ELEMENTS OF CALCULUS

AND ANALYTIC GEOMETRY

ELEMENTS OF CALCULUS

AND ANALYTIC GEOMETRY

GEORGE B. THOMAS, Jr.

Massachusetts Institute of Technology

ADDISON-WESLEY PUBLISHING COMPANY

MENLO PARK, CALIFORNIA · READING, MASSACHUSETTS

LONDON · DON MILLS, ONTARIO

REVISED EDITION

SECONDARY
MATHEMATICS
SERIES

THIS BOOK IS IN THE

ADDISON-WESLEY
SECONDARY MATHEMATICS SERIES

CONSULTING EDITORS

Richard S. Pieters   Paul Rosenbloom

George B. Thomas, Jr.   John Wagner

PREFACE

Calculus is a subject in which much can be learned by doing problems. In this text special attention has been given to selecting an unusually ample supply. These problems are arranged in three different fashions to give the student as wide a variety of experiences as possible. First, the exercise sets at the end of each section contain not only problems which require straightforward application of the material, but also problems which involve subtle use of new ideas in conjunction with concepts already developed. Further, at the end of each chapter there are two additional problem sets: review questions and exercises, and miscellaneous problems. Numerical answers are given for odd-numbered problems to provide a check for the student's own solutions. In cases where equivalent answers of different forms are correct, only one answer is given.

This book closely follows the recommendations of the Committee on Mathematics of the Advanced Placement Program. It contains the material on analytic geometry and essentially all of the material on functions of one variable from the author's *Calculus and Analytic Geometry*, Third Edition. In addition, there is a more leisurely introduction to such topics as inequalities, absolute value, intervals and neighborhoods, functions, and limits.

Some significant features of the book are worth noting. In order to motivate the idea of limit of a function, the concepts of slope of a curve and derivative of a function are introduced in Chapter 2, prior to the theory of limits in Chapter 3. Here the Greek letter ϵ (epsilon) is used in the usual way to restrict variation in the range of the function. But the introduction of the Greek letter δ (delta), which is ordinarily used to restrict variation in the domain, is deferred until the student is accustomed to thinking in terms of neighborhoods. (For a further treatment of limits, including limits of sequences, see the author's booklet, *Limits*, Addison-Wesley, 1963.) A teacher may, in some classes, wish to skip the theory of limits in Chapter 3 and go directly on to Chapter 4. If so, a brief, intuitive discussion of the key theorems about limits of sums, differences, products, and quotients—without proofs—could be substituted in place of Chapter 3.

A knowledge of algebra, geometry, and some trigonometry is necessary for the study of calculus. Some of the key formulas in trigonometry are derived in the text in Chapter 6, Article 4.

Chapters 11 and 12 deal with topics in analytic geometry in Cartesian and polar coordinates. These chapters could be studied before Chapter 2, Article 5, if one omits all applications of calculus to analytic geometry. Alternatively, they could be taken up following Chapter 8 (omitting all references to determinants). The order in this book, however, has been found to be quite satisfactory in many schools.

The work on determinants and linear equations in Chapter 10 is not essential to a first calculus course, but the same method that is used to reduce the determinant to triangular form by operating on its rows (or columns) is also used in reducing a matrix to such a form. It is also necessary to know something about determinants in order to find the characteristic equation of a matrix, or a system of ordinary differential equations. (See Example 3 of Article 10-7.) Since many students will go on to study linear algebra, advanced calculus, or differential equations, the introduction to determinants and linear equations should be included if there is enough time.

The many analogies between hyperbolic functions and trigonometric functions, and some of the contrasts, are brought out in Chapter 13. The derivation, and solution, of the equation that describes equilibrium of a hanging cable is also included in this chapter as a mathematical model of a physical situation. The study of velocity and acceleration in terms of vectors provides another such model, closely related to planetary and earth-satellite orbital mechanics.

Many of the miscellaneous problems were provided by Professors T. M. Apostol of the California Institute of Technology and A. W. Tucker of Princeton. Most of the answers to these problems were provided by Richard T. Bumby, Robert R. D. Kemp, and C. Peter Wolk. The author is grateful for this friendly and valuable help.

It is a pleasure to acknowledge the expert assistance from the editorial and production staffs of the Addison-Wesley Publishing Company in producing this book. The author also acknowledges the many helpful suggestions from users of the first edition of *Elements of Calculus and Analytic Geometry* and related books.

Any errors, in the text or in the answers to problems, are the responsibility of the author. He will very much appreciate having them brought to his attention.

G. B. T., Jr.

CONTENTS

5   APPLICATIONS

6   INTEGRATION

7   APPLICATIONS OF THE DEFINITE INTEGRAL

8   TRANSCENDENTAL FUNCTIONS

9   METHODS OF INTEGRATION

14   VECTORS AND PARAMETRIC EQUATIONS

SELECTED ANSWERS TO PROBLEMS

TABLES

INDEX

Analytic Preparation

1–1   Introduction.   Calculus is the mathematics of change and motion. Where there is motion or growth, where forces are at work producing acceleration, calculus is the right mathematical tool. This was true in the beginnings of the subject, and it is true today. Calculus is used to predict the orbits of earth satellites; in the design of inertial navigation systems, cyclotrons, and radar systems; to explore problems of space travel; and to test scientific theories about such things as the dynamics of the atmosphere, ocean currents, and even theories about economic, sociologic, and psychological behavior. Of course the scientist needs a great deal more than mathematical competence, and he needs more mathematics than calculus. But calculus is a tool of great importance and usefulness and is prerequisite for further study in nearly all branches of higher mathematics.

One of the great mathematicians of the twentieth century, John von Neumann (1903–57), has written:* "The calculus was the first achievement of modern mathematics, and it is difficult to overestimate its importance. I think it defines more unequivocally than anything else the inception of modern mathematics, and the system of mathematical analysis, which is its logical development, still constitutes the greatest technical advance in exact thinking."

The calculus is a branch of mathematics which provides methods for solving two large classes of problems. The first of these involves finding the rate at which a variable quantity is changing. For example, when a body, say a stone dropped from a tower, travels in a straight line, its distance from its starting point changes with time and we may ask *how fast* it is moving at any given instant. *Differential calculus* is the branch of calculus which treats such problems.

The second type of problem the calculus deals with is that of finding a function when its rate of change is given. Thus, for example, if we are given the *velocity* of a moving body at every instant of time, we may seek to find the distance it has moved as a function of time. This problem belongs to the domain of *integral calculus*.

Modern science and engineering use both branches of the calculus as a language for expressing physical laws in precise mathematical terms, and

---

* *World of Mathematics*, Vol. 4, "The Mathematician," by John von Neumann, pp. 2053–2063.

as a tool for studying the consequences of those laws. Thus Sir Isaac
Newton (1642–1727) was able to explain the motion of the planets relative
to the sun as a consequence of the physical assumption known today as
the law of gravitational attraction. Some appreciation of the magnitude
of his achievement may be gained from realizing that Kepler (1571–1630)
spent some twenty years studying observational data and using empirical
methods to discover the three laws now known as *Kepler's laws*. They are:

(a) Each planet describes an orbit about the sun which is an ellipse
with the sun at one focus.
(b) The line joining the planet and the sun sweeps over equal areas in
equal intervals of time.
(c) The squares of the periods of revolution of the planets are proportional to the cubes of their mean distances from the sun.

All three of these laws can be derived, using the calculus as the main
mathematical tool, from the "inverse-square" law of gravitational attraction and Newton's laws of motion. A large part of the subject matter
of this branch of mathematics was developed by Newton as a tool to help
him solve problems which arose in connection with his investigations in
physics and astronomy. Credit for the invention of the calculus must
also be shared, however, with a German mathematician and philosopher,
Gottfried Wilhelm Leibniz (1646–1716), who independently and approximately concurrently also developed a large part of the subject, and whose
notation has been almost universally adopted in preference to that used
by Newton.

Analytic geometry, which forms a third division of the subject matter of
this book, was the creation of several mathematicians.* Two French
mathematicians, Pierre de Fermat (1601–1665) and René Descartes (1596–
1650) are the chief claimants to the title of inventor of analytic geometry
as we now know it. Descartes is credited with the important idea of locating a point in the plane by means of its distances from two perpendicular axes, and his name is commemorated in the terminology "Cartesian
coordinates." We discuss coordinates in Article 1–2. The distinguishing
characteristic of analytic geometry is that it uses algebraic methods and
equations to study geometric problems. Conversely, it permits us to
visualize algebraic equations in terms of geometric curves. This frequently
adds clarity to abstract concepts. We shall see that most of the theory
in calculus can be presented in geometrical terms, so that calculus and
analytic geometry may profitably be united and studied as a whole.

---

* See, for example, *World of Mathematics*, Vol. 1, "Commentary on Descartes
and Analytical Geometry," pp. 235–237. Also the article "The Invention of
Analytic Geometry," by Carl B. Boyer, *Scientific American*, January, 1949.

1-2 Coordinates. The basic idea in analytic geometry is the establishment of a one-to-one correspondence between the points of a plane on the one hand and pairs of numbers (x, y) on the other hand. This correspondence may be established in many ways, but the one most commonly used is as follows.

A horizontal line in the plane, extending indefinitely to the left and to the right, is chosen as the x-axis or axis of *abscissas*. A reference point O on this line and a unit of length are then chosen. The axis is scaled off in terms of this unit of length in such a way that the number zero is attached to O, the number $+a$ is attached to the point which is a units to the right of O, and $-a$ is attached to the symmetrically located point to the left of O. In this way a one-to-one correspondence is established between the points of the x-axis and the set of all *real numbers* (that is, numbers which may be represented by terminating or nonterminating decimals).

Now through O take a second, vertical line in the plane, extending indefinitely up and down. This line becomes the y-axis, or axis of *ordinates*. The unit of length used to represent $+1$ on the y-axis need not be the same as the unit of length used to represent $+1$ on the x-axis. The y-axis is scaled off in terms of the unit of length adopted for it, with the positive number $+b$ attached to the point b units above O and negative number $-b$ attached to the symmetrically located point b units below O.

If a line parallel to the y-axis is drawn through the point marked a on the x-axis, and a line parallel to the x-axis is drawn through the point marked b on the y-axis, their point of intersection P is to be labeled $P(a, b)$. Thus, given the pair of real numbers a and b, we find one and only one point with abscissa a and ordinate b, and this point we denote by $P(a, b)$.

Conversely, if we start with any point P in the plane, we may draw lines through it parallel to the coordinate axes. If these lines intersect the x-axis at a and the y-axis at b, we then regard the pair of numbers (a, b) as corresponding to the point P. We say that the coordinates of P are (a, b).

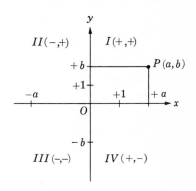

Figure 1-1

The two axes divide the plane into four quadrants, called the first quadrant, second quadrant, and so on, and labeled I, II, III, IV in Fig. 1-1. Points in the first quadrant have both coordinates positive, in the second quadrant the x-coordinate (abscissa) is negative and the y-coordinate (ordinate) is positive. The notations $(-, -)$ and $(+, -)$ in quadrants III and IV of Fig. 1–1 represent the signs of the coordinates of points in these quadrants.

Remark. There are times when it is quite obvious that there is no physical relationship between the unit of measurement of x and the unit of measurement of y. For example, if y is the total cost in dollars, to a certain shoe manufacturer, to produce x pairs of shoes per week, then "1" on the x-scale stands for one pair of shoes, while "1" on the y-scale stands for one dollar. Clearly, there is no reason for using the same scale on the two axes.

On the other hand, in surveying, one foot measured north-and-south should be the same as one foot measured east-and-west. In trigonometry, therefore, it is usually assumed that the units of length on the two axes are the same. This assumption is also made in analytic geometry.

In this book, if coordinates of points are given as pure numbers (i.e., without any physical units attached), it is to be assumed that the scales on the two axes are the same. In particular, this assumption is made wherever angles between lines or lengths of skew line segments are involved.

PROBLEMS

In each of the following problems (1–15), plot the given point P and such of the following points as may apply:

(a) The point Q such that the line segment* $\overline{QP}$ is perpendicular to the x-axis and is bisected by it. Give the coordinates of Q.

(b) The point R such that the line segment $\overline{PR}$ is perpendicular to and is bisected by the y-axis. Give the coordinates of R.

(c) The point S such that the line segment $\overline{PS}$ is bisected by the origin. Give the coordinates of S.

(d) The point T such that the line segment $\overline{PT}$ is perpendicular to and is bisected by the 45° line L through the origin bisecting the first and third quadrants. Give the coordinates of T, assuming equal units on the axes.

[*Note:* Q and P are symmetric with respect to the x-axis, R and P with respect to the y-axis, S and P with respect to the origin, and T and P with respect to L.] State rules for finding coordinates of Q, R, S, T in terms of the coordinates of P.

1. $(1, -2)$	2. $(2, -1)$	3. $(-2, 2)$
4. $(-2, 1)$	5. $(2, 2)$	6. $(-2, -2)$
7. $(0, 1)$	8. $(1, 0)$	9. $(-2, 0)$
10. $(0, -3)$	11. $(-1, -3)$	12. $(\sqrt{2}, -\sqrt{2})$
13. $(-\pi, -\pi)$	14. $(-1.5, 2.3)$	15. $(\sqrt{2}, 0)$

In each of the following problems (16 through 20), take the units of length on the two axes to be equal.

---

* See Article 1–3.

16. A straight line is drawn through the point $(0, 0)$ and the point $(1, 1)$. What acute angle does it make with the positive x-axis? Sketch.

17. A straight line is drawn through the point $A(1, 2)$ and the point $B(2, 4)$. Find $\tan \alpha$, where α is the acute angle that this line makes with the horizontal line through A. Sketch.

18. Show that the line through the pair of points $(1, 1)$ and $(2, 0)$ is parallel to the line through the pair of points $(-1, -1)$ and $(0, -2)$. Sketch.

19. The line through the pair of points $(2, 3)$ and $(1, 1)$ cuts the y-axis at the point $(0, b)$. Find b by using similar triangles. Sketch.

20. Does the line through the pair of points $(-1, -1)$ and $(1, 2)$ pass through the origin? Sketch. Give a reason, other than the evidence of your sketch, for your answer.

1–3 Directed distance. In our work we shall distinguish between lines and line segments in the following manner.

For any two points A and B we indicate the *line* that contains A and B by $\overleftrightarrow{AB}$. (See Fig. 1–2a.)

For any two points A and B we indicate the set which consists of points A and B together with all points between A and B by $\overline{AB}$. This set is called a *line segment.* (See Fig. 1–2b.) If A and B are any two points on the x-axis, or on a line parallel to the x-axis, we define the *directed distance from A to B* as follows:

Figure 1–2

directed distance from A to B equals (x-coordinate of B) minus (x-coordinate of A).

The notation we use for this directed distance is AB. In Fig. 1–2(c) the x-coordinate of A is x_1 and the x-coordinate of B is x_2, so $AB = x_2 - x_1$. When we change the order of the two points, and apply the definition, we get

directed distance from B to A equals (x-coordinate of A) minus (x-coordinate of B).

Thus, for points A and B as shown in Fig. 1–2(c),

$$AB = x_2 - x_1, \qquad BA = x_1 - x_2. \qquad (1)$$

It is clear from Eq. (1) that the directed distances AB and BA differ only in sign:

$$AB = -BA. \qquad (2)$$

The *length* of the line segment $\overline{AB}$ is the absolute value of either of these directed distances. We denote this length by $|AB|$. (See Article 1–7.)

For example, the directed distance from the point $(-2, 0)$ to the point $(3, 0)$ is $3 - (-2) = 5$; while the directed distance from $(-1, 0)$ to $(-4, 0)$ is $-4 - (-1) = -3$. The segment joining the first pair of points has length 5 and the second has length 3.

If we apply the definition of directed distance to the origin O and points A and B, respectively, we get

$$OA = (x\text{-coordinate of } A) - (x\text{-coordinate of } O)$$
$$= x_1$$

and

$$OB = (x\text{-coordinate of } B) - (x\text{-coordinate of } O)$$
$$= x_2.$$

The equation

$$x_2 = x_1 + (x_2 - x_1),$$

which is true for all real numbers x_1 and x_2, is the same as

$$OB = OA + AB. \tag{3}$$

We can interpret the right side of Eq. (3) in terms of motion of a particle that starts at the origin, travels to A (the directed distance OA) and from A travels to B (the directed distance AB). The net result is the same as traveling from O to B (the directed distance OB). In traveling from A to B the abscissa of the particle changes from x_1 to x_2. In calculus it is customary to use the notation Δx (read "delta x") to represent the amount of change in x, which is the difference $x_2 - x_1$:

$$\boxed{\Delta x = x_2 - x_1.}$$

The symbol Δx thus denotes "change in x" or "difference between two values of x," and does not mean a number multiplied by x.

In Fig. 1–3(a), for example, if we think of a particle that starts at $x_1 = -2$ and travels to $x_2 = +3$, then its abscissa x undergoes a change given by

$$\Delta x = x_2 - x_1 = 3 - (-2) = +5.$$

(a)   (b)

Figure 1–3

In Fig. 1–3(b), if the particle travels from $x_1 = -1$ to $x_2 = -4$, then its abscissa changes by the amount

$$\Delta x = x_2 - x_1 = -4 - (-1) = -3.$$

In an analogous fashion, we define the directed distance from a point C to a point D, when both points are on the y-axis (or on a line parallel to the y-axis) as

CD equals (y-coordinate of D) minus (y-coordinate of C).

Thus if y_1 is the ordinate of C and y_2 is the ordinate of D, and both points have the same abscissa, the directed distance CD is Δy, where

$$\Delta y = y_2 - y_1$$

is equal to the ordinate of the terminal point D minus the ordinate of the initial point C.

Figure 1–4 shows two points $P_1(x_1, y_1)$ and $P_2(x_2, y_2)$ on a line that is not parallel to either axis. If a particle were to travel from P_1 to P_2 along any path whatever, its abscissa would change by an amount

$$\Delta x = x_2 - x_1$$

and its ordinate would change by an amount

$$\boxed{\Delta y = y_2 - y_1.}$$

These changes correspond to the directed distances P_1R and RP_2 in the right triangle P_1RP_2 shown in Fig. 1–4.

For our purposes it is not important to try to assign a positive direction to a line that is not parallel to either coordinate axis, so we do not bother about directed distances between points P_1 and P_2 on such a line. However we shall have occasion to talk about the distance between such points, but only when the same unit of measurement is used on both coordinate axes. Then we can express all distances in the plane in terms of this fundamental unit. In particular, we readily find by applying the theorem of

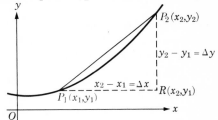

Figure 1–4

Pythagoras to the right triangle P_1RP_2 in Fig. 1–4 that the distance d between the two points $P_1(x_1, y_1)$ and $P_2(x_2, y_2)$ is simply

$$d = \sqrt{(\Delta x)^2 + (\Delta y)^2} = \sqrt{(x_2 - x_1)^2 + (y_2 - y_1)^2}. \qquad (4)$$

For example, if a particle starts from $P_1(-1, 2)$ and travels in a straight line to the point $P_2(2, -2)$, then its abscissa undergoes a change

$$\Delta x = x_2 - x_1 = 2 - (-1) = 3$$

and its ordinate changes by an amount

$$\Delta y = y_2 - y_1 = -2 - 2 = -4.$$

The distance the particle travels from P_1 to P_2 is

$$d = |P_1P_2| = \sqrt{(\Delta x)^2 + (\Delta y)^2} = \sqrt{9 + 16} = 5.$$

PROBLEMS

In each of the following problems, points A and B are given and point C is to be found at the intersection of the horizontal line through A and the vertical line through B. Sketch, and find

(a) the coordinates of C,
(b) the directed distance $AC = \Delta x$,
(c) the directed distance $CB = \Delta y$, and
(d) the length of $\overline{AB}$ under the assumption that the unit of length on the y-axis is the same as the unit of length on the x-axis.

1. $A(1, 1)$, $B(3, 4)$ 2. $A(3, 4)$, $B(1, 1)$
3. $A(-1, 2)$, $B(2, -1)$ 4. $A(2, -1)$, $B(-1, 2)$
5. $A(-1, -1)$, $B(1, 2)$ 6. $A(1, 2)$, $B(-1, -1)$
7. $A(-3, 2)$, $B(-1, -2)$ 8. $A(-1, -2)$, $B(-3, 2)$
9. $A(-3, -2)$, $B(-1, -1)$ 10. $A(-1, -1)$, $B(-3, -2)$

11. What equation must be satisfied by the coordinates of a point $P(x, y)$ if P is on the circle of radius 5 with center at $C(h, k)$ if:

(a) $(h, k) = (0, 0)$,   (b) $(h, k) = (5, 0)$,
(c) $(h, k) = (3, 4)$,   (d) $(h, k) = (h, k)$?

1–4   Slope of a straight line. Let L be a straight line which is not parallel to the y-axis. Let $P_1(x_1, y_1)$ and $P_2(x_2, y_2)$ be any two distinct points on L (Fig. 1–5a). Then we call

$$\Delta y = y_2 - y_1$$

the "rise" and

$$\Delta x = x_2 - x_1$$

the "run" along L from P_1 to P_2. (Note that either Δx or Δy, or both,

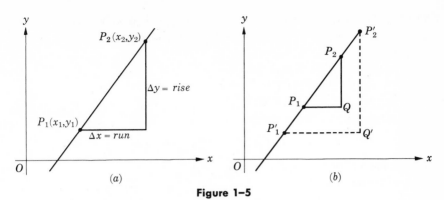

Figure 1-5

may be negative.) We define the *slope of L* as the rate of rise per unit of run,

$$\text{slope} = \frac{\text{rise}}{\text{run}}. \tag{1a}$$

If we denote the slope by m, we have

$$m = \frac{\Delta y}{\Delta x} = \frac{y_2 - y_1}{x_2 - x_1}. \tag{1b}$$

Remark 1. Suppose that instead of using the pair of points P_1 and P_2 to calculate the slope, Eq. (1a), we were to choose a different pair of points $P_1'(x_1', y_1')$, $P_2'(x_2', y_2')$ on L and calculate

$$m' = \frac{y_2' - y_1'}{x_2' - x_1'} = \frac{\Delta y'}{\Delta x'}.$$

Would we get the same answer for the slope? In other words, does

$$m' = m?$$

The answer is "yes." For, in Fig. 1-5(b) the triangles P_1QP_2 and $P_1'Q'P_2'$ are similar, hence

$$m' = \frac{Q'P_2'}{P_1'Q'} = \frac{QP_2}{P_1Q} = m.$$

In other words, Eq. (1b) relates the change in x and the change in y between *any* pair of points (x, y) and $(x + \Delta x, y + \Delta y)$ on L.

Remark 2. If we multiply the first two terms of Eq. (1b) by Δx, we obtain

$$\Delta y = m \, \Delta x. \tag{2}$$

This means, in the light of the comment above, that as a particle moves along L, the change in y is proportional to the change in x, and the slope m is the proportionality factor.

For example, suppose L is the line determined by the points $P_1(1, 2)$ and $P_2(3, 8)$, Fig. 1–6. Then the slope of L is

$$m = \frac{8 - 2}{3 - 1} = 3.$$

And, if $P(x, y)$, $Q(x + \Delta x, y + \Delta y)$ are any two points on L, then

$$\Delta y = 3\,\Delta x.$$

That is, for every unit of run, there are three units of rise. Thus, starting from $P_1(1, 2)$, if we increase x by 1 unit we should increase y by 3 units, which would bring us to the point $P_3(2, 5)$. Or, we could decrease x by 1 unit and y by 3 units and obtain the point $P_4(0, -1)$. [*Question:* At what point does L cross the x-axis?]

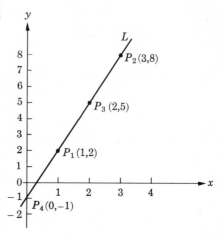

Figure 1–6

Remark 3. *Interpolation.* In using a table of logarithms, we may, for example, want to find log 3.1416. Suppose the table gives

$$\log 3.1410 = 0.49707, \qquad \log 3.1420 = 0.49721,$$

and no intermediate values. Then, for any x between 3.1410 and 3.1420, we could approximate the graph of $y = \log x$ by the chord L through the two points $P_1(3.1410, 0.49707)$ and $P_2(3.1420, 0.49721)$. The slope of this chord is

$$m = \frac{\Delta y}{\Delta x} = \frac{14 \times 10^{-5}}{10 \times 10^{-4}} = 1.4 \times 10^{-1}.$$

Then, corresponding to

$$\Delta x = 3.1416 - 3.1410 = 6 \times 10^{-4},$$

we may take

$$\Delta y = 0.14\,\Delta x = 8.4 \times 10^{-5} \approx 8 \times 10^{-5}.$$

Hence, the ordinate of the point on L with abscissa 3.1416 is

$$0.49707 + 0.00008 = 0.49715.$$

That is, using the chord to approximate the curve, we find

$$\log 3.1416 \approx 0.49715.$$

Remark 4. If we take equal scales on the x- and y-axes, we may interpret the slope of the line L as the tangent of the angle of inclination that L makes with the positive x-axis. That is,

$$m = \tan \phi.$$

Here ϕ is the angle, $0 \le \phi < 180°$, that the line makes with the positively directed portion of the x-axis (Fig. 1–7).

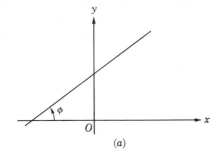

(a)   (b)

Figure 1–7

For a line that slopes upward to the right, Fig. 1–7(a), Δy is positive when Δx is. Also, $0 < \phi < 90°$, and $\tan \phi = \Delta y/\Delta x$ is positive.

For a line that slopes downward to the right, Fig. 1–7(b), Δy is negative when Δx is positive. Also, $90° < \phi < 180°$, and $\tan \phi = \Delta y/\Delta x$ is negative.

For a horizontal line, Δy is zero for any Δx. Also $\phi = 0°$ and $\tan \phi = \Delta y/\Delta x$ is zero.

For a vertical line, Δx is zero for any Δy. Then $\Delta y/\Delta x$ is meaningless, since we cannot divide by zero. Also $\phi = 90°$, and $\tan 90°$ does not exist.

Let us examine the slopes of lines whose inclination angles are near $90°$, such as

$$\phi_1 = 89°59', \qquad m_1 = \tan \phi_1 \approx 3437.7$$

and

$$\phi_2 = 90°01', \qquad m_2 = \tan \phi_2 \approx -3437.7.$$

We see that such lines have slopes which are numerically very large. And by taking the angle still closer to $90°$, we can make the slope numerically larger than any preassigned positive number N, no matter how large N may be. It is this fact which is sometimes summarized by the statement that "a vertical line has infinite slope" or, "the slope of the line becomes infinite as its inclination angle approaches $90°$."

The symbol ∞ is used to represent infinity, but we should not use this symbol in computations involving addition, subtraction, multiplication, or division in the way we use ordinary real numbers.   (See Article 3–4.)

 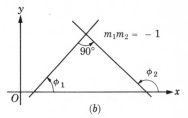

(a)   (b)

Figure 1–8

Two *parallel* lines (Fig. 1–8a) have equal angles of inclination and hence have equal slopes

$$m_1 = m_2.$$

Conversely, two lines having equal slopes

$$m_1 = \tan \phi_1, \qquad m_2 = \tan \phi_2$$

also have equal inclinations, since

$$\tan \phi_1 = \tan \phi_2$$

together with

$$0 \le \phi_1 < 180°, \qquad 0 \le \phi_2 < 180°$$

implies that ϕ_1 and ϕ_2 are equal.

Next, consider two *perpendicular* lines (Fig. 1–8b).   Their inclinations differ by 90°.   Suppose, for example, that

$$\phi_2 = 90° + \phi_1.$$

Case 1.   If one line is vertical, then the other must be horizontal.
Case 2.   If neither line is vertical, then neither ϕ_1 nor ϕ_2 is 90° and

$$
\begin{aligned}
m_2 &= \tan \phi_2 \\
&= \tan (90° + \phi_1) \\
&= -\cot \phi_1 = -\frac{1}{\tan \phi_1} \\
&= -1/m_1.
\end{aligned}
$$

Thus the condition for *perpendicularity* in this case is

$$m_2 = -\frac{1}{m_1}. \tag{3}$$

PROBLEMS

In each of the following problems (1 through 15), plot the given points A and B and find the slope of the straight line determined by them and of a line perpendicular to it.

1. $A(1, 2)$, $B(2, -1)$
2. $A(-1, 2)$, $B(-2, -1)$
3. $A(-2, -1)$, $B(1, -2)$
4. $A(2, -1)$, $B(-2, 1)$
5. $A(1, 0)$, $B(0, 1)$
6. $A(-1, 0)$, $B(1, 0)$
7. $A(2, 3)$, $B(-1, 3)$
8. $A(0, 3)$, $B(2, -3)$
9. $A(0, -2)$, $B(-2, 0)$
10. $A(1, 2)$, $B(1, -3)$
11. $A(\frac{1}{2}, 0)$, $B(0, -\frac{1}{3})$
12. $A(0, 0)$, $B(x, y)$ $(x \neq 0, y \neq 0)$
13. $A(0, 0)$, $B(x, 0)$ $(x \neq 0)$
14. $A(0, 0)$, $B(0, y)$ $(y \neq 0)$
15. $A(a, 0)$, $B(0, b)$ $(a \neq 0, b \neq 0)$

In each of the following problems (16 through 20), plot the given points A, B, C, and D. Determine in each case whether or not $ABCD$ is a parallelogram. Also indicate those parallelograms that are rectangles.

16. $A(0, 1)$, $B(1, 2)$, $C(2, 1)$ $D(1, 0)$
17. $A(3, 1)$, $B(2, 2)$, $C(0, 1)$, $D(1, 0)$
18. $A(-2, 2)$, $B(1, 3)$, $C(2, 0)$, $D(-1, -1)$
19. $A(1, -2)$, $B(2, -1)$, $C(2, 1)$, $D(1, 0)$
20. $A(-1, 0)$, $B(0, -1)$, $C(2, 0)$, $D(0, 2)$

21. Find the coordinates of a point $P(x, y)$ which is so located that the line $\overleftrightarrow{OP}$ through the origin and P has slope equal to $+2$, and the line $\overleftrightarrow{AP}$ through the point $A(-1, 0)$ and P has slope equal to $+1$.

22. A line L goes through the origin and has slope equal to $+3$. If $P(x, y)$ is a point other than the origin and on the line L, show that $y = 3x$. Sketch the line.

In each of the following problems (23 through 27), plot the given points and determine analytically whether or not they all lie on a straight line. Give reasons for your answers.

23. $A(1, 0)$, $B(0, 1)$, $C(2, -1)$
24. $A(-2, 1)$, $B(0, 5)$, $C(-1, 2)$
25. $A(-2, -1)$, $B(-1, 1)$, $C(1, 5)$, $D(2, 7)$
26. $A(-2, 3)$, $B(0, 2)$, $C(2, 0)$
27. $A(-3, -2)$, $B(-2, 0)$, $C(-1, 2)$, $D(1, 6)$

28. Let $P_1(x_1, y_1)$ and $P_2(x_2, y_2)$ be two points. Find the mid-point of the segment $\overline{P_1P_2}$.

29. Given $A(0, -1)$, $B(4, 0)$, and $C(3, 4)$, show that ABC is a right triangle and find the center and radius of the circumscribed circle. Sketch.

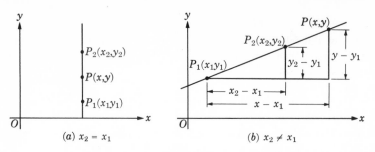

$(a)\ x_2 = x_1$ $(b)\ x_2 \neq x_1$

Figure 1–9

1–5   Equations of a straight line. In this article we shall discuss algebraic equations that represent straight lines. Suppose we ask ourselves how the two coordinates x and y of a point $P(x, y)$ on the straight line determined by the two points $P_1(x_1, y_1)$ and $P_2(x_2, y_2)$ are related to each other. It is desirable to distinguish between the cases (see Fig. 1–9)

$$x_2 = x_1 \quad \text{and} \quad x_2 \neq x_1.$$

Case 1. If $x_2 = x_1$, then the line $\overleftrightarrow{P_1P_2}$ is vertical and all points on it have the same x-coordinate. Then $P(x, y)$ is on the line if and only if

$$x = x_1. \tag{1}$$

In this case the x- and y-coordinates of P are not related to each other. The ordinate y may have any value whatsoever and the point $P(x, y)$ will be on the line provided its abscissa x has the value x_1.

Case 2. If $x_2 \neq x_1$, we know the slope of the line is

$$m = \frac{y_2 - y_1}{x_2 - x_1}. \tag{2}$$

Then the point $P(x, y)$ is also on the line if the slope of $\overleftrightarrow{P_1P}$ is the same as the slope of $\overleftrightarrow{P_1P_2}$. That is, x and y must satisfy the equation

$$\frac{y - y_1}{x - x_1} = m$$

or

$$y - y_1 = m(x - x_1), \tag{3}$$

if P is on the line; and conversely, if x and y do satisfy Eq. (3), then $P(x, y)$ is on the line. If P coincides with P_1, Eq. (3) is still satisfied, even though the slope of $\overleftrightarrow{P_1P}$ is then undefined.

Equation (3) is called the *point-slope* form of the equation of the line, since it gives the equation in terms of one point $P_1(x_1, y_1)$ on the line and the slope m. The three numbers x_1, y_1, and m are constants in Eq. (3), while x and y are variables. By a *variable* we mean a symbol, such as x, which may take any value in some set of numbers. In Eq. (3), x may take any real value whatever, $-\infty < x < +\infty$,

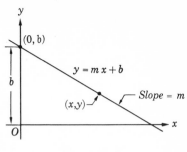

Figure 1–10

and as x varies continuously from a negative value $-N$ to a positive value $+M$, the corresponding point $P(x, y)$ traces an unbroken portion of the line from left to right.

We may also write Eq. (3) in the equivalent form

$$y = mx + b, \qquad (4)$$

where m is the slope of the line and

$$b = y_1 - mx_1$$

is a constant. In fact, $(0, b)$ is the point where the line crosses the y-axis. The ordinate of this point is called the y-intercept of the line. Equation (4) is expressed in terms of the slope m and the y-intercept b, and is therefore called the *slope-intercept* equation of the line.

For example, the equation

$$y = 2x + 3$$

may be compared with (4), with

$$m = 2, \qquad b = 3.$$

Thus it represents a straight line having y-intercept 3 and slope 2.

More generally, an equation

$$Ax + By + C = 0, \qquad (5)$$

where A, B, and C are constants with at least one of A and B different from zero, represents a *straight line*. For if

$$B = 0, \qquad Ax + C = 0, \qquad x = -(C/A)$$

and the line is a vertical line as in Eq. (1). On the other hand, if

$$B \neq 0, \qquad y = -\frac{A}{B}x - \frac{C}{B},$$

and this represents a straight line of the form of Eq. (4), with

$$m = -\frac{A}{B}, \qquad b = -\frac{C}{B}.$$

An equation like (5) that contains only first powers of x and y is said to be "linear in x and in y." Thus we may summarize our discussion by saying that every straight line in the plane is represented by a linear equation and, conversely, every linear equation represents a straight line.

EXAMPLE. Find the slope of the line $2x + 3y = 5$.

Solution. Solving for y we have

$$y = -\tfrac{2}{3}x + \tfrac{5}{3},$$

which compares with $y = mx + b$, with $m = -\tfrac{2}{3}$ and $b = \tfrac{5}{3}$. Hence the slope is $-\tfrac{2}{3}$.

PROBLEMS

In each of the following problems (1 through 10), plot the given pair of points and find an equation for the line determined by them.

1. $(0, 0)$, $(2, 3)$
2. $(1, 1)$, $(2, 1)$
3. $(1, 1)$, $(1, 2)$
4. $(-2, 1)$, $(2, -2)$
5. $(-2, 0)$, $(-2, -2)$
6. $(1, 3)$, $(3, 1)$
7. $(0, 0)$, $(1, 0)$
8. $(0, 0)$, $(0, 1)$
9. $(2, -1)$, $(-2, 3)$

10. Find an equation for the line determined by the pair of points $(a, 0)$, $(0, b)$ where $a \neq 0$ and $b \neq 0$.

In each of the following problems (11 through 20), find the slope of the given line.

11. $y = 3x + 5$
12. $2y = 3x + 5$
13. $x + y = 2$
14. $2x - y = 4$
15. $x - 2y = 4$
16. $3x + 4y = 12$
17. $4x - 3y = 12$
18. $x = 2y - 5$

19. $\dfrac{x}{a} + \dfrac{y}{b} = 1$ (a, b constants $\neq 0$)

20. $x_1 x + y_1 y = 1$ (x_1, y_1 constants $\neq 0$)

21. Find the line that passes through the point $(1, 2)$ and is parallel to the line $x + 2y = 3$.

22. (a) Find the line L through $A(-2, 2)$ and perpendicular to the line L': $2x + y = 4$

(b) Find the point B where the lines L and L' of part (a) intersect.

(c) Using the result of part (b), find the distance from the point A to the line L' of part (a).

23. Find the line through $(1, 4)$ and having inclination angle $\phi = 60°$.

24. What is the inclination of the line $x + y = 4$?

25. If A, B, C, C' are constants, show that (a) the lines

$$Ax + By + C = 0,$$
$$Ax + By + C' = 0$$

are parallel, and (b) the lines

$$Ax + By + C = 0,$$
$$Bx - Ay + C' = 0$$

are perpendicular.

26. (a) Let C and F denote, respectively, corresponding centigrade and Fahrenheit temperature readings. Given that the F vs. C graph is a straight line, find its equation from the following data: $C = 0$, $F = 32$ and $C = 100$, $F = 212$ are coordinates of two points on the graph.

(b) Is there a temperature at which $C = F$? If so, what is it?

27. The perpendicular distance $|ON|$ from the origin to line L is p, and $\overleftrightarrow{ON}$ makes an angle α with the positive x-axis. Show that L has equation

$$x \cos \alpha + y \sin \alpha = p.$$

1–6   Inequalities. If a and b are real numbers, we say that a is *less than* b and write

$$a < b, \tag{1}$$

provided

$$b - a > 0. \tag{2}$$

Using the properties of addition and multiplication over the reals, we can easily prove the following theorems.

THEOREM 1. *If $a < b$ and c is any real number, then*

$$a + c < b + c.$$

Proof. Suppose $a < b$. Then

$$b - a = p$$

is positive. But

$$(b + c) - (a + c) = b - a,$$

so
$$(b + c) - (a + c) = p$$
is positive. Therefore,
$$a + c < b + c. \quad \text{Q.E.D.}$$

EXAMPLE 1. Since $2 < 5$ and -7 is a real number,
$$2 + (-7) < 5 + (-7);$$
that is,
$$-5 < -2.$$

THEOREM 2. *If $a < b$ and c is positive, then $ca < cb$.*

Proof. Suppose that $a < b$ so that
$$b - a = p$$
is positive. If c also is positive, then
$$cp = c(b - a)$$
$$= cb - ca$$
is positive, so
$$ca < cb. \quad \text{Q.E.D.}$$

EXAMPLE 2. Since $-3 < 2$ and 5 is positive, $-15 < 10$.

Remark 1. Suppose the numbers a and b are coordinates of points A and B on a number line, as in Fig. 1–11 where the positive direction is to the right. Then $a < b$ if and only if the point A of coordinate a is to the left of the point B of coordinate b.

Figure 1–11

In particular, every point to the left of the origin has a coordinate that is negative:

$$\boxed{a < 0 \text{ if and only if } a \text{ is negative.}}$$

Likewise, every point to the right of the origin has a positive coordinate, so

$$\boxed{0 < b \text{ if and only if } b \text{ is positive.}}$$

Remark 2. If a is *less then* b, we also say that b is *greater than* a, and write
$$b > a.$$

Thus,

$$\boxed{a < b \text{ if and only if } b > a.}$$

Notice that the lesser number, in this case a, is always on the pointed, smaller end of the inequality sign, while the greater number is on the side that opens wide:

smaller number on small side of the inequality symbol $<$,
greater number on large side of the inequality symbol $<$.

But we must be careful in applying this mnemonic (memory) device because negative numbers might fool us. Thus, -4 is *less* than -2, so it is true that $-4 < -2$, but $4 > 2$. Another mnemonic device is this:

Figure 1–12

pointed end of the inequality symbol toward the left,
lesser coordinate on the left and the greater coordinate on the right,
in the same order in which they appear on the number line.

Figure 1–12 illustrates $a < b$ when a and b are both negative.

In Problems 11 through 15 you are asked to prove the following theorems.

THEOREM 3. *If $a < b$ and $c < 0$, then $ac > bc$.*

THEOREM 4. *If $a > b > 0$, then*

$$\frac{1}{a} < \frac{1}{b}.$$

THEOREM 5. *If $a > 0 > b$, then*

$$\frac{1}{a} > 0 > \frac{1}{b}.$$

THEOREM 6. *If $a < b < 0$, then*

$$\frac{1}{a} > \frac{1}{b}.$$

THEOREM 7. *If $a < b$ and $b < c$, then $a < c$.*

Remark 3. Theorem 7 is known as the transitive property of inequalities.

PROBLEMS

For each of the following ordered pairs of numbers (a, b) (Problems 1 through 10), write $a < b$ or $b < a$, whichever is correct. For example, for $(2, -3)$ write $-3 < 2$, and for $(5, 7)$ write $5 < 7$. Illustrate on a number line like that in Fig. 1–11.

1. $(0, -1)$ 2. $(1, 0)$ 3. $(2, 3)$
4. $(1, -2)$ 5. $(-2, -3)$ 6. $(\sqrt{2}, \sqrt{3})$
7. $(2, \sqrt{2})$ 8. $(3, 2\sqrt{2})$ 9. $(\frac{1}{2}, \frac{1}{3})$

10. $\left(\dfrac{1}{(-2)}, \dfrac{1}{(-3)} \right)$ 11. Prove Theorem 3.

12. Prove Theorem 4.   13. Prove Theorem 5.

14. Prove Theorem 6.   15. Prove Theorem 7.

16. Prove: If $a > b > 0$, then $a^2 > b^2$.

17. Prove: If $a > b > 0$, then $\sqrt{a} > \sqrt{b}$.

18. Prove: If a and b are positive real numbers, then

$$\frac{a + b}{2} \geq \sqrt{ab}.$$

1–7   Absolute value. It is often useful to have a symbol that represents the *magnitude* of a number without regard to its sign. For example, in the sense we intend, both $+3$ and -3 have the same magnitude, 3. The technical name used, in addition to the word *magnitude*, is *absolute value*. The absolute value of a real number x is denoted by $|x|$, which is read "absolute value of x." Thus,

$$|3| = 3, \qquad |-3| = 3, \qquad |0| = 0.$$

There are three equivalent ways that $|x|$ can be defined in terms of x. Of course, when x is positive, we just have $|x| = x$. But if x is negative, the positive number of the same magnitude is $-x$. Thus, if $x = -3$, then $-x = 3$ and $|x| = -x$. The first way of defining $|x|$ follows from these considerations.

DEFINITION. (a) *Let x be a real number. The absolute value of x is x itself when x is positive or zero, and is $-x$ when x is negative:*

$$|x| = \begin{cases} x & \text{if } x \geq 0 \\ -x & \text{if } x < 0. \end{cases} \tag{1}$$

Notice that

$$(-x)^2 = x^2 = |x|^2.$$

Thus by taking $|x|$ as the nonnegative square root of x^2, we have a second (but equivalent) definition for absolute value.

DEFINITION. (b) $$|x| = \sqrt{x^2}.$$ (2)

EXAMPLE 1. $|-7| = \sqrt{(-7)^2} = \sqrt{49} = 7.$

Finally, given the real number x, we can examine both x and $-x$. If $x \neq 0$, one of these is positive and the other is negative. The positive number is greater than the negative, so we can also say that $|x|$ is the maximum of the two numbers x and $-x$.

DEFINITION. (c) $$|x| = \max \{x, -x\}.$$ (3)

EXAMPLE 2. $$|5| = \max \{5, -5\} = 5,$$
$$|-5| = \max \{-5, 5\} = 5,$$
and
$$|0| = \max \{0, 0\} = 0.$$

Geometric interpretations of |x|. By applying Eq. (4) of Article 1-3, the distance between the point $P(x, 0)$ and the origin $O(0, 0)$ is

$$d = \sqrt{(x - 0)^2 + (0 - 0)^2} = \sqrt{x^2} = |x|.$$ (4)

Thus we can say that

$|x|$ is the distance, in x-units, between the origin and the point $P(x, 0)$.

Figure 1-13(a) illustrates

$$|x_2| = P_2 O, \qquad |x_1| = OP_1$$

for points $P_2(x_2, O)$ and $P_1(x_1, 0)$, with x_2 negative and x_1 positive.

If we want to describe the set of points on the x-axis that are not more than two units away from the origin, we simply require that

$$|x| \leq 2.$$ (5a)

Figure 1-13

Figure 1–13(b) shows these points; they are those for which

$$-2 \leq x \leq 2. \tag{5b}$$

Note that we can apply the distance formula to the points $P(x, y)$ and $Q(0, y)$ to get

$$d = \sqrt{(x - 0)^2 + (y - y)^2} = \sqrt{x^2} = |x|,$$

because P and Q have the same y-coordinates. Thus, another interpretation for $|x|$ is the distance from a point $Q(0, y)$ on the y-axis to a point $P(x, y)$.

Sometimes we want to interpret an inequality like

$$|x - a| < 3 \tag{6}$$

geometrically. Now

$$|x - a| = \sqrt{(x - a)^2} \tag{7}$$

is just the distance between the points $P(x, 0)$ and $A(a, 0)$ on the x-axis. Hence the given inequality describes those points P that are on the x-axis and less than three units away from A. Such points have x-coordinates between $a - 3$ and $a + 3$. (See Fig. 1–13c.)

An inequality like

$$|x - a| > 3 \tag{8}$$

can be interpreted geometrically also. Since

$$|x - a| = \sqrt{|x - a|^2} \tag{9}$$

is the distance between the points $P(x, 0)$ and $A(a, 0)$ on the x-axis, the given inequality describes those points P that are on the x-axis and more than three units away from A. Such points have x-coordinates which are either greater than $a + 3$ or less than $a - 3$ (see Fig. 1–13d).

There is an algebraic way of converting the statement

$$|x - a| < 3 \tag{10a}$$

into the equivalent statement

$$a - 3 < x < a + 3. \tag{10b}$$

This is how it goes:

$$|x - a| < 3 \Leftrightarrow x - a \text{ is a number between } -3 \text{ and } +3$$
$$\Leftrightarrow -3 < x - a < +3$$
$$(\text{now add } a)$$
$$\Leftrightarrow a - 3 < x < a + 3.$$

The double-headed double arrow, $\Leftrightarrow$, is read either "if and only if" or "is equivalent to."

EXAMPLE 3. Which points on the x-axis satisfy the inequality $|x - 3| < 5$?

Solution. $|x - 3| < 5 \Leftrightarrow -5 < x - 3 < 5$

$$\Leftrightarrow 3 - 5 < x < 3 + 5, \quad \text{or} \quad -2 < x < 8.$$

Notice that these points are in an interval 10 units long (from -2 to $+8$), with center at $x = 3$. (See Fig. 1–14a.)

In the next example, we again consider the inequality $|x - 3| < 5$, but now we interpret this as describing a *set of points in the xy-plane*, where y need not be zero.

Figure 1–14(a)

EXAMPLE 4. Which points $P(x, y)$ in the plane satisfy the inequality

$$|x - 3| < 5?$$

Solution. The distance between the points $P(x, y)$ and $Q(3, y)$ is

$$|QP| = \sqrt{(x - 3)^2 + (y - y)^2} = |x - 3|,$$

because P and Q have the same y-coordinate. The locus* of $Q(3, y)$ is the line $x = 3$ parallel to the y-axis. The given inequality describes points P that lie within five units of this line; that is, between the parallel lines

$$x = -2 \quad \text{and} \quad x = 8.$$

(See Fig. 1–14b.)

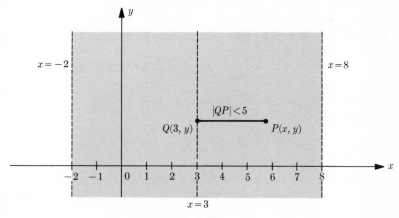

Figure 1–14(b)

---

* The *locus* is the set of points which satisfies a given condition. For instance, the set of points on the x-axis, $-2 < x < 4$, is the locus of the inequality $|x - 1| < 3$.

Remark. When an inequality of the form

$$|x - a| < h \tag{11a}$$

is given, it is always equivalent to

$$- h < x - a < h \quad \text{or} \quad a - h < x < a + h. \tag{11b}$$

But the corresponding points may be

(a) an interval of length $2h$, centered at a, on the x-axis, or
(b) a strip between the parallel lines $x = a - h$ and $x = a + h$ in the xy-plane.

EXAMPLE 5.   Use inequalities and absolute values to describe the points inside the rectangle with vertices $A(-1, -2)$, $B(5, -2)$, $C(5, 4)$, and $D(-1, 4)$.

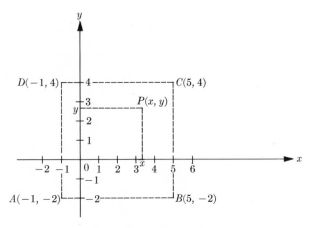

Figure 1–15

Solution. The rectangle $ABCD$ (actually a square) is shown in Fig. 1–15. A point $P(x, y)$ is inside it if and only if

$$-1 < x < 5 \quad \text{and} \quad -2 < y < 4.$$

The interval on the x-axis from -1 to 5 is six units long and is centered at $x = 2$. The points with x between -1 and 5 therefore satisfy the Inequality (11a) with $a = 2$ and $h = 3$:

$$|x - 2| < 3.$$

That is,

$$-1 < x < 5 \Leftrightarrow |x - 2| < 3.$$

Similarly, the y-interval from -2 to 4 is six units long, but its center is at $y = 1$. Therefore,

$$-2 < y < 4 \Leftrightarrow |y - 1| < 3.$$

Hence, $P(x, y)$ is inside the square $ABCD$ if and only if

$$|x - 2| < 3 \quad \text{and} \quad |y - 1| < 3.$$

Examples 4 and 5 have illustrated some of the ways that absolute values can be used to describe sets of points in the plane. In Example 4, there is no restriction on y and the resulting set of points is the intersection of the half-plane to the right of the line $x = -2$ and the half-plane to the left of the line $x = +8$. In Example 5, the interior of the rectangle is the intersection of four half-planes:

(a) the half-plane to the right of the line $x = -1$,

(b) the half-plane to the left of the line $x = 5$,

(c) the half-plane above the line $y = -2$,

(d) the half-plane below the line $y = 4$.

A point $P(x, y)$ is in this intersection if and only if its coordinates simultaneously satisfy the four inequalities

$$x > -1, \quad x < 5, \quad y > -2, \quad y < 4.$$

In the next two examples, we will use the algebraic definitions of $|x|$ and $|y|$ to find the sets of points described by $|x| + |y| = 2$ and $|x| + |y| > 2$.

EXAMPLE 6. Describe (without the use of absolute value) and sketch the graph described by $|x| + |y| = 2$.

Solution. Because $|y|$ is never negative, the given equation cannot be satisfied by any points for which $|x| > 2$. Likewise, there are no points on the locus with $|y| > 2$. Hence the entire locus lies inside or on the square bounded by the lines $x = 2$, $x = -2$, $y = 2$, $y = -2$. Also, because

$$|-x| = |x| \quad \text{and} \quad |-y| = |y|,$$

the points $P_2(-x, y)$, $P_3(-x, -y)$, and $P_4(x, -y)$ in the second, third, and fourth quadrants are in the set if and only if the point $P_1(x, y)$ in the first

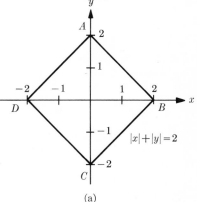

(a)

Figure 1–16(a)

quadrant is on it. Now the points where $x \geq 0$ and $y \geq 0$ also satisfy $|x| = x$ and $|y| = y$, and $|x| + |y| = 2$ becomes just $x + y = 2$. Therefore,

> in the first quadrant, the desired locus coincides with the line segment $\overline{AB}$ joining the points $A(0, 2)$ and $B(2, 0)$.

In the second quadrant, $x \leq 0$ so $|x| = -x$ but $|y| = y$; therefore we have $-x + y = 2$ for points on $\overline{DA}$. The segment in the fourth quadrant is the intersection of the line $x - y = 2$ and the half-planes $x > 0$, $y < 0$, together with the points $B(2, 0)$ and $C(0, -2)$. (How would you describe the segment in the third quadrant?) The entire locus consists of points on the square $ABCD$ as shown in Fig. 1–16(a).

EXAMPLE 7. Describe (without the use of absolute value) and sketch the points $P(x, y)$ in the plane that satisfy the inequality

$$|x| + |y| > 2.$$

Solution. By definition (a) of absolute value the inequality

$$|x| + |y| > 2$$

implies the following inequalities:

$$
\begin{array}{lll}
x + y > 2 & \text{for} & x \geq 0, y \geq 0, \\
-x + y > 2 & \text{for} & x < 0, y \geq 0, \\
-x - y > 2 & \text{for} & x < 0, y < 0, \\
x - y > 2 & \text{for} & x \geq 0, y < 0.
\end{array}
$$

Rewritten, the first two inequalities become

$$y > -x + 2$$
$$y > x + 2.$$

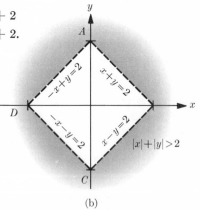

So from algebra we know that the region *above* each of the lines $x + y = 2$ and $-x + y = 2$ is shaded. The last two inequalities become

$$y < -x - 2, \; y < x - 2.$$

So the region *below* each of the lines $-x - y = 2$ and $x - y = 2$ is shaded. (See Fig. 1–16b.) The locus consists of all points that are outside the square $ABCD$.

(b)

Figure 1–16(b)

PROBLEMS

The following inequalities and equations (1 through 12) describe certain sets of points on the x-axis. Describe each set (without the use of absolute values) and sketch.

1. $|x| < 4$
2. $|2x| < 4$
3. $|x - 2| \leq 5$
4. $|x + 2| < 5$
5. $|2x - 4| \geq 5$
6. $|2x + 4| < 6$
7. $|x - 2| > 3$
8. $|x + 3| > 2$
9. $|2x + 3| \leq 4$
10. $|x| + |x - 1| = 3$
11. $|x| + |x - 3| = 3$
12. $|x| + |x - 3| < 3$

The following inequalities and equations describe sets of points $P(x, y)$ in the plane. Describe each set (without the use of absolute values) and sketch.

13. $|x| < 1$
14. $|y| < 1$
15. $|x| = |y|$
16. $|y| < |x|$
17. $|y| > |x|$
18. $|x + y| = 2$
19. $|x + y| < 2$
20. $|x + y| > 2$
21. $|x| + |y| = 1$
22. $|x| + |y| < 1$
23. $|x - 3| < 1 \quad$ and $\quad |y - 2| < 5$
24. $|x + 1| < 1 \quad$ and $\quad -2 < y < 3$

1-8 Absolute values of sums, products, quotients, and differences.
Sums. If a and b are real numbers, then

$$a \leq |a| \qquad \text{and} \qquad b \leq |b|.$$

Adding, we get

$$a + b \leq |a| + |b|, \tag{1a}$$

Similarly,

$$-a \leq |a| \qquad \text{and} \qquad -b \leq |b|,$$

so

$$-a - b \leq |a| + |b|. \tag{1b}$$

Since both $a + b$ and $-(a + b)$ are less than or equal to $|a| + |b|$, we conclude that their maximum is also $\leq |a| + |b|$. Therefore,

$$|a + b| = \max \{a + b, -a - b\}$$
$$\leq |a| + |b|.$$

This result,

$$\boxed{|a + b| \leq |a| + |b|,} \tag{2}$$

is often called the *triangle inequality*, because it resembles the theorem *the length of any side of a triangle is less than the sum of the lengths of the other two sides.*

EXAMPLE 1. If a is either 7 or -7 and b is either 4 or -4, then $a + b$ can equal 11, 3, -3, or -11. In every case, $|a| = 7$, $|b| = 4$, so $|a| + |b| = 11$, but $|a + b| = 3$ or $|a + b| = 11$. Hence, for every combination of signs, $|a + b|$ is either less than or equal to $|a| + |b|$.

Products. If a and b are any real numbers,

$$(ab)^2 = a^2 b^2.$$

By Definition (b) of Article 1–7

$$|ab| = \sqrt{(ab)^2} = \sqrt{a^2 b^2} = \sqrt{a^2} \sqrt{b^2},$$

so

$$\boxed{|ab| = |a|\,|b|.} \tag{3}$$

EXAMPLE 2. If $a = -2$, $b = 3$, then

$$ab = -6$$

and

$$|ab| = 6, \qquad |a| = 2, \qquad |b| = 3,$$

so

$$|ab| = |a|\,|b|.$$

Quotients. If a and b are real numbers and $b \neq 0$, then

$$\left(\frac{a}{b}\right)^2 = \frac{a^2}{b^2}.$$

Hence

$$\left|\frac{a}{b}\right| = \sqrt{\left(\frac{a}{b}\right)^2} = \sqrt{\frac{a^2}{b^2}} = \frac{\sqrt{a^2}}{\sqrt{b^2}} = \frac{|a|}{|b|}.$$

$$\boxed{\left|\frac{a}{b}\right| = \frac{|a|}{|b|} \qquad \text{if} \qquad b \neq 0.} \tag{4}$$

Differences. There are two kinds of inequalities that apply to $|a - b|$. In the first place, because we can apply the triangle inequality to the equation

$$a - b = a + (-b),$$

we get

$$|a - b| = |a + (-b)| \leq |a| + |-b|.$$

But $|-b| = |b|$, so Inequality (2) leads to

$$\boxed{|a - b| \leq |a| + |b|.} \tag{5}$$

This is really not anything new; it is just (2) in another form.

The second kind of inequality results from applying the triangle inequality to the equation

$$a = (a - b) + b$$

to get

$$|a| = |(a - b) + b| \leq |a - b| + |b|.$$

If we add $- |b|$ to both sides of this we get

$$|a| - |b| \leq |a - b|,$$

or, turning things around, we have

$$\boxed{|a - b| \geq |a| - |b|.} \tag{6}$$

Inequality (6) can be stated as "the absolute value of the difference of two numbers is greater than or equal to the difference of their absolute values."

EXAMPLE 3.

(a) $\quad |7 - 4| \geq |7| - |4|$

$\qquad 3 \geq 3,$

(b) $\quad |4 - 7| \geq |4| - |7|$

$\qquad 3 \geq -3,$

(c) $|4 - (-7)| \geq |4| - |-7|$

$\qquad 11 \geq -3,$

(d) $|7 - (-4)| \geq |7| - |-4|$

$\qquad 11 \geq 3.$

PROBLEMS

1. Use the triangle inequality twice in succession to prove that, if a, b, and c are real numbers, then

$$|a + b + c| \leq |a| + |b| + |c|.$$

Try to generalize this result.

2. Prove that $|a - b - c| \geq |a| - |b| - |c|$. Try to generalize this result.

If it is known that $|a| < 3$ and $|b| \leq 0.5$, which of the following statements (3 through 8) must be true, and which might be false? Prove the ones that must be true and give examples showing why the others might be false.

3. $|a + b| < 3.5$

4. $|a + b| \geq 3.5$

5. $|a + b| \geq 2.5$

6. $|ab| \leq 1.5$

7. $|ab| \geq 1.5$

8. $\left| \dfrac{a}{b} \right| < 6, \quad b \neq 0$

9. Prove that, if $|a| \leq m$ and $|b| \leq n$, then

(a) $|a + b| \leq m + n$,

(b) $|ab| \leq mn$.

Illustrate with specific numerical values of a, b, m, and n.

10. Prove that, if $|a| \geq m$ and $|b| \leq n$, then

(a) $|a + b| \geq m - n$,

(b) $\left|\dfrac{b}{a}\right| \leq \dfrac{n}{m}$ if $m > 0$.

Illustrate with specific numerical values of a, b, m, and n.

11. Prove that if $a^2 < b^2$, then $|a| < |b|$. Is the converse true?

1–9 Intervals and neighborhoods. There are four kinds of intervals of real numbers which we shall consider:

$$\{x \mid a < x < b\} \text{ (also written } (a, b) \text{ or }]a, b[ ) \qquad (1a)$$

is all x between a and b;

$$\{x \mid a \leq x < b\} \text{ (also written } [a, b)) \qquad (1b)$$

is a and all x between a and b;

$$\{x \mid a < x \leq b\} \text{ (also written } (a, b]) \qquad (1c)$$

is b and all x between a and b;

$$\{x \mid a \leq x \leq b\} \text{ (also written } [a, b]) \qquad (1d)$$

is a and b and all x between a and b.

The first of these is called an *open interval*. Figure 1–17 shows how we can represent an open interval (a, b) graphically. The open circles at a and at b indicate that points a and b are omitted from the interval. The heavy line between the open circles indicates the set of all x's between a and b.

Figure 1–17

Figure 1–18

The interval $[a, b]$ described by (1d) is called a *closed interval*. It contains both endpoints. Figure 1–18 shows how we can represent such a closed interval graphically.

Figure 1-19

The intervals in (1b) and (1c) are called *half-open* (or *half-closed*). In each case, only the endpoint where the square bracket occurs is to be included, along with the points (or numbers) between a and b. Figure 1-19 shows graphs of these intervals.

If c is any real number and $a < c < b$, we say that "c is in the open interval (a, b)" or that "the open interval (a, b) contains (or covers) c."

DEFINITION. *The set of all numbers in an open interval (a, b) that contains c is called a* neighborhood *of* c.

For example, if $c = 2$, the open intervals

$$(1, 3), \quad (0, 5), \quad (-1, 3) \tag{2a}$$

are three different neighborhoods of c. But

$$(2, 4), \quad (0, 2), \quad [2, 4), \quad [-1, 3] \tag{2b}$$

are not neighborhoods of 2, because the first two intervals do not contain 2 and the last two are not open.

The special features of a *neighborhood* of c are:
  (a) It is an open interval.
  (b) It contains c.
As a consequence, every open interval is a neighborhood of every point in it. Thus, the open interval $(0, 3)$ is a neighborhood of every number between 0 and 3.

In the theory of limits (see Chapter 3) we shall be interested in functions in a *deleted neighborhood* of c, that is a neighborhood of c from which c is omitted. For instance, if

$$f(t) = \frac{t^2 - 9}{t - 3} \tag{3a}$$

is the value of a function f at t and t is a real number different from 3, we can study how the function values $f(t)$ behave when t is near, but not at, 3. In this example, $t^2 - 9 = (t - 3)(t + 3)$, so,

$$f(t) = \frac{(t - 3)(t + 3)}{(t - 3)} = t + 3, t \neq 3. \tag{3b}$$

Now we see right away that when t is near 3, $t + 3$ is near 6, so $f(t)$ has values near 6 when t has any value near, but different from, 3.

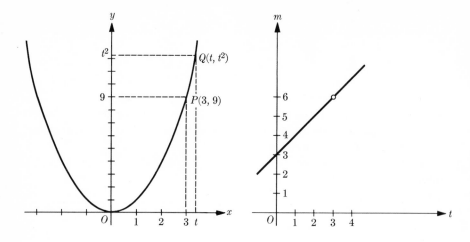

Figure 1–20   **Figure 1–21**

The particular expression (3a) could arise in the following way. The point $P(3, 9)$ is on the graph of $y = x^2$. If t is a number near 3, but not equal to 3, the point $Q(t, t^2)$ is a second point on the graph and $\overleftrightarrow{PQ}$ is a secant line through P and the nearby point Q. The slope of that secant line (see Fig. 1–20) is

$$\frac{\text{rise from } P \text{ to } Q}{\text{run from } P \text{ to } Q} = \frac{y_Q - y_P}{x_Q - x_P} = \frac{t^2 - 9}{t - 3}. \qquad (4a)$$

Because Q is not the same point as P, $t \neq 3$. Therefore, $t - 3$ is not zero, and the slope of $\overleftrightarrow{PQ}$ is

$$m_{PQ} = t + 3, \qquad t \neq 3. \qquad (4b)$$

Figure 1–21 shows the graph of this slope function $m = t + 3$ for t near, but not at, 3. The open circle indicates that the point $(3, 6)$ is not on the graph. But when t is near 3, $t + 3$ is near 6.

Remark 1. In Fig. 1–20, we show Q above and to the right of P, indicating $t > 3$. This means that the slope of $\overleftrightarrow{PQ}$ is greater than (but near) 6 when t is greater than (but near) 3. Had we chosen Q to the left of, and below, P on the curve, we would still have found $t + 3$ for the slope of $\overleftrightarrow{PQ}$, and this would be slightly less than 6, when t is slightly less than 3. So secant lines $\overleftrightarrow{PQ}$ through P have slopes very close to 6 when Q is near P, and in Chapter 2 we will define the tangent to the graph of $y = x^2$ at $P(3, 9)$ as the line through P with slope 6.

Remark 2. In the example discussed above, the slope function of $\overleftrightarrow{PQ}$ is given by $m = t + 3$, $t \neq 3$. The number $t = 3$ is not in the *domain* of this function.* But we could choose a small positive number h, and

Figure 1–22

every point of the neighborhood from $3 - h$ to $3 + h$, *except 3 itself*, would be in the domain. Such a neighborhood of 3, from which the single point $t = 3$ has been deleted, is an example of a deleted neighborhood of 3 (Fig. 1–22).

Remark 3. Ordinarily, we find that *symmetric* deleted neighborhoods (like the one shown in Fig. 1–22) work as well as nonsymmetric ones. An example of a nonsymmetric deleted neighborhood of 3 would be the union of the intervals

Figure 1–23

$$(3 - h, 3) \quad \text{and} \quad (3, 3 + 2h)$$

as shown in Fig. 1–23.

One advantage of a symmetric deleted neighborhood is that it can always be characterized briefly by using absolute values. For example, the deleted neighborhood of $t = 3$ in Fig. 1–22 is the set of all values of t such that

$$0 < |t - 3| < h, \tag{5}$$

because the left inequality in (5) requires that $t \neq 3$ and the right inequality specifies that the distance between 3 and t be less than h; that is, t is within h units of 3.

PROBLEMS

1. Describe the set of t values that satisfies

$$0 < |t - 2| < 5,$$

and sketch the corresponding deleted neighborhood. What number is deleted? How far is it from one end to the other of this deleted neighborhood?

2. Suppose that Inequality (5) is changed to $|t - 3| < h$. How do you describe the set of t values that satisfies this new inequality? Sketch. How does it differ from Fig. 1–22?

---

* Chapter 2 is an extensive treatment of functions. Domain is defined in Article 2–2.

3. For the curve $y = x^2$ shown in Fig. 1–20, suppose that $A(2, 4)$ and $B(t, t^2)$ are two points on the graph, with B near A, but different from A. Find an equation for the slope m of the secant line $\overleftrightarrow{AB}$. If B is very near A, what number is m very nearly equal to?

4. If $C(x, x^2)$ and $D(t, t^2)$ are two points ($C \neq D$) on the graph of the curve $y = x^2$, what is the slope m of the secant line $\overleftrightarrow{CD}$? If t is very nearly equal to x (that is, t is in a deleted neighborhood $0 < |t - x| < h$, for h a small positive number) what is m very nearly equal to?

5. If $A(x, 1/x)$ and $B(t, 1/t)$ are two points ($A \neq B$) on the graph of $y = 1/x$, what is the slope of the secant line $\overleftrightarrow{AB}$? What is m approximately equal to when t is close to x?

6. If $A(x, \sqrt{x})$ and $B(t, \sqrt{t})$ are two points ($A \neq B$) on the graph of $y = \sqrt{x}$, what is the slope m of the secant line $\overleftrightarrow{AB}$? What number is m approximately equal to if $x = 4$ and t is close to 4?

REVIEW QUESTIONS AND EXERCISES FOR CHAPTER 1

1. Define what is meant by the *slope* of a straight line. How would you find the slope of a straight line from its graph? From its equation?

2. In Fig. 1–24, the lines L_1, L_2, and L_3 have slopes m_1, m_2, m_3, respectively. Which slope is algebraically least? Greatest? Write the three slopes in order of increasing size with the symbols for "less than" or "greater than" correctly inserted between them.

3. Describe the family of lines $y - y_1 = m(x - x_1)$:

(a) If (x_1, y_1) is fixed and different lines are drawn for different values of m.

(b) If m and x_1 are fixed and different lines are drawn for different values of y_1.

4. Give three equivalent definitions of absolute value. What is the geometric interpretation of $|x|$ on the x-axis? of $|x - a|$?

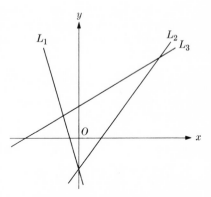

Fig. 1–24. Lines L_1, L_2, L_3 have slopes m_1, m_2, m_3 respectively.

5. Which points on the x-axis satisfy the inequality $|x - a| < h$? Which points $P(x, y)$ in the plane satisfy the inequality $|x - a| < h$?

6. What is the triangle inequality? How did it get its name? Using absolute values, write equivalent expressions for $|ab|$ and $|a/b|$. Complete the following inequality using $|a|$ and $|b|$: _____ $\leq |a - b| \leq$ _____.

7. Use inequalities to describe four kinds of intervals. Use square brackets and parentheses to represent these intervals in another way. What is the geometric interpretation of each of these intervals?

8. Define what is meant by a neighborhood of r, a real number. What are two special features of such a neighborhood? Give an example of a neighborhood of r and represent it in three different ways. What is the difference between a neighborhood of r and the corresponding deleted neighborhood?

1.   (a) Plot the points $A(8, 1)$, $B(2, 10)$, $C(-4, 6)$, $D(2, -3)$, $E(4\frac{2}{3}, 6)$.

(b) Find the slopes of the lines $\overleftrightarrow{AB}$, $\overleftrightarrow{BC}$, $\overleftrightarrow{CD}$, $\overleftrightarrow{DA}$, $\overleftrightarrow{CE}$, $\overleftrightarrow{BD}$.

(c) Do four of the five points A, B, C, D, E form a parallelogram? (Why?)

(d) Do three of the five points lie on a common straight line? (Why?)

(e) Does the origin $(0, 0)$ lie on a straight line through two of the five points? (Why?)

(f) Find equations of the lines $\overleftrightarrow{AB}$, $\overleftrightarrow{CD}$, $\overleftrightarrow{AD}$, $\overleftrightarrow{CE}$, $\overleftrightarrow{BD}$.

(g) Find the coordinates of the points in which the lines $\overleftrightarrow{AB}$, $\overleftrightarrow{CD}$, $\overleftrightarrow{AD}$, $\overleftrightarrow{CE}$, $\overleftrightarrow{BD}$ intersect the x- and y-axes.

2.   Given the straight line $2y - 3x = 4$ and the point $(1, -3)$.

(a) Find the equation of the straight line through the given point and perpendicular to the given line.

(b) Find the shortest distance from the given point to the given line.

3.   Plot the three points $A(6, 4)$, $B(4, -3)$, and $C(-2, 3)$.

(a) Is triangle ABC a right triangle? Why?

(b) Is it isosceles? Why?

(c) Does the origin lie inside, outside, or on the boundary of the triangle? Why?

(d) If C is replaced by a point $C'(-2, y)$ such that angle $C'BA$ is a right angle, find y, the ordinate of C'.

4.   Find the equations of the straight lines passing through the origin which are tangent to the circle of center $(2, 1)$ and radius 2.

5.   Let $P_1(x_1, y_1)$ and $P_2(x_2, y_2)$ be any two points. Find the coordinates of the midpoint of $\overline{P_1P_2}$.

6.   The x- and y-intercepts of a line L are respectively a and b. Show that an equation of L is $(x/a) + (y/b) = 1$.

7.   Given the line L: $ax + by + c = 0$. Find (a) its slope, (b) its y-intercept, (c) its x-intercept, (d) the line through the origin perpendicular to L.

8.   Show that the distance from a point $P(x_1, y_1)$ to a line $ax + by + c = 0$ is equal to

$$\frac{|ax_1 + by_1 + c|}{\sqrt{a^2 + b^2}}.$$

(There are neat solutions of this problem in Vol. 59, 1952, of the *American Mathematical Monthly*, pp. 242 and 248.)

9.   How many circles can you find that are tangent to the three lines

$$L_1: \ x + y = 1; \qquad L_2: \ y = x + 1; \qquad L_3: \ x - 3y = 1?$$

Give the center and radius of at least one such circle. You may use the result of Problem 8 that the distance from a point $P(x_1, y_1)$ to a line $ax + by + c = 0$ is

$$\frac{|ax_1 + by_1 + c|}{\sqrt{a^2 + b^2}}.$$

10. Find, in terms of b, b', and m, the perpendicular distance between the parallel lines $y = mx + b$ and $y = mx + b'$.

11. Given the two lines

$$L_1: a_1x + b_1y + c_1 = 0; \qquad L_2: a_2x + b_2y + c_2 = 0.$$

If k is a constant, what is the locus whose equation is

$$(a_1x + b_1y + c_1) + k(a_2x + b_2y + c_2) = 0?$$

12. Determine the coordinates of the point on the straight line $y = 3x + 1$ that is equidistant from $(0, 0)$ and $(-3, 4)$.

13. Find the equation of a straight line which is perpendicular to $5x - y = 1$ and is such that the area of the triangle formed by the x-axis, the y-axis, and the straight line is equal to 5.

The following inequalities describe sets of points $P(x, y)$ in the plane. Sketch each set.

14. $1 < x \leq 3 \qquad$ and $\qquad 2 \leq y < 3$

15. $-4 < x < 7 \qquad$ and $\qquad -9 < y < 5$

16. $|x - 3| \leq 2 \qquad$ and $\qquad |y + 2| < 3$

Use absolute values and inequalities to express the following facts.

17. The point t is closer to -3 than it is to the point b.

18. The point t is closer to the point b than it is to the origin.

19. The point t is farther from 2 than from the point b.

For each of the following inequalities give the interval or intervals on which the inequality is true.

20. $x^2 - x - 2 > 0$ $\qquad\qquad$ 21. $x^2 - 1 \geq 0$

22. $x^2 - 6x + 9 < 0$ $\qquad\qquad$ 23. $x^2 + 7x + 12 \leq 0$

Functions

2–1 Introduction. Calculus is used to study the behavior of functions. Conversely, specific functions and their graphs are often used to illustrate facts in calculus, to suggest theorems, or to provide counterexamples that disprove conjectures. In this chapter we are concerned with some properties of functions that do not depend upon our knowing any calculus.

For example, we know from algebra that the graph of the function

$$f(x) \;=\; 2x - 1, \qquad -3 \le x \le 3 \tag{1}$$

is a line segment joining the points $(-3, -7)$ and $(3, 5)$, as shown in Fig. 2–1. Looking at the graph, we can say that the function given by (1) is strictly increasing, is bounded below by -7, is bounded above by 5, has exactly one value $f(a)$ for any number a in $[-3, 3]$, has the value 0 for just one number x between 0 and 1, has range $[-7, 5]$, and maps the interval $[-3, 3]$ onto the interval $[-7, 5]$.

The words *range*, *increasing*, *bounded above*, and some others in the preceding sentence are technical terms that we shall define later. In the next section, we start with a definition of *function* and show how functions can be interpreted in a variety of ways. The following problems should be handled intuitively, using graphs to answer the questions in the way Fig. 2–1 was used above.

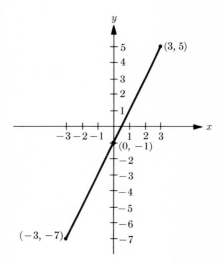

Figure 2–1

PROBLEMS

Graph each of the following problems (1 through 5) and then answer these questions:

(a) Is the function increasing or decreasing?

(b) Is it bounded above? bounded below? If so, by what numbers?

(c) How many zeros (solutions of $f(x) = 0$) does the function have? Where are they located?

39

(d) What is the range of the function?

1. $f(x) = 2x + 3, \quad -2 \le x \le 3$
2. $f(x) = 3 - 2x, \quad -2 \le x \le 3$
3. $f(x) = x, \quad 0 < x < 1$
4. $f(x) = |x|, \quad {}^{-}1 \le x \le 1$
5. $f(x) = \sin x, \quad -\pi \le x \le \pi$

2–2   What is a function?   There are three equivalent answers to this question, and they all involve a variety of ideas. Before stating any formal definition of function, we list the three answers in outline and block-diagram form:

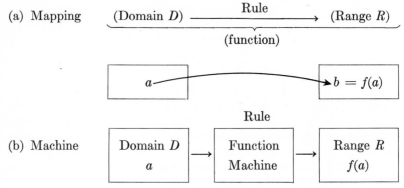

(a) Mapping   (Domain D) $\xrightarrow{\text{Rule}}$ (Range R)

$\underbrace{\hspace{5cm}}_{\text{(function)}}$

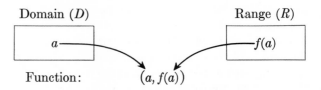

(b) Machine

(c) Set of ordered pairs: $\{(a, f(a)) \mid a \in D\}$

Domain (D) Range (R)

Function: $(a, f(a))$

Corresponding to these three equivalent ways of looking at a function, we have the following equivalent definitions.

DEFINITIONS.

(a) *A function f is a mapping that associates with each element a, in some set D (called the domain of f), a unique element b, in a set R, called the range of f. We also say that b is the value of function f at a, and write $b = f(a)$.*

(b) *A function f consists of a domain D and a rule for assigning to any element a in D a unique element $f(a)$. The collection of all elements $f(a)$, for a in D, is called the range of f.*

(c) *A function f is a set of ordered pairs of elements* $(a, f(a))$ *such that no two ordered pairs have the same first members and different second members.*

A *variable* is a symbol, such as x, that may take any value in some specified set of numbers. If we look at a function as an ordered pair, say (a, b), we call the variable a which yields the first of the two numbers in the ordered pair the *independent variable*. The second variable b is called the *dependent variable*. So the *domain* of the function is the set of all values taken on by the independent variable, and the range is the set of all values taken on by the dependent variable.

Remark 1. We can show that the three definitions of function are equivalent. To get one of the ordered pairs referred to in the third definition, from the mapping referred to in the first definition, one would select any element a from D, find the image $b = f(a)$ in R, and form the pair $(a, f(a)) = (a, b)$. If this is done for *all* elements a in D, the collection of all resulting ordered pairs (a, b) has the property that no two pairs (a_1, b_1) and (a_2, b_2) have $a_1 = a_2$ and $b_1 \neq b_2$, because the image of $a_1 = a_2$ under the mapping f is *unique*. Conversely, given a collection of ordered pairs as described in (c), if a is the first member of an ordered pair $(a, f(a))$, then there is only one such pair; thus the second member $f(a)$ is uniquely determined, and we call it the *image* of a under f. Thus the mapping for every a in D is indicated by

$$a \to f(a) = b,$$

and the first definition of function is equivalent to the third.

Finally, let us see whether the second definition of function (domain and rule) is equivalent to the third definition (set of ordered pairs). Starting with the domain-and-rule definition, if a is in D and the function machine gives a rule which assigns $f(a)$ as the unique associated value of the function, we form the pair $(a, f(a))$, and this is one of the ordered pairs called for in the third definition. Conversely, given all the ordered pairs $\{(a, f(a)) \mid a \in D\}$, the *rule* can be stated as follows:

Given any $a \in D$, find the unique ordered pair (a, b) in the set of ordered pairs and let $b = f(a)$.

So the second and third definitions of function are equivalent.

We have shown that the first and third as well as the third and second definitions of function are equivalent. Therefore, the three definitions are equivalent. (The first definition emphasizes *mapping*, the second emphasizes the *rule* given by a function machine for computing $f(a)$, and the third emphasizes *set* and is the most abstract of the three.)

Notations. We sometimes use a single letter, like f, g, h, F, F_1, F_2, or ϕ, to represent a function. Thus, if we want to emphasize the *mapping* action of f, we might write

$$f: x \to x^2, \qquad -\infty < x < \infty, \tag{1a}$$

read "f maps x into x^2."

The rule is implicit in the formula

$$f(x) = x^2, \tag{1b}$$

because Eq. (1b) says "square x to get the value of the function for any x in the domain of f."

Using ordered pairs, we might write the function defined by $f(x) = x^2$ as

$$f = \{(x, x^2) \mid x \text{ is any real number}\}, \tag{1c}$$

which is read: "f is the set of all ordered pairs of the form (x, x^2) such that x is any real number."

How is the *domain* specified in Eqs. (1a, b, c)? In (1a), the inequalities,

$$-\infty < x < \infty,$$

and in (1c), the words "x is any real number" say that the *domain* is the set of all real numbers. As written, Eq. (1b) does not say what the domain is. It is customary among mathematicians to rely on a general understanding that,

> when a rule (or formula) is given for $f(x)$ and the domain is not stated explicitly, the *natural domain* of f is the set of all values of x for which the formula makes sense when these values are substituted for x in that formula.

Thus, if the formula reads

$$f(x) = \sqrt{x}, \tag{2}$$

it is understood:

(a) that only real values are to be considered for x and for $\sqrt{x}$, and, therefore,

(b) the domain is the set of all $x \geq 0$.

Again, if

$$g(x) = \frac{1}{x}, \tag{3}$$

the understanding is that the natural domain of g is the set of all $x \neq 0$, because every nonzero real number has a reciprocal, but zero does not. (No number times zero is equal to one.)

Two restrictions should always be kept in mind. First, we must **never divide by zero.** Thus if we see $y = x/(x - 2)$, we must always think "$x \neq 2$," even if this restriction is not stated explicitly. Second, we are dealing exclusively with real-valued functions. This means that the domain must be suitably restricted when we have square roots, or fourth roots, or other even roots. For example, if $y = \sqrt{4 - x^2}$, we should also think "x^2 must not be greater than 4; that is, the domain must not extend beyond the interval $-2 \leq x \leq +2$, or $|x| \leq 2$."

Remark 2. Since a function is determined by the domain and a rule, we shall often resort to such shorthand expressions as "consider the function $f(x) = x/(x - 2)$" in place of the more precise expression "let f be a function whose domain is the set of all real numbers $x \neq 2$ and which associates with x the number $f(x) = x/(x - 2)$." Or again we may say, simply, "consider the function $y = x^2$," when we actually mean "the function defined on the domain of all real numbers which assigns the value x^2 to the function at x."

PROBLEMS

1. Suppose f is a function whose domain is the interval $[-3, 2]$ with values given by the rule

$$f(x) = \begin{cases} 2 & \text{when} & -3 \leq x < 0 \\ x & \text{when} & 0 \leq x < 1 \\ 2 - x & \text{when} & 1 \leq x \leq 2. \end{cases}$$

Sketch a graph of f. What is the range? How many solutions are there of the equation $f(x) = 0$? of $f(x) = 1$? of $f(x) = 2$?

2. A function g has the following rule: "Choose any number x, add 3, multiply the result by x, add 4, multiply that result by x, subtract 7." Give a formula for $g(x)$, in two forms: (a) follow the steps given verbally, and (b) state as a polynomial in x.

In each problem (3 through 10) state an equivalent rule for computing $f(x)$, not using absolute values or square roots. The rule may take different forms on different parts of the domain. Sketch the graph of $y = f(x)$.

3. $f(x) = |2x|$, $\quad -3 \leq x \leq 3$

4. $f(x) = x + |x|$, $\quad -2 \leq x \leq 2$

5. $f(x) = |\sin x|$, $\quad -\pi \leq x \leq \pi$

6. $f(x) = \sin x + |\sin x|$, $\quad -\pi \leq x \leq \pi$

7. $f(x) = |x - 2|$, $\quad 0 \leq x \leq 5$

8. $f(x) = |2x - 1|$, $\quad 0 \leq x \leq 3$

9. $f(x) = \sqrt{x^2 - 2x + 1}$, $\quad -1 \leq x \leq 3$

10. $f(x) = x + \sqrt{4x^2 - 4x + 1}$, $\quad 0 \leq x \leq 2$

In each problem (11 through 21) what is the *natural domain* of the given function?

11. $f(x) = \dfrac{x}{\sqrt{x-1}}$ 12. $f(x) = \dfrac{\sqrt{x-1}}{x}$

13. $f(x) = \dfrac{\sqrt{1-x}}{x}$ 14. $f(x) = x\sqrt{2+x}$

15. $f(x) = \sqrt{(2+2x)(3-x)}$ 16. $f(x) = \sqrt{x^2-1}$

17. $f(x) = \sqrt{x^3-x}$ 18. $f(x) = \sqrt[4]{-x^2}$

19. $y = \dfrac{x^2}{x^2+1}$ 20. $y = \sqrt{\dfrac{x}{x+1}}$ 21. $y = x - \dfrac{1}{x}$

22. Describe the domain of the variable x without the use of the "absolute value" symbol in each of the following cases: (a) $|x| < 2$, (b) $|x| \geq 2$, (c) $|x - 1| \leq 3$, (d) $|x - 2| < 2$ and simultaneously x must satisfy the additional restriction $|x - 3| \geq 1$.

23. When does $|1 - x|$ equal $1 - x$ and when does it equal $x - 1$?

2–3   Equal functions. Functions of more than one variable.   When a familiar formula is used along with a domain that is stated explicitly, the resulting function need not be the same as it would be if the same formula were applied to its natural domain.   Thus, for example, the functions f_1, f_2, and f_3, given by

$$f_1(x) = \frac{1}{x}, \quad x \neq 0 \text{ (the natural domain)}, \tag{4a}$$

$$f_2(x) = \frac{1}{x}, \quad x > 0 \text{ (domain, the positive real numbers)}, \tag{4b}$$

$$f_3(x) = \frac{1}{x}, \quad 0 < x < 1 \text{ (domain, the interval } (0, 1)), \tag{4c}$$

are not the same.   The graphs of f_1, f_2, f_3 are indicated in Fig. 2–2.   In Fig. 2–2(c), note the different scales on the x- and y-axes.   (The point $(1, 1)$ is not on the curve.)

DEFINITION.   *Two functions, f and g, are equal if and only if they have the same domain, $D_f = D_g$, and the values of $f(x)$ and $g(x)$ are equal for each x in their domain.*

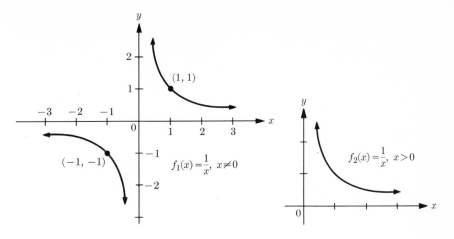

Figure 2–2(a), (b)

For example, since $|x|$ and $\sqrt{x^2}$ are both defined for all real numbers x, and the values are the same for every x, the two functions

$$f(x) = |x|$$

and

$$g(x) = \sqrt{x^2}$$

are equal. But the functions

$$h(x) = x$$

and

$$\phi(x) = \frac{x(x-1)}{x-1}$$

are not equal, because the domain of h contains the number $x = 1$ and the domain of ϕ does not.

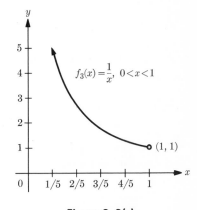

Figure 2–2(c)

Remark 1. Once the domain and the rule of a function are given, the set of all ordered pairs (x, y) can, at least in theory, be computed by a machine into which the elements of the domain are fed, one after another. The machine computes the value of y for the input x. Thus if the domain is the set of all real numbers and with the number x the function associates the number

$$y = f(x) = x^2 + 5,$$

we think of a machine so constructed that when a real number x is fed into it, the machine produces $x^2 + 5$ as the result (Fig. 2–3). Whatever argument is substituted for x, the machine squares it and adds 5. For instance,

$$f(2) = 2^2 + 5 = 9,$$

and

$$f(a + 3) = (a + 3)^2 + 5$$
$$= a^2 + 6a + 14.$$

Figure 2–3

Remark 2. Another way that a machine can be used to give the value of a function at a particular x is to store in the machine's "memory" a complete table of the pairs (x, y) that constitute the function. Then tell the machine the value of x and ask it to produce the corresponding y. Or, instead of a complete table, we may store in the machine a partial set of function-values, and compute others from these by interpolation. In practice, the memory of a computer has limited capacity. Hence it is better to compute the function-values as needed, rather than storing them. But whether they are computed or stored in the form of a table, what is important is that there be just one "answer" y corresponding to any given x (from the domain of the function). And when the values are given by a table, we may still say that there is a "rule" for determining the value of the function at a given x—the rule being, "look it up in the table." This is just what we do in evaluating logarithms.

Remark 3. The "function-is-a-machine" idea can be applied to functions defined by rules that are not simple formulas.

For example, suppose f is a function whose domain is the interval $[-2, 2]$ with values given by the rule

$$f(x) = \begin{cases} x & \text{when} & -2 \le x < 0, & (5a) \\ 1 & \text{when} & x = 0, & (5b) \\ 2 - x & \text{when} & 0 < x \le 2. & (5c) \end{cases}$$

A computer could be programmed to compute the values of $f(x)$, according to the flow diagram of Fig. 2–4. Start at the base and follow the arrows upward. The three ovals containing question marks are decision makers. They tell whether x is in the domain, and if so, whether $x < 0$ or $x = 0$ or $x > 0$. (If x is neither less than zero nor greater than zero, we conclude that $x = 0$.)

Functions of more than one independent variable. Occasionally we have functions which depend upon several independent variables. For example,

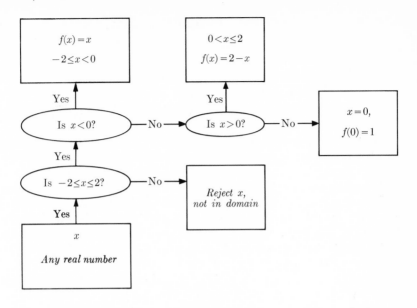

Figure 2-4

if r is the base radius and h is the altitude of a right circular cone (Fig. 2-5), then the volume

$$v = \tfrac{1}{3}\pi r^2 h$$

is uniquely determined when r and h are given definite values. The physical meaning requires that r, h, and v be positive. The set of all ordered triples (r, h, v) with

$$v = \tfrac{1}{3}\pi r^2 h, \qquad r > 0, \quad h > 0$$

Figure 2-5

is an example of a function of two independent variables (r and h). Its *domain* is the set of all pairs (r, h) with $r > 0$, $h > 0$. Its *range* is the set of positive numbers $v > 0$. The variables r and h are *independent* in the sense that the value assigned to either of them need not depend upon the other. But the value of v is fixed by the other two variables, so we call v the *dependent* variable. It is also customary to be briefer, and somewhat less precise, and to say that "the volume of a right circular cone is a function of the radius and altitude," or, still more briefly, "v is a function of r and h." This means two things:

(a) r and h can be assigned values independently, and
(b) when r and h are given, v is uniquely determined.

Similarly, the set of all ordered triples (r, h, s) with

$$s = \pi r \sqrt{r^2 + h^2}, \qquad r > 0, \quad h > 0,$$

is another example of a function of the same two independent variables r and h. Here s is the lateral surface area of the cone. And again we might say, "the lateral surface area of a right circular cone is a function of the radius and altitude," or "s is a function of r and h."

More generally, suppose that some quantity y is uniquely determined by n other quantities $x_1, x_2, x_3, \ldots, x_n$. The set of all ordered $(n + 1)$-tuples $(x_1, x_2, x_3, \ldots, x_n, y)$ that can be obtained by substituting permissible values of the variables $x_1, x_2, \ldots, x_n$ and the corresponding values of y is a function whose domain is the set of all allowable n-tuples $(x_1, x_2, x_3, \ldots, x_n)$ and whose range is the set of all possible values of y corresponding to this domain. If values can be assigned independently to each of the x's, we call them independent variables and say that y is a function of the x's. We also write

$$y = f(x_1, x_2, x_3, \ldots, x_n)$$

to indicate that y is a function of the n x's, just as we write

$$y = f(x)$$

to indicate that y is a function of one independent variable x.

Our primary concern in this book will be with functions of a single independent variable. In such cases there are at least four different ways of representing the functional relationship between the variables x and y, and all four of these methods are probably familiar to the reader. They are:

1. *By tables of values.* For example, the functions $y = \log_{10} x$, $y = \sin (x°)$, $y = \sqrt{x}$, $y = 1/x$, and many others are given in most numerical tables.

2. *By corresponding scales.* For example, the scales of a slide rule may be lined up so that opposite any number x on one scale, we may read $\sqrt{x}$, or x^2, or $\log_{10} x$, and so on, on other scales.

3. *By means of graphs.* Here we usually lay off the x-axis horizontally and the y-axis vertically on graph paper, with their origins coinciding. Then we plot points (x, y) with x in the domain of the function and with $y = f(x)$, and draw a smooth curve through the plotted points, as for example in Fig. 2–2. Observe that it is also customary to make a *table of values* of corresponding numbers x and y before we plot the curve.

4. *By means of equations,* from which we can calculate the value of y that corresponds to any given x.

Of these four methods, the ones most often used in this book will be the third and fourth, namely graphs and equations. However, any rule, whether expressed algebraically or verbally, that produces a unique value for y when x is given satisfies the requirements of expressing y as a function of x. There need not be a simple equation which gives y in terms of x. Thus, for example, a person's weight is a function of time (the value of his weight can be determined by stepping on scales at a given time), but there is unlikely to be any simple equation relating weight to time. On the other hand, a person's age is a function of time, and this relationship may be expressed by a linear equation.

An example of an interesting function given by a verbal statement is one known as "the greatest integer function." This function is defined on the domain of all real numbers. With any x in the domain, the function associates the algebraically greatest integer which is less than or equal to x. The integer thus associated with x is designated by writing brackets around x, $[x]$. And it has the property of being less than or equal to x, while the next larger integer is greater than x. That is,

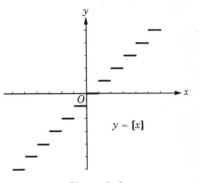

$$[x] \le x < [x] + 1.$$

For example, if $x = 3.4$, then $[x] = 3$ is the greatest integer in x. If x is negative, the greatest integer in x, which always lies at or to the left of x on the usual

Figure 2–6

x-axis number scale, may have a larger absolute value than x has. For instance, $[-4.7] = -5$ is the greatest integer in -4.7. The graph of the function $y = [x]$ is shown in Fig. 2–6. Its *range* is just the set of all integers . . . , -3, -2, -1, 0, 1, 2, 3, . . . negative, zero, and positive. It is clear from the graph why such a function is called a "step function." There are many examples of step functions in everyday life. The following are typical of situations that may be encountered:

1. The cash value y dollars of a \$100 Series E savings bond x years after the date of issue, $0 \le x \le 20$.

2. The postage y cents on a first-class letter weighing x ounces.

3. The toll charge y dollars on a long distance telephone call from Boston to Chicago lasting x minutes.

4. Some physical property y (for example, density, thermal conductivity, or coefficient of thermal expansion) at distance x inches from one end of a compound metal bar composed of two or more different metals joined end-to-end.

Such functions exhibit points of *discontinuity* where the function suddenly jumps from one value to another without taking on any of the intermediate values, as in Fig. 2–6 at $x = 2$ where, as x approaches 2 from the left, y jumps from 1 to 2 without taking any of the intervening values.

PROBLEMS

1. Sketch the graphs of the following functions to show that they are not the same:

$$f_1(x) = x^2, \quad \text{the natural domain}$$
$$f_2(x) = x^2, \quad x \geq 0$$
$$f_3(x) = x^2, \quad -2 \leq x \leq 2$$
$$f_4(x) = x^2, \quad -2 \leq x \leq 2, \text{ where } x \text{ is an integer.}$$

2. State which of the following functions are equal to the function

$$f(x) = \frac{x^2 - 2x}{x}.$$

Give reasons for your answers.

$$g(x) = x - 2$$

$$h(x) = \frac{4x - 8}{4}$$

$$k(x) = \frac{x^3 - 2x^2}{x^2}$$

$$m(x) = \frac{2x^2 - 4x}{2x}$$

$$n(x) = \frac{x^2 - 3x + 2}{x - 1}$$

3. State which of the following functions are equal to the function

$$r(x) = |x - 2|.$$

Give reasons for your answers.

$$s(x) = \sqrt{x^2 - 4x + 4}$$

$$t(x) = \sqrt{\frac{(x - 2)^3}{x - 2}}$$

$$u(x) = \frac{|x - 2|^2}{|x - 2|}$$

$$v(x) = \frac{|6x - 12|}{6}$$

$$w(x) = \left| \frac{x^2 + x - 6}{x + 3} \right|$$

4. State which of the following functions are equal to the function

$$\phi(x) = \frac{\sin^2 x + 1}{x}.$$

Give reasons for your answers.

$$f(x) = \frac{\sin^2 x}{x} + \frac{1}{x}$$

$$g(x) = \frac{\sin^2 x}{x} + \frac{x-1}{x^2 - x}$$

$$h(x) = \frac{2\sin^2 x + \cos^2 x}{x}$$

$$j(x) = \frac{2x - x\cos^2 x}{x^2}$$

5. Given the function $f(x) = x^2 + \left(\dfrac{1}{x}\right)$ find $f(2)$, $f(-1)$, $f\left(\dfrac{1}{x}\right)$, $f(x + \Delta x)$.

6. Make a table corresponding to $x = 0, \frac{1}{2}, 1, \frac{3}{2}, 2$ and sketch a graph to represent the function

$$y = \begin{cases} x, & \text{when} \quad 0 \le x \le 1 \\ 2 - x, & \text{when} \quad 1 < x \le 2. \end{cases}$$

7. Given the function

$$y = |4 - x^2|, \quad -3 \le x \le 3,$$

compute the values of y corresponding to each whole number in the domain and make a table of these values. Use this table to sketch a graph of the function.

8. Sketch graphs of the following functions for $-3 \le x \le 3$.
   (a) $f(x) = x - [x]$
   (b) $g(x) = [x] + [-x]$
   (c) $h(x) = \dfrac{[x]}{x}, \quad x \ne 0$

9. Sketch a graph of the function defined by

$$f(x) = \begin{cases} \dfrac{x}{|x|} & \text{for } x \ne 0 \\ 0 & \text{for } x = 0. \end{cases}$$

This is known as the signum function, sgn (x).

10. Consider the function
$$V = f(l, w, h),$$

which gives the volume v of a rectangular solid with length l, width w, and height h.
   (a) Name each independent variable.
   (b) Name each dependent variable.
   (c) What is the domain of each of the independent variables?
   (d) What is the range of the function?

11. Rewrite the function in problem 10 so that the dependent variable is h.

12. Separate the equation $x^2 + xy + y^2 = 3$ into two equations, each of which determines y as a function of x.

13. Let us define Δf as a function of two variables, x and h such that

$$\Delta f(x, h) = f(x + h) - f(x).$$

(a) Name a sufficient condition for $\Delta f(x, h) = 0$.

(b) If $f(x) = x^2$, find $\Delta f(0, 0)$, $\Delta f(-2, 4)$, $\Delta f(0.0001, -0.0001)$.

(c) If $0 < h \leq 1$ and $|x| < 3$ determine the range of Δf for $f(x) = x^2$.

2–4 Ways of combining functions. If f and g are two functions with domains D_f and D_g, then $f(x)$ and $g(x)$ exist for any x that is in both domains and we can compute $f(x) + g(x)$, $f(x) \cdot g(x)$, $f(x) - g(x)$. We can also find $f(x)/g(x)$ provided $g(x) \neq 0$. The new functions so constructed are called the

$$\text{sum} \qquad f + g: x \to f(x) + g(x), \tag{1a}$$

$$\text{product} \qquad f \cdot g: x \to f(x) \cdot g(x), \tag{1b}$$

$$\text{difference} \quad f - g: x \to f(x) - g(x), \tag{1c}$$

$$\text{quotient} \qquad \frac{f}{g}: x \to \frac{f(x)}{g(x)}. \tag{1d}$$

The domain of $f + g$, $f - g$, and $f \cdot g$ is the intersection of the domains of f and of g. The points at which $g(x) = 0$ must be excluded, however, to obtain the domain of f/g.

EXAMPLE 1. $\qquad f(x) = \sqrt{x}, \qquad g(x) = \sqrt{1 - x}. \tag{2a}$

The natural domains of f and g are:

$$D_f = \{x \mid x \geq 0\}, \qquad D_g = \{x \mid x \leq 1\}. \tag{2b}$$

The intersection of D_f and D_g is

$$D_f \cap D_g = \{x \mid 0 \leq x \leq 1\} = [0, 1]. \tag{3}$$

$$\text{Sum} \qquad f + g: x \to \sqrt{x} + \sqrt{1 - x},$$

$$\text{Difference} \quad f - g: x \to \sqrt{x} - \sqrt{1 - x},$$

$$\text{Product} \qquad f \cdot g: x \to \sqrt{x(1 - x)},$$

$$\text{Quotients} \qquad \frac{f}{g}: x \to \sqrt{\frac{x}{1 - x}},$$

$$\frac{g}{f}: x \to \sqrt{\frac{1 - x}{x}}.$$

The domains of $f + g$, $f - g$, and $f \cdot g$ are all the same, $[0, 1]$. Since $g(x) = 0$ when $x = 1$, the domain of f/g is $[0, 1)$. Similarly, the domain of g/f is $(0, 1]$.

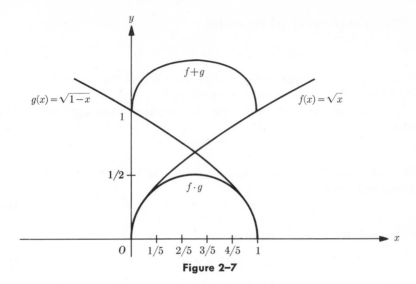

Figure 2–7

We can construct graphs of $f + g, f - g, fg, f/g$, or g/f from the separate graphs of f and g in the obvious way. For example, Fig. 2–7 shows a sketch of graphs of $f, g, f + g$, and $f \cdot g$.

EXAMPLE 2. If $f(x) = x$ and $g(x) = 1/x$, then $D_f = (-\infty, \infty)$, $D_g = \{x \mid x \neq 0\}$. The domain of $f \cdot g$ is the set of all nonzero real numbers. Hence, although $f(x) \cdot g(x) = 1$ when $x \neq 0$, we cannot say that $f \cdot g$ is the constant function 1, because the domain of that function is $(-\infty, \infty)$, and this is different from the domain of $f \cdot g$.

Translation and change of scale. It is well known that the graphs of

$$f(x) = x^2 \quad \text{and} \quad g(x) = (x - c)^2 \qquad (4)$$

are very much alike, for any number c. Figure 2–8(a) shows the parabolas for f and for g, with $c = 2$.

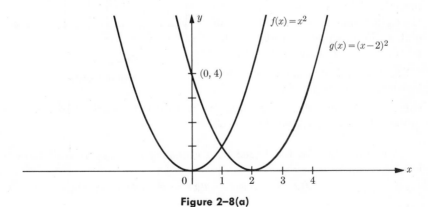

Figure 2–8(a)

The formulas in Eq. (4) are related:

$$g(x) = f(x - c) = (x - c)^2. \tag{5}$$

If we look at the graphs in Fig. 2–8(a), we see that the graph of g is that of f *translated* or shifted two units to the right.

What can we say in general about the graphs of functions f and g that satisfy

$$g(x) = f(x - c) \tag{6}$$

for some number c? Assume that the domain of f is $[a, b]$. Then $f(x - c)$ is only defined when

$$a \leq x - c \leq b \tag{7a}$$

or, by adding c throughout, when

$$a + c \leq x \leq b + c. \tag{7b}$$

Thus, $g(x) = f(x - c)$ is defined on the domain

$$D_g = [a + c, b + c] \tag{8a}$$

while f itself has domain

$$D_f = [a, b]. \tag{8b}$$

Equations (8) show that the domain of g is the interval we get by shifting $[a, b]$ to the right c units, or to the left $|c|$ units if $c < 0$. Now take any x in that new interval $[a + c, b + c]$. Equation (6) shows that the value of g at that x is equal to the value of f at $x - c$. In other words, take the ordinate of f at $x - c$ and shift it to the right c units to get the ordinate of g at x. Figure 2–8(b) illustrates this situation for a positive value of c.

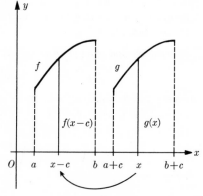

Figure 2–8(b)

EXAMPLE 3. How is the graph of $y = |x|$ related to the graph of $y = |x - 2|$?

Figure 2–9 shows the two graphs. We just shift the graph of $|x|$ two units to the right to get the graph of $|x - 2|$.

A function can also be altered by a *change of scale*. This is illustrated by the example

$$f(x) = \sin x, \qquad g(x) = \sin(\pi x). \tag{9}$$

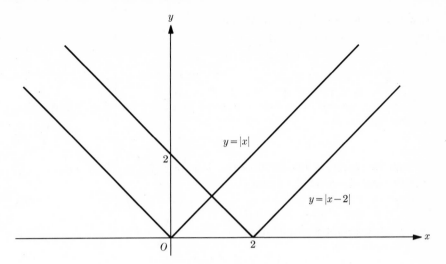

Figure 2–9

The natural domain is $(-\infty, \infty)$ for both functions f and g. But as x varies from 0 to 1, πx varies from 0 to π. Graphs of f, for $-\pi \leq x \leq \pi$, and of g, for $-1 \leq x \leq 1$, are shown in Fig. 2–10. The situation in Eq. (9) and Fig. 2–10 (a) is that

$$g(x) = f(\pi x). \tag{10}$$

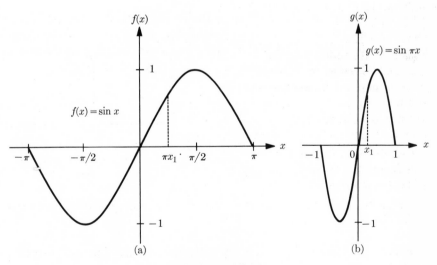

Figure 2–10(a),(b)

If we want πx, the argument of f in Eq. (10), to cover the interval $[-\pi, \pi]$ which corresponds to one complete sine wave, then

$$-\pi \leq \pi x \leq \pi$$

corresponds to

$$-1 \leq x \leq 1.$$

We get the g curve in Fig. 2–10(b) by compressing the f curve horizontally in the ratio π to 1.

We can also alter a function by changing its vertical scale. Let us take, for example,

$$f(x) = \sin x,$$
$$q(x) = 2 \sin x. \qquad (11)$$

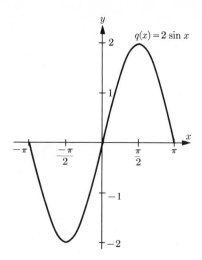

Figure 2–10(c)

The graph of q for $-\pi \leq x \leq \pi$ is shown in Fig. 2–10(c). The range of f (in Fig. 2–10a) is $[-1, 1]$, but the range of q is $[-2, 2]$. We get the q curve by stretching the f curve vertically in the ratio of 2 to 1.

More generally, suppose k is any positive constant and that

$$g(x) = f(kx). \qquad (12)$$

How is the graph of $g(x)$ related to the graph of $f(x)$? Figure 2–10(a) suggests that the answer is "compress or stretch the x-axis by shrinking (if $k > 1$) or stretching (if $k < 1$) every interval of length k on the x-axis into an interval of length 1."

For example, if D_f, the domain of f, is

$$D_f = [a, b],$$

and

$$g(x) = f(kx), \qquad (13)$$

then g is defined by (13) if and only if

$$a \leq kx \leq b$$

or, assuming $k > 0$,

$$\frac{a}{k} \leq x \leq \frac{b}{k}.$$

That is, D_g, the domain of g, is

$$D_g = \left[\frac{a}{k}, \frac{b}{k}\right], \qquad (14)$$

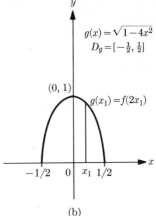

Figure 2–11

and for any x in D_g, we find kx in D_f, and take $g(x) = f(kx)$. Figure 2–10 illustrates for $k = \pi, f(x) = \sin x, g(x) = \sin (\pi x) = f(\pi x)$.

Another example is illustrated by Fig. 2–11 which shows the effect for $k = 2$, $f(x) = \sqrt{1 - x^2}, g(x) = f(2x) = \sqrt{1 - 4x^2}$.

We can also look at the situation in Fig. 2–10(c) more generally. Suppose k is a positive constant and that

$$q(x) = kf(x).$$

The figure suggests that we can obtain the graph of q from the graph of f in either of the following two equivalent ways:

stretch the f curve vertically (if $k > 1$), or compress it (if $k < 1$),

or

change the scale on the y-axis so that points labeled 1, 2, 3, ... for the graph of f are relabeled $k, 2k, 3k, \ldots$ for the graph of q.

PROBLEMS

For each of the following pairs of functions f and g in Problems 1 through 3, specify the natural domains of f and g and the corresponding domains of $f + g$, $f \cdot g, f/g$, and g/f.

1. $f(x) = x, \quad g(x) = \sqrt{x - 1}$

2. $f(x) = \dfrac{1}{x - 2}, \quad g(x) = \dfrac{1}{\sqrt{x - 1}}$

3. $f(x) = \sqrt{x}, \quad g(x) = \sqrt[4]{x + 1}$

4. Suppose $f(x) = |x|$ and $g(x) = f(x - 3)$. Graph f and g. Compare the graphs of f and g.

5. Suppose c is positive and $g(x) = f(x + c)$. If $D_f = [a, b]$, what is D_g? How can you get the graph of g from the graph of f? Illustrate with $f(x) = \sin x$, $-\pi \le x \le \pi$, and $g(x) = f(x + \pi/2)$.

6. If $\phi(x) = \sin x$, $-\pi \le x \le \pi$, sketch the graph of each of the following and state the domain and range of each.

(a) $p(x) = \phi\left(\dfrac{x}{2}\right)$ (b) $r(x) = \phi(3x)$ (c) $q(x) = \phi(-x)$

7. If $f(x) = 2x^2 - 2[|x|]^2$, $-2 < x < 2$, sketch the graph of each of the following and state the domain and range of each.

(a) $g(x) = f\left(\dfrac{x}{4}\right)$ (b) $h(x) = f(\tfrac{3}{2}x)$ (c) $k(x) = f(-2x)$

8. If $F(x) = 1 + 3\cos 2x$, $-\pi \le x \le \pi$, sketch the graph of each of the following and state the domain and range of each.

(a) $f(x) = \tfrac{1}{2}F(x)$ (b) $g(x) = F\left(\dfrac{x}{4}\right)$

(c) $h(x) = F\left(x + \dfrac{\pi}{2}\right)$ (d) $H(x) = -F(x)$

9. Sketch the graph of

$$f(x) = \frac{1 + \operatorname{sgn}(x^2 - 4)}{3}, \qquad -4 \le x \le 4,$$

and state its range.*

10. Sketch the graph of each of the following and state the domain and range of each, where $f(x) = \sqrt{1 - x^2}$ for $|x| \le 1$.

(a) $g(x) = \tfrac{3}{2}f(x)$ (b) $h(x) = f(\tfrac{2}{3}x)$
(c) $F(x) = 3f(2x)$ (d) $H(x) = -f(-x)$

11. Sketch the graphs of

(a) $f(x) = |x|$ (b) $g(x) = |2x|$
(c) $h(x) = |x^2 - 2x - 3|$ (d) $f(x) = |1 - x^2| - 2$

(e) $g(x) = \dfrac{2 + \operatorname{sgn}(-x)}{2}$ (f) $h(x) = 3 - [3x]$

(g) $f(x) = (\operatorname{sgn} x)(x - 1)^2 + x^2[\operatorname{sgn}(x - 1)]$

2–5 Behavior of functions. We know that the linear function

$$f(x) = 3x \tag{1}$$

has as its graph a straight line, through the origin of slope $+3$. As x increases, the function values increase at a rate three times as fast, because a one-unit change in x produces a three-unit change in $f(x)$.

For example, if x_1 is an initial value of x, and $x_2 = x_1 + h$ is a new value obtained by increasing x by h units, then the corresponding increase in the value of the function is

$$f(x_1 + h) - f(x_1) = 3(x_1 + h) - 3x_1 = 3h, \tag{2}$$

---

* See Problem 9, page 51.

which is exactly three times the increase in x. So when $f(x) = 3x$, and x increases from x_1 to $x_1 + h$, $f(x)$ increases from $3x_1$ to $3x_1 + 3h = 3(x_1 + h)$. See Fig. 2–12.

Remark 1. In Article 1–3, the notation Δx was introduced to represent the difference $x_2 - x_1$ between two values of x. That is,

$$\Delta x = x_2 - x_1. \qquad (3)$$

In the preceding example we located x_2, the new value of x, by increasing the initial value x_1 by h units

$$x_2 = x_1 + h. \qquad (4)$$

Notice from (4) that

$$h = x_2 - x_1. \qquad (5)$$

Therefore, we can see from (3) and (5) that

$$\Delta x = h.$$

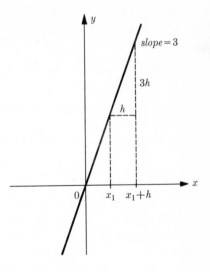

Figure 2–12

In other words Δx and h are different representations of the same thing, a change in the value of x. We will use these two notations interchangeably. It is important to remember that they are equivalent.

Not all functions are as simple as the one just discussed. The function

$$f(x) = x^2 \qquad (6)$$

increases over some intervals of x-values and decreases over others. Its rate of change, per unit change in x, is not constant. Substituting $x_1 + h$ and x_1 on both sides of Eq. (6) and subtracting, we get

$$\begin{aligned} f(x_1 + h) - f(x_1) &= (x_1 + h)^2 - x_1^2 \\ &= 2x_1h + h^2. \end{aligned} \qquad (7)$$

The increase in $f(x) = x^2$ depends upon x_1, the initial value of x, and also upon h, the amount of increase in x. We want to compare the increase in $f(x)$ with the increase in x. For the linear function $3x$ we saw that the increase in $f(x) = 3x$ was three times the increase in x. For the function $f(x) = x^2$, we see from Eq. (7) that we can write

$$f(x_1 + h) - f(x_1) = (2x_1 + h)h \qquad (8)$$

Here, h represents the increase in x from x_1 to $x_1 + h$. Therefore, we can say "the increase in x^2, as x increases from x_1 to $x_1 + h$, is $2x_1 + h$ times the increase in x." Alternately, we can divide the increase in $f(x)$ by the increase in x. This ratio,

$$\frac{f(x_1 + h) - f(x_1)}{(x_1 + h) - x_1} = \frac{f(x_1 + h) - f(x_1)}{h} = \frac{\text{change in } f(x)}{\text{change in } x}, \tag{9}$$

is called the *average rate of increase* of $f(x)$, *per unit of increase* in x, from x_1 to $x_1 + h$.

For the example $f(x) = x^2$, Eqs. (8) and (9) lead to the result

$$\frac{f(x_1 + h) - f(x_1)}{h} = 2x_1 + h, \tag{10}$$

for the average rate of increase of x^2 per unit of increase in x. Thus, if $x_1 = 2$ and $h = 1$, the right side of Eq. (10) gives $2x_1 + h = 5$, so that x^2 increases five times as much as x does in going from $x_1 = 2$ to $x_1 + h = 3$. The following table shows how the average rate of increase of x^2, per unit of increase in x, varies for four different starting values, x_1, and several different values of $h > 0$.

h	$2x_1 + h$ $x_1 = 2$	$2x_1 + h$ $x_1 = 3$	$2x_1 + h$ $x_1 = -2$	$2x_1 + h$ $x_1 = -3$
1	5	7	−3	−5
0.5	4.5	6.5	−3.5	−5.5
0.25	4.25	6.25	−3.75	−5.75
0.1	4.1	6.1	−3.9	−5.9
0.01	4.01	6.01	−3.99	−5.99
0.001	4.001	6.001	−3.999	−5.999

Two things are evident from the above table or from Eq. (10):

(a) If we fix x_1 and take smaller and smaller values of h, the average rate of change of x^2 per unit change in x tends to become almost equal to $2x_1$.

(b) When x_1 is negative, a small *increase* in x, from x_1 to $x_1 + h$, corresponds to a *negative increase* (that is, a *decrease*) in x^2.

Figure 2–13 illustrates some of these ideas. There, the slope of the secant line through points (x_1, x_1^2) and $((x_1 + h), (x_1 + h)^2)$ is $2x_1 + h$.

For a *constant function*, such as

$$f(x) = 5,$$

of course, there is no change in the value of $f(x)$ when x increases from x_1 to $x_1 + h$, because

$$f(x_1 + h) = f(x_1) = 5.$$

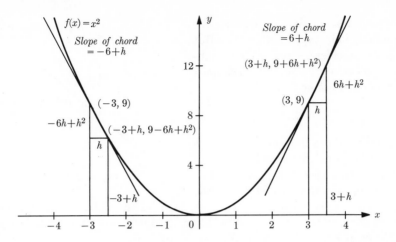

Figure 2-13

For any such constant function, Eq. (9) leads to the result

$$\frac{f(x_1 + h) - f(x_1)}{h} = \frac{0}{h} = 0,$$

for any $h \neq 0$. We interpret this to say that "the average rate of increase of a constant function is zero," which is just what we would expect. (See Fig. 2-14.)

Remark 2. In the next chapters we shall develop systematic rules for calculating the rate of increase of a function $f(x)$ per unit change in x. *Differential calculus* (one of the two main branches of calculus—the other being integral calculus) is concerned with the *instantaneous* rate of increase, rather than with the average rate. For constant functions $f(x) = c$, and for linear functions $f(x) = mx + b$, the average rate of increase

Figure 2-14

is constant and we need not distinguish between average rate and instantaneous rate. (By analogy, if an automobile is travelling at a steady rate of 45 miles per hour, its average speed and its instantaneous speed are the same.) But we saw that the square function does not have the same average rate of increase everywhere, because if $f(x) = x^2$, and $h \neq 0$, then

$$\frac{f(x_1 + h) - f(x_1)}{h} = 2x_1 + h. \tag{11}$$

Notice the restriction $h \neq 0$: We cannot divide by 0 in Eq. (11). But we can consider h's in a deleted neighborhood of zero. Figure 2–15 shows a graph of the *slope function*

$$m(h) = 2x_1 + h \qquad (12)$$

for a typical positive value of x_1 and h in a deleted neighborhood of zero (in other words, for h "near zero"). The point $(0, 2x_1)$ that would be on the

Figure 2–15

graph if we allowed h to be equal to zero on the right side of Eq. (12), is *not included* because h must be different from zero if we want to identify $m(h)$ from Eq. (12) with the difference quotient

$$\frac{f(x_1 + h) - f(x_1)}{h}$$

from Eq. (11). But $m(h)$ is bounded between $2x_1 + 0.01$ and $2x_1 - 0.01$ when $|h|$ is, say, less than 0.01. In fact, if ϵ (Greek letter read "epsilon") is any positive number, and we choose $|h| < \epsilon$, then from Eq. (12) we see that $m(h)$ is between $2x_1 - \epsilon$ and $2x_1 + \epsilon$ because

$$-\epsilon < h < \epsilon \Rightarrow 2x_1 - \epsilon < 2x_1 + h < 2x_1 + \epsilon$$

(double arrow, $\Rightarrow$, read "implies"). We also say that $m(h)$ is *approximated by $2x_1$ to within ϵ* when $0 < |h| < \epsilon$. Figure 2–16 illustrates the idea. The number $2x_1$ is called "the *limit* of $2x_1 + h$, as h approaches zero." This limit is also called the *instantaneous rate of increase* of $f(x) = x^2$, at $x = x_1$, and is indicated by the notation $f'(x_1)$, read "f prime at x_1." Formally, we make the following definition.

DEFINITION. *We say $m(h)$ is approximated by L to within ϵ on an interval (a, b), provided*

$$L - \epsilon < m(h) < L + \epsilon$$

when

$$a < h < b.$$

Figure 2–16

EXAMPLE 1. Show $m(h) = 2h + 1$ is approximated by $L = 1$ to within $\epsilon = 0.5$ on the interval $(-\frac{1}{4}, \frac{1}{4})$.
We have

$$-\tfrac{1}{4} < h < \tfrac{1}{4}.$$

By using the properties of inequalities we get

$$2(-\tfrac{1}{4}) + 1 < 2h + 1 < 2(\tfrac{1}{4}) + 1.$$

Rewritten, we have

$$1 - 0.5 < m(h) < 1 + 0.5$$

which demonstrates that the preceding definition applies and the approximation of $m(h)$ on the given interval is always within the given ϵ of L.

EXAMPLE 2. Find values of L and ϵ so that $m(h) = 3h + 2$ is approximated by L to within ϵ on the interval $(-0.5, 0.5)$.
A very large ϵ would always meet our conditions. We shall try to find a small ϵ. We know that

$$-0.5 < h < 0.5. \tag{13}$$

We want to find L and ϵ, so that

$$L - \epsilon < m(h) < L + \epsilon.$$

From (13) we have

$$3(-0.5) + 2 < 3h + 2 < 3(0.5) + 2,$$

or

$$2 - 1.5 < 3h + 2 < 2 + 1.5.$$

So we can conclude that if we take $\epsilon = 1.5$ and $L = 2$, all possible values of $m(h)$ over the given interval will be between $2 + 1.5$ and $2 - 1.5$ and hence we would accept 2 as an approximation of $m(h)$. Obviously, had we chosen $\epsilon > 1.5$, 2 would also have been a reasonable approximation for $m(h)$. But the major question we pose at this time is not what is a reasonable approximation for $m(h)$ when ϵ is large, but what is a reasonable approximation of $m(h)$ regardless of the magnitude of ϵ.

In the next chapter we shall take up the subject of limits in more general terms. Before studying that chapter, answer the questions in the problems following.

PROBLEMS

1. For each of the following functions write the expression for $m(h)$ where the initial value x_1 increases by h units. Compute $m(h)$ for the given values of x_1 and h.

   (a) $f(x) = 2x - 1$ $x_1 = -1, \quad h = 4$

   (b) $g(x) = x^2 + x$ $x_1 = 4, \quad h = 2$

(c) $F(x) = \dfrac{1}{x}$ $\qquad\qquad x_1 = 1, \quad h = \dfrac{1}{4}$

(d) $f(x) = \dfrac{x}{x-3}$ $\qquad x_1 = 0, \quad h = \dfrac{1}{10}$

(e) $g(x) = |x|$ $\qquad\qquad x_1 = -1, \quad h = \frac{1}{2}$

(f) $F(x) = \sin x$ $\qquad\quad x_1 = \dfrac{\pi}{3}, \quad h = \dfrac{\pi}{6}$

2. For each of the following functions sketch the graph and, if possible, find an appropriate value for L when $-0.1 < h < 0.1$, and $x_1 = 0$.

(a) $f(x) = 3x + 2$ $\qquad\qquad$ (b) $g(x) = \frac{1}{2}x^2 - x$

(c) $f(x) = \dfrac{x}{x+2}$ $\qquad\qquad$ (d) $F(x) = \dfrac{1}{|x|}$

In Problems 3 through 7, demonstrate the truth or falsity of "$m(h)$ is approximated by L to within ϵ" on the given interval (a, b) for the given values of L and ϵ. Sketch graphs showing $m(h)$, L, $L - \epsilon$, $L + \epsilon$, (a, b).

3. $m(h) = h^2 + 4$, $\quad L = 4$, $\quad \epsilon = 0.01$, $\quad (a, b) = (-0.1, 0.1)$
4. $m(h) = 2h + 3$, $\quad L = 3$, $\quad \epsilon = 0.5$, $\quad (a, b) = (-\frac{1}{4}, \frac{1}{4})$
5. $m(h) = 2h + 3$, $\quad L = 4$, $\quad \epsilon = 0.5$, $\quad (a, b) = (-\frac{1}{4}, \frac{1}{4})$
6. $m(h) = 2h + 3$, $\quad L = 3$, $\quad \epsilon = 0.5$, $\quad (a, b) = (-\frac{1}{2}, \frac{1}{2})$
7. $m(h) = 3 + (2/h)$, $\quad L = 3$, $\quad \epsilon = 1$, $\quad (a, b) = (10, 20)$

Find values of L and of ϵ so that it is true that $m(h)$ is approximated by L to within ϵ on (a, b) for each of the following problems (8 through 12). (Answers are not unique: One could always take ϵ very large and use many different values of L. Try to answer with small values of ϵ.)

8. $m(h) = 5 + 6h$, $\quad (a, b) = (-0.1, 0.1)$
9. $m(h) = 4 - 6h$, $\quad (a, b) = (-0.1, 0.1)$
10. $m(h) = \dfrac{3 + h}{2 - h}$, $\quad (a, b) = (-\frac{1}{2}, \frac{1}{2})$
11. $m(h) = (2 + h)(3 - h)$, $\quad (a, b) = (-\frac{1}{2}, \frac{1}{2})$
12. $m(h) = (2 + h) + (5 - h^2)$, $\quad (a, b) = (-0.1, 0.1)$

2–6   Slope of a curve. In Article 1–4 we discussed the slope of a straight line. In this article we shall define what we mean by the *slope of a curve* at a point $P(x, y)$ on the curve. This is the way in which Leibniz himself approached the "differential calculus."

In Fig. 2–17, $P(x_1, y_1)$ is any point on the curve $y = f(x)$, and $Q(x_2, y_2)$ is another point on the same curve. Then the slope of the secant line joining the points P and Q is

$$m_{\text{sec}} = \text{slope of } \overrightarrow{PQ} = \frac{y_2 - y_1}{x_2 - x_1} = \frac{\Delta y}{\Delta x}. \qquad (1)$$

Suppose now we hold P fixed and move Q along the curve toward P. As we do so, the slope of the secant line $\overleftrightarrow{PQ}$ will probably vary. But it may happen (and does for most curves encountered in practice) that as Q moves closer and closer to P, the slope of the secant line varies by smaller and smaller amounts and, in fact, approaches a constant lim-

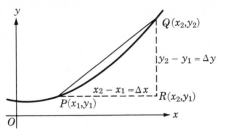

Figure 2–17

iting value. When this happens, as it does in the following example, we call this limiting value *the slope of the tangent to the curve at P* or, more briefly, *the slope of the curve at P*.

EXAMPLE. Consider the curve

$$y = x^3 - 3x + 3. \tag{2}$$

If $P(x_1, y_1)$ is a point on this curve, then its coordinates must satisfy the equation

$$y_1 = x_1^3 - 3x_1 + 3. \tag{3a}$$

If $Q(x_2, y_2)$ is a second point on the curve, and if

$$\Delta x = x_2 - x_1, \qquad \Delta y = y_2 - y_1,$$

then

$$x_2 = x_1 + \Delta x, \qquad y_2 = y_1 + \Delta y$$

must also satisfy Eq. (2). That is,

$$
\begin{aligned}
y_1 + \Delta y &= (x_1 + \Delta x)^3 - 3(x_1 + \Delta x) + 3 \\
&= x_1^3 + 3x_1^2 \Delta x + 3x_1 (\Delta x)^2 + (\Delta x)^3 - 3x_1 - 3\Delta x + 3. \tag{3b}
\end{aligned}
$$

When we subtract the members of Eq. (3a) from Eq. (3b) we obtain

$$\Delta y = 3x_1^2 \Delta x + 3x_1 (\Delta x)^2 + (\Delta x)^3 - 3\Delta x. \tag{4}$$

From this we readily find the slope of the secant line $\overleftrightarrow{PQ}$ to be

$$m_{\text{sec}} = \frac{\Delta y}{\Delta x} = 3x_1^2 + 3x_1 \Delta x + (\Delta x)^2 - 3. \tag{5}$$

Now comes the most important step! When Q approaches P along the curve, Δx and Δy both approach zero. Thus the slope of $\overleftrightarrow{PQ}$ will be the ratio of two small numbers. This information is not helpful, since the ratio of two small numbers may be practically anything. But we have further information here, since we also know from Eq. (5) that

$$m_{\text{sec}} = (3x_1^2 - 3) + (3x_1 + \Delta x)\, \Delta x.$$

The right side of this equation is the sum of two terms, one of which,

$$3x_1^2 - 3,$$

remains constant as Δx approaches zero, while the other,

$$(3x_1 + \Delta x)\,\Delta x,$$

becomes smaller and, in fact, itself approaches zero when Δx does. We summarize this by saying that

the limit* of m_{sec} as Δx approaches zero is $3x_1^2 - 3$,

and by definition, this limit is the slope of the tangent to the curve, or the slope of the curve, at the point (x_1, y_1). Since (x_1, y_1) might have been *any* point on the curve of Eq. (2), we may delete the subscript 1 and say that

$$m = 3x^2 - 3 \tag{6}$$

gives the slope of the curve at any point $P(x, y)$ on it. In other words, for the set of points on the curve $\{x_1, x_2, x_3, \ldots\}$, this process gives us a corresponding set of values $\{m_1, m_2, m_3, \ldots\}$. Therefore we are getting a new function $\{(x_n, m_n)\}$; the rule for this function is $x \to 3x^2 - 3$, i.e., $m(x) = 3x^2 - 3$.

We can make use of the slope as well as the equation of the curve itself to learn more about the shape of the curve than we would be likely to discover if we did not have this additional information. For example, we see that the tangent to the curve is horizontal, that is, $m = 0$, when $x = \pm 1$. We also see that the slope is negative for x between -1 and $+1$, and that elsewhere it is positive. If we substitute values of x between -2 and $+2$, say, into Eq. (2) to find y and into Eq. (6) to find m, we obtain the following table of values:

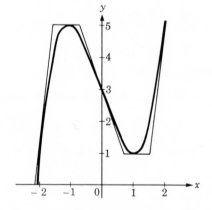

Figure 2–18

x	y	m
-2	1	9
-1	5	0
0	3	-3
1	1	0
2	5	9

When these points are plotted and the tangent line at each point is drawn, we get a very good picture of the shape of the curve. Of course the curve itself is smooth and does not follow the tangent lines, but these lines do afford material aid in sketching the curve (Fig. 2–18).

---

* Limits are defined and discussed in more detail in Chapter 3.

PROBLEMS

For the following curves, find the slope at the given point:

1. $y = x^2 - 3$ at $P(0, -3)$ 2. $y = x^2 - 2x + 1$ at $P(0, 1)$
3. $y = 5 - 2x - x^2$ at $P(-1, 6)$ 4. $y = 2x - x^2$ at $P(3, -3)$
5. $y = 2x^2 - 7$ at $P(-2, 1)$ 6. $y = x^2 - 3x + 3$ at $P(x_1, y_1)$
7. $y = x^3 - 3x^2 + 5$ at $P(2, -3)$ 8. $y = 3x^2 - 5$ at $P(c, d)$
9. $y = 3x + 4x^2$ at $P(-a, b)$ 10. $y = 2 - 3x - x^2$ at $P(-x', y')$

Use the method illustrated in this article to find the slope of each of the following curves at a point (x, y) on the curve. Use the equation of the curve and the equation you get for its slope to make a table of values. Include in your table all points where the curve has a horizontal tangent. Sketch the curve, making use of all the information in your table of values.

11. $y = x^2 - 2x - 3$ 12. $y = 2x^2 - x - 1$
13. $y = 4 - x^2$ 14. $y = x^2 - 4x$
15. $y = x^2 + 3x + 2$ 16. $y = 2 - x - x^2$
17. $y = 2x^3 + 3x^2 - 12x + 7$ 18. $y = x^3 - 3x$
19. $y = x^3 - 12x$ 20. $y = x^2(4x + 3) + 1$
21. $y = x^3 - 3x^2 + 4$ 22. $y = 5|x| + 2$
23. $y = |x^2 - 4|$ 24. $y = x^{-1} + 2x$
25. $y = (x^2 + 4x)^{-1}$

2–7 Derivative of a function. We now formulate the method for finding the slope of a curve representing the more general functional equation $y = f(x)$. Let $P(x_1, y_1)$ be a fixed point on the curve. The subscript 1 is used to emphasize that x_1 and y_1 are to be held constant throughout the following discussion. If $Q(x_1 + \Delta x, y_1 + \Delta y)$ is another point on the curve, then

$$y_1 + \Delta y = f(x_1 + \Delta x),$$

and from this we subtract

$$y_1 = f(x_1)$$

to obtain (Fig. 2–19)

$$\Delta y = f(x_1 + \Delta x) - f(x_1).$$

Then the slope of the secant line $\overrightarrow{PQ}$ is

$$m_{\text{sec}} = \frac{\Delta y}{\Delta x} = \frac{f(x_1 + \Delta x) - f(x_1)}{\Delta x}.$$

$$(1)$$

Figure 2–19

The division in Eq. (1) can only be *indicated* when we are talking about a general function $f(x)$. But for any specific equation such as the one in Eq. (2) of Article 2–6, $f(x) = x^3 - 3x + 3$, this division of Δy by Δx is actually to be carried out [as we did in going from Eq. (4) to Eq. (5)] *before* we do the next operation.

Having performed the division indicated in Eq. (1), we now investigate what happens if we hold x_1 fixed and take Δx to be smaller and smaller, approaching zero. If m_{sec} approaches a constant value, we call this value its *limit* and define this to be the slope m_{tan} of the tangent to the curve at P. The mathematical symbols which summarize this discussion are

$$m_{\text{tan}} = \lim_{Q \to P} m_{\text{sec}} = \lim_{\Delta x \to 0} \frac{\Delta y}{\Delta x} = \lim_{\Delta x \to 0} \frac{f(x_1 + \Delta x) - f(x_1)}{\Delta x}. \tag{2}$$

The symbol "lim" with "$\Delta x \to 0$" written beneath it is read "the limit, as Δx approaches zero, of . . ."

The result of carrying out the operations represented by the last term in Eq. (2) produces a number which we have called m_{tan}, or the slope of the tangent to the curve $y = f(x)$ at the point $P(x_1, y_1)$. It is also customary to indicate that this number is related to the original function f by writing it as $f'(x_1)$ (read "f-prime at x_1"). Thus $f'(x_1)$ is *defined* by

$$f'(x_1) = \lim_{\Delta x \to 0} \frac{f(x_1 + \Delta x) - f(x_1)}{\Delta x}. \tag{3}$$

As mentioned above, the subscript 1 is used to emphasize the fact that x_1 is held constant while the various operations indicated on the right side of Eq. (3) are performed. The indicated limit may exist for some values of x_1 and fail to exist for other values. (We shall discuss this situation in more detail below.) At each point x_1 where the limit does exist, the function f is said to have a *derivative* (or to be *differentiable*) and the number $f'(x_1)$ is said to be the derivative of f at x_1.

The process of *finding the derivative of a function* is the fundamental operation of differential calculus. In fact we may now define *differential calculus* to be that branch of mathematics which is concerned with studying the following two general problems.

Problem I. Given a function f, determine those values of x (in the domain of f) at which the function possesses a derivative.

Problem II. Given a function f and an x at which the derivative exists, find $f'(x)$.

For example, in studying Eq. (2) of Article 2–6,

$$f(x) = x^3 - 3x + 3, \tag{4}$$

we found that for any x_1 whatever, the result of applying the operations on the right side of Eq. (3) gave us $3x_1^2 - 3$. That is, the function f in Eq. (4) possesses a derivative whose value at *any* x_1 is

$$f'(x_1) = 3x_1^2 - 3. \tag{5}$$

Thus the answer to Problem I above is: "The function f, Eq. (4), possesses a derivative at any x in the domain $-\infty < x + \infty$," and the answer to Problem II is given by Eq. (5).

Now for most of the functions considered in this book, it will turn out that the answer to Problem I is that the derivative exists at all but a few values of x; that is, the places where the derivative fails to exist will be exceptional. Then the x_1 in Eq. (3) may be *any* of the nonexceptional values of x. Therefore, we might as well write x instead of x_1 in Eq. (3) if we remember that

x is to be held constant, while
Δx varies and approaches zero

in the calculation of the derivative

$$f'(x) = \lim_{\Delta x \to 0} \frac{f(x + \Delta x) - f(x)}{\Delta x}. \tag{6}$$

With this understanding, we shall henceforth omit the subscript 1 in talking about the derivative and shall use Eq. (6) to define the derivative of f, with respect to x, at any x in its domain for which the limit exists.

The derived function. Let x be a number in the domain of the function f. If the limit indicated in Eq. (6) exists, then it provides a rule for associating a number $f'(x)$ with the number x. The set of all pairs of numbers $(x, f'(x))$ that can be formed by this process is called the *derived function* f'. The *domain* of f' is a subset of the domain of f. It contains all numbers x in the domain of f such that the limit in (6) exists, but does not contain those exceptional values where the *derivative* fails to exist. The derived function f' is also called the *derivative* of f. Its value at any point x in its domain will be $f'(x)$.

EXAMPLE 1. Consider the absolute value function

$$f(x) = |x|, \qquad -\infty < x < +\infty.$$

From the graph in Fig. 2–9 it is clear that the slope is $+1$ when x is positive and -1 when x is negative. But at $x = 0$, the derivative fails to exist [the graph has no tangent at $(0, 0)$]. Hence the *domain* of the derived function does not include 0. It consists of all real numbers $x \neq 0$. The values of the derived function are given by the rule

$$f'(x) = \begin{cases} -1 & \text{if} \quad x < 0, \\ +1 & \text{if} \quad x > 0. \end{cases}$$

(See Problem 21, at the end of this section.)

Notations. In addition to $f'(x)$, various notations are used to denote the derivative of $y = f(x)$ with respect to x. The ones most commonly used are

$$y', \qquad \frac{dy}{dx}, \qquad \text{and} \qquad D_x y.$$

The last two of these may be interpreted as

$$\frac{dy}{dx} = \frac{d}{dx}(y),$$

where $\frac{d}{dx} \ldots$ stands for the operation "derivative with respect to x of" the expression following, and

$$D_x y = D_x(y)$$

with $D_x \ldots$ meaning the same thing as $\frac{d}{dx} \ldots$, namely, "derivative with respect to x of" the expression which follows it.

EXAMPLE 2. Find $f'(x)$ for the function

$$f(x) = x^2 + \frac{1}{x}, \qquad x \neq 0.$$

Solution. We carry out the operations indicated on the right side of Eq. (6) in the following order:

1. $f(x + \Delta x) = (x + \Delta x)^2 + \dfrac{1}{x + \Delta x}$

   $\qquad\qquad = x^2 + 2x\,\Delta x + (\Delta x)^2 + \dfrac{1}{x + \Delta x}.$

2. $f(x) = x^2 + \dfrac{1}{x}.$

Subtract 2 from 1:

3. $f(x + \Delta x) - f(x) = 2x\,\Delta x + (\Delta x)^2 + \dfrac{1}{x + \Delta x} - \dfrac{1}{x}$

$$= 2x\,\Delta x + (\Delta x)^2 + \frac{x - (x + \Delta x)}{x(x + \Delta x)}$$

$$= \Delta x \left(2x + \Delta x - \frac{1}{x(x + \Delta x)} \right).$$

Divide by Δx:

4. $\dfrac{f(x + \Delta x) - f(x)}{\Delta x} = 2x + \Delta x - \dfrac{1}{x(x + \Delta x)}.$

5. $f'(x) = \lim\limits_{\Delta x \to 0} \dfrac{f(x + \Delta x) - f(x)}{\Delta x}$

$$= \lim_{\Delta x \to 0} \left(2x + \Delta x - \frac{1}{x(x + \Delta x)} \right) \tag{a}$$

$$= 2x + 0 - \frac{1}{x(x + 0)} \tag{b}$$

$$= 2x - \frac{1}{x^2}.$$

In Chapter 3 we shall discuss the validity of the various limit operations involved in going from (a) to (b) above. If we anticipate these results, we may say that *after* the division by Δx has been carried out and the expression has been reduced to a form [as in (a) above] which "makes sense" (that is, does not involve division by zero) when Δx is taken equal to zero, then the limit as Δx *approaches* zero does exist and may be found by simply replacing Δx by zero in this reduced form.

EXAMPLE 3. Find dy/dx if $y = \sqrt{x}$ and $x > 0$.

Solution. Let $y = \sqrt{x}$, $y + \Delta y = \sqrt{x + \Delta x}$, so that

$$\frac{\Delta y}{\Delta x} = \frac{\sqrt{x + \Delta x} - \sqrt{x}}{\Delta x}$$

$$= \frac{(\sqrt{x + \Delta x} - \sqrt{x})(\sqrt{x + \Delta x} + \sqrt{x})}{\Delta x(\sqrt{x + \Delta x} + \sqrt{x})} \tag{a}$$

$$= \frac{(x + \Delta x) - x}{\Delta x(\sqrt{x + \Delta x} + \sqrt{x})} = \frac{1}{\sqrt{x + \Delta x} + \sqrt{x}}.$$

In step (a) we multiplied by a fraction equal to 1 and having a form such that it enabled us to get rid of the square roots in the numerator. Then in the next step we were able to carry out the division by Δx. Now we let Δx approach zero in the final form and have

$$\frac{dy}{dx} = \lim_{\Delta x \to 0} \frac{\Delta y}{\Delta x} = \lim_{\Delta x \to 0} \frac{1}{\sqrt{x + \Delta x} + \sqrt{x}} = \frac{1}{2\sqrt{x}}.$$

PROBLEMS

For each of the following functions f, find the derivative $f'(x)$, by means of the definition in Eq. (6).

1. $f(x) = 2x + 3$

2. $f(x) = x^2$

3. $f(x) = x^3$

4. $f(x) = x^2 - x + 1$

5. $f(x) = \dfrac{1}{x}$

6. $f(x) = \dfrac{1}{x^2}$

7. $f(x) = \dfrac{1}{2x + 1}$

8. $f(x) = \dfrac{x}{x + 1}$

9. $f(x) = 2x^2 - x + 5$

10. $f(x) = x^3 - 12x + 11$

11. $f(x) = x^4$

12. $f(x) = ax^2 + bx + c$ (a, b, c constants)

13. $f(x) = x - \dfrac{1}{x}$

14. $f(x) = ax + \dfrac{b}{x}$ (a, b constants)

15. $f(x) = \sqrt{2x}$

16. $f(x) = \sqrt{x + 1}$

17. $f(x) = \sqrt{2x + 3}$

18. $f(x) = \dfrac{1}{\sqrt{x}}$

19. $f(x) = \dfrac{1}{\sqrt{2x + 3}}$

20. $f(x) = \sqrt{x^2 + 1}$

21. In Example 1, $f(x) = |x|$, what is the *range* of the derived function f'? What is its graph? Compare the graphs of $y = f'(x)$ and $y = |x|/x,\ x \neq 0$.

2–8   Velocity and rates. When a body moves in a straight line, it is customary to represent the line of motion by a coordinate axis, select a reference point O on the line as origin, adopt a positive direction and a unit of distance on the line, and then describe the motion by means of an equation which gives the coordinate of the body as a function of the time t that has elapsed since the start of the motion.

Thus for a freely falling body, the equation of motion is

$$s = \tfrac{1}{2}gt^2, \tag{1}$$

where g is the acceleration due to gravity and is approximately 32 (ft/sec^2), and s is the distance in feet that the body has fallen in t seconds from the start.

More generally, suppose the law of motion is given by a function f,

$$s = f(t), \tag{2}$$

and that we are required to find the *velocity* of the body at some instant of time t. First of all, how shall we *define* the instantaneous velocity of a moving body?

If we assume that *distance* and *time* are the fundamental physical quantities which we can measure, we may be led to reason as follows. At time t, the body is in the position

$$s = f(t), \tag{3}$$

and at time $t + \Delta t$ the body is in the position

$$s + \Delta s = f(t + \Delta t). \tag{4}$$

Hence during the interval of time from t to $t + \Delta t$, it has undergone a displacement

$$\Delta s = f(t + \Delta t) - f(t). \tag{5}$$

The quantities in Eqs. (3), (4), and (5) are all physical quantities which can be measured (by clocks and tapelines, say).

We now define the *average velocity* to be Δs divided by Δt:

$$v_{\text{av}} = \frac{\Delta s}{\Delta t} = \frac{f(t + \Delta t) - f(t)}{\Delta t}. \tag{6}$$

We are all familiar with applications of Eq. (6) in everyday life. For example, a sprinter runs 100 yards in 10 seconds. His average velocity is therefore

$$v_{\text{av}} = \frac{\Delta s}{\Delta t} = \frac{100 \text{ (yd)}}{10 \text{ (sec)}} = 10 \text{ (yd/sec)}.$$

In order to obtain the *instantaneous* velocity at time t, we take the average velocity over shorter and shorter intervals of time Δt. We are thereby led to the definition of instantaneous velocity, or what we call the velocity at time t, as the *limit* of v_{av} as Δt approaches zero; that is,

$$v = \lim_{\Delta t \to 0} \frac{\Delta s}{\Delta t} = \lim_{\Delta t \to 0} \frac{f(t + \Delta t) - f(t)}{\Delta t}. \tag{7}$$

We recognize that Eq. (7) is the same as the definition of the derivative

$$v = \frac{ds}{dt} = f'(t). \tag{8}$$

EXAMPLE. For the motion governed by Eq. (1).

$$s = \tfrac{1}{2}gt^2,$$

we find, by the methods of the previous article, that the velocity at time t is

$$v = \frac{ds}{dt} = gt.$$

Figure 2–20

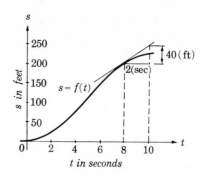

Figure 2–21

When we refer to Fig. 2–20, we see that

$$v_{\text{av}} = \frac{\Delta s}{\Delta t}$$

is the slope of the secant line $\overleftrightarrow{PQ}$ in the sense of measuring its rate of rise in units of s per unit of t. Here there is no reason to suppose that the unit of length used on the t-axis to represent one second is the same as the unit of length used on the s-axis to represent one foot. And certainly the geometrical inclination ϕ of the secant line $\overleftrightarrow{PQ}$ depends upon the scales used to represent the units of time and distance on the two axes. We can still say, however, that the average velocity equals the ratio of the opposite side to the adjacent side in the triangle PRQ, each with its proper units (and proper sign). Then the instantaneous velocity can also be interpreted geometrically as the rate of rise of the tangent line in units of s per unit of t.

This geometrical interpretation is sometimes used to estimate the velocity when the motion is given by means of a graph instead of by an equation $s = f(t)$.

For example, in the graph of Fig. 2–21, s represents the coordinate of some point of a bicycle which a boy is riding along a straight road. At $t = 8$, the tangent line appears to be rising at the rate of 40 s-units in an interval of 2 t-units; that is, the velocity at time $t = 8$ is apparently

$$\frac{40 \ (\text{ft})}{2 \ (\text{sec})} = 20 \ (\text{ft/sec}).$$

We say the velocity is "apparently" 20 ft/sec because we cannot be sure that we have accurately constructed the tangent to the curve. Indeed, an accurate construction would require that we know the derivative $f'(t)$, exactly, at $t = 8$ and this is the very thing we are trying to estimate. On the other hand, we can make a fair approximation to the tangent line by inspection and this is what we have done in the graph.

There are many other applications of the notion of average rate and instantaneous rate. For example, the quantity of water Q (gal) in a reservoir at time t (min) is a function of t. Water may flow into or out of the reservoir. As it does so, suppose that Q changes by an amount ΔQ from time t to time $t + \Delta t$. Then the average rate of change of Q with respect to t is

$$\frac{\Delta Q}{\Delta t} \ (\text{gal/min})$$

and the instantaneous rate of change of Q with respect to t is

$$\frac{dQ}{dt} = \lim_{\Delta t \to 0} \frac{\Delta Q}{\Delta t} \ (\text{gal/min}).$$

Derivatives are important in economic theory, where they are usually indicated by the adjective *"marginal."* Suppose, for example, that a manufacturer produces x tons of steel per week at a total cost of $y = f(x)$ dollars. This total cost includes such items as a proportionate part of the cost of building and maintaining the company's steel mills, salaries of executives, taxes, office maintenance, cost of raw materials, labor, etc. Suppose that in order to produce $x + \Delta x$ tons of steel weekly, it would cost $y + \Delta y$ dollars. The increase in cost per unit increase in output would be $\Delta y / \Delta x$. The limit of this ratio, as Δx tends to zero, is called the *marginal cost*. In other words, if total cost is y for weekly output x, then the *marginal* cost is just the derivative of y with respect to x. It gives the rate of increase of cost per unit increase of output from the level x.

The manufacturer is also interested in revenue and in profits. In order to sell his output of x tons per week he finds that he may charge a price $P = F(x)$ per ton. [Usually, at a higher price he would sell less; at a lower price he could sell more.] Then his *revenue* is the product $xP = xF(x)$. The *marginal* revenue is the *derivative* of xP with respect to x. It gives the rate of increase of revenue per unit increase in output. The manufacturer's profit, T, is the difference between revenue and cost:

$$T = xP - y.$$

In Chapter 5 we shall see how the manufacturer should adjust his production to achieve maximum profit. The adjustment involves his *marginal* profit, $\dfrac{dT}{dx}$, which is the rate of increase of profit per unit increase of production. (For a further discussion of applications to economics, see the book *Mathematical Analysis for Economists* by R. G. D. Allen, published by the Macmillan Co., New York, 1939. In particular, marginal cost and marginal revenue are discussed on pp. 152 ff.)

Any derivative may be interpreted as the instantaneous rate of change of one variable per unit change in the other. Thus, if the function defined by $y = f(x)$ has a derivative

$$f'(x) = \lim_{\Delta x \to 0} \frac{\Delta y}{\Delta x} = \lim_{\Delta x \to 0} \frac{f(x + \Delta x) - f(x)}{\Delta x},$$

we may interpret $\Delta y / \Delta x$ as *average* rate of change and

$$f'(x) = \lim_{\Delta x \to 0} \frac{\Delta y}{\Delta x}$$

as *instantaneous* rate of change of y with respect to x. Such a rate tells us the amount of change that would be produced in y by a change of one unit in x, provided the rate of change remained constant.

The *average* rate of change of y per unit change in x, $\Delta y / \Delta x$, when multiplied by the number of units change in x, Δx, gives the actual change in y:

$$\Delta y = \frac{\Delta y}{\Delta x} \Delta x.$$

The *instantaneous* rate of change of y per unit change in x, $f'(x)$, multiplied by the number of units change in x, Δx, gives the change that would be produced in y if the point (x, y) were to move along the *tangent line* instead of moving along the curve; that is (Fig. 2–22),

$$\boxed{\Delta y_{\tan} = f'(x) \cdot \Delta x.}$$

One reason calculus is important is that it enables us to find quantitatively how a change in one of two related variables affects the second variable.

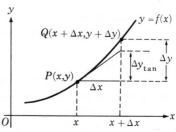

Figure 2–22

PROBLEMS

1. If a, b, c are constants and

$$f(t) = at^2 + bt + c,$$

show that

$$f'(t) = \lim_{\Delta t \to 0} \frac{f(t + \Delta t) - f(t)}{\Delta t} = 2at + b.$$

In the following problems (2 through 10), the law of motion gives s as a function of t. Apply the *result* found in Problem 1 above to write the velocity, $v = \dfrac{ds}{dt}$, by inspection.

2. $s = 2t^2 + 5t - 3$

3. $s = \frac{1}{2}gt^2 + v_0 t + s_0$
   (g, v_0, s_0 constants)

4. $s = 4t + 3$

5. $s = t^2 - 3t + 2$

6. $s = 4 - 2t - t^2$

7. $s = (2t + 3)^2$

8. $s = (2 - t)^2$

9. $s = 3 - 2t^2$

10. $s = 64t - 16t^2$

11. The following data give the coordinate s of a moving body for various values of t. Plot s vs. t on coordinate paper and sketch a smooth curve through the given points. Assuming that this smooth curve represents the motion of the body, estimate the velocity (a) at $t = 1.0$, (b) at $t = 2.5$, (c) at $t = 2.0$.

s (in ft)	10	38	58	70	74	70	58	38	10
t (in sec)	0	0.5	1.0	1.5	2.0	2.5	3.0	3.5	4.0

12. A swimming pool is to be drained for cleaning. If Q represents the number of gallons of water in the pool t minutes after the pool has started to drain, and $Q = 200\,(30 - t)^2$, how fast is the water running out at the end of 10 minutes? What is the *average* rate at which the water flows out during the first 10 minutes?

13. (a) If the radius of a circle changes from r to $r + \Delta r$, what is the average rate of change of the area of the circle with respect to the radius? (b) Find the instantaneous rate of change of the area with respect to the radius.

14. The volume V (ft^3) of a sphere of radius r (ft) is $V = \frac{4}{3}\pi r^3$. Find the rate of change of V with respect to r.

15. The radius r and altitude h of a certain cone are equal at all times. Find the rate of change of the volume $V = \frac{1}{3}\pi r^2 h$ with respect to h.

REVIEW QUESTIONS AND EXERCISES FOR CHAPTER 2

1. Define *function* in three ways. What is the *domain* of a function? What is its *range*?

2. The domain of a certain function is the set $0 \le x \le 2$. The range of the function is the single number $y = 1$.
   (a) Sketch and describe the graph of the function.
   (b) Write an expression for the function.
   (c) If we interchange the axes in part (a), does the new graph so obtained represent a function? Explain.

3. If $f(x) = 1/x$ and $g(x) = 1/\sqrt{x}$, what are the natural domains of f and g and the corresponding domains of $f - g$, $f \cdot g$, f/g, and g/f?

4. If f is a function with domain $[a, b]$ and $g(x) = f(x - c)$ for some positive number c, how can the graph of g be obtained from the graph of f? What is the name given to this process? What is the domain of g?

5. If $g(x) = f(kx)$, $k > 0$, what process is used to obtain the graph of g from the graph of f?

6. Give an example, different from those mentioned in the text, of a step-function.

7. Give an example, different from those in the text, of a function whose domain could be the set of all real numbers, $-\infty < x < +\infty$.

8. Is it appropriate to define a *tangent line* to a curve C at a point P on C as a line that has just the one point P in common with C? Illustrate your discussion with graphs.

9. Define, carefully, the concept of slope of a tangent to a curve at a point on the curve.

10. Define the concept of *average velocity*, of *instantaneous velocity*.

11. What more general concept includes both the concept of slope of the tangent to a curve and the concept of instantaneous velocity?

12. Define the derivative of a function at a point in its domain. Illustrate your definition by applying it to the function f defined by $f(x) = x^2$, at the point $x = 2$.

1. Given the equation $y = (x^2 + 2)/(x^2 - 1)$. Express x in terms of y and determine the range of values of y for which x is real.

2. Express the area A and the circumference C of a circle as functions of the radius r. Express A as a function of C.

3. In each of the following functions, what is the largest domain of x and the corresponding range of y?

(a) $y = \dfrac{1}{1+x}$; (b) $y = \dfrac{1}{1+x^2}$; (c) $y = \dfrac{1}{1+\sqrt{x}}$.

4. Without the use of the absolute value symbol, describe the domain of x for which $|x + 1| < 4$.

5. If $y = 2x + |2 - x|$, determine x as a function of y.

6. For what range of values of y does the equation $y = x + |2 - x|$ determine x as a single-valued function of y? Solve for x in terms of y on this range of values.

7. If $y = x + (1/x)$, express x as the union of two functions of y and determine the domain of y for which x is real.

8. DEFINITION. *A rational number is one that can be expressed in the form p/q, where p and q are integers with no common divisor greater than one, and $q > 0$. A real number that is not rational is called* irrational.
  With these definitions in mind, plot a few points on the graph of the function that maps the rational number p/q (reduced to lowest terms as above) into $1/q$, and maps each irrational number into zero. This function has been described as the "ruler function" because of the resemblance of its graph to the markings on an ordinary ruler showing inches, half-inches, quarters, eighths, and sixteenths by lines of different lengths. The edge of the ruler corresponds to the x-axis. Do you see why this terminology is rather appropriate?

9. (a) If $f(x) = x^2 + 2x - 3$, find $f(-2); f(-1); f(x_1); f(x_1 + \Delta x)$.
  (b) If $f(x) = x - (1/x)$, show that $f(1/x) = -f(x) = f(-x)$.

10. Sketch the graph of each of the following equations:

(a) $y = |x - 2| + 2$; (b) $y = x^2 - 1$.

(c) Find the point on the curve in part (b) where the tangent to the curve makes an angle of $45°$ with the positive x-axis.

11. Sketch a graph of the function $y = |x + 2| + x$ for the domain $-5 \le x \le 2$. What is the range?

12. Show that the expression $M(a, b) = (a + b)/2 + |a - b|/2$ is equal to a when $a \ge b$ and is equal to b when $b \ge a$. In other words, $M(a, b)$ gives the larger of the two numbers a and b. Find a similar expression, $m(a, b)$, which gives the smaller of the two numbers.

For each of the following expressions for $f(x)$ in Problems 13–16, sketch first the graph of $y = f(x)$, then the graph of $y = |f(x)|$ and finally the graph of $y = f(x)/2 + |f(x)|/2$.

13. $f(x) = (x - 2)(x + 1)$ 14. $f(x) = x^2$

15. $f(x) = -x^2$ 16. $f(x) = 4 - x^2$

17. *Lagrange interpolation formula.*   Let (x_1, y_1), (x_2, y_2), ..., (x_n, y_n) be n points in the plane, no two of them having the same abscissas. Find a polynomial, $f(x)$, of degree $(n - 1)$ which takes the value y_1 at x_1, y_2 at x_2, ..., y_n at x_n; that is, $f(x_i) = y_i$ $(i = 1, 2, ..., n)$. [*Hint:* $f(x) = y_1\phi_1(x) + y_2\phi_2(x) + \cdots + y_n\phi_n(x)$, where $\phi_k(x)$ is a polynomial which is zero at $x_i(i \neq k)$ and $\phi_k(x_k) = 1$.]

18. If $f(x) = x/(x - 1)$, find (a) $f(1/x)$, (b) $f(-x)$.

Find $f'(x)$ using the definition of the derivative for each of the following expressions for $f(x)$.

19. $(x - 1)/(x + 1)$ 20. $x^{3/2}$ 21. $x^{1/3}$

Use the definition of the derivative in Problems 22 to 24.

22. Find $f'(x)$ if $f(x) = x^2 - 3x - 4$

23. Find $\dfrac{dy}{dx}$ if $y = \dfrac{1}{3x} + 2x$

24. Find $f'(t)$ if $f(t) = \sqrt{t - 4}$

25. (a) By means of the Δ-method, find the slope of the curve $y = 2x^3 + 2$ at the point $(1, 4)$. (b) At which point of the curve in (a) is the tangent to the curve parallel to the x-axis? Sketch the curve.

26. If $f(x) = 2x/(x - 1)$, find (a) $f(0), f(-1), f(1/x)$; (b) $\Delta f(x)/\Delta x$; (c) $f'(x)$, using the result of part (b).

27. Given $y = 180x - 16x^2$. Using the method of Article 2–6, find the slope of the curve at the point (x_1, y_1). Sketch the curve. At what point does the curve have a horizontal tangent?

28. Find the velocity $v = ds/dt$ if the distance a particle moves in time t is given by $s = 180t - 16t^2$. When does the velocity vanish?

29. If the pressure P and volume V of a certain gas are related by the formula $P = 1/V$, find (a) the average rate of change of P with respect to V, (b) the rate of change of P with respect to V at the instant when $V = 2$.

30. The volume V (in^3) of water remaining in a leaking pail after t sec is $V = 2000 - 40t + 0.2t^2$. How fast is the volume decreasing when $t = 30$?

31. Let f be a function defined on an interval, and x_1 and x_2 a pair of numbers on the interval with $x_1 < x_2$. (a) If $f(x_1) < f(x_2)$, then f is an *increasing function*. (b) If $f(x_1) > f(x_2)$, then f is a *decreasing function*. (c) If $f(x_1) \leq f(x_2)$, then f is a *weakly increasing function*. (d) If $f(x_1) \geq f(x_2)$, then f is a *weakly decreasing function*.

DEFINITION. *A monotone function is one which is either weakly increasing or weakly decreasing. A strongly monotone function is one which is either increasing or decreasing.*

For each of the following functions state whether it is monotone increasing, monotone decreasing, or not monotone. If it is not monotone, divide its domain into parts such that the restriction of f to any of these parts gives a monotone or strongly monotone function.

(a) $f(x) = c$ (b) $f(x) = |x|$

(c) $f(x) = [x]$ (d) $f(x) = -x^2$

(e) $f(x) = x|x|$ (f) $f(x) = |x^2 - 4|$

(g) $f(x) = \dfrac{1}{x}$ (h) $f(x) = x^3$

Limits

3–1 Definition of limit of a function. The purpose of this chapter is to introduce the formal definition of *limit* as an operation applied to a function at a point, and to prove theorems about limits of sums, products, and quotients of functions. We have already seen in Article 2–5 that the average rate of increase of a function $f(x)$, when x goes from x_1 to $x_1 + h$ is

$$\frac{f(x_1 + h) - f(x_1)}{h}, \quad h \neq 0.$$

The *instantaneous* rate of increase of f at x_1 is the limit (if there is one) of this expression as h tends to zero. We cannot just put $h = 0$ in the quotient because $0/0$ is meaningless. Thus, it is necessary to study the theory of limits before proceeding. We shall apply the various limit theorems in Chapter 4 when we resume the study of the rate of change of a function.

DEFINITION. *Suppose $f(x)$ is a function defined for values of x near a. (The domain of f need not include a, although it may.) We say that*

> L *is the* limit *of $f(x)$ as x approaches a,*

and write

$$L = \lim_{x \to a} f(x) \tag{1}$$

provided that, for any $\epsilon > 0$ there corresponds a deleted neighborhood N of a such that

$$L - \epsilon < f(x) < L + \epsilon \tag{2}$$

whenever x is in N.

Intuitively, what we are looking for is some L so that we can make "$f(x)$ as close to L as we please" by taking x in a "small enough" deleted neighborhood of a. What we are doing is giving a precise mathematical formulation of the rather vague phrases enclosed in quotes in the previous sentence.

EXAMPLE. Find $\lim_{x \to 1} (5x - 3)$, and prove that your answer is correct.

Solution. Let

$$f(x) = 5x - 3 \quad \text{and} \quad a = 1. \tag{3}$$

83

We first guess an appropriate value of L by asking, what number is $f(x) = 5x - 3$ close to when x is close to 1? The obvious answer is

$$L = 2.$$

We try to satisfy the conditions in (2), assuming that $L = 2$ and ϵ is a given positive number. Thus we require that

$$2 - \epsilon < 5x - 3 < 2 + \epsilon, \qquad (4a)$$

which, after adding 3 throughout, is seen to be equivalent to

$$5 - \epsilon < 5x < 5 + \epsilon \qquad (4b)$$

or, after division by 5,

$$1 - \frac{\epsilon}{5} < x < 1 + \frac{\epsilon}{5}. \qquad (4c)$$

The inequalities in (4c) describe the open interval $(1 - \epsilon/5, 1 + \epsilon/5)$, which is a neighborhood of $a = 1$. If we delete 1 from that neighborhood, the resulting *deleted* neighborhood is described by

$$0 < |x - 1| < \frac{\epsilon}{5}. \qquad (4d)$$

Figure 3-1 shows that, if N_0 is this deleted neighborhood of 1, the inequalities in (4a) are satisfied whenever x is in N_0. Therefore, $\lim\limits_{x \to 1} (5x - 3) = 2$.

Figure 3-1

Remark 1. Notice that the half-width of the deleted neighborhood in (4d) is $\epsilon/5$. Thus the neighborhood gets smaller if ϵ is decreased.

Remark 2. The half-width $\epsilon/5$ is the largest that will work for the above example. But the deleted neighborhood N_0 is not unique: we could, for example, use a smaller neighborhood N_1 such as $0 < |x - 1| < \epsilon/10$ or use a nonsymmetric deleted neighborhood N_2 like the union of the intervals

$$(1 - \epsilon/6, 1) \qquad \text{and} \qquad (1, 1 + \epsilon/8).$$

Since $\epsilon/10$, $\epsilon/6$, and $\epsilon/8$ are all less than $\epsilon/5$, these nonsymmetric deleted neighborhoods lie inside N_0. Thus if x_1 is in N_2 it is also in N_0 and the value of f at x_1 is between $2 - \epsilon$ and $2 + \epsilon$.

PROBLEMS

Find an appropriate number L and a deleted neighborhood N, of a, such that, given $\epsilon > 0$,

$$L - \epsilon < f(x) < L + \epsilon \qquad \text{when } x \text{ is in } N.$$

Illustrate each problem (1 through 7) with a graph similar to Fig. 3–1.

1. $f(x) = 5 - 3x$, $\qquad a = 2$

2. $f(x) = 7$, $\qquad a = -1$

3. $f(x) = 4/x$, $\qquad a = 2$

4. $f(x) = \dfrac{x^2 - 4}{x - 2}$, $\qquad a = 2$

5. $f(x) = \dfrac{x^2 + 6x + 5}{x + 5}$, $\qquad a = 5$

6. $f(x) = \dfrac{3x^2 + 8x - 3}{2x + 6}$, $\qquad a = -3$

7. $f(x) = \dfrac{(1/x) - (1/3)}{x - 3}$, $\qquad a = 3$

8. In the next article we use the fact that if N_1 and N_2 are deleted neighborhoods of a, so is their intersection $N_1 \cap N_2$. Prove this fact, by telling what the intersection is if

$$N_1 = \{x \mid h_1 < x < a \qquad \text{or} \qquad a < x < k_1\}$$

and

$$N_2 = \{x \mid h_2 < x < a \qquad \text{or} \qquad a < x < k_2\}.$$

Illustrate with a sketch. (Hint: First set up conditions for h_3 and k_3 in terms of h_1 and h_2 and k_1 and k_2 respectively, such that for N_3, the intersection of N_1 and N_2, we have

$$N_3 = \{x \mid h_3 < x < a \qquad \text{or} \qquad a < x < k_3\}.)$$

9. Find some neighborhood of $t = 3$, that is, a domain $0 < |t - 3| < \delta$, such that when t is restricted to this domain, the difference between $t^2 + t$ and 12 will be numerically smaller than (a) $\frac{1}{10}$, (b) $\frac{1}{100}$, (c) ϵ, where ϵ may be any positive number.

3–2   Theorems about limits. In Chapter 2 we saw how to combine functions by adding, multiplying, subtracting, and dividing. In this and the following article we shall prove some useful theorems about limits of such combinations of functions. Our first theorem, however, is suggested by the example of Article 3–1.

THEOREM 1. *If m, b, and a are any real numbers, and*

$$f(x) = mx + b, \tag{1}$$

then

$$\lim_{x \to a} f(x) = ma + b. \tag{2}$$

Proof. Let $\epsilon > 0$ be given, and let $L = ma + b$. We need to prove that there exists a deleted neighborhood N, of a, such that

$$(ma + b) - \epsilon < mx + b < (ma + b) + \epsilon \tag{3}$$

when x is in N. Subtract $(ma + b)$ from the three expressions in (3) and get

$$-\epsilon < mx - ma < \epsilon \tag{4a}$$

which is the same as

$$|m(x - a)| < \epsilon. \tag{4b}$$

In the statement of the theorem, m is an arbitrary real number, so it may be positive, negative, or zero.

Case 1. If m is positive, divide both sides of (4b) by m and get the equivalent inequality

$$|x - a| < \frac{\epsilon}{m}. \tag{5a}$$

Case 2. If m is negative, use the fact that

$$|m(x - a)| = |m|\,|x - a|$$

and divide both sides of (4b) by $|m|$ and get,

$$|x - a| < \frac{\epsilon}{|m|}. \tag{5b}$$

Case 3. If $m = 0$, Inequality (4b) is satisfied for all values of x because

$$|0(x - a)| = 0 < \epsilon.$$

For either Case 1 or Case 2 we can take, for the deleted neighborhood N, the set of all x which satisfies

$$0 < |x - a| < \frac{\epsilon}{|m|}, \tag{6a}$$

and when $m = 0$ $(f(x) = b = \text{constant})$ we can take N to be any deleted neighborhood, for example those x such that

$$0 < |x - a| < 1. \tag{6b}$$

Therefore, given m, b, a, and $\epsilon > 0$, we can always find a deleted neighborhood N of a such that the inequalities in (3) hold for all x in N. Therefore, $L = ma + b$ satisfies Condition (2) in the definition of a limit, Article 3–1, and we conclude that

$$\lim_{x \to a} (mx + b) = ma + b. \qquad \text{Q.E.D.}$$

EXAMPLE 1. $\lim\limits_{x \to 5} (3x - 7) = 15 - 7 = 8, \qquad (m = 3, b = -7).$

EXAMPLE 2. $\qquad\qquad \lim\limits_{x \to a} x = a, \qquad (m = 1, b = 0).$

EXAMPLE 3. $\qquad\qquad \lim\limits_{x \to a} b = b, \qquad (m = 0).$

Uniqueness of limit. Is it possible for a function to approach two different limits as x approaches a? The answer is "No," as the following theorem shows.

THEOREM 2. *If $f(x)$ has a limit as x approaches a, that limit is unique.*

Proof. (Indirect proof: by contradiction.) Suppose L_1 and L_2 are two different numbers, and

$$\lim_{x \to a} f(x) = L_1, \qquad \lim_{x \to a} f(x) = L_2. \tag{7}$$

Then $L_1 \neq L_2$ means that $|L_1 - L_2|$ is positive and we let

$$\epsilon = \tfrac{1}{2}|L_1 - L_2|. \tag{8}$$

You will see why this choice is made later in the proof.

By definition of limit, applied to L_1, we know there is a deleted neighborhood N_1 of a (see Fig. 3–2) such that

$$|f(x) - L_1| < \epsilon \qquad (9a)$$

when x is in N_1. Likewise there is a deleted neighborhood N_2 of a such that

$$|f(x) - L_2| < \epsilon \qquad (9b)$$

Figure 3–2

when x is in N_2. If

$$N_1 = \{x \mid h_1 < x < a \quad \text{or} \quad a < x < k_1\} \tag{10a}$$

and

$$N_2 = \{x \mid h_2 < x < a \quad \text{or} \quad a < x < k_2\}, \tag{10b}$$

then the intersection of N_1 and N_2 is a nonempty deleted neighborhood N_3 such that

$$N_3 = \{x \mid h_3 < x < a \quad \text{or} \quad a < x < k_3\} \tag{10c}$$

where

$$h_3 = \max \{h_1, h_2\}$$
$$k_3 = \min \{k_1, k_2\}.$$

Figure 3–2 illustrates these ideas. N_1 goes from h_1 to k_1, N_2 from h_2 to k_2. Here points $\neq a$ between h_1 and k_2 are in both N_1 and N_2, hence are in $N_3 = N_1 \cap N_2$ where $h_3 = h_1$ and $k_3 = k_2$. But for any x in N_3, both (9a) and (9b) hold simultaneously, and lead to the false conclusion

$$|L_1 - L_2| = |L_1 - f(x) + f(x) - L_2|$$
$$\leq |L_1 - f(x)| + |f(x) - L_2| < \epsilon + \epsilon = 2\epsilon = |L_1 - L_2|.$$

Since the assumption that

$$L_1 \neq L_2$$

leads to the contradiction

$$|L_1 - L_2| < |L_1 - L_2|,$$

that assumption must be false. Therefore $L_1 = L_2$, so the limit is unique.

Q.E.D.

Remark 1. Theorem 2 shows that if we can guess an answer to the question of finding a limit L for a function $f(x)$ as x approaches a, and then prove that this number L satisfies the conditions in the definition of a limit, then it is *the* answer—there is no other.

EXAMPLE 4. Prove that $\lim\limits_{x \to 3} (x^3 - 27)/(x - 3) = 27$.

Solution. Since $x^3 - 27 = (x - 3)(x^2 + 3x + 9)$, we have

$$f(x) = \frac{x^3 - 27}{x - 3} = x^2 + 3x + 9, \quad \text{if} \quad x \neq 3.$$

When x is *close* to (but not equal to) 3, $x^2 + 3x + 9$ is *close* to 27, and we guess that $L = 27$ is the answer. Now we can see if we can prove it. Suppose ϵ is a given positive number. Can we find a deleted neighborhood N of 3 such that

$$|f(x) - L| = |(x^2 + 3x + 9) - 27| < \epsilon \qquad \text{(11a)}$$

when x is in N? We observe that

$$
\begin{aligned}
x^2 + 3x + 9 - 27 &= x^2 + 3x - 18 \\
&= (x - 3)(x + 6)
\end{aligned}
$$

so Inequality (11a) is the same as

$$|x - 3|\,|x + 6| < \epsilon. \qquad \text{(11b)}$$

When x is near 3, the factor $x - 3$ is near zero and $x + 6$ is near 9. Consider now the deleted neighborhood N_0

$$0 < |x - 3| < 1. \qquad \text{(12)}$$

If x is in N_0, $-1 < x - 3 < 1$ or (by adding 9) $8 < x + 6 < 10$. Therefore $|x + 6| < 10$ and it follows that

$$|x - 3|\,|x + 6| < 10|x - 3|.$$

If we now make

$$0 < 10|x - 3| < \epsilon$$

and consider the deleted neighborhood N_1

$$0 < |x - 3| < \frac{\epsilon}{10}, \qquad \text{(13)}$$

we shall satisfy the Inequalities (11a) and (11b) if we take for N the smaller of the two neighborhoods N_0 and N_1. If x is in N it follows that

$$
\begin{aligned}
|f(x) - 27| &= |(x^2 + 3x + 9) - 27| \\
&= |x^2 + 3x - 18| \\
&= |x + 6|\,|x - 3| \\
&< 10\,|x - 3| \quad \text{since } x \text{ belongs to } N \subseteq N_0^* \\
&< 10\,\frac{\epsilon}{10} \qquad \text{since } x \text{ belongs to } N \subseteq N_1 \\
&< \epsilon.
\end{aligned}
$$

Therefore

$$\lim_{x \to 3} f(x) = 27.$$

---

* We write $A \subseteq B$ to mean A is a subset of B which may be equal to B.

Remark 2. The foregoing example reduced to showing that

$$\lim_{x \to 3} (x^2 + 3x + 9) = 27.$$

If we could say

$$\lim (x^2 + 3x + 9) = \lim (x^2) + \lim (3x + 9)$$

and

$$\lim (x^2) = (\lim x) \cdot (\lim x)$$

the problem would have been much simpler. These are, in fact, correct statements, as the next theorems will show.

THEOREM 3. LIMIT OF SUMS. *If* $\lim f(x) = L_1$ *and* $\lim g(x) = L_2$, *then*

$$\lim \big(f(x) + g(x)\big) = \lim f(x) + \lim g(x)$$
$$= L_1 + L_2,$$

where all limits are taken as $x \to a$.

Proof. Suppose $\epsilon > 0$ is given. We want to find a deleted neighborhood N of a, such that

$$|f(x) + g(x) - (L_1 + L_2)| < \epsilon \tag{14}$$

when x is in N. We use the fact that

$$|(f(x) + g(x)) - (L_1 + L_2)| = |(f(x) - L_1) + (g(x) - L_2)|$$
$$\leq |(fx) - L_1| + |g(x) - L_2| \tag{15}$$

Because $\epsilon/2$ is positive and $f(x) \to L_1$, there is a deleted neighborhood N_1 of a such that

$$|f(x) - L_1| < \frac{\epsilon}{2} \tag{16a}$$

when x is in N_1. Likewise there is a deleted neighborhood N_2 of a such that

$$|g(x) - L_2| < \frac{\epsilon}{2} \tag{16b}$$

when x is in N_2. Let N be the intersection of N_1 and N_2:

$$N = N_1 \cap N_2.$$

Then the inequalities of (16a) and (16b) both hold when x is in N, and so (14) also holds, since

$$|(f(x) + g(x)) - (L_1 + L_2)| \leq |f(x) - L_1| + |g(x) - L_2|$$
$$< \frac{\epsilon}{2} + \frac{\epsilon}{2} = \epsilon. \quad \text{Q.E.D.}$$

PROBLEMS

Evaluate the limits indicated in Problems 1 through 8.

1. $\lim_{x \to 2} 2x$

2. $\lim_{x \to 0} 2x$

3. $\lim_{x \to 4} 4$

4. $\lim_{x \to -2} 4$

5. $\lim_{x \to 1} (3x - 1)$

6. $\lim_{x \to 1/3} (3x - 1)$

7. $\lim_{y \to 2} \dfrac{y^2 + 5y + 6}{y + 2}$

8. $\lim_{y \to 2} \dfrac{y^2 - 5y + 6}{y - 2}$

9. Suppose $\lim_{x \to b} f(x) = 7$ and $\lim_{x \to b} g(x) = -3$, what is $\lim_{x \to b} (f(x) + g(x))$?

10. Prove that $\lim_{x \to a} (p(x) + r(x) + s(x)) = \lim_{x \to a} p(x) + \lim_{x \to a} r(x) + \lim_{x \to a} s(x)$, provided the last three limits exist.

11. Suppose $\lim_{x \to -2} p(x) = 4$, $\lim_{x \to -2} r(x) = 0$, $\lim_{x \to -2} s(x) = -3$. What is the $\lim_{x \to -2} (p(x) + r(x) + s(x))$?

12. (a) Find $\lim_{x \to 3} 2x - 3$.

    (b) Find $\lim_{x \to 3} 3x + 2$.

    (c) Find $\lim_{x \to 3} 5x - 1$ in two ways.

In Problems 13 through 18 guess the limit, then prove that your guess is correct.

13. $\lim_{x \to 5} x^2$

14. $\lim_{x \to 2} x(2 - x)$

15. $\lim_{x \to 0} (x^2 - 2x + 1)$

16. $\lim_{x \to 5} (x^2 - 3x - 18)$

17. $\lim_{x \to 2} (x^3 - 4x + 1)$

18. $\lim_{x \to 4} \sqrt{x}$

19. Give an example of functions f and g such that $f(x) + g(x)$ approaches a limit as x approaches zero, even though $f(x)$ and $g(x)$, separately, do not approach limits as $x \to 0$.

3-3 More theorems about limits. In Article 3-2 we proved a very useful theorem involving the limit of a sum. In this article we shall prove two theorems involving the limit of a product and the limit of a quotient.

THEOREM 4. LIMIT OF PRODUCTS. *If* $\lim f(x) = L_1$ *and* $\lim g(x) = L_2$, *then*

$$\lim f(x)g(x) = (\lim f(x))(\lim g(x)) = L_1 L_2,$$

where all limits are taken as $x \to a$.

Proof. Let $\epsilon > 0$ be given. We need to show that there is a deleted neighborhood N of a such that

$$|f(x)g(x) - L_1L_2| < \epsilon \tag{1}$$

when x is in N.

We write

$$f(x) = L_1 + (f(x) - L_1)$$
$$g(x) = L_2 + (g(x) - L_2)$$

so that

$$
\begin{aligned}
f(x)g(x) - L_1L_2 &= [L_1 + (f(x) - L_1)][L_2 + (g(x) - L_2)] - L_1L_2 \\
&= [L_1(g(x) - L_2) + L_2(f(x) - L_1) \\
&\quad + (f(x) - L_1)(g(x) - L_2) + L_1L_2] - L_1L_2 \\
&= L_1(g(x) - L_2) + L_2(f(x) - L_1) \\
&\quad + (f(x) - L_1)(g(x) - L_2).
\end{aligned}
$$

Therefore,

$$
\begin{aligned}
|f(x)g(x) - L_1L_2| &\leq |L_1(g(x) - L_2)| + |L_2(f(x) - L_1)| \\
&\quad + |(f(x) - L_1)(g(x) - L_2)|
\end{aligned}
$$

and

$$
\begin{aligned}
|f(x)g(x) - L_1L_2| &\leq |L_1| \cdot |g(x) - L_2| + |L_2| \cdot |f(x) - L_1| \\
&\quad + |f(x) - L_1| \cdot |g(x) - L_2|. \tag{2}
\end{aligned}
$$

By hypothesis there is a deleted neighborhood N_1 of a such that

$$|g(x) - L_2| < \frac{\epsilon}{3(1 + |L_1|)}$$

when x is in N_1, because $\lim g(x) = L_2$ and

$$\frac{\epsilon}{3(1 + |L_1|)}$$

is a positive number. Likewise, there are deleted neighborhoods N_2, N_3, and N_4 such that

$$|f(x) - L_1| < \frac{\epsilon}{3(1 + |L_2|)} \qquad \text{when } x \text{ is in } N_2,$$

$$|f(x) - L_1| < \sqrt{\epsilon/3} \qquad \text{when } x \text{ is in } N_3,$$

and

$$|g(x) - L_2| < \sqrt{\epsilon/3} \qquad \text{when } x \text{ is in } N_4.$$

(It will be apparent later why the particular positive numbers $\epsilon/3(1 + |L_1|)$, $\epsilon/3(1 + |L_2|)$, and $\sqrt{\epsilon/3}$, are chosen.) If N is the intersection of N_1, N_2,

N_3, and N_4, the above inequalities all hold when x is in N, so that the right side of Inequality (2) is less than

$$\frac{|L_1|\epsilon}{3(1 + |L_1|)} + \frac{|L_2|\epsilon}{3(1 + |L_2|)} + \sqrt{\frac{\epsilon}{3}} \cdot \sqrt{\frac{\epsilon}{3}}. \tag{3}$$

Since

$$\frac{|L_1|}{1 + |L_1|} < 1 \quad \text{and} \quad \frac{|L_2|}{1 + |L_2|} < 1$$

we have

$$\frac{|L_1|\epsilon}{3(1 + |L_1|)} < \frac{\epsilon}{3} \quad \text{and} \quad \frac{|L_2|\epsilon}{3(1 + |L_2|)} < \frac{\epsilon}{3}.$$

Therefore (3) is less than

$$\frac{\epsilon}{3} + \frac{\epsilon}{3} + \frac{\epsilon}{3} = \epsilon. \qquad \text{Q.E.D.}$$

Remark 3. There is a reason for using $1 + |L_1|$ and $1 + |L_2|$ in the denominators in (3) instead of $|L_1|$ and $|L_2|$. If $L_1 = 0$, we do not want $|L_1|$ in the denominator. But $1 + |L_1|$ cannot be zero, and, as noted, $|L|/(1 + |L|)$ is always less than 1 because the denominator is greater than the numerator.

COROLLARY 4.1. *If* $\lim f(x) = L$ *and k is a constant, then* $\lim kf(x) = kL$, *where both limits are taken as $x \to a$.*

Proof. Apply Theorem 4 with $g(x) = k$, so that

$$L_2 = \lim g(x) = k.$$

COROLLARY 4.2. *The* $\lim_{x \to a} x^n = a^n$ *for any positive integer n.*

Proof. (By induction on n.) If $n = 1$,

$$\lim_{x \to a} x = a,$$

by Theorem 1 with $m = 1$, $b = 0$.

If $n - 1$ is a positive integer such that

$$\lim_{x \to a} x^{n-1} = a^{n-1},$$

then

$$\lim_{x \to a} x^n = \lim_{x \to a} (x \cdot x^{n-1}) = a \cdot a^{n-1} = a^n$$

by Theorem 4 with $f(x) = x$, $g(x) = x^{n-1}$, $L_1 = a$, and $L_2 = a^{n-1}$.

$$\text{Q.E.D.}$$

COROLLARY 4.3. *If*

$$f(x) = c_0 x^n + c_1 x^{n-1} + \cdots + c_n$$

is a polynomial in x, then

$$\lim_{x \to a} f(x) = c_0 a^n + c_1 a^{n-1} + \cdots + c_n = f(a).$$

Proof. (Again by induction on n.) Since we have already proved it for $n = 1$ in Theorem 1, assume that the result holds for the polynomial

$$g(x) = c_1 x^{n-1} + \cdots + c_n.$$

Then

$$\lim_{x \to a} \left(c_0 x^n + g(x) \right) = \lim_{x \to a} \left(c_0 x^n \right) + \lim_{x \to a} g(x)$$

$$= c_0 a^n + g(a)$$

$$= f(a),$$

from Corollaries 4.1 and 4.2 with $k = c_0$.   Q.E.D.

EXAMPLE 5. $\lim_{x \to 2} (5x^2 + 4x - 10) = 20 + 8 - 10 = 18.$

Is it true that

$$\lim \frac{1}{g(x)} = \frac{1}{\lim g(x)} ?$$

Since division by zero is not valid, we must assume that

$$\lim g(x) \neq 0.$$

With this proviso, the answer is "yes."

THEOREM 5. LIMIT OF QUOTIENTS. *Let* $\lim_{x \to a} g(\dot{x}) = L \neq 0$. *Then*

$$\lim_{x \to a} \left(\frac{1}{g(x)} \right) = \frac{1}{L}. \tag{4}$$

Proof. Given: $\epsilon > 0$. We want a deleted neighborhood N of a such that

$$\left| \frac{1}{g(x)} - \frac{1}{L} \right| < \epsilon \tag{5}$$

when x is in N. Inequality (5) is the same as

$$\left| \frac{L - g(x)}{L \cdot g(x)} \right| < \epsilon. \tag{6}$$

The numerator on the left can be made as small as we like, by taking x sufficiently near a since $\lim_{x \to a} g(x) = L$. To the denominator we apply Corollary 4.1:

$$\lim_{x \to a} L \cdot g(x) = L \lim_{x \to a} g(x) = L^2.$$

By definition of limit, with $\epsilon = L^2/2$, there is a deleted neighborhood N_1 of a such that, whenever x is in N_1,

$$L^2 - \epsilon < L \cdot g(x) < L^2 + \epsilon$$

or since $\epsilon = L^2/2$

$$\frac{L^2}{2} < L \cdot g(x) < \frac{3L^2}{2}.$$

Hence $L \cdot g(x)$ is positive and, on taking reciprocals, we get

$$\frac{2}{L^2} > \frac{1}{L \cdot g(x)}$$

when x is in N_1. Therefore,

$$\left| \frac{L - g(x)}{L \cdot g(x)} \right| = \frac{|L - g(x)|}{L \cdot g(x)} < \frac{2}{L^2} |L - g(x)| \qquad (7)$$

when x is in N_1. Finally, to satisfy (6), there is a deleted neighborhood N_2 such that

$$|L - g(x)| < \frac{\epsilon L^2}{2} \qquad (8)$$

when x is in N_2. Now let N be the intersection of N_1 and N_2. When x is in N, Inequalities (7) and (8) both hold, so that

$$\left| \frac{L - g(x)}{L \cdot g(x)} \right| < \frac{2}{L^2} |L - g(x)| < \frac{2}{L^2} \left(\frac{\epsilon L^2}{2} \right) = \epsilon. \qquad \text{Q.E.D.}$$

COROLLARY 5.1. *If* $\lim_{x \to a} f(x) = L_1$ *and* $\lim_{x \to a} g(x) = L_2$, *and* $L_2 \neq 0$, *then*

$$\lim_{x \to a} \frac{f(x)}{g(x)} = \frac{L_1}{L_2} = \frac{\lim f(x)}{\lim g(x)}.$$

Proof. Combine Theorems 4 and 5.

$$\lim \frac{f(x)}{g(x)} = \lim \left[f(x) \cdot \frac{1}{g(x)} \right] = \lim f(x) \cdot \lim \left(\frac{1}{g(x)} \right)$$

$$= L_1 \cdot \frac{1}{L_2}. \qquad \text{Q.E.D.}$$

COROLLARY 5.2.   *If $f(x) = b_0 x^m + b_1 x^{m-1} + \ldots + b_m$ and $g(x) = c_0 x^n + c_1 x^{n-1} + \ldots + c_n$ are polynomials and $g(a) \neq 0$, then*

$$\lim_{x \to a} \frac{f(x)}{g(x)} = \frac{f(a)}{g(a)}.$$

Proof. Combine Corollaries 5.1 and 4.3 to get

$$\lim \frac{f(x)}{g(x)} = \frac{\lim f(x)}{\lim g(x)} = \frac{f(a)}{g(a)}. \qquad \text{Q.E.D.}$$

Remark 4.   In effect, Corollary 5.2 says that to find the limit of the quotient of two polynomials as x *approaches* a, substitute $x = a$ and compute $f(a)/g(a)$, provided the denominator turns out to be *different from zero*. But you cannot find

$$\lim_{x \to 3} \frac{x^2 - 9}{x - 3} = \lim_{x \to 3} (x + 3) = 6,$$

by dividing $3^2 - 9 = 0$ by $3 - 3 = 0$.

EXAMPLE 6. $\displaystyle \lim_{x \to 1} \frac{x^2 - x + 2}{x^2 + x + 2} = \frac{1 - 1 + 2}{1 + 1 + 2} = \frac{1}{2}.$

We conclude this article with a theorem which is used repeatedly in our later work.

THEROEM 6.   *Suppose $f(x) \leq g(x) \leq h(x)$ for all values of x near c. Furthermore, suppose that the function values $f(x)$ and $h(x)$ approach a common limit L as x approaches c. Then $g(x)$ also approaches L as limit when x approaches c.*

Proof. By hypothesis, to any positive number ϵ there corresponds a deleted neighborhood N of c such that both $f(x)$ and $h(x)$ lie between $L - \epsilon$ and $L + \epsilon$ when x is in N; that is

$$L - \epsilon < f(x) < L + \epsilon, \qquad L - \epsilon < h(x) < L + \epsilon.$$

But this also implies

$$L - \epsilon < f(x) \leq g(x) \leq h(x) < L + \epsilon.$$

or

$$L - \epsilon < g(x) < L + \epsilon.$$

In other words,

$$|g(x) - L| < \epsilon \quad \text{when } x \text{ is in } N.$$

This establishes the conclusion,

$$\lim_{x \to c} g(x) = L \qquad \text{Q.E.D.}$$

PROBLEMS

1. Suppose $\lim\limits_{x \to c} f(x) = 5$ and $\lim\limits_{x \to c} g(x) = -2$. (a) What is $\lim\limits_{x \to c} f(x)g(x)$?
(b) What is $\lim\limits_{x \to c} 2f(x)g(x)$?

Evaluate the limits indicated in Problems 2 through 24.

2. $\lim\limits_{x \to 1} [(2x - 1)(x)]$

3. $\lim\limits_{x \to 2} [3(2x - 1)(x)]$

4. $\lim\limits_{x \to 2} [3(2x - 1)(x + 1)]$

5. $\lim\limits_{x \to 2} [3(2x - 1)(x^2)]$

6. $\lim\limits_{x \to 2} [3(2x - 1)(x + 1)^2]$

7. $\lim\limits_{x \to -1} (x + 3)$

8. $\lim\limits_{x \to -1} (x + 3)^2$

9. $\lim\limits_{x \to -1} (x^2 + 6x + 9)$

10. $\lim\limits_{x \to -2} (x + 3)^{171}$

11. $\lim\limits_{x \to -4} (x + 3)^{1967}$

12. $\lim\limits_{x \to 1} (x^3 + 3x^2 - 2x - 17)$

13. Suppose $\lim\limits_{x \to c} f(x) = 2$ and $\lim\limits_{x \to c} g(x) = 5$.

(a) What is $\lim\limits_{x \to c} \dfrac{f(x)}{g(x)}$?

(b) What is $\lim\limits_{x \to c} \dfrac{f(x)}{3g(x)}$?

14. $\lim\limits_{t \to 2} \dfrac{t + 3}{t + 2}$

15. $\lim\limits_{x \to 5} \dfrac{x^2 - 25}{x - 5}$

16. $\lim\limits_{x \to 5} \dfrac{x^2 - 25}{x + 5}$

17. $\lim\limits_{x \to 5} \dfrac{x - 5}{x^2 - 25}$, if it exists.

18. $\lim\limits_{x \to 5} \dfrac{x + 5}{x^2 - 25}$, if it exists.

19. $\lim\limits_{x \to 1} \dfrac{x^2 - x - 2}{x^2 - 1}$

20. $\lim\limits_{x \to 0} \dfrac{5x^3 + 8x^2}{3x^4 - 16x^2}$

21. Give an example of functions f and g such that $\lim\limits_{x \to 0} f(x)g(x)$ exists, but at least one of the functions f and g fails to have a limit as $x \to 0$.

22. As $x \to 0+$, the functions $1/x$, $1/x^2$, $1/\sqrt{x}$ all become very large. Which one increases most rapidly and which one least rapidly? [$x \to 0+$ means that x approaches 0 through positive values, that is, from the right.]

23. Suppose F is a function whose values are all less than or equal to some constant M; $F(t) \leq M$. Prove: If $\lim_{t \to c} F(t) = L$, then $L \leq M$. [Suggestion: An indirect proof may be used to show that $L > M$ is false. For, if $L > M$, we may take $\frac{1}{2}(L - M)$ as a positive number ϵ, apply the definition of limit, and arrive at a contradiction.]

3–4   Infinity. The function

$$f(x) = \frac{1}{x}, \qquad (x \neq 0), \tag{1}$$

has as its domain the set of all real nonzero numbers. The graph is the curve shown in Fig. 3–3.

There are some facts about $1/x$ that are evident:

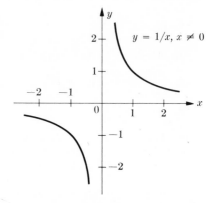

(a) When x is a small positive number, $1/x$ is a large positive number. For example, $1/0.001 = 1000$.
(b) When x is a large number, $1/x$ is small. For example, $1/10,000 = 0.0001$.
(c) When x is negative, $1/x$ is negative. For example, $1/(-0.001) = -1000$ and $1/(-10,000) = -0.0001$.

Figure 3–3

These facts are sometimes abbreviated by saying that

(a) $1/x$ approaches 0 as x tends to either $+\infty$ or $-\infty$,
(b) $1/x$ tends to $+\infty$ as x approaches 0 through positive values,
(c) $1/x$ tends to $-\infty$ as x approaches 0 through negative values.

The symbol ∞, is read *infinity*, but it does not represent any real number.

(In more advanced mathematics, a new system consisting of the real numbers and two additional elements, called $+\infty$ and $-\infty$, is sometimes used. It is called the *extended* real number system. However, special rules have to be set up, such as

$$\begin{aligned}
a + (+\infty) &= +\infty & &\text{for any real number } a, \\
a - (+\infty) &= -\infty, & & \\
a \cdot (+\infty) &= +\infty & &\text{if} \quad a > 0, \\
a \cdot (+\infty) &= -\infty & &\text{if} \quad a < 0, \\
(+\infty) \cdot (+\infty) &= +\infty, & & \\
(+\infty) + (+\infty) &= +\infty. & &
\end{aligned}$$

But such operations as $(+\infty) + (-\infty)$ and $0 \cdot (+\infty)$, or $(+\infty)/(+\infty)$ are not permitted because no consistent (unique) values can be assigned to such operations.

Mainly we shall avoid using the extended real number system in this book. And even in that system, division by zero has to be excluded if we hope to retain the usual laws of arithmetic and algebra.)

DEFINITION. *If $f(x)$ is defined for large values of x, we say that $f(x)$ approaches the real number L as limit as x tends to infinity, and write*

$$\lim_{x \to \infty} f(x) = L,$$

provided that, to each positive number ϵ there corresponds a number M such that

$$L - \epsilon < f(x) < L + \epsilon \quad \text{when} \quad x > M. \tag{2}$$

Remark 1. Graphically, the inequalities in (2) mean that the curve $y = f(x)$ stays between the lines $y = L - \epsilon$ and $y = L + \epsilon$ for x sufficiently large. The part of the statement that reads

$$\text{when } x > M$$

can also be written

$$\text{for } M < x < \infty$$

or

$$\text{for } x \text{ in the open interval } (M, \infty).$$

Such an open interval, consisting of all numbers greater than some fixed number M is also called a neighborhood of ∞. Thus we could say that $f(x)$ stays inside the neighborhood $(L - \epsilon, L + \epsilon)$ when x is in the neighborhood (M, ∞).

EXAMPLE 1. $$\lim_{x \to \infty} \frac{1}{x} = 0.$$

EXAMPLE 2. $$\lim_{x \to \infty} \frac{x}{x + 1} = \lim_{x \to \infty} \frac{1}{1 + (1/x)} = 1.$$

EXAMPLE 3. $$\lim_{x \to \infty} \frac{2x^2 - x + 3}{3x^2 + 5} = \lim_{x \to \infty} \frac{2 - (1/x) + (3/x^2)}{3 + (5/x^2)} = \frac{2}{3}.$$

For Example 1, $f(x) = 1/x$, we have

$$-\epsilon < \frac{1}{x} < \epsilon \tag{3a}$$

for any $\epsilon > 0$, provided

$$|x| > \frac{1}{\epsilon}. \tag{3b}$$

Thus, $f(x)$ is in the neighborhood $(-\epsilon, \epsilon)$ of zero, when x is in the neighborhood $(1/\epsilon, \infty)$ of ∞. See Fig. 3–4.

See Fig. 3–5 for the example

$$f(x) = 2 + \frac{\sin x}{x}.$$

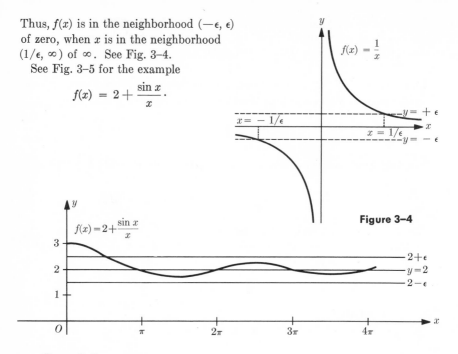

Figure 3–4

Figure 3–5

The graph of this function oscillates about the line $y = 2$. The amplitude of the oscillations decreases toward zero as $x \to \infty$, and the curve lies between $y = 2 + \epsilon$ and $y = 2 - \epsilon$ when $x > 1/\epsilon$. When x is large, $\sin x/x \to 0$ and $f(x) \to L = 2$.

The following theorems about limits of sums, differences, products, and quotients are analogous to the corresponding theorems for limits when $x \to a$.

THEOREM 7. *If*

$$\lim_{x \to \infty} f(x) = L_1 \qquad and \qquad \lim_{x \to \infty} g(x) = L_2,$$

where L_1 and L_2 are (finite) real numbers, then:

$$\lim_{x \to \infty} [f(x) + g(x)] = L_1 + L_2, \tag{4a}$$

$$\lim_{x \to \infty} f(x)g(x) = L_1 L_2, \tag{4b}$$

$$\lim_{x \to \infty} [f(x) - g(x)] = L_1 - L_2, \tag{4c}$$

$$\lim_{x \to \infty} \frac{f(x)}{g(x)} = \frac{L_1}{L_2}, \qquad if \qquad L_2 \neq 0. \tag{4d}$$

In order to prove these theorems, one only needs to repeat the proofs for the corresponding theorems for limits as $x \to a$ with only minor changes.

Finally, we sometimes want to say such things as

$$\lim_{x \to a} f(x) = \infty \qquad (5a)$$

or

$$\lim_{x \to a^+} f(x) = \infty \qquad (5b)$$

or

$$\lim_{x \to a^-} f(x) = \infty \qquad (5c)$$

or

$$\lim_{x \to \infty} f(x) = \infty. \qquad (5d)$$

In every instance, the symbol ∞ means the same as

$$f(x) \to +\infty$$

or that, for any real number M that is given, no matter how large M may be, the condition

$$f(x) > M$$

is satisfied for all values of x in some restricted set, usually depending upon M. The appropriate set in (5a) is

in some deleted neighborhood of a.

In (5b), $x \to a^+$ means that we consider numbers close to a but greater than a; that is, an interval of the form $(a, a + h)$ for some $h > 0$. In (5c), $x \to a^-$ means we restrict attention to values of x that are near a and less than a; an interval of the form $(a - h, a)$ with $h > 0$. In (5d), the neighborhood is of the form (c, ∞); that is, for x large, or for $x > c$ for some c.

The following theorems are stated without proof. The problems ask for proofs of some of them. They involve the ideas of *bounded below* and *bounded* functions.

DEFINITIONS.   *If there is a real number b such that for all x in the domain of g*

$$g(x) \geq b,$$

then g(x) is bounded below.

If there is a real number b and a large positive real number c such that for all x in the domain of g

$$g(x) \geq b \quad for \quad x > c,$$

then g(x) is bounded below for x large.

If there is a real number a such that for all x in the domain of g

$$g(x) \leq a,$$

then g(x) is bounded above.

If there are real numbers a, b, and c such that

$$a < g(x) < b \quad when \quad x > c,$$

then g(x) is bounded for x large.

For example,

$$g(x) = \frac{2x}{x+1} + \frac{1}{x}$$

is bounded for x large because

$$0 < g(x) < 2 \quad \text{when } x > 1.$$

THEOREM 8. *If* $\lim_{x \to \infty} f(x) = \infty$ *and* $g(x)$ *is bounded below, for x large, then*

$$\lim_{x \to \infty} [f(x) + g(x)] = \infty.$$

EXAMPLE. $\lim_{x \to \infty} x = \infty$ and $\sin x \geq -1.$

Hence

$$\lim_{x \to \infty} (x + \sin x) = \infty,$$

even though $\sin x$ does *not* have a limit as $x \to \infty$.

THEOREM 9. *If* $\lim_{x \to \infty} f(x) = 0$ *and* $g(x)$ *is bounded for x large, then*

$$\lim_{x \to \infty} f(x)g(x) = 0.$$

EXAMPLE. $\lim_{x \to \infty} (1/x) = 0$ and $-1 \leq \cos x \leq 1,$

that is $\cos x$ is bounded. Hence

$$\lim_{x \to \infty} \frac{\cos x}{x} = 0.$$

PROBLEMS

Use Theorems 7, 8, and 9 to find the following limits:

1. $\lim\limits_{x \to \infty} \dfrac{2x + 3}{5x + 7}$

2. $\lim\limits_{x \to \infty} \dfrac{3x^3 + 5x^2 - 7}{10x^3 - 11x^2 + 5x}$

3. $\lim\limits_{x \to \infty} \dfrac{3x^2 - 6x}{4x - 8}$

4. $\lim\limits_{x \to \infty} \dfrac{7x - 28}{x^3}$

5. $\lim\limits_{x \to \infty} \dfrac{2x^2 + 3}{x^3 + x - 5} \operatorname{sgn} x$

6. $\lim\limits_{x \to \infty} \left(\dfrac{1}{x} + 1 \right) \left(\dfrac{5x^2 - 1}{x^2} \right)$

7. $\lim\limits_{x \to \infty} \left(\sqrt{x} + \dfrac{1}{[x]} \right)$

8. $\lim\limits_{x \to \infty} [\tan x + \sec x(5 \cos x - \sin x)]$

9. $\lim\limits_{x \to \infty} \dfrac{\sqrt{x + 1}}{\sqrt{4x - 1}}$

10. What is $\lim\limits_{x \to \infty} \dfrac{f(x)}{g(x)}$ if $f(x)$ is a polynomial of degree less than polynomial $g(x)$?

11. What does $f(x)/g(x)$ tend to, as $x \to \infty$, if the degree of the polynomial $g(x)$ is less than the degree of the polynomial $f(x)$?

12. Prove Eq. (4a) of Theorem 7.

13. Use Eq. (4b) of Theorem 7 to prove the following corollary: If $\lim\limits_{x \to \infty} f(x) = L$ where L is finite, $\lim\limits_{x \to \infty} [-f(x)] = -L$.

14. Use the result of Problem 13 to prove Eq. (4c) of Theorem 7.

15. Prove Theorem 8.

16. Prove Theorem 9.

17. (a) Is the polynomial $g(x) = x^2 - 3x + 4$ bounded below for x large?
    (b) Is it bounded below for all values of x?
    (c) Is it bounded for x large?

18. State and prove a theorem like Theorem 6 as x approaches ∞.

19. If $\dfrac{2x - 3}{x} < f(x) < \dfrac{2x^2 + 5x}{x^2}$, find $\lim\limits_{x \to \infty} f(x)$.

20. Suppose that $f(x)$ and $g(x)$ are two polynomials, and that $g(x)$ is bounded below for x large. If the degree of $f(x)$ is less than the degree of $g(x)$, prove that $f(x) + g(x)$ is bounded below for x large.

REVIEW QUESTIONS AND EXERCISES FOR CHAPTER 3

1. Define what it means to say that:

(a) $\lim\limits_{x \to 2} f(x) = 5$

(b) $\lim\limits_{x \to c} g(x) = k$

2. Give two examples of deleted neighborhoods of the point $x = 2$, of which one is symmetric about 2 and the other is not.

3. Describe the intersection of the deleted neighborhoods $0 < |x - a| < 2$ and $(a - 1, a) \cup (a, a + 3)$.

4. What is wrong with the following "proof" of Theorem 5? Let

$$f_1(x) = g(x), \quad f_2(x) = 1/g(x),$$

$$L_1 = \lim_{x \to a} f_1(x), \quad L_2 = \lim_{x \to a} f_2(x).$$

Then, by Theorem 4,

$$\lim_{x \to a} f_1(x)f_2(x) = L_1 L_2.$$

But $f_1(x)f_2(x) = 1$, so we have, by Theorem 1 with $m = 0$, $b = 1$,

$$1 = \lim_{x \to a} f_1(x)f_2(x) = L_1 L_2.$$

Therefore,

$$L_2 = 1/L_1.$$

5. Corollary 4.2, with $n = 2$, asserts that $\lim_{x \to a} x^2 = a^2$, but it does not say that $\lim_{x \to a} \sqrt{x} = \sqrt{a}$. Try to prove this result, for $a > 0$. (Do not assume the existence of the limit of $\sqrt{x}$. Work directly from the definition of limit.)

6. A function f, whose domain is the set of all real numbers, has the property that $f(x + h) = f(x) \cdot f(h)$ for all x and h; and $f(x) \neq 0$.

(a) Show that $f(0) = 1$. [Hint: Let $h = x = 0$.]

(b) If f has a derivative at 0, show that f has a derivative at every real number x, and that

$$f'(x) = f(x) \cdot f'(0).$$

7. Give an example of a function, defined for all real x, that fails to have a derivative (a) at some point, (b) at several points, (c) at infinitely many points.

MISCELLANEOUS PROBLEMS FOR CHAPTER 3

Evaluate the following limits, or show that the limit does not exist:

1. $\lim\limits_{x \to \infty} \dfrac{x + \sin x}{2x + 5}$

2. $\lim\limits_{x \to \infty} \dfrac{1 + \sin x}{x}$

3. $\lim\limits_{x \to 1} \dfrac{x^2 - 4}{x^3 - 8}$

4. $\lim\limits_{x \to 2} \dfrac{x^2 - 4}{x^3 - 8}$

5. $\lim\limits_{x \to \infty} \dfrac{x \sin x}{x + \sin x}$

6. $\lim\limits_{x \to a} \dfrac{x^2 - a^2}{x - a}$

7. $\lim\limits_{x \to a} \dfrac{x^2 - a^2}{x + a}$

8. $\lim\limits_{h \to 0} \dfrac{(x + h)^2 - x^2}{h}$

9. $\lim\limits_{h \to 0} \dfrac{\sqrt{x + h} - \sqrt{x}}{h}$

10. $\lim\limits_{\Delta x \to 0} \dfrac{1/(x + \Delta x) - 1/x}{\Delta x}$

11. $\lim\limits_{x \to 0^+} \dfrac{1}{x}$

12. $\lim\limits_{x \to 1} \dfrac{1 - \sqrt{x}}{1 - x}$

13. $\lim\limits_{x \to 1} \dfrac{(2x - 3)(\sqrt{x} - 1)}{2x^2 + x - 3}$

14. $\lim\limits_{x \to \infty} (1 - \cos x)$

The following problems deal with limits of sequences. A function whose domain is the set of positive integers $1, 2, \ldots$ is said to be a *sequence*. Instead of writing the value of the function at n as $f(n)$, it is customary to write the nth term of the sequence as a_n, or S_n, or something similar. A sequence a_n is said to converge to the limit L as $n \to \infty$ if and only if to each positive number ϵ there corresponds an integer N such that

$$|a_n - L| < \epsilon \text{ for all values of } n \text{ greater than } N.$$

The following theorems about limits of sequences are analogous to theorems in this chapter about limits of other functions. Prove them.

15. If

$$\lim_{n \to \infty} a_n = A \text{ and } \lim_{n \to \infty} b_n = B,$$

then

$$\lim_{n \to \infty} (a_n + b_n) = A + B.$$

16. If

$$\lim_{n \to \infty} a_n = A \text{ and } k \text{ is a number,}$$

then

$$\lim_{n \to \infty} (ka_n) = kA.$$

17. If $\lim a_n$ exists (is a finite real number), then the sequence a_n is bounded.

18. If

$$\lim_{n \to \infty} a_n = A \text{ and } \lim_{n \to \infty} b_n = B,$$

then

$$\lim_{n \to \infty} (a_n b_n) = AB.$$

19. If

$$\lim_{n \to \infty} b_n = B \neq 0,$$

then

$$\lim_{n \to \infty} 1/b_n = 1/B.$$

Evaluate the following limits:

20. $\lim\limits_{n \to \infty} \dfrac{3n^2 - 5n + \sin n}{4n^2 + 7n + 6}$

[Hint: divide the numerator and denominator by n^2.]

21. $\lim\limits_{n \to \infty} \dfrac{2n^2 + 5n - 3}{n^3 + 2n}$

22. $\lim\limits_{n \to \infty} \left(\sqrt{n^2 + n} - \sqrt{n^2 + 10} \right)$

23. Suppose that $h_n = \sqrt[n]{n} - 1$. Then

$$n = (1 + h_n)^n = 1 + nh_n + \frac{n(n-1)}{2} h_n^2 + \cdots > \frac{n(n-1)}{2} h_n^2$$

when $n > 2$. From the above inequality, and the definition of h_n, deduce that

$$0 < h_n < \sqrt{\frac{2}{n-1}} \quad \text{when} \quad n > 2.$$

Find: (a) $\lim\limits_{n \to \infty} h_n$ (b) $\lim\limits_{n \to \infty} \sqrt[n]{n}$

The *right-hand limit b* of a function f at a point a is the limit of the function at a for a right-hand domain $(a, a + \delta)$, $\delta > 0$. We write

$$\lim_{x \to a^+} f(x) = b.$$

Similarly, the *left-hand limit c* of a function f at a point a is the limit of the function at a for a left-hand domain $(a - \delta, a)$, $\delta > 0$. We write

$$\lim_{x \to a^-} f(x) = c.$$

For example, $\lim_{x \to 5^+} [x] = 5$, but $\lim_{x \to 5^-} [x] = 4$.

Find each of the following limits:

24. $\lim_{x \to 0^+} \dfrac{|x|}{x}$

25. $\lim_{x \to 0^-} \dfrac{|x|}{x}$

26. $\lim_{x \to 4^-} [x] - x$

27. $\lim_{x \to 4^+} [x] - x$

28. $\lim_{x \to 3^+} \dfrac{[x]^2 - 9}{x^2 - 9}$

29. $\lim_{x \to 3^-} \dfrac{[x]^2 - 9}{x^2 - 9}$

30. $\lim_{x \to 4^+} [[x]]$

31. $\lim_{x \to 0^+} \dfrac{\sqrt{x}}{\sqrt{4 + \sqrt{x}} - 2}$

Derivatives of Algebraic Functions

4–1 Polynomial functions and their derivatives. A single term of the form cx^n, where c is a constant and n is zero or a positive integer, is called a *monomial* in x. A function which is the sum of a finite number of monomial terms is called a *polynomial* in x. For example,

$$f(x) = x^3 - 5x + 7, \qquad g(x) = (x^2 + 3)^3, \qquad h(x) = 4x, \qquad \phi(x) = 5$$

are special cases of polynomials in x and

$$s = \tfrac{1}{2}gt^2, \qquad v = v_0 + gt$$

are polynomials in t.

We shall now derive some formulas which will enable us to find the derivatives of polynomial functions very easily. In every case we derive the formula by means of the basic definition:

Let $y = f(x)$ define a function f. If the limit

$$\frac{dy}{dx} = \lim_{\Delta x \to 0} \frac{\Delta y}{\Delta x}, \tag{1a}$$

meaning

$$f'(x) = \lim_{\Delta x \to 0} \frac{f(x + \Delta x) - f(x)}{\Delta x}, \tag{1b}$$

exists and is finite, we call this limit the derivative of y with respect to x and say that f is differentiable at x.

1. *The derivative of a constant is zero.* The geometric meaning of this result is that the graph of the equation $y = c$ is everywhere parallel to the x-axis (Fig. 4–1). To prove it analytically, let

$$y = c,$$

where c is a constant. Then when $x = x_1$ and again when $x = x_1 + \Delta x$, y has the same value c, hence

$$y = c$$

and

$$y + \Delta y = c,$$

so that

$$\Delta y = 0.$$

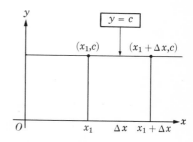

Figure 4–1

109

Then, dividing by Δx, we have

$$\frac{\Delta y}{\Delta x} = 0$$

and

$$\frac{dy}{dx} = \lim_{\Delta x \to 0} \frac{\Delta y}{\Delta x} = 0.$$

2. *The derivative, with respect to x, of x^n is nx^{n-1} when n is any positive integer.* To prove this result, we let

$$y = x^n,$$

where n may be any positive integer. Then, by the binomial theorem,

$y + \Delta y =$

$$(x + \Delta x)^n = \begin{cases} x + \Delta x & \text{if } n = 1, \\ x^2 + 2x\,\Delta x + (\Delta x)^2 & \text{if } n = 2, \\ x^3 + 3x^2\,\Delta x + 3x\,(\Delta x)^2 + (\Delta x)^3 & \text{if } n = 3, \\ x^n + nx^{n-1}\,\Delta x + (\text{terms in } x \text{ and } \Delta x) \cdot (\Delta x)^2 & \text{if } n > 3. \end{cases}$$

From this we subtract $y = x^n$ and obtain

$$\Delta y = \begin{cases} \Delta x & \text{if } n = 1, \\ 2x\,\Delta x + (\Delta x)^2 & \text{if } n = 2, \\ 3x^2\,\Delta x + (3x + \Delta x) \cdot (\Delta x)^2 & \text{if } n = 3, \\ nx^{n-1}\,\Delta x + (\text{terms in } x \text{ and } \Delta x) \cdot (\Delta x)^2 & \text{if } n > 3. \end{cases}$$

Dividing by Δx, we find next that

$$\frac{\Delta y}{\Delta x} = \begin{cases} 1 & \text{if } n = 1, \\ 2x + \Delta x & \text{if } n = 2, \\ 3x^2 + (3x + \Delta x) \cdot \Delta x & \text{if } n = 3, \\ nx^{n-1} + (\text{terms in } x \text{ and } \Delta x) \cdot \Delta x & \text{if } n > 3. \end{cases}$$

Finally, we let Δx approach zero and find

$$\frac{dy}{dx} = \lim_{\Delta x \to 0} \frac{\Delta y}{\Delta x} = \begin{cases} 1 & \text{if } n = 1, \\ 2x & \text{if } n = 2, \\ 3x^2 & \text{if } n = 3, \\ nx^{n-1} & \text{if } n > 3. \end{cases}$$

In particular, the case $n = 1$ tells us that

$$\frac{dx}{dx} = 1.$$

Since the results for $n = 1, 2, 3$ are simply special cases of the general result, we have

$$\frac{dy}{dx} = nx^{n-1} \qquad \text{if} \qquad y = x^n \tag{2}$$

and

$$n = \text{any positive integer.}$$

In words, this says: *"To find the derivative of x to the power n, simply multiply that power times x to a power one less."*

3. *If $u = f(x)$ is a differentiable function of x and c is a constant, then*

$$\frac{d(cu)}{dx} = c \frac{du}{dx}. \tag{3}$$

Proof. Let

$$y = cu, \tag{4a}$$

where

$$u = f(x).$$

Then if x is replaced by $x + \Delta x$, we have

$$y + \Delta y = c(u + \Delta u), \tag{4b}$$

where

$$u + \Delta u = f(x + \Delta x).$$

Subtracting (4a) from (4b), we obtain

$$\Delta y = c \, \Delta u$$

and dividing this by Δx, we have

$$\frac{\Delta y}{\Delta x} = c \frac{\Delta u}{\Delta x}. \tag{4c}$$

Since u has a derivative

$$\frac{du}{dx} = \lim_{\Delta x \to 0} \frac{\Delta u}{\Delta x},$$

the limit of the right side of Eq. (4c), when Δx approaches zero, is simply

$$\lim_{\Delta x \to 0} c \frac{\Delta u}{\Delta x} = c \frac{du}{dx}.$$

Since both sides of Eq. (4c) are equal, its left side must have the same limit. But this limit is also equal to dy/dx from the definition of the derivative. All of this is summarized in the following equation, which follows by taking limits in Eq. (4c):

$$\frac{dy}{dx} = \lim_{\Delta x \to 0} \frac{\Delta y}{\Delta x} = \lim_{\Delta x \to 0} c\frac{\Delta u}{\Delta x} = c\frac{du}{dx}.$$

Since $y = cu$, this is the same as

$$\boxed{\frac{d(cu)}{dx} = c\frac{du}{dx},}$$

which we wished to show.

In particular, if c is a constant and n is a positive integer, Eqs. (3) and (2) together tell us that

$$\boxed{\frac{d(cx^n)}{dx} = cnx^{n-1}.} \tag{5}$$

For example, if

$$y = 7x^5$$

then

$$\frac{dy}{dx} = 35x^4.$$

4. *The derivative of the sum of a finite number of differentiable functions is equal to the sum of their derivatives.* To prove this, we first consider the sum of two terms,

$$y = u + v,$$

where we suppose that u and v are differentiable functions of x whose derivatives are

$$\frac{du}{dx} = \lim_{\Delta x \to 0} \frac{\Delta u}{\Delta x}$$

and

$$\frac{dv}{dx} = \lim_{\Delta x \to 0} \frac{\Delta v}{\Delta x}.$$

When x is replaced by $x + \Delta x$, the new values of the variables will satisfy the equation

$$y + \Delta y = (u + \Delta u) + (v + \Delta v).$$

We subtract

$$y = u + v$$

from this and obtain

$$\Delta y = \Delta u + \Delta v,$$

and hence

$$\frac{\Delta y}{\Delta x} = \frac{\Delta u}{\Delta x} + \frac{\Delta v}{\Delta x}.$$

When Δx approaches zero, we get

$$\frac{dy}{dx} = \lim_{\Delta x \to 0} \frac{\Delta y}{\Delta x} = \lim_{\Delta x \to 0} \left(\frac{\Delta u}{\Delta x} + \frac{\Delta v}{\Delta x} \right),$$

$$\boxed{\frac{d(u+v)}{dx} = \frac{du}{dx} + \frac{dv}{dx}.}$$

This equation expresses the result that the derivative of the sum of two terms is the sum of their derivatives.

We may proceed by induction to establish the result for the sum of any finite number of terms. For example, if

$$y = u_1 + u_2 + u_3,$$

where u_1, u_2, and u_3 are differentiable functions of x, then we may take

$$u = u_1 + u_2, \qquad v = u_3,$$

and apply the result already established for the sum of two terms, namely,

$$\frac{dy}{dx} = \frac{d(u_1 + u_2)}{dx} + \frac{du_3}{dx}.$$

Since the first term is again a sum of two terms, we have

$$\frac{d(u_1 + u_2)}{dx} = \frac{du_1}{dx} + \frac{du_2}{dx},$$

so that

$$\frac{d(u_1 + u_2 + u_3)}{dx} = \frac{du_1}{dx} + \frac{du_2}{dx} + \frac{du_3}{dx}.$$

Finally, if it has been established for some integer n that

$$\frac{d(u_1 + u_2 + \cdots + u_n)}{dx} = \frac{du_1}{dx} + \frac{du_2}{dx} + \cdots + \frac{du_n}{dx},$$

and we let

$$y = u + v,$$

with

$$u = u_1 + u_2 + \cdots + u_n,$$

$$v = u_{n+1},$$

we find in the same way as above that

$$\frac{d(u_1 + u_2 + \cdots + u_{n+1})}{dx} = \frac{du_1}{dx} + \frac{du_2}{dx} + \cdots + \frac{du_{n+1}}{dx}.$$

This enables us to conclude that if the theorem is true for a sum of n terms it is also true for a sum of $(n + 1)$ terms, and since it is already established for the sum of two terms, we conclude that it is true for the sum of any finite number of terms.

EXAMPLE 1. Find dy/dx if $y = x^3 + 7x^2 - 5x + 4$.

By the result just established, we may find the derivatives of the separate terms of a sum and add the results. Thus

$$\frac{dy}{dx} = \frac{d(x^3)}{dx} + \frac{d(7x^2)}{dx} + \frac{d(-5x)}{dx} + \frac{d(4)}{dx}$$

$$= 3x^2 + 14x - 5x^0 + 0$$

$$= 3x^2 + 14x - 5.$$

EXAMPLE 2. What is the slope of the curve

$$y = x^3 - 6x + 2$$

where it crosses the y-axis?

The slope at the point (x, y) is equal to

$$\frac{dy}{dx} = 3x^2 - 6.$$

The curve crosses the y-axis when $x = 0$. Hence its slope at that point is

$$m = (3x^2 - 6)_{x=0} = -6.$$

The derivative with respect to x of $y' = dy/dx$ is called the *second derivative* of y with respect to x and is denoted by y''. That is,

$$y' = \frac{dy}{dx}$$

is the first derivative of y with respect to x, and its derivative

$$y'' = \frac{dy'}{dx} = \frac{d}{dx}\left(\frac{dy}{dx}\right)$$

is the second derivative of y with respect to x. The operation of taking the derivative of a function twice in succession, denoted by

$$\frac{d}{dx}\left(\frac{d}{dx}\cdots\right),$$

is also indicated by the notation

$$\frac{d^2}{dx^2}(\cdots).$$

In this notation, we write the second derivative of y with respect to x as

$$\frac{d^2 y}{dx^2}.$$

More generally, the result of differentiating a function $y = f(x)$ n times in succession is denoted by $y^{(n)}$, $f^{(n)}(x)$, or by $d^n y/dx^n$.

EXAMPLE 3. For example, if $y = x^3 - 3x^2 + 2$, then

$$y' = \frac{dy}{dx} = 3x^2 - 6x, \qquad y''' = \frac{d^3 y}{dx^3} = 6,$$

$$y'' = \frac{d^2 y}{dx^2} = 6x - 6, \qquad y^{(iv)} = \frac{d^4 y}{dx^4} = 0.$$

In mechanics, if $s = f(t)$ gives the position of a moving body at time t, then

the first derivative ds/dt gives the *velocity*, and

the second derivative d^2s/dt^2 gives the *acceleration*

of the body at time t.

EXAMPLE 4. A body moves in a straight line according to the law of motion

$$s = t^3 - 4t^2 - 3t.$$

Find its acceleration at each instant when the velocity is zero.

Here we find the velocity v and acceleration a are

$$v = \frac{ds}{dt} = 3t^2 - 8t - 3, \qquad a = \frac{dv}{dt} = 6t - 8.$$

The velocity is zero when

$$3t^2 - 8t - 3 = (3t + 1)(t - 3) = 0,$$

that is, when

$$t = -\tfrac{1}{3} \qquad \text{or} \qquad t = 3.$$

The corresponding values of the acceleration are

$$t = -\tfrac{1}{3}, \quad a = -10; \qquad t = 3, \quad a = 10.$$

In Problems 1–5, s represents the position of a moving body at time t. Find the velocity $v = ds/dt$ and the acceleration $a = dv/dt = d^2s/dt^2$.

1. $s = t^2 - 4t + 3$ 2. $s = 2t^3 - 5t^2 + 4t - 3$

3. $s = gt^2/2 + v_0t + s_0$; (g, v_0, s_0 constants)

4. $s = 3 + 4t - t^2$ 5. $s = (2t + 3)^2$

Find $y' = dy/dx$ and $y'' = dy'/dx$ in Problems 6–15.

6. $y = x^4 - 7x^3 + 2x^2 + 5$ 7. $y = 5x^3 - 3x^5$

8. $y = 4x^2 - 8x + 1$ 9. $y = \dfrac{x^4}{4} - \dfrac{x^3}{3} + \dfrac{x^2}{2} - x + 3$

10. $y = 2x^4 - 4x^2 - 8$ 11. $12y = 6x^4 - 18x^2 - 12x$

12. $y = 3x^7 - 7x^3 + 21x^2$ 13. $y = x^2(x^3 - 1)$

14. $y = (x - 2)(x + 3)$ 15. $y = (3x - 1)(2x + 5)$

16. A particle projected vertically upward with a speed of 160 ft/sec reaches an elevation $s = 160t - 16t^2$ at the end of t seconds. (a) How high does it rise? (b) How fast is it traveling when it reaches an elevation of 256 feet going up and again when it reaches this elevation coming down?

17. Find the line tangent to the curve $y = 2x^2 + 4x - 3$ at the point $(1, 3)$.

18. Find the lines tangent to the curve $y = x^3 + x$, where the slope is equal to 4. What is the smallest value the slope of this curve can ever have and where on the curve does the slope equal this smallest value?

19. Find the points on the curve $y = 2x^3 - 3x^2 - 12x + 20$, where the tangent is parallel to the x-axis.

20. Find the values of the constants a, b, and c if the curve $y = ax^2 + bx + c$ is to pass through the point $(1, 2)$ and is to be tangent to the line $y = x$ at the origin.

21. Find the constants a, b, and c so that the two curves $y = x^2 + ax + b$ and $y = cx - x^2$ shall be tangent to each other at the point $(1, 0)$.

22. Find the constant c if the curve $y = x^2 + c$ is to be tangent to the line $y = x$.

4–2　Rational functions and their derivatives. In the preceding article we learned how to find the derivative of a polynomial very quickly by using certain simple formulas. First we found the derivative of a monomial in x,

$$\frac{d}{dx}(cx^n) = cnx^{n-1},$$

and then we proved that the derivative of the sum of a finite number of such terms is the sum of their derivatives.

In this article we shall derive formulas for finding the derivative with respect to x of

$$\text{products: } y = uv,$$

$$\text{quotients: } y = u/v,$$

$$\text{powers: } \quad y = u^n,$$

when u and v are any differentiable functions of x. For the present, this will mean that u and v may be polynomials in x, for example; but after we learn to differentiate other functions like $\sin x$ and $\log x$, the same basic formulas will apply to combinations of these as well.

The product of two polynomials in x is again a polynomial in x; hence if u and v are polynomials the product uv is also a polynomial. Similarly, if n is a positive integer and u is a polynomial, then u^n is again a polynomial. For example, if

$$u = x^2 + 1, \quad v = x^3 + 3, \qquad \text{then} \qquad uv = x^5 + x^3 + 3x^2 + 3,$$

and if

$$u = x^2 + 1, \quad n = 2, \qquad \text{then} \qquad u^n = x^4 + 2x^2 + 1.$$

But the ratio u/v of two polynomials is, in general, not a polynomial in x. Such a function is called a *rational* function of x, where the word *ratio* is the key to the real meaning of the word rational.

1. *The derivative of the product*

$$y = uv$$

of two differentiable functions of x is given by

$$\boxed{\frac{d(uv)}{dx} = u\,\frac{dv}{dx} + v\,\frac{du}{dx}.}$$

(1)

To prove this result, we let

$$y = uv,$$

where u and v are differentiable functions of x. Let x be given an increment Δx, and let the corresponding increments in y, u, v be denoted by Δy, Δu, Δv. (These "increments" may be either positive or negative.) Then the new values of the variables satisfy the equation

$$y + \Delta y = (u + \Delta u)(v + \Delta v)$$
$$= uv + u\,\Delta v + v\,\Delta u + \Delta u\,\Delta v.$$

When we subtract from this the equation

$$y = uv,$$

we obtain

$$\Delta y = u \, \Delta v + v \, \Delta u + \Delta u \, \Delta v.$$

Next we must divide by Δx,

$$\frac{\Delta y}{\Delta x} = u \, \frac{\Delta v}{\Delta x} + v \, \frac{\Delta u}{\Delta x} + \Delta u \, \frac{\Delta v}{\Delta x}.$$

Finally, when Δx approaches zero, so will Δu and Δv, since

$$\lim \Delta u = \lim \left(\frac{\Delta u}{\Delta x} \, \Delta x \right) = \lim \frac{\Delta u}{\Delta x} \lim \Delta x = \frac{du}{dx} \cdot 0.$$

Thus,

$$\lim \frac{\Delta y}{\Delta x} = \lim \left(u \, \frac{\Delta v}{\Delta x} + v \, \frac{\Delta u}{\Delta x} + \Delta u \, \frac{\Delta v}{\Delta x} \right)$$

$$= \lim u \, \frac{\Delta v}{\Delta x} + \lim v \, \frac{\Delta u}{\Delta x} + \lim \Delta u \, \frac{\Delta v}{\Delta x}$$

$$= \lim u \lim \frac{\Delta v}{\Delta x} + \lim v \lim \frac{\Delta u}{\Delta x} + \lim \Delta u \lim \frac{\Delta v}{\Delta x}$$

$$= u \, \frac{dv}{dx} + v \, \frac{du}{dx} + 0 \cdot \frac{dv}{dx}.$$

That is,

$$\frac{dy}{dx} = u \, \frac{dv}{dx} + v \, \frac{du}{dx},$$

which establishes (1).

Note that the derivative of a product is *not* the product of the derivatives. Instead, we add together two terms $u(dv/dx)$ and $v(du/dx)$. In the first of these we leave u untouched and differentiate v, and in the second we differentiate u and leave v alone. In fact, it is possible to extend the formula, by the method of mathematical induction, to show that the derivative of a product

$$y = u_1 u_2 \ldots u_n$$

of a finite number of differentiable functions is given by

$$\frac{d}{dx} (u_1 u_2 \cdots u_n) = \frac{du_1}{dx} \cdot u_2 \cdots u_n + u_1 \, \frac{du_2}{dx} \cdots u_n + \cdots + u_1 u_2 \cdots \frac{du_n}{dx}, \quad (2)$$

where the right side of the equation consists of the sum of the n terms obtained by multiplying the derivative of each one of the factors by the other $(n - 1)$ factors undifferentiated.

2. *At a point where $v \neq 0$, the derivative of the quotient*

$$y = \frac{u}{v}$$

of two differentiable functions u and v is given by

$$\frac{d}{dx}\left(\frac{u}{v}\right) = \frac{v\frac{du}{dx} - u\frac{dv}{dx}}{v^2}.$$

(3)

To prove this, consider a point $x = c$ where $v \neq 0$ and where u and v are differentiable. Let x be given an increment Δx and let Δy, Δu, Δv be the corresponding increments in y, u, v. Then, as $\Delta x \to 0$,

$$\lim (v + \Delta v) = \lim v + \lim \Delta v$$

while

$$\lim \Delta v = \lim \frac{\Delta v}{\Delta x} \cdot \Delta x = \frac{dv}{dx} \cdot 0 = 0.$$

Therefore the value of $v + \Delta v$ is close to the value of v when $x + \Delta x$ is close to c, that is, when Δx is near zero. In particular, since $v \neq 0$ at $x = c$, it follows that $v + \Delta v \neq 0$ when Δx is *near* zero, say when $0 < |\Delta x| < h$. Let Δx be so restricted. Then $v + \Delta v \neq 0$ and

$$y + \Delta y = \frac{u + \Delta u}{v + \Delta v}.$$

From this we subtract

$$y = \frac{u}{v}$$

and obtain

$$\Delta y = \frac{u + \Delta u}{v + \Delta v} - \frac{u}{v}$$

$$= \frac{(vu + v\,\Delta u) - (uv + u\,\Delta v)}{v(v + \Delta v)}$$

$$= \frac{v\,\Delta u - u\,\Delta v}{v(v + \Delta v)}.$$

We divide this by Δx by dividing the numerator of the fraction on the right by Δx and have

$$\frac{\Delta y}{\Delta x} = \frac{v\frac{\Delta u}{\Delta x} - u\frac{\Delta v}{\Delta x}}{v(v + \Delta v)}.$$

When Δx approaches zero, we obtain

$$\lim \frac{\Delta u}{\Delta x} = \frac{du}{dx},$$

$$\lim \frac{\Delta v}{\Delta x} = \frac{dv}{dx},$$

$$\lim v(v + \Delta v) = \lim v \lim (v + \Delta v) = v^2 \neq 0,$$

and

$$\lim \frac{\Delta y}{\Delta x} = \frac{\lim \left(v \dfrac{\Delta u}{\Delta x} - u \dfrac{\Delta v}{\Delta x} \right)}{\lim v(v + \Delta v)},$$

or

$$\frac{dy}{dx} = \frac{v \dfrac{du}{dx} - u \dfrac{dv}{dx}}{v^2},$$

which establishes Eq. (3).

3. *If $u = g(x)$ is a differentiable function of x and n is a positive integer or zero, then*

$$\frac{d}{dx} (u^n) = nu^{n-1} \frac{du}{dx}. \tag{4}$$

We let

$$y = u^n,$$

where u and n satisfy the hypotheses, give x an increment Δx, and call the increments of y and u, Δy and Δu. Then

$$y + \Delta y = (u + \Delta u)^n$$

$$= u^n + nu^{n-1} \Delta u + \frac{n(n - 1)}{2} u^{n-2} (\Delta u)^2 + \cdots + (\Delta u)^n.$$

From this we subtract the original equation and obtain

$$\Delta y = nu^{n-1} \Delta u + (\text{terms in } u \text{ and } \Delta u)(\Delta u)^2.$$

Next, we divide by Δx:

$$\frac{\Delta y}{\Delta x} = nu^{n-1} \frac{\Delta u}{\Delta x} + (\text{terms in } u \text{ and } \Delta u) \frac{(\Delta u)^2}{\Delta x}.$$

Now when Δx approaches zero,

$$\lim \frac{\Delta u}{\Delta x} = \frac{du}{dx}$$

by the definition of the derivative, while

$$\lim \frac{(\Delta u)^2}{\Delta x} = \lim \left(\frac{\Delta u}{\Delta x} \Delta u \right)$$

$$= \lim \frac{\Delta u}{\Delta x} \lim \Delta u = \frac{du}{dx} \cdot 0 = 0.$$

Hence,
$$\lim \frac{\Delta y}{\Delta x} = \lim \left[nu^{n-1} \frac{\Delta u}{\Delta x} + (\cdots) \frac{(\Delta u)^2}{\Delta x} \right]$$

$$= \lim nu^{n-1} \frac{\Delta u}{\Delta x} + \lim (\cdots) \frac{(\Delta u)^2}{\Delta x}$$

$$= nu^{n-1} \frac{du}{dx} + 0,$$

that is,

$$\frac{dy}{dx} = nu^{n-1} \frac{du}{dx},$$

which establishes Eq. (4).

4. *At a point where* $u = g(x)$ *is differentiable and different from zero, the derivative of*

$$y = u^n$$

is given by

$$\frac{d(u^n)}{dx} = nu^{n-1} \frac{du}{dx} \qquad (5)$$

if n *is a negative integer.*

Note that this formula (5) is the extension of (4) to the case where n is a *negative integer*. To prove it, we combine the results in Eqs. (3) and (4) as follows. Let

$$y = u^{-m} = \frac{1}{u^m},$$

where $n = -m$ is a negative integer, so that m is a positive integer. Then, using (3) for the derivative of a quotient, we have

$$\frac{dy}{dx} = \frac{d\left(\frac{1}{u^m}\right)}{dx} = \frac{u^m \frac{d(1)}{dx} - 1 \frac{d(u^m)}{dx}}{(u^m)^2} \qquad (6)$$

at any point where u is differentiable and different from zero. Now the various derivatives on the right side of (6) can be evaluated by formulas already proved, namely,

$$\frac{d(1)}{dx} = 0,$$

since 1 is a constant, and

$$\frac{d(u^m)}{dx} = mu^{m-1} \frac{du}{dx},$$

since m is a *positive integer*. Therefore,

$$\frac{dy}{dx} = \frac{u^m \cdot 0 - 1 \cdot mu^{m-1} \frac{du}{dx}}{u^{2m}} = -mu^{-m-1} \frac{du}{dx}.$$

If $-m$ is replaced by its equivalent value n, the formula reduces to Eq. (5).

EXAMPLE 1. $y = x^2 + 1/x^2$, $x \neq 0$. We may write

$$y = x^2 + x^{-2}.$$

Then

$$\frac{dy}{dx} = 2x^{2-1}\frac{dx}{dx} + (-2)x^{-2-1}\frac{dx}{dx}$$

$$= 2x - 2x^{-3}.$$

EXAMPLE 2. $y = \dfrac{x^2 + 1}{x^2 - 1}$, $x^2 \neq 1$. We apply the formula, Eq. (3), for the derivative of a fraction and have

$$\frac{dy}{dx} = \frac{(x^2 - 1) \cdot 2x - (x^2 + 1) \cdot 2x}{(x^2 - 1)^2}$$

$$= \frac{-4x}{(x^2 - 1)^2}.$$

EXAMPLE 3. $y = (x^2 + 1)^3(x^3 - 1)^2$. We could, of course, expand everything here and write y as a polynomial in x, but this is not necessary. Instead, we use Eq. (1) for the derivative of a product:

$$\frac{dy}{dx} = (x^2 + 1)^3 \frac{d}{dx}(x^3 - 1)^2 + (x^3 - 1)^2 \frac{d}{dx}(x^2 + 1)^3.$$

The derivatives which are now to be evaluated are of the type in Eq. (4),

$$\frac{d}{dx}(x^3 - 1)^2 = 2(x^3 - 1)\frac{d}{dx}(x^3 - 1)$$

$$= 2(x^3 - 1) \cdot 3x^2 = 6x^2(x^3 - 1),$$

and

$$\frac{d}{dx}(x^2 + 1)^3 = 3(x^2 + 1)^2 \frac{d}{dx}(x^2 + 1)$$

$$= 3(x^2 + 1)^2 \cdot 2x = 6x(x^2 + 1)^2.$$

We substitute these into the earlier equation and have

$$\frac{dy}{dx} = (x^2 + 1)^3 6x^2(x^3 - 1) + (x^3 - 1)^2 6x(x^2 + 1)^2$$

$$= 6x(x^2 + 1)^2(x^3 - 1)[x(x^2 + 1) + (x^3 - 1)]$$

$$= 6x(x^2 + 1)^2(x^3 - 1)(2x^3 + x - 1).$$

PROBLEMS

Find dy/dx in each of the following problems (1 through 8).

1. $y = x^3/3 - x^2/2 + x - 1$ 2. $y = (x - 1)^3(x + 2)^4$
3. $y = (x^2 + 1)^5$ 4. $y = (x^3 - 3x)^4$

5. $y = (x + 1)^2 (x^2 + 1)^{-3}$ 6. $y = \dfrac{2x + 1}{x^2 - 1}$

7. $y = \dfrac{2x + 5}{3x - 2}$ 8. $y = \left(\dfrac{x + 1}{x - 1}\right)^2$

Find ds/dt in each of the following problems (9 through 15).

9. $s = \dfrac{t}{t^2 + 1}$ 10. $s = (2t + 3)^3$

11. $s = (t^2 - t)^{-2}$ 12. $s = t^2 (t + 1)^{-1}$

13. $s = \dfrac{2t}{3t^2 + 1}$ 14. $s = (t + t^{-1})^2$

15. $s = (t^2 + 3t)^3$

16. With the book closed, state and prove the formula for the derivative of the product of two differentiable functions u and v.

17. With the book closed, state and prove the formula for the derivative of the quotient u/v of two differentiable functions u and v.

18. With the book closed, state and prove the formula for the derivative with respect to x of u^n, where n is a positive integer and u is a differentiable function of x.

4-3   Implicit relations and their derivatives.   The functions we have dealt with so far have been of the form $y = f(x)$, which express y explicitly in terms of x. Quite often, however, we encounter equations like

$$x^2 + y^2 = 1, \qquad\qquad xy = 1,$$
$$y^2 = x, \qquad x^2 + xy + y^2 = 3,$$

which involve x and y in such a manner that they do not give y explicitly in terms of x. Nevertheless each of the equations listed defines a relation between y and x. When a definite number from some domain is substituted for x, the resulting equation determines one or more values of y to be associated with the given value of x. We therefore say that the equation determines y as one or more *implicit functions* of x. The domain of x is usually restricted so that y is real.

It happens that each of the equations given above can actually be solved to give y explicitly in terms of x, but such is not the case for an equation like

$$x^5 + 4xy^3 - 3y^5 = 2. \tag{1}$$

Nevertheless, it is possible to calculate dy/dx from such an equation by the method known as *implicit differentiation*. In this method we simply treat y as an unknown but differentiable function of x and apply the rules for finding derivatives of u^n, uv, u/v, etc., which we have already developed. [For a discussion of the validity of the assumption that the equation does define y as one or more differentiable functions of x, we must refer the reader to more advanced textbooks such as Fine, *Calculus*, p. 248; Macmillan (1937).]

EXAMPLE 1. Find dy/dx if y is related to x by Eq. (1).

Solution. We simply differentiate both sides of the given equation with respect to x, thus

$$\frac{d}{dx}(x^5) + \frac{d}{dx}(4xy^3) - \frac{d}{dx}(3y^5) = \frac{d}{dx}(2),$$

or

$$5x^4 + 4\left(x\frac{d(y^3)}{dx} + y^3\frac{dx}{dx}\right) - 15y^4\frac{dy}{dx} = 0,$$

$$5x^4 + 4\left(3xy^2\frac{dy}{dx} + y^3\right) - 15y^4\frac{dy}{dx} = 0,$$

$$(12xy^2 - 15y^4)\frac{dy}{dx} = -(5x^4 + 4y^3),$$

and finally, at all points where

$$12xy^2 - 15y^4 \neq 0,$$

we have

$$\frac{dy}{dx} = \frac{5x^4 + 4y^3}{15y^4 - 12xy^2}.$$

Note that the rule

$$\frac{d}{dx}u^n = nu^{n-1}\frac{du}{dx}$$

becomes

$$\frac{dy^5}{dx} = 5y^4\frac{dy}{dx}$$

when applied to y^5.

The result of applying this method to any of the equations listed above will be to give an expression for dy/dx in terms of both x and y. This is no real handicap since, if we want the slope of the tangent to a curve at a point (x_1, y_1), for instance, we need merely substitute x_1 for x and y_1 for y in the final expression for dy/dx.

EXAMPLE 2. Find the slope of the tangent to the curve $x^2 + xy + y^2 = 7$ at the point (1, 2).

Solution. We differentiate both sides of the equation with respect to x, noting that xy is a product, uv, and that y^2 is of the form u^n, while 7 is a constant.

Thus

$$2x \frac{dx}{dx} + \left(x \frac{dy}{dx} + y \frac{dx}{dx} \right) + 2y \frac{dy}{dx} = 0,$$

$$(x + 2y) \frac{dy}{dx} = -(2x + y),$$

and wherever $x + 2y \neq 0$, we have

$$\frac{dy}{dx} = -\frac{2x + y}{x + 2y}.$$

In particular, at $(1, 2)$ we have

$$\left(\frac{dy}{dx} \right)_{(1,2)} = -\frac{4}{5}.$$

The method of implicit differentiation enables us to show also that *if u is a differentiable function of x and*

$$y = u^{p/q},$$

where p and q are integers with $q > 0$, then

$$\frac{dy}{dx} = \frac{p}{q} u^{(p/q)-1} \frac{du}{dx}$$

provided $u \neq 0$ if $p/q < 1$.

Note that this is the familiar rule for the derivative of u^n, but this time applied to the case where $n = p/q$ is any rational number. Of course, the domain of x is restricted to values for which $u^{p/q}$ is well defined. For example, if $u = 1 - x^2$ and $p/q = \frac{1}{2}$, then $|x| \leq 1$ in order to produce real values of

$$y = (1 - x^2)^{1/2}.$$

The restriction $u \neq 0$ if $p/q < 1$ is necessary in order to avoid division by zero, which is never permitted.

To establish the result, let

$$y = u^{p/q},$$

which means that

$$y^q = u^p.$$

Then, differentiating both sides of the equation implicitly and using the familiar formulas for the derivatives of y^q and u^p (since p and q are integers, these formulas are valid), we obtain

$$qy^{q-1} \frac{dy}{dx} = pu^{p-1} \frac{du}{dx}.$$

Hence if $y \neq 0$, we have

$$\frac{dy}{dx} = \frac{pu^{p-1}}{qy^{q-1}} \frac{du}{dx}.$$

But

$$y^{q-1} = (u^{p/q})^{q-1} = u^{p-(p/q)},$$

so that

$$\frac{dy}{dx} = \frac{p}{q} \frac{u^{p-1}}{u^{p-(p/q)}} \frac{du}{dx}$$

$$= \frac{p}{q} u^{(p/q)-1} \frac{du}{dx}.$$

The restriction $y \neq 0$ is the same as the restriction $u \neq 0$ but was made without reference to whether p/q was or was not less than one. The restriction is certainly not needed if $p/q = 1$, since then we simply have $y = u$ and

$$\frac{dy}{dx} = \frac{du}{dx}.$$

The case

$$y = x^{3/2}$$

is typical of the case

$$y = u^{p/q}, \qquad p/q > 1,$$

and we shall show that for this case the slope of the curve is 0 at $x = 0$. We may work directly with the definition of the tangent to the curve at $(0, 0)$ as the limiting position of a secant line through $(0, 0)$ and a second point $P_1(x_1, y_1)$ on the curve as P_1 approaches the origin. Then the slope of $\overleftrightarrow{OP_1}$ is

$$m = \frac{\text{rise}}{\text{run}} = \frac{y_1 - 0}{x_1 - 0} = \frac{x_1^{3/2}}{x_1} = x_1^{1/2}.$$

Now as P_1 approaches O, we have

$$m_0 = \lim_{x_1 \to 0} m = \lim_{x_1 \to 0} x_1^{1/2} = 0;$$

that is, the slope of the tangent to the curve at O is zero. If we use the formula just derived, we obtain

$$y = x^{3/2},$$

$$\frac{dy}{dx} = \frac{3}{2} x^{1/2},$$

and at $x = 0$ this also equals zero.

In the strictest sense, this curve doesn't actually have a derivative at $x = 0$, since the curve does

Figure 4–2

not exist to the left of the origin. This means that only the right-hand limit,

$$\lim_{\Delta x \to 0+} \frac{f(x + \Delta x) - f(x)}{\Delta x},$$

can be calculated at $x = 0$. Nevertheless, it is customary to say that the curve (see Fig. 4–2) has a horizontal tangent at the origin, since the only secant lines which can be drawn from $O(0, 0)$ to points P on the curve tend to a unique limiting position as P approaches O along the curve.

PROBLEMS

In Problems 1–23, find dy/dx.

1. $x^2 + y^2 = 1$

2. $y^2 = \dfrac{x - 1}{x + 1}$

3. $x^2 + xy = 2$

4. $x^2 y + xy^2 = 6$

5. $y^2 = x^3$

6. $x^{2/3} + y^{2/3} = 1$

7. $x^{1/2} + y^{1/2} = 1$

8. $x^3 - xy + y^3 = 1$

9. $x^2 = \dfrac{x - y}{x + y}$

10. $y = \dfrac{x}{\sqrt{x^2 + 1}}$

11. $y = x\sqrt{x^2 + 1}$

12. $y^2 = x^2 + \dfrac{1}{x^2}$

13. $2xy + y^2 = x + y$

14. $y = \sqrt{x} + \sqrt[3]{x} + \sqrt[4]{x}$

15. $y^2 = \dfrac{x^2 - 1}{x^2 + 1}$

16. $(x + y)^3 + (x - y)^3 = x^4 + y^4$

17. $(3x + 7)^5 = 2y^3$

18. $y = (x + 5)^4 (x^2 - 2)^3$

19. $\dfrac{1}{y} + \dfrac{1}{x} = 1$

20. $y = (x^2 + 5x)^3$

21. $y^2 = x^2 - x$

22. $x^2 y^2 = x^2 + y^2$

23. $y = \dfrac{\sqrt[3]{x^2 + 3}}{x}$

24. (a) By differentiating the equation $x^2 - y^2 = 1$ implicitly, show that $dy/dx = x/y$.

(b) By differentiating both sides of the equation $dy/dx = x/y$ implicitly, show that

$$\frac{d^2 y}{dx^2} = \frac{y - x\left(\dfrac{dy}{dx}\right)}{y^2} = \frac{y - \dfrac{x^2}{y}}{y^2} = \frac{y^2 - x^2}{y^3}$$

or, since $y^2 - x^2 = -1$ from the original equation,

$$\frac{d^2 y}{dx^2} = \frac{-1}{y^3}.$$

Use the method outlined in Problem 24 to find dy/dx and d^2y/dx^2 in each of the following problems (25 through 28).

25. $x^2 + y^2 = 1$ 26. $x^3 + y^3 = 1$

27. $x^{2/3} + y^{2/3} = 1$ 28. $xy + y^2 = 1$

29. A particle of mass m moves along the x-axis. The velocity $v = dx/dt$ and position x satisfy the equation

$$m(v^2 - v_0^2) = k(x_0^2 - x^2),$$

where k, v_0, and x_0 are constants. Show, by implicitly differentiating this equation with respect to t, that whenever $v \neq 0$,

$$m\frac{dv}{dt} = -kx.$$

Find the lines that are respectively *tangent* and *normal* to the following curves at the points indicated as P_0. (A line is said to be *normal* to a curve at a point P_0 if it is perpendicular to the tangent at P_0.)

30. $x^2 + xy - y^2 = 1,$ $P_0(2, 3)$

31. $x^2 + y^2 = 25,$ $P_0(3, -4)$

32. $x^2y^2 = 9,$ $P_0(-1, 3)$

33. $\dfrac{x - y}{x - 2y} = 2,$ $P_0(3, 1)$

34. $(y - x)^2 = 2x + 4,$ $P_0(6, 2)$

4–4   The increment of a function. In this article, we shall learn how to estimate the change Δy produced in a function $y = f(x)$ when x changes by a small amount Δx. To be precise, let us focus our attention on a portion of the graph of $y = f(x)$ in the neighborhood of a point $P(x, y)$ where the function is differentiable. Then, if $Q(x + \Delta x, y + \Delta y)$ is a second point on the curve, with $\Delta x \neq 0$, we know that

$$\text{the slope of the secant line } \overleftrightarrow{PQ} = \frac{\Delta y}{\Delta x}$$

approaches the limiting value

$$\frac{dy}{dx} = f'(x)$$

as Δx approaches zero. Therefore, the difference

$$\frac{\Delta y}{\Delta x} - \frac{dy}{dx}$$

is numerically small when $|\Delta x|$ is small. Let us denote this difference by ϵ:

$$\frac{\Delta y}{\Delta x} - \frac{dy}{dx} = \epsilon. \tag{1}$$

Then, saying that

$$\lim_{\Delta x \to 0} \frac{\Delta y}{\Delta x} = \frac{dy}{dx} = f'(x) \tag{2}$$

is equivalent to saying that

$$\lim_{\Delta x \to 0} \epsilon = 0. \tag{3}$$

In other words, we may deduce from Eqs. (1), (2), and (3) that

$$\frac{\Delta y}{\Delta x} = \frac{dy}{dx} + \epsilon, \tag{4a}$$

where

$$\epsilon \to 0 \quad \text{as} \quad \Delta x \to 0. \tag{4b}$$

If we multiply both sides of (4a) by Δx, we also have

$$\boxed{\Delta y = \frac{dy}{dx} \Delta x + \epsilon \, \Delta x.} \tag{4c}$$

Although Eq. (4c) was derived under the assumption that $\Delta x \neq 0$, it is still a true equation even when $\Delta x = 0$. In fact, if we define ϵ by Eq. (1) when $\Delta x \neq 0$, and take $\epsilon = 0$ when $\Delta x = 0$, then Eqs. (4b, c) hold whether $\Delta x = 0$ or not.

If we compare Fig. 4–3 with Fig. 2–22, Article 2–7, we see that the first term on the right side of Eq. (4c) is equal to the change Δy_{tan} that would be produced in y by a change Δx in x if the point (x, y) were to move along the tangent line. This is called the *principal part* of Δy since, for small values of Δx, it usually is large in comparison with the second term, $\epsilon \, \Delta x$.

The significance of Eqs. (4b, c) is that

$$\boxed{\Delta y = \Delta y_{\text{tan}} + \epsilon \, \Delta x = \text{change in } y \text{ } \textit{along the curve}}$$

and

$$\boxed{\Delta y_{\text{tan}} = \frac{dy}{dx} \Delta x = \text{change in } y \text{ } \textit{along the tangent line}}$$

differ by an amount

$$\epsilon \, \Delta x,$$

which tends to zero more rapidly than Δx does when Δx approaches zero.

Figure 4–3

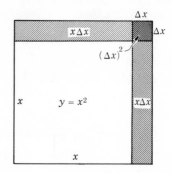

Figure 4–4

For example, if

$$y = x^2 = f(x),$$

then

$$\frac{dy}{dx} = 2x = f'(x)$$

and the principal part of Δy is

$$\frac{dy}{dx} \Delta x = 2x \, \Delta x.$$

On the other hand, the exact value of Δy is

$$\Delta y = 2x \, \Delta x + (\Delta x)^2.$$

We compare this with Eq. (4c) and see that, for this particular example, the part which is denoted by $\epsilon \, \Delta x$ in (4c) is

$$\epsilon \, \Delta x = (\Delta x)^2.$$

When Δx is small, $(\Delta x)^2$ is the square of a small number and this is much smaller than Δx itself.

This example,

$$y = x^2, \qquad \text{(principal part of } \Delta y) = 2x \, \Delta x,$$

also lends itself to an interesting geometrical interpretation, as illustrated by Fig. 4–4. The original square, having sides x by x, has area $y = x^2$. When the sides are increased to $x + \Delta x$ by $x + \Delta x$, the area is increased by $\Delta y = 2x \, \Delta x + (\Delta x)^2$. When Δx is small in comparison with x, most of the change in y is given by the two rectangular pieces x by Δx and only a very small part is given by the small square Δx by Δx. Thus, if the original square has sides

$$x = 2 \text{ (in.)}$$

and the larger square has sides

$$x + \Delta x = 2.01 \text{ (in.)},$$

so that

$$\Delta x = +0.01 \text{ (in.)},$$

the area of the original square is

$$y = x^2 = 4 \text{ (in}^2)$$

and the area of the larger square is

$$y + \Delta y = (x + \Delta x)^2 = x^2 + 2x\,\Delta x + (\Delta x)^2$$
$$= 4 + 0.04 + 0.0001 \text{ (in}^2).$$

The increment,

$$\Delta y = 0.04 + 0.0001 \text{ (in}^2)$$

has its principal part equal to

$$2x\,\Delta x = 0.04 \text{ (in}^2)$$

and its remainder

$$(\Delta x)^2 = 0.0001 \text{ (in}^2).$$

If we were to use only the principal part of Δy as an approximation to Δy itself, we would thereby introduce an error of magnitude 0.0001 (in^2), which is just under one-fourth of one percent of Δy.

Since the principal part of Δy usually gives a good approximation to Δy itself (at least when Δx is small compared with dy/dx), it is customary to use the approximation

$$\Delta y \approx \frac{dy}{dx}\,\Delta x = \Delta y_{\text{tan}} \tag{5}$$

in numerical calculations. (The symbol $\approx$ means "is approximately equal to.")

EXAMPLE 1. Use the approximation in Eq. (5) to approximate the change in $y = x^3$ when x changes from 3 to 2.98.

Solution. We take $x = 3$ and $x + \Delta x = 2.98$, so that $\Delta x = 2.98 - 3 = -0.02$. Since

$$\frac{dy}{dx} = 3x^2,$$

we find, using Eq. (5), that

$$\Delta y \approx 3x^2\,\Delta x = 27\,(-0.02) = -0.54.$$

EXAMPLE 2. Using the approximation in Eq. (5), determine a reasonable approximation to $(2.98)^3$.

Solution. As in Example 1, we consider

$$y = x^3.$$

Since 2.98 is near to 3 and $3^3 = 27$ is easily calculated, we think of starting from the point

$$x = 3, \qquad y = 27$$

and trying to reach the point

$$x + \Delta x = 2.98, \qquad y + \Delta y = (2.98)^3 = ?$$

Now instead of calculating $(2.98)^3$ exactly, we shall make use of the *approximation*

$$\Delta y \approx \frac{dy}{dx} \Delta x = 3x^2 \Delta x = -0.54.$$

Hence, adding this to $y = x^3 = 27$, we have

$$(2.98)^3 = y + \Delta y \approx y + \frac{dy}{dx} \Delta x = 27 - 0.54$$

or

$$(2.98)^3 \approx 26.46.$$

PROBLEMS

For each of the following functions, find (a) Δy, (b) the principal part of Δy, namely, $\Delta y_{\tan} = (dy/dx)\Delta x$, (c) the difference, $\Delta y - \Delta y_{\tan}$.

1. $y = x^2 + 2x$ 2. $y = 2x^2 + 4x - 3$
3. $y = x^3 - x$ 4. $y = x^4$
5. $y = x^{-1}$

For each of the following functions $y = f(x)$, *estimate* $y + \Delta y = f(x + \Delta x)$ by calculating y plus the principal part of Δy for the given data.

6. $y = \sqrt{x}, \quad x = 4, \quad \Delta x = 0.5$ 7. $y = \sqrt[3]{x}, \quad x = 8, \quad \Delta x = -0.5$
8. $y = x^{-1}, \quad x = 2, \quad \Delta x = 0.1$
9. $y = \sqrt{x^2 + 9}, \quad x = -4, \quad \Delta x = -0.2$
10. $y = \dfrac{x}{x + 1}, \quad x = 1, \quad \Delta x = 0.3$

11. The volume $y = x^3$ of a cube of edge x increases by an amount Δy when x increases by an amount Δx. Show that Δy may be represented geometrically as the sum of the volumes of:

(a) three slabs of dimensions x by x by Δx,
(b) three bars of dimensions x by Δx by Δx,
(c) one cube of dimensions Δx by Δx by Δx.

Illustrate by a sketch.

4–5   The chain rule for derivatives.   When a particle moves in a curved plane path rather than in a straight line, it is customary to specify its position at any time t by means of equations which give both x and y as functions of t. For example, the equations of the trajectory of a projectile have approximately the form

$$x = c_1 t, \qquad y = c_2 t - \tfrac{1}{2}gt^2,$$

Figure 4–5

where c_1 and c_2 are the initial velocity components at time $t = 0$.

The exact equations, which must also take air resistance and other factors into account, are much more complicated. We are not in a position to go into details here.

More generally, equations of the form

$$x = f(t), \qquad y = g(t) \tag{1}$$

can be used to specify the position of (x, y) in terms of t. Such equations are called *parametric equations* and t is called the parameter. If we eliminate t from the equations, then we obtain an equation of the form

$$y = F(x). \tag{2}$$

One might reasonably ask how $dy/dx = F'(x)$ from Eq. (2) is related to $dy/dt = g'(t)$ and $dx/dt = f'(t)$ from Eq. (1). The answer to this question is contained in the following *chain rule for derivatives*.

If $y = F(x)$ is a differentiable function of x and $x = f(t)$ is a differentiable function of t, then $y = F[f(t)] = g(t)$ is a differentiable function of t and

$$g'(t) = F'(x)f'(t), \tag{3a}$$

or, in other words,

$$\boxed{\frac{dy}{dt} = \frac{dy}{dx}\frac{dx}{dt}.} \tag{3b}$$

This is called the chain rule of differentiation, since finding the derivative with respect to t of

$$y = F[f(t)]$$

involves the following chain of steps. *First*, differentiate the outside function

$$y = F(x)$$

with respect to x. *Second*, differentiate the inside function

$$x = f(t)$$

with respect to t.

The product of these derivatives gives dy/dt.

To establish the result, we let t be given an increment $\Delta t \neq 0$ and denote the corresponding x and y increments by Δx and Δy. Then, since $y = F(x)$ is a differentiable function of x, we know, from Eqs. (4a, b, c) of Article 4–4, that we may write

$$\Delta y = \frac{dy}{dx} \Delta x + \epsilon \, \Delta x, \tag{4a}$$

where

$$\epsilon \to 0 \quad \text{as} \quad \Delta x \to 0. \tag{4b}$$

We divide (4a) by Δt

$$\frac{\Delta y}{\Delta t} = \frac{dy}{dx} \frac{\Delta x}{\Delta t} + \epsilon \frac{\Delta x}{\Delta t} \tag{4c}$$

and take limits as $\Delta t \to 0$. Since $x = f(t)$ is a differentiable function of t, we have

$$\lim_{\Delta t \to 0} \Delta x = \lim_{\Delta t \to 0} \left(\frac{\Delta x}{\Delta t} \Delta t \right) = \frac{dx}{dt} \cdot 0 = 0.$$

Therefore Δx approaches zero when Δt does, and

$$\lim_{\Delta t \to 0} \epsilon = \lim_{\Delta x \to 0} \epsilon = 0.$$

Hence the last term in Eq. (4c) has the limit zero and we have

$$\frac{dy}{dt} = \lim_{\Delta t \to 0} \frac{\Delta y}{\Delta t} = \lim_{\Delta t \to 0} \frac{dy}{dx} \frac{\Delta x}{\Delta t} + \lim_{\Delta t \to 0} \left(\epsilon \frac{\Delta x}{\Delta t} \right) = \frac{dy}{dx} \frac{dx}{dt} + 0,$$

as we wished to show.

EXAMPLE 1.

$$y = x^3 - 3x^2 + 5x - 4 = F(x), \qquad x = t^2 + t = f(t).$$

Solution. From these equations, we find

$$\frac{dy}{dx} = 3x^2 - 6x + 5 = 3(t^2 + t)^2 - 6(t^2 + t) + 5,$$

$$\frac{dx}{dt} = 2t + 1,$$

so that Eq. (3b) becomes

$$\frac{dy}{dt} = \frac{dy}{dx} \frac{dx}{dt}$$

$$= [3(t^2 + t)^2 - 6(t^2 + t) + 5](2t + 1).$$

If, on the other hand, we first substitute the value of x in terms of t into the equation for y, we have

$$y = (t^2 + t)^3 - 3(t^2 + t)^2 + 5(t^2 + t) - 4.$$

When we differentiate this with respect to t, we get

$$\frac{dy}{dt} = 3(t^2 + t)^2(2t + 1) - 6(t^2 + t)(2t + 1) + 5(2t + 1)$$

$$= [3(t^2 + t)^2 - 6(t^2 + t) + 5](2t + 1),$$

which agrees with the previous answer.

Remark 1. So far we have not defined dy and dx as separate entities, but have used the complete symbol dy/dx as the name for $\lim (\Delta y/\Delta x)$ as $\Delta x \to 0$. Now that we have established Eq. (3), we are in a position where we can (and we shall in the next article) define dy and dx as separate quantities whose ratio is the derivative of y with respect to x. Then Eq. (3b) is the form of the chain rule which is most easily remembered, since it suggests that dx may be cancelled from the two fractions on the right.

Remark 2. If $dx/dt \neq 0$, we may divide both sides of Eq. (3b) by dx/dt and write it in the equivalent form

$$\boxed{\frac{dy}{dx} = \frac{dy/dt}{dx/dt}.} \qquad (5)$$

This form of the equation is particularly useful in dealing with the parametric equations

$$x = f(t), \qquad y = g(t),$$

since it enables us to find the derivative of y with respect to x directly from these equations.

EXAMPLE 2. The parametric equations

$$x = 2t + 3, \qquad y = t^2 - 1$$

represent a curve whose equation in the form of $y = f(x)$ may be found by substituting

$$t = \frac{x - 3}{2}$$

from the first equation into the second; that is,

$$y = \tfrac{1}{4}(x - 3)^2 - 1.$$

If we work with the original equations and calculate

$$\frac{dx}{dt} = 2, \qquad \frac{dy}{dt} = 2t,$$

then Eq. (5a) gives

$$\frac{dy}{dx} = \frac{dy/dt}{dx/dt} = \frac{2t}{2} = t = \frac{x-3}{2}.$$

On the other hand, from the equation for y in terms of x, we find

$$\frac{dy}{dx} = \frac{1}{2}(x-3)\frac{d}{dx}(x-3) = \frac{x-3}{2}.$$

Remark 3. The chain rule is also frequently expressed using other letters to represent the variables. The most common of these is the case where y is a function of u and u is a function of x,

$$y = F(u), \qquad u = f(x).$$

Then the rule says

$$\boxed{\frac{dy}{dx} = \frac{dy}{du}\frac{du}{dx}.} \tag{6}$$

We have already had an illustration of this formula in the case of the derivative with respect to x of

$$y = u^n.$$

Then

$$\frac{dy}{du} = nu^{n-1}$$

and

$$\frac{dy}{dx} = \frac{dy}{du}\frac{du}{dx} = nu^{n-1}\frac{du}{dx}.$$

Remark 4. The term *composite function** is used to describe a *function of a function*. For example, if

$$g(x) = x^2$$

and

$$h(x) = \sin x,$$

we can compose them in two different orders and get two different composite functions. One of these is

$$g\big(h(x)\big) = g\,(\sin x) = \sin^2 x$$

and the other is

$$h\big(g(x)\big) = h(x^2) = \sin\,(x^2).$$

---

* For a longer discussion of composite functions and their properties, see *Continuity*, by G. B. Thomas, pp. 45–49.

In general, if g and h are two functions, the composition of g with h is the function f defined by the equation

$$f(x) = g(h(x)). \qquad (7)$$

The chain rule for derivatives says that the derivative of this composite function is

$$f'(x) = g'(h(x)) \cdot h'(x). \qquad (8)$$

PROBLEMS

In Problems 1–4, each pair of equations represents a curve in parametric form. In each case, find the equation of the curve in the form $y = F(x)$ by eliminating t, then calculate dy/dt, dy/dx, and dx/dt and verify that they satisfy the chain rule, Eq. (3b).

1. $x = 3t + 1$, $y = t^2$ 2. $x = t^2$, $y = t^3$

3. $x = \dfrac{t}{1-t}$, $y = t^2$ 4. $x = \dfrac{t}{1+t}$, $y = \dfrac{t^2}{1+t}$

5. If a point traces the circle $x^2 + y^2 = 25$ and if $dx/dt = 4$ when the point reaches $(3, 4)$, find dy/dt there.

In each of the following problems (6 through 10), find dy/dx, (a) by using the chain rule and also (b) by first expressing y directly in terms of x, and then differentiating.

6. $y = u^2 + 3u - 7$; $u = 2x + 1$ 7. $y = \dfrac{u^2}{u^2+1}$; $u = \sqrt{2x+1}$

8. $y = z^{2/3}$; $z = x^2 + 1$ 9. $y = w^2 - w^{-1}$; $w = 3x$

10. $y = 2v^3 + \dfrac{2}{v^3}$; $v = (3x + 2)^{2/3}$

4–6 The differentials dx and dy. We are now prepared to define dx and dy in such a way that their ratio, when $dx \neq 0$, will be the same as the derivative of y with respect to x. This is very easy to do in the case where x is the *independent variable* and y is a function of x. When x is the independent variable and

$$y = F(x),$$

we shall adopt the following *definitions:*

(a) dx, called the *"differential of x,"* may be any real number whatever; that is, dx is another independent variable and its domain is $-\infty < dx < +\infty$, and

(b) *dy, called the "differential of y," is a function of x and dx given by*

$$dy = F'(x)\, dx, \tag{1}$$

where $F'(x)$ is the derivative at x of the function F.

It is clear from (1) that the differentials dx and dy have the properties

(1) if $dx = 0$, then $dy = 0$, and
(2) if $dx \neq 0$, then

$$\frac{dy}{dx} = \frac{\text{the differential of } y \text{ in terms of } x \text{ and } dx}{\text{the differential of } x}$$

$$= \frac{F'(x)\, dx}{dx} = F'(x) \tag{2}$$

is the derivative of y with respect to x.

There is certainly nothing mysterious about this last result, since we deliberately defined dy by Eq. (1) so that Eq. (2) would be true. In other words, we planned it that way!

For example, if

$$y = x^3 = F(x)$$

then

$$F'(x) = 3x^2$$

and

$$dy = F'(x)\, dx = 3x^2\, dx.$$

We also have been accustomed to writing

$$\frac{dy}{dx} = 3x^2,$$

and if we treat this as a fraction and multiply both sides by dx, we obtain again

$$dy = 3x^2\, dx.$$

Again, if

$$y = x = F(x)$$

then

$$F'(x) = 1$$

and

$$dy = F'(x)\, dx = dx.$$

That is, the *function $F(x) = x$* has its differential, as given by Eq. (1), equal to the differential of the *independent variable x*. This is not a profound result; it simply shows that in the case where both (a) and (b) apply, the differential is the same whether given by (a) or by (b); that is, the two rules are *consistent*.

The geometric interpretation of dy becomes clear when we refer to Fig. 4–6, where in each part we indicate a curve $y = F(x)$ and a line segment $\overline{PT}$ tangent to the curve at P. The differential $dx = PR$ in each figure is considered positive if R is to the right of P [as in (a) and (c)], and negative when R is to the left of P. The sign of dy is positive if T is above R [as in (a) and (d)] and negative if T is below R. In any

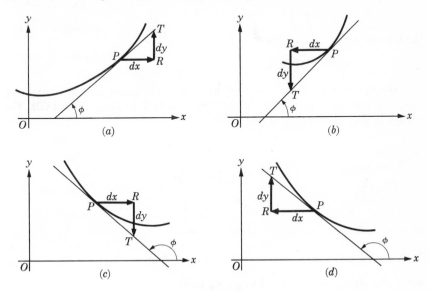

Figure 4–6

case, we find that

$$\frac{dy}{dx} = \frac{RT}{PR} = \tan \phi = F'(x)$$

gives the slope of the tangent to the curve at P, and

$$dy = F'(x)\, dx = (\tan \phi)(PR) = RT$$

is the *amount* of change in y along this tangent line that would be produced by a change dx in x. We thus have

(a) dy/dx is the *rate* of change of y per unit change in x, and

(b) dy is the *amount* of change of y for dx units of change in x along the *tangent* to the curve at P.

Therefore, if we take $dx = \Delta x$, then dy is the same as Δy_{tan} (Fig. 2–22), which is the principal part of Δy. In problems dealing with increments we therefore do take $dx = \Delta x$ and use dy as an approximation to Δy.

EXAMPLE. Find a reasonable approximation to the value of

$$(1.001)^7 - 2(1.001)^{4/3} + 3.$$

Solution. At

$$x_0 = 1$$

the function

$$F(x) = x^7 - 2x^{4/3} + 3$$

has the easily calculated value

$$y_0 = F(1) = 2.$$

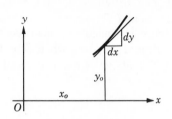

Figure 4-7

The tangent to this curve $y = F(x)$ at $(1, 2)$ will remain near the curve for values of x close to x_0. As x changes from $x_0 = 1$ to $x_0 + dx = 1.001$, the change in y *along this tangent line will be*

$$dy = F'(x_0)\, dx.$$

Since

$$F'(x) = 7x^6 - \tfrac{8}{3}x^{1/3}$$

has the value

$$F'(x_0) = \tfrac{13}{3}$$

at $x_0 = 1$, when we take $dx = 0.001$, we have

$$dy = \tfrac{13}{3}(0.001) = 0.0043.$$

When this change in y is added to y_0, we have

$$y_0 + dy = 2.0043$$

as a good approximation to the value of y at the point on the curve for which $x = x_0 + dx$.

Suppose next that x is not the independent variable, but that x and y are both to be regarded as functions of t. Let

$$y = F(x), \qquad x = f(t),$$
$$y = F[f(t)] = g(t), \tag{3}$$

with t now the independent variable. Then to be consistent with our previous definitions, we shall have the definitions:

(a) dt is arbitrary, that is, another independent variable with the range $-\infty < dt < +\infty$, but

(b) $dx = f'(t)\, dt$, and $\hspace{6cm}$ (4a)

(c) $dy = g'(t)\, dt$. $\hspace{6.5cm}$ (4b)

Our notation is the same as that used in establishing Eq. (3a), Article 4–5, so we may substitute

$$g'(t) = F'(x)f'(t)$$

into (4b) and find

$$dy = F'(x)f'(t) \, dt,$$

and reference to (4a) shows that this implies

$$dy = F'(x) \, dx. \tag{4c}$$

What is the significance of (4c) and how does it differ from (1)? To answer the latter question first: In (4c), $dy = g'(t) \, dt$ is expressed in terms of t and dt; likewise $dx = f'(t) \, dt$ is expressed in terms of t and dt, whereas in (1), dx is an independent variable and dy is expressed directly in terms of x and dx. Thus the significance of (4c) is that from it we may write

$$F'(x) = \frac{dy \text{ (in terms of } t \text{ and } dt)}{dx \text{ (in terms of } t \text{ and } dt)}, \qquad \text{if } dx \neq 0,$$

that is,

$$\text{the derivative of } y \text{ with respect to } x = \frac{\text{the differential of } y}{\text{the differential of } x}, \qquad \text{if } dx \neq 0,$$

whether the differentials are in terms of x and dx or in terms of t and dt. [When dx equals zero, Eq. (4c) tells us only that dy also equals zero, and of course tells us nothing about $F'(x)$.]

It is this property of the differentials that makes it possible to treat the derivative as the ratio of dy and dx, whether x is the independent variable or not, and enables us to take full advantage of the Leibniz notation.

As an illustration of these ideas, if we let

$$y = t^2 \qquad \text{and} \qquad x = t^3,$$

we have

$$\frac{dy}{dt} = 2t, \qquad \frac{dx}{dt} = 3t^2,$$

$$dy = 2t \, dt, \qquad dx = 3t^2 \, dt,$$

$$\frac{dy}{dx} = \frac{2t \, dt}{3t^2 \, dt} = \frac{2}{3t}.$$

If we eliminate t before taking derivatives,

$$y = x^{2/3},$$

$$\frac{dy}{dx} = \frac{2}{3} x^{-1/3} = \frac{2}{3x^{1/3}} = \frac{2}{3t},$$

in agreement with the answer above.

Second derivative. The second derivative of y with respect to x has been interpreted as the result obtained from y by doing twice in succession the operation "differentiate with respect to x"; i.e.,

$$\frac{d^2y}{dx^2} = \frac{d}{dx}\left[\frac{d}{dx}(y)\right].$$

It is also possible to define a second differential, d^2y, in such a way that the second derivative of y with respect to x is equal to d^2y divided by $(dx)^2$. However, things get rather complicated in the case of parametric equations

$$x = f(t), \qquad y = F(x) = F[f(t)] = g(t).$$

In such cases, it is simplest to calculate second and higher order derivatives by using such rules as

$$\frac{dy}{dx} = y' = \frac{dy/dt}{dx/dt},$$

$$\frac{d^2y}{dx^2} = y'' = \frac{dy'}{dx} = \frac{dy'/dt}{dx/dt}.$$

It is important to note that to get the second derivative of y with respect to x, when the first derivative $dy/dx = y'$ is expressed in terms of t, we may differentiate y' with respect to t, provided we divide the result by dx/dt.

EXAMPLE. Find d^2y/dx^2 if $x = t - t^2$ and $y = t - t^3$.

Solution. $\quad y' = \dfrac{dy}{dx} = \dfrac{dy/dt}{dx/dt} = \dfrac{1 - 3t^2}{1 - 2t},$

$$\frac{d^2y}{dx^2} = y'' = \frac{dy'}{dx} = \frac{dy'/dt}{dx/dt} = \frac{\dfrac{d}{dt}\left[\dfrac{1 - 3t^2}{1 - 2t}\right]}{(1 - 2t)}$$

$$= \frac{(1 - 2t)\cdot(-6t) - (1 - 3t^2)\cdot(-2)}{(1 - 2t)^3} = \frac{2 - 6t + 6t^2}{(1 - 2t)^3}.$$

4-7   Formulas for differentiations repeated in the notation of differentials.
Earlier in this chapter we derived formulas for the derivatives listed below
on the left. By multiplying each one by dx we now obtain the corresponding formulas for differentials.

Derivatives	*Differentials*
I. $\dfrac{dc}{dx} = 0$	I'. $dc = 0$
II. $\dfrac{d(cu)}{dx} = c\dfrac{du}{dx}$	II'. $d(cu) = c\,du$
III. $\dfrac{d(u+v)}{dx} = \dfrac{du}{dx} + \dfrac{dv}{dx}$	III'. $d(u+v) = du + dv$
IV. $\dfrac{d(uv)}{dx} = u\dfrac{dv}{dx} + v\dfrac{du}{dx}$	IV'. $d(uv) = u\,dv + v\,du$
V. $\dfrac{d\left(\frac{u}{v}\right)}{dx} = \dfrac{v\dfrac{du}{dx} - u\dfrac{dv}{dx}}{v^2}$	V'. $d\left(\dfrac{u}{v}\right) = \dfrac{v\,du - u\,dv}{v^2}$
VI. $\dfrac{du^n}{dx} = nu^{n-1}\dfrac{du}{dx}$	VI'. $d(u^n) = nu^{n-1}\,du$
VIa. $\dfrac{dcx^n}{dx} = cnx^{n-1}$	VI'a. $d(cx^n) = cnx^{n-1}\,dx$

We collect these formulas primarily for future reference. Any problem
involving differentials, say that of finding dy when y is a given function
of x, may be handled either

(a) by finding the derivative dy/dx and then multiplying by dx, or
(b) by direct use of formulas I'–VI'a.

For instance, if we let
$$y = x^3 + 5x^2 - 7x + 4,$$

then
$$\frac{dy}{dx} = 3x^2 + 10x - 7,$$
and
$$dy = (3x^2 + 10x - 7)\,dx,$$

or we may calculate directly:

$$dy = d(x^3 + 5x^2 - 7x + 4)$$
$$= d(x^3) + d(5x^2) + d(-7x) + d(4) \qquad \text{(III')}$$
$$= 3x^2\,dx + 10x\,dx - 7\,dx + 0 \qquad \text{(VI'a)}$$
$$= (3x^2 + 10x - 7)\,dx.$$

It should be noted that a *differential* on the left side of an equation, say dy, also calls for a *differential*, usually dx, on the right side of the equation. Thus we never have $dy = 3x^2$, but instead $dy = 3x^2\,dx$.

The term "differentiate" means either to find the derivative or to find the differential and either operation is referred to as "differentiation."

PROBLEMS

In each of the following problems (1 through 8), find dy.

1. $y = x^3 - 3x^2 + 5x - 7$　　　　2. $y^2 = (3x^2 + 1)^{3/2}$

3. $xy^2 + x^2 y = 4$　　　　　　　　4. $y = \dfrac{2x}{1 + x^2}$

5. $y = x\sqrt{1 - x^2}$　　　　　　　6. $y = \dfrac{x + 1}{x^2 - 2x + 4}$

7. $y = \dfrac{(1 - x)^3}{2 - 3x}$　　　　　　8. $y = \dfrac{1 + x - x^2}{1 - x}$

Use differentials to obtain reasonable approximations to the following:

9. $\sqrt{145}$　　　　　　　　　　　10. $(2.1)^3$

11. $\sqrt[4]{17}$　　　　　　　　　　12. $\sqrt[3]{0.126}$

13. $(8.01)^{4/3} + (8.01)^2 - \dfrac{1}{\sqrt[3]{8.01}}$

Given the following functions $x = f(t)$, $y = g(t)$.
(a) Express dx and dy in terms of t and dt.

(b) Use the results of (a) to find, at the point for which $t = 2$, the slope of the locus of the point (x, y).

(c) Use the results of (b) to find an equation of the line tangent to the curve at the point for which $t = 2$.

14. $x = t + \dfrac{1}{t}, \quad y = t - \dfrac{1}{t}$　　　15. $x = \sqrt{2t^2 + 1}, \quad y = (2t + 1)^2$

16. $x = t\sqrt{2t + 5}, \quad y = (4t)^{1/3}$　　　17. $x = \dfrac{t - 1}{t + 1}, \quad y = \dfrac{t + 1}{t - 1}$

18. $x = \dfrac{1}{t^2}$, $\ y = \sqrt{t^2 + 12}$

19. Find d^2y/dx^2 from the parametric equations in Problem 14.

20. Find d^2y/dx^2 from the parametric equations in Problem 17.

21. Given the parametric equations $x = f(t)$, $y = g(t)$. Show that

$$\frac{d^2y}{dx^2} = \frac{\dfrac{dx}{dt}\dfrac{d^2y}{dt^2} - \dfrac{d^2x}{dt^2}\dfrac{dy}{dt}}{(dx/dt)^3}.$$

22. [Franklin: *Treatise on Advanced Calculus* (Wiley, 1940), p. 110.] Let

$$y = F(x), \quad x = f(t); \quad F[f(t)] = g(t).$$

Using a subscript to denote the independent variable, define second differentials as follows:

$$(d^2y)_x = F''(x) \cdot (dx)^2, \ (d^2y)_t = g''(t) \cdot (dt)^2, \ (d^2x)_t = f''(t) \cdot (dt)^2.$$

Then show that

$$(d^2y)_t = (d^2y)_x + F'(x)(d^2x)_t.$$

[*Hint:* By the chain rule, $g'(t) = F'(x)f'(t)$. From this deduce that $g''(t) = F'(x)f''(t) + F''(x)[f'(t)]^2$.]

4-8 . Continuity. Before we take up applications of differentiation (Chapter 5), it is desirable to discuss the *continuity* of a function. We shall see that continuity is even more basic than differentiability.

DEFINITION. *A function f which is defined in some neighborhood of c is said to be* continuous *at c provided*

(a) *the function has a definite finite value $f(c)$ at c, and*

(b) *as x approaches c, $f(x)$ approaches $f(c)$ as limit:*

$$\boxed{\lim_{x \to c} f(x) = f(c).}$$

If a function is continuous at all points of an interval $a \le x \le b$ (or $a < x < b$, etc.), then it is said to be continuous on, or in, that interval.

As an example of a continuous function, let us investigate

$$f(x) = x^2$$

at some fixed value $x = c$. Certainly requirement (a) of the definition is satisfied, since the function has the value

$$f(c) = c^2$$

at $x = c$. Furthermore, the difference

$$f(x) - f(c) = x^2 - c^2 = (x - c)(x + c)$$

approaches zero as a limit when $x - c$ approaches zero, since as $x \to c$ we have

$$\lim [f(x) - f(c)] = \lim (x - c) \lim (x + c)$$
$$= 0 \cdot 2c = 0.$$

Therefore this function, $f(x) = x^2$, is continuous at *any* $x = c$; that is, it is continuous for all x, $-\infty < x < +\infty$.

The graph of a function which is continuous on an interval $a \le x \le b$ consists of an unbroken curve over that interval. This fact is of practical importance in using curves to represent functions. It makes it possible, for example, to sketch a curve by constructing a table of values (x, y), plotting relatively few points from this table, and then sketching a continuous (i.e., unbroken) curve through these points. For example, suppose we carry through the steps discussed for the simple case $y = x^2$.

We first make a short table of values:

x	0	± 0.5	± 1	± 2
y	0	0.25	1	4

then plot these points and draw a continuous curve through them, as shown in Fig. 4–8. Then we might go one step further and use the curve itself to find the value of x^2 corresponding to an x different from those used in making the table of values. For example, in Fig. 4–8, $x = 1.6$ is indicated on the x-scale and the corresponding reading on the y-scale gives $x^2 \approx 2.6$. Of course, the graph probably won't give *exact* values except at those points which have been plotted exactly. But it will give values which are near the exact values, if the calculated points aren't spread too far apart.

In order to appreciate the concept of continuity more fully, it is desirable to have some examples of the opposite behavior which some functions exhibit at certain points, that is, discontinuity. For example, the function $F(t) = 1/t$ is discontinuous at $t = 0$ because it violates both requirements (a) and (b) (see Fig. 4–9). This function has an infinite discontinuity at $t = 0$.

Figure 4–8   Figure 4–9

The function

$$F(t) = \text{greatest integer in } t = [t],$$

on the other hand, is discontinuous at $t = n$ for every integer $n = 0, \pm 1,$ $\pm 2, \ldots,$ but its discontinuities are all finite. This function changes abruptly by unity when t decreases by ever so small an amount from 3 to $3 - \delta$, for example, no matter how small the positive number δ may be. (See Fig. 4–10.)

Figure 4–10   Figure 4–11

An extreme example of a discontinuous function is afforded by the function defined by the rule

$$f(x) = \begin{cases} 0, & \text{when } x \text{ is rational,} \\ 1, & \text{when } x \text{ is irrational.} \end{cases}$$

This function has a perfectly definite value for every x in the interval $0 \leq x \leq 1$. But no matter what c is chosen in this interval, there are points x which are arbitrarily close to c but having functional values $f(x)$ which differ from $f(c)$ by unity. That is, $|f(x) - f(c)|$ is not arbitrarily small for all $x \neq c$ in some small neighborhood of c. This function is discontinuous at all points in the interval $(0, 1)$. Its graph cannot be drawn, but it can be described by saying that it consists of all the-rational points on the x-axis from 0 to 1, with the irrational points all pushed up one unit above the x-axis. (See Fig. 4–11.) Thus it consists of two parallel line segments, each of which is full of holes!

With these examples before us, the question arises as to how, in practice, we can tell whether or not a given function is continuous. When we sketch its graph, should we be sure to sketch a connected, unbroken curve, as for the graph of $y = x^2$, or must we be careful *not* to connect all of the points as, for example, in the case $y = 1/x$, where points in the third quadrant must not be connected with points in the first quadrant?

Since we have studied differentiation, the following theorem, which says that every function which has a derivative at a point is also continuous at that point, enables us to conclude that:

(a) every polynomial
$$f(x) = ax^n + bx^{n-1} + \cdots + px + q$$

is continuous for all x, $-\infty < x < +\infty$, and

(b) every rational function

$$f(x) = \frac{F(x)}{G(x)},$$

$F(x)$ and $G(x)$ being polynomials, is continuous for all x where the denominator, $G(x)$, is not zero.

Thus, for example, the graphs of

$$y = x^3, \qquad y = 2x^2 - x + 3, \qquad y = \frac{x^2 - 1}{x^2 + 1}$$

are continuous, connected curves over the domain $-\infty < x < +\infty$. On the other hand, the graph of

$$y = \frac{x^2 + 1}{x^3 - 4x} \tag{1}$$

goes shooting off toward $\pm\infty$ as x approaches one of the three values

$$x = -2, \qquad x = 0, \qquad x = +2,$$

where the denominator vanishes. But, over the intervals $-\infty < x < -2$,

$-2 < x < 0, 0 < x < 2$, and $2 < x < +\infty$, the graph consists of separate continuous curves, since the denominator does not vanish in any of these intervals. The reader will find it instructive to work out the graph of Eq. (1) for himself on the basis of the discussion above.

Let us now state and prove the theorem we mentioned above.

THEOREM 1. *If the function f has a finite derivative*

$$f'(c) = \lim_{\Delta x \to 0} \frac{f(c + \Delta x) - f(c)}{\Delta x} \qquad (2)$$

at $x = c$, *then f is continuous at* $x = c$.

Proof. For the limit in (2) to exist, it is necessary that $f(c)$ and $f(c + \Delta x)$ both exist, at least for all Δx near zero. We change the notation slightly by writing x in place of $c + \Delta x$. Then

$$x = c + \Delta x$$

is near c when

$$\Delta x = x - c$$

is near zero. Equation (2) now may be written in the form

$$f'(c) = \lim_{x \to c} \frac{f(x) - f(c)}{x - c}.$$

Suppose then that $f'(c)$ exists and is finite. We want to prove that $f(x) - f(c)$ tends to zero as $x \to c$. This follows at once from

$$\lim_{x \to c} [f(x) - f(c)] = \lim_{x \to c} \left[(x - c) \frac{f(x) - f(c)}{x - c} \right]$$

$$= \lim_{x \to c} (\dot{x} - c) \cdot \lim_{x \to c} \frac{f(x) - f(c)}{x - c}$$

$$= 0 \cdot f'(c) = 0. \qquad \text{Q.E.D.}$$

We have just shown that differentiability implies continuity. The converse, however, is not true, as is easily seen by considering the example

$$f(x) = |x|,$$

which is continuous at $x = 0$ but does not possess a derivative at that point.

The fact that $f(x) = |x|$ has no derivative at $x = 0$ follows from the fact that

$$\frac{f(0 + \Delta x) - f(0)}{\Delta x} = \frac{|\Delta x|}{\Delta x}$$

$$= \begin{cases} +1, & \text{when} \quad \Delta x > 0, \\ -1, & \text{when} \quad \Delta x < 0, \end{cases}$$

and

$$\lim_{\Delta x \to 0} \frac{|\Delta x|}{\Delta x} \text{ does not exist.}$$

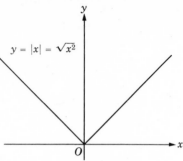

Figure 4–12

Until the middle of the 19th century it was generally believed that a continuous function would at least have a derivative at most places, even though there might be isolated points (as at $x = 0$, in our example) where the derivative did not exist. However, the German mathematicians Riemann (1826–1866) and Weierstrass (1815–1897) gave examples of functions which are continuous but which fail to have derivatives anywhere. For a readable account of this, see *World of Mathematics*, Vol. 3, p. 1963.

The following theorem means that sums, differences, products, and quotients of continuous functions are also continuous on their respective domains. The proof is immediate from the corresponding theorems about limits (Article 3–2).

THEOREM 2. *Suppose f and g are two functions that are continuous at $x = c$. Then the functions F_1, F_2, F_3 defined by*

$$F_1(x) = f(x) + g(x),$$

$$F_2(x) = kf(x), \qquad k \text{ any number,}$$

$$F_3(x) = f(x) \cdot g(x)$$

are also continuous at $x = c$. Furthermore, if $g(c)$ is not zero, then F_4,

$$F_4(x) = \frac{f(x)}{g(x)}$$

is also continuous at $x = c$.

The following theorem is much more difficult to prove because it requires a more penetrating study of the properties of the real number system than we care to make at this time. (The pamphlet *Continuity*, pp. 18–44, contains a proof; as do more advanced books such as Buck, R. C., *Advanced Calculus*, McGraw-Hill Book Co., and Rudin, W., *Principles of Mathematical Analysis*, McGraw-Hill Book Co.)

THEOREM 3. *A function f that is continuous for all x in the closed interval* $a \leq x \leq b$ *has the following properties:*

(i) *It has a minimum value m and a maximum value M; that is, there are numbers α and β in the interval such that $m = f(\alpha)$ and $M = f(\beta)$, and such that for all x in the interval, the condition*

$$m \leq f(x) \leq M$$

is satisfied.

(ii) *If N is any number between $f(a)$ and $f(b)$, then there is at least one number c between a and b such that $f(c) = N$.**

(iii) *Given any positive number ϵ there is a positive number δ (which may depend upon ϵ but does not depend upon x_1 or x_2) such that if x_1 and x_2 belong to the interval $a \leq x \leq b$ and $|x_1 - x_2| < \delta$, then $|f(x_1) - f(x_2)| < \epsilon$.*

Remark. A function that satisfies the condition (iii) above is said to be *uniformly continuous* for $a \leq x \leq b$ and the theorem says that a function that is continuous on a *closed* interval is automatically *uniformly continuous* there. The function $f(x) = 1/x$ is, on the other hand, continuous in the *open* interval $0 < x < 1$, but is not uniformly continuous there.

 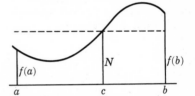

Figure 4–13

The following physical interpretation of continuity may be of some value in throwing more light on the distinction between the notion of "continuous at every point of an interval" on the one hand and "uniformly continuous in an interval" on the other. We recall that a function is continuous at $x = c$ if $f(c)$ exists and $f(x) \to f(c)$ as $x \to c$. This means that if we are challenged with a positive "tolerance limit" ϵ and required to make

$$|f(x) - f(c)| < \epsilon \qquad (3)$$

for *all* x sufficiently close to c, we must produce a positive number δ such that condition (3) is met whenever

$$|x - c| < \delta. \qquad (4)$$

Let us translate this into physical terms.

---

* This is known as the Intermediate Value Theorem.

Suppose we have a pair of dividers (Fig. 4–14) with a meter attached and having the property that when the points of the dividers are set at c and x respectively, the meter registers the numerical value of the difference in the functional values at c and x; that is,

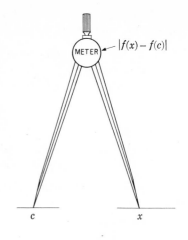

Figure 4–14

the meter reads $|f(x) - f(c)|$ when the points touch x and c.

Suppose now we hold one prong of the dividers at c and move the other prong around near c, either to the left of c or to its right. Suppose that to *each* positive number ϵ we are able to assign a band of width 2δ around c,

$$c - \delta < x < c + \delta,$$

such that whenever the second prong is inside this band the meter reading is less than ϵ. Then the function is, by our definition, continuous at c.

Now the "bandwidth" 2δ will in general depend upon ϵ. That is, the smaller the tolerance limit ϵ that is required, the more narrowly must we restrict the range of x around c. Furthermore, the "bandwidth" 2δ will also, in general, depend upon c. That is, for a given function $f(x)$,

$$\delta = \delta(c, \epsilon)$$

is a function of both c and ϵ. Now if the function $f(x)$ is continuous for all values of x in some domain, then with each x_0 in the domain and with each $\epsilon > 0$ we can associate a positive number $\delta = \delta(x_0, \epsilon)$ such that if x is in the domain and if $|x - x_0| < \delta(x_0, \epsilon)$, then

$$|f(x) - f(x_0)| < \epsilon.$$

Finally, as we vary x_0, it may happen that all of these numbers $\delta(x_0, \epsilon)$ are at least as large as some positive number $k = k(\epsilon)$. Then, given $\epsilon > 0$, we could use a band of constant width $2k$ around *any* x_0 of the domain, and have

$$|f(x) - f(x_0)| < \epsilon$$

whenever x is in the domain and $|x - x_0| < k$. For, the band $x_0 - k < x < x_0 + k$ surely lies inside the band $x_0 - \delta(x_0, \epsilon) < x < x_0 + \delta(x_0, \epsilon)$, since $\delta(x_0, \epsilon) \geq k$. In other words, if the two prongs of the dividers are spread apart any distance smaller than this k and the dividers are then placed so that they touch *any two points* x_1, x_2, in the domain of x, in the circumstances described above it will turn out that the meter reading is less than ϵ. This exemplifies what is meant by *uniform* continuity.

To summarize these remarks we may say that

(a) *ordinary continuity* at a point c means that the bandwidth depends not only upon the tolerance ϵ but also upon c, whereas

(b) *uniform continuity* means that with any positive ϵ we may associate *one* bandwidth that works for *all* points in the domain.

PROBLEMS

1. (a) Prove that the function $f(x) = x^3$ is continuous at $x = c$ for any real c. (b) If $c = 5$, and ϵ is a preassigned positive number, find

$$\delta \text{ such that } |x^3 - 5^3| < \epsilon \qquad \text{when} \qquad |x - 5| < \delta.$$

2. For what values of x is each of the following functions discontinuous?

(a) $f(x) = \dfrac{x}{x + 1}$,

(b) $f(x) = \dfrac{x + 1}{x^2 - 4x + 3}$.

3. Is the function f defined by the rule

$$f(x) = \begin{cases} \dfrac{x^2 - 1}{x - 1}, & \text{when} \quad x \neq 1, \\ 2, & \text{when} \quad x = 1, \end{cases}$$

continuous or discontinuous at $x = 1$? Prove your result.

4. The function $f(x) = |x|$ is continuous at $x = 0$. Given a positive number ϵ, how large may δ be in order that $|f(x) - 0| < \epsilon$ when $|x - 0| < \delta$?

5. What is the maximum of $f(x) = |x|$ for $-1 \leq x \leq 1$? What is the minimum? Sketch.

6. Does the function $f(x) = x^2$ have a maximum for $0 < x < 1$? Does it have a minimum? Give reasons for your answers.

7. A continuous function $y = f(x)$ is known to be negative at $x = 0$ and positive at $x = 1$. Why is it true that the equation $f(x) = 0$ has at least one root between $x = 0$ and $x = 1$? Illustrate with a sketch.

8. Is the function $f(x) = \sqrt[3]{x}$ continuous at $x = 0$? Is it differentiable there? Give reasons for your answers.

9. *Prove the following theorem.* Let f be continuous and positive at $x = c$. Prove that there is some interval around $x = c$, say $c - \delta < x < c + \delta$, throughout which $f(x)$ remains positive. [*Hint:* In the definition of continuity, Eqs. (3) and (4), take $\epsilon = \frac{1}{2}f(c)$.] Illustrate with a sketch.

10. For $x \neq 2$, the function $f(x)$ is equal to $(x^2 + 3x - 10)/(x - 2)$. What value should be assigned to $f(2)$ to make $f(x)$ continuous at $x = 2$?

REVIEW QUESTIONS AND EXERCISES FOR CHAPTER 4

1. Using the definition of the derivative, deduce the formula for the derivative of a product uv of two differentiable functions.

2. In the formula for the derivative of uv, let $v = u$, and thereby deduce a formula for the derivative of u^2. Repeat the process, with $v = u^2$, and get a formula for the derivative of u^3. Extend the result, by the method of mathematical induction, to deduce the formula for the derivative of u^n for every positive integer n.

3. Explain how the three formulas

$$\text{(a)} \quad \frac{d(x^n)}{dx} = nx^{n-1}, \qquad \text{(b)} \quad \frac{d(cu)}{dx} = c\,\frac{du}{dx}, \qquad \text{(c)} \quad \frac{d(u+v)}{dx} = \frac{du}{dx} + \frac{dv}{dx}$$

are sufficient to differentiate any polynomial.

4. What formula do we need, in addition to the three listed in Problem 3 above, in order to differentiate rational functions?

5. Does the derivative of a polynomial function exist at every point of its domain? What is the largest domain the function can have? Does the derivative of a rational function exist at every point in its domain? What real numbers, if any, must be excluded from the domain of a rational function?

6. *Definition of algebraic function.* Let $y = f(x)$ define a function of x such that every pair of numbers (x, y) belonging to f satisfy an irreducible equation of the form

$$P_0(x)y^n + P_1(x)y^{n-1} + \cdots + P_{n-1}(x)y + P_n(x) = 0 \qquad (\alpha)$$

for some positive integer n, with coefficients $P_0(x), \ldots, P_n(x)$ polynomials in x, and $P_0(x)$ not identically zero. Then f is said to be an *algebraic function*. What technique of this chapter can be used to find the derivative of an algebraic function if the polynomial coefficients $P_0(x), \ldots, P_n(x)$ in its defining equation (α) are given?

7. Show that the function f defined by $f(x) = x^{2/3}$ is an algebraic function by finding an appropriate equation of the type (α) in the definition in Problem 6 above. On what domain of values of x is this function defined? Where is it continuous? Where is it differentiable?

8. Show that every rational function is algebraic. Do you think the converse is also true? Explain.

9. It can be shown (though not very easily) that sums, quotients, products, powers, and roots of algebraic functions are algebraic functions. Thus

$$f(x) = x\sqrt{3x^2 + 1} + 5x^{4/3}/(3x + 2), \qquad x \neq -\tfrac{2}{3},$$

defines an algebraic function. Find its derivative. What formulas of this chapter are used in finding derivatives of functions like this one?

10. Show that $y = |x|$ satisfies the equation $y^2 - x^2 = 0$. Is the absolute value function algebraic? What is its derivative? Where does the derivative exist? Where is the absolute value function continuous?

11. Define differentials. If $y = f(x)$ defines a differentiable function, how are dy and dx related? Give geometrical interpretations of dx and dy.

12. State the chain rule for derivatives. Prove it, with the book closed.

13. Show how the chain rule is used to prove that the derivative of y with respect to x is the ratio of dy to dx when x and y are both differentiable functions of t, and $dx \neq 0$.

14. Give an example of a function that is defined and bounded on $0 \leq t \leq 1$, continuous in the open interval $0 < t < 1$, and discontinuous at $t = 0$.

15. State and prove a theorem about the relationship between continuity and differentiability of a function, at a point in its domain.

16. Read the article "The Lever of Mahomet," by R. Courant and H. Robbins, and the accompanying "Commentary on Continuity," by J. R. Newman, in *World of Mathematics*, Vol. 4, pp. 2410–2413.

MISCELLANEOUS PROBLEMS FOR CHAPTER 4

Find dy/dx in each of the following problems (1 through 33).

1. $y = \dfrac{x}{\sqrt{x^2 - 4}}$

2. $x^2 + xy + y^2 - 5x = 2$

3. $xy + y^2 = 1$

4. $x^3 + 4xy - 3y^3 = 2$

5. $x^2 y + xy^2 = 6$

6. $y = (x + 1)^2 (x^2 + 2x)^{-2}$

7. $y = \dfrac{x}{\sqrt{1 - x^2}}$

8. $x^2 + 3xy^2 + y^3 = 2$

9. $y = \dfrac{x}{x + 1}$

10. $y = \sqrt{2x + 1}$

11. $y = x^2 \sqrt{x^2 - a^2}$

12. $y = \dfrac{2x + 1}{2x - 1}$

13. $y = \dfrac{x^2}{1 - x^2}$

14. $y = (x^2 + x + 1)^3$

15. $y = \dfrac{1}{\sqrt{x^2 + x - 1}}$

16. $y = \dfrac{x^3 - 1}{x - 1}$

17. $y = \dfrac{(2x^2 + 5x)^{3/2}}{3}$

18. $y = \dfrac{3}{(2x^2 + 5x)^{3/2}}$

19. $xy^2 + \sqrt{xy} = 2$

20. $x^2 + y^2 = xy$

21. $x^{2/3} + y^{2/3} = a^{2/3}$

22. $x^{1/2} + y^{1/2} = a^{1/2}$

23. $xy = 1$

24. $\sqrt{xy} = 1$

25. $(x + 2y)^2 + 2xy^2 = 6$

26. $y = \sqrt{\dfrac{1 - x}{1 + x^2}}$

27. $y^2 = \dfrac{x}{x + 1}$

28. $x^2 y + xy^2 = 6(x^2 + y^2)$

29. $xy + 2x + 3y = 1$

30. $y = u^2 - 1, x = u^2 + 1$

31. $y = \sqrt{2t + t^2}, t = 2x + 3$

32. $x = \dfrac{t}{1 + t^2}, y = 1 + t^2$

33. $t = \dfrac{x}{1 + x^2}, y = x^2 + t^2$

34. Find the slope of $y = x/(x^2 + 1)$ at the origin. Write the equation of the tangent line at the origin.

35. Write the equation of the tangent to the curve $x^2 - 2xy + y^2 + 2x + y - 6 = 0$ at $(2, 2)$.

36. Determine the constant c such that the straight line joining the points $(0, 3)$ and $(5, -2)$ is tangent to the curve $y = c/(x + 1)$.

37. What is the slope of the curve $y = 2x^2 - 6x + 3$ at the point on the curve where $x = 2$? What is the equation of the tangent line to the curve at this point?

38. Find the points on the curve $y = 2x^3 - 3x^2 - 12x + 20$ where the tangent is parallel to the x-axis.

39. Find the derivatives of the following functions:

(a) $y = (x^2 + 2x)^5$;   (b) $f(t) = \sqrt{3t^2 - 2t}$;

(c) $f(r) = \sqrt{r^2 + 5} + \sqrt{r^2 - 5}$;   (d) $f(x) = \dfrac{x^2 - 1}{x^2 + 1}$.

40. Find the equation of the tangent to the curve $y = 2/\sqrt{x} - 1$ at the point on the curve where $x = 10$.

41. Write the equation of the straight line passing through the point $(1, 2)$ and normal to the curve $x^2 = 4y$.

42. Use the definition of the derivative to find dy/dx for $y = \sqrt{2x + 3}$ and then check the result by finding the same derivative by the power formula.

43. Find the value of

$$\lim_{\Delta x \to 0} \frac{[2 - 3(x + \Delta x)]^2 - [2 - 3x]^2}{\Delta x}$$

and specify the function $f(x)$ of which this is the derivative.

44. Find the slope of the curve $x^2 y + xy^2 = 6$ at the point $(1, 2)$.

45. A cylindrical can of height 6 (in.) and radius r (in.) has volume $V = 6\pi r^2$ (in³). What is the difference between ΔV and its principal part as r varies? What is the geometric significance of the principal part?

46. If a hemispherical bowl of radius 10 in. is filled with water to a depth of x in., the volume of water is given by $v = \pi[10 - (x/3)]x^2$. Find the rate of increase of the volume per inch increase of the depth.

47. A bus will hold 60 people. If the number x of persons per trip who use the bus is related to the fare charged (p nickels), by the law $p = [3 - (x/40)]^2$, write the function expressing the total revenue per trip received by the bus company. What is the number x_1 of people per trip that will make the marginal revenue equal to zero? What is the corresponding fare?

48. Prove Eq. (2), Article 4–2, by mathematical induction.

49. Given $y = x - x^2$, find the rate of change of y^2 with respect to x^2 (expressed in terms of x).

50. If $x = 3t + 1$ and $y = t^2 + t$, find dy/dt, dx/dt, and dy/dx. Eliminate t to obtain y as a function of x, and then determine dy/dx directly. Do the results check?

51. A particle projected vertically upward with a speed of a ft/sec reaches an elevation $s = at - 16t^2$ ft at the end of t sec. What must the initial velocity be in order for the particle to travel 49 ft upward before it starts coming back down?

52. Find the rate of change of $\sqrt{x^2 + 16}$ with respect to $x/(x - 1)$ at $x = 3$.

53. The circle $(x - h)^2 + (y - k)^2 = r^2$, center at (h, k), radius $= r$, is tangent to the curve $y = x^2 + 1$ at the point $(1, 2)$. (a) Find the locus of the point (h, k). (b) If, also, the circle and the curve have the same second derivative at $(1, 2)$, find h, k, and r. Sketch the curve and the circle.

54. If $y = x^2 + 1$ and $u = \sqrt{x^2 + 1}$, find dy/du.

55. If $x = y^2 + y$ and $u = (x^2 + x)^{3/2}$, find dy/du.

56. If $f'(x) = \sqrt{3x^2 - 1}$ and $y = f(x^2)$, find dy/dx.

57. If $f'(x) = \sin(x^2)$ and $y = f\left(\dfrac{2x - 1}{x + 1}\right)$, find $\dfrac{dy}{dx}$.

58. Find $y' = dy/dx$ and $y'' = dy'/dx$ if $y = x^2 - 3x + 5$.

59. If s represents the distance a body moves in time t, determine the acceleration $a = d^2s/dt^2$ if $s = 250 + 40t - 16t^2$.

60. If $y = x\sqrt{2x - 3}$, find d^2y/dx^2.

61. Find the value of d^2y/dx^2 in the equation $y^3 + y = x$ at the point $(2, 1)$.

62. If $x = t - t^2$, $y = t - t^3$, find the values of dy/dx and d^2y/dx^2 at $t = 1$.

63. Prove Leibniz's rule:

(a) $\dfrac{d^2(uv)}{dx^2} = \dfrac{d^2u}{dx^2} \cdot v + 2\,\dfrac{du}{dx}\dfrac{dv}{dx} + u\,\dfrac{d^2v}{dx^2}$,

(b) $\dfrac{d^3(uv)}{dx^3} = \dfrac{d^3u}{dx^3} \cdot v + 3\,\dfrac{d^2u}{dx^2}\dfrac{dv}{dx} + 3\,\dfrac{du}{dx}\dfrac{d^2v}{dx^2} + u\,\dfrac{d^3v}{dx^3}$,

(c) $\dfrac{d^n(uv)}{dx^n} = \dfrac{d^nu}{dx^n} \cdot v + n\,\dfrac{d^{n-1}u}{dx^{n-1}}\dfrac{dv}{dx} + \cdots$

$\qquad + \dfrac{n(n - 1) \cdots (n - k + 1)}{k!}\,\dfrac{d^{n-k}u}{dx^{n-k}}\dfrac{d^kv}{dx^k} + \cdots + u\,\dfrac{d^nv}{dx^n}$.

The terms on the right side of this equation may be obtained from the terms in the binomial expansion $(a + b)^n$ by replacing $a^{n-k}b^k$ by $(d^{n-k}u/dx^{n-k}) \cdot (d^kv/dx^k)$ for $k = 0, 1, 2, \ldots, n$, and interpreting d^0u/dx^0 as being u itself.

64. Find d^3y/dx^3 in each of the following cases:

(a) $y = \sqrt{2x - 1}$;   (b) $y = \dfrac{1}{3x + 2}$;   (c) $y = ax^3 + bx^2 + cx + d$.

65. If $f(x) = (x - a)^n g(x)$, where $g(x)$ is a polynomial and $g(a) \neq 0$, show that $f(a) = 0 = f'(a) = \cdots = f^{(n-1)}(a)$; but $f^{(n)}(a) = n!g(a) \neq 0$.

66. If $y = 2x^2 - 3x + 5$, find Δy for $x = 3$ and $\Delta x = 0.1$. Approximate Δy by finding its principal part.

67. Find an approximate value of $\sqrt{26}$ by considering the function $y = \sqrt{x}$ when $x = 25$ and $\Delta x = 1$. Also find an approximate value of $\sqrt[3]{26}$. (Specify the function used for the purpose and the values of x and Δx.)

68. By means of differentials, find an approximate value of $\sqrt[10]{0.999}$.

69. To compute the height h of a lamppost, the length a of the shadow of a six-foot pole is measured. The pole is 20 ft from the lamppost. If $a = 15$ ft, with a possible error of less than one inch, find the height of the lamppost and estimate the error in height.

70. Find the differential dy in each of the following cases:

(a) $y = x^2/(1 + x)$;   (b) $x^2 - y^2 = 1$;   (c) $xy + y^2 = 1$.

71. Given a function f satisfying the following two conditions for all x and y:

(a) $f(x + y) = f(x) \cdot f(y)$;   (b) $f(x) = 1 + xg(x)$, where $\lim\limits_{x \to 0} g(x) = 1$.

Prove that (a) the derivative $f'(x)$ exists, (b) $f'(x) = f(x)$.

72. Let $f(x) = x^2 + 1$. Given $\epsilon > 0$, find $\delta > 0$ such that $|f(x_1) - f(x_2)| < \epsilon$ whenever $|x_1 - x_2| < \delta$ and x_1, x_2 both lie in the closed interval $-2 \leq x \leq 2$. State precisely what this means concerning the continuity of this function.

73. Given a function $f(x)$, defined for all real x, and a positive constant c such that $|f(x + h) - f(x)| \leq ch^2$ for all real h. Prove that (a) $f(x)$ is uniformly continuous, (b) $f'(x) = 0$ for all x.

74. A function $f(x)$ is said to satisfy a Lipschitz condition of order m on the closed interval $a \leq x \leq b$ if there is a constant C such that

$$|f(x_2) - f(x_1)| \leq C|x_2 - x_1|^m$$

for all values of x_1, x_2 on $[a, b]$. Prove that a function which satisfies a Lipschitz condition of order $m > 0$ on $[a, b]$ is uniformly continuous there.

75. Suppose $[a, b]$ is the interval $[-1, 1]$ and $f(x) = \sqrt{1 - x^2}$. Find appropriate values of C and of m to satisfy the conditions in Problem 74. [*Hint:* Show that if $y_2 > y_1 > 0$ and $y_2 - y_1 = h$, then $|\sqrt{y_2} - \sqrt{y_1}| \leq \sqrt{h}$.]

Applications

5-1   Sign of the first derivative. Application to curve sketching.   We
have previously illustrated the use of the slope of a curve to gain information beyond that given by the table of (x, y) values.   We wish now to
consider how just the sign of the de-
rivative at a point gives information
about the curve.   Figure 5–1 shows a
curve $y = f(x)$ on which we have indicated certain points $A, B, C, D,$ and E.
At A we say that y is an increasing
function of x, by which we mean that
the function values increase as x increases.   At such a point the slope of
the tangent to the curve, dy/dx, is
positive.   The same applies at E, while

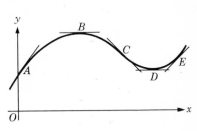

Figure 5–1

at C we say the function f is a decreasing function of x and this will be indicated by a negative value of dy/dx at C.   At B and D the slope is zero.

We apply these ideas to the problem of sketching the curve:

$$y = \tfrac{1}{3}x^3 - 2x^2 + 3x + 2.$$

The slope at (x, y) is

$$\frac{dy}{dx} = x^2 - 4x + 3 = (x - 1)(x - 3).$$

To determine where dy/dx is positive and where it is negative, we first
determine where it is zero:

$$\frac{dy}{dx} = 0 \qquad \text{when} \qquad x = 1 \quad \text{or} \quad x = 3,$$

since these points will mark the transition from positive to negative or
from negative to positive slopes.   The sign of dy/dx depends upon the
signs of both factors $(x - 1)$ and $(x - 3)$, and since the sign of $(x - 1)$
is negative when x is to the left of 1 and positive to the right, we have the
pattern of signs indicated in Fig. 5–2(a).   Similarly, the sign of $(x - 3)$
is a shown in Fig. 5–2(b), the sign of $dy/dx = (x - 1)(x - 3)$ as shown
in Fig. 5–2(c).   We can get a rough idea of the shape of the curve
just from this pattern of signs of its slope, if we sketch a curve which is

161

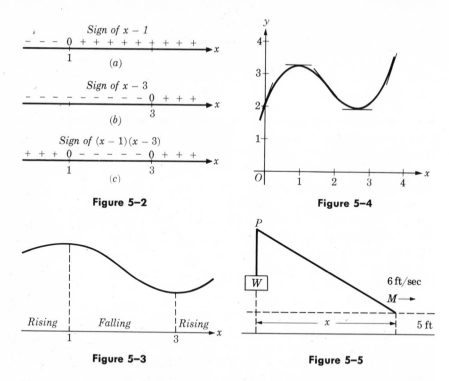

Figure 5-2

Figure 5-4

Figure 5-3

Figure 5-5

rising, falling, and rising again for $x < 1$, $1 < x < 3$, and $x > 3$, respectively (Fig. 5-3).

To get a more accurate curve, we would construct a table for some range of values extending, say, from $x = 0$ to $x = 4$, which includes the transition points between rising and falling portions of the curve (Fig. 5-4).

The terms "rising" and "falling," or "increasing" and "decreasing" are always taken to apply to the behavior of the curve as the point that is tracing it moves from left to right or, in other words, relative to its behavior as x increases.

The same concepts apply to functions that vary with time. For example, Fig. 5-5 represents a rope running through a pulley at P, bearing a weight W at one end. The other end is held in a man's hand M at a distance of 5 feet above the ground as he walks in a straight line at the rate of 6 ft/sec. If, as in the figure, x represents the distance in feet of the man's hand away from the vertical line $\overleftrightarrow{PW}$, then x is an increasing function of t and we are given the rate at which it changes with t, namely, 6 ft/sec. This would be stated in mathematical terms by saying $dx/dt = +6$ (ft/sec). On the other hand, if the man were to walk toward the line $\overleftrightarrow{PW}$ at the rate of 6 ft/sec, we would have $dx/dt = -6$ (ft/sec), because x would then be a decreasing function of t.

PROBLEMS

In each of the following exercises, determine dy/dx and find the sets of values of x where the graph of y versus x is rising (to the right) and where it is falling. Sketch each curve, showing in particular the points of transition between falling and rising portions of the curve.

1. $y = x^2 - x + 1$

2. $y = \dfrac{x^3}{3} - \dfrac{x^2}{2} - 2x + \dfrac{1}{3}$

3. $y = 2x^3 - 3x^2 + 3$

4. $y = x^3 - 27x + 36$

5. $y = x^4 - 8x^2 + 16$

5-2 Related rates. In the example at the end of Article 5-1, suppose that the pulley is 25 ft above the ground, the rope is 45 ft long, and at a given instant the distance x is 15 ft and the man is walking away from the pulley. How fast is the weight being raised at this particular instant?

In Fig. 5-6, M represents the man's hand, P the pulley, W the weight, and $\overleftrightarrow{OM}$ is a horizontal line at the level of the man's hand which is 5 ft above the ground, so that P is 20 ft above O. The figure is drawn to illustrate the situation at any time t and *not just at* the instant in question. The reason for this is that certain of the distances, namely, x, y, z, and h in the illustration, are quantities which vary and it is important to treat them as such and not as constants.

Having drawn a figure to illustrate the relationship between the various variable quantities involved in the problem, let us now state what is given and what the problem asks for in terms of these variables.

Given: (a) Relationships between the variables which are to hold for all instants of time:

$$y + z = 45,$$

$$h + y = 20,$$

$$20^2 + x^2 = z^2.$$

Figure 5-6

(b) At a given instant, which we may take to be $t = 0$:

$$x = 15, \qquad \frac{dx}{dt} = 6.$$

To find: $dh/dt = (?)$ at the given instant $t = 0$.

Such a problem involving rates of related variables is called "a problem in related rates." It is typical of such problems that

(a) certain variables are related in a definite way for all values of t under consideration,

(b) the values of some or all of these variables and the rates of change of some of them are given at some particular instant, and

(c) it is required to find the rate of change of one or more of them at this instant.

The variables may then all be considered to be functions of time, and if the equations which relate them for all values of t are differentiated with respect to t, the new equations so obtained will tell how their rates of change are related. From this information it should be possible to answer the question posed by the problem.

In our problem, we shall modify the procedure outlined above by first obtaining a single equation relating the variable x (whose rate is given) and the variable h (whose rate is wanted) before we take derivatives. Using the equations given, we find successively:

$$z = 45 - y, \qquad y = 20 - h,$$
$$z = 45 - (20 - h) = (25 + h),$$
$$20^2 + x^2 = z^2 = (25 + h)^2,$$

that is,

$$20^2 + x^2 = (25 + h)^2.$$

This last equation relates the variables x and h for all values of t under consideration (namely, in an interval of values of t near $t = 0$). Both sides of this equation are functions of t, and the equality says they represent the same function of t. Thus when we differentiate both sides of the equation with respect to t, we will have another equation:

$$\frac{d}{dt}(20^2 + x^2) = \frac{d}{dt}(25 + h)^2,$$

$$0 + 2x\frac{dx}{dt} = 2(25 + h)\frac{dh}{dt}.$$

This may be solved for the rate we want, namely,

$$\frac{dh}{dt} = \frac{x}{25 + h}\frac{dx}{dt}.$$

Now at the given instant, we have

$$x = 15, \qquad \frac{dx}{dt} = 6,$$

and we find h at this instant from the equation

$$20^2 + 15^2 = (25 + h)^2, \qquad 25 + h = 25.$$

When we substitute these values, we obtain

$$\frac{dh}{dt} = \frac{18}{5} = 3\tfrac{3}{5} \text{ (ft/sec)}$$

Figure 5–7

as the rate at which the weight is being raised at the instant in question.

As a second example, consider a ladder 26 ft long which leans against a vertical wall. At a particular instant, the foot of the ladder is 10 ft out from the base of the wall and is being drawn away from the wall at the rate of 4 ft/sec. How fast is the top of the ladder moving down the wall at this instant? Figure 5–7 represents the position of the ladder, with the distance from the base of the wall to the foot of the ladder labeled x to indicate the fact that it is a variable, and the distance from the ground to the top of the ladder labeled y because it varies also. The statement of the problem may then be translated into mathematical terms as follows:

Given: $x^2 + y^2 = 26^2$.

To find: $\dfrac{dy}{dt} = (?)$

when

$$x = 10 \text{ (ft)} \qquad \text{and} \qquad \frac{dx}{dt} = 4 \text{ (ft/sec)}.$$

We differentiate the given equation implicitly with respect to t and get

$$2x\frac{dx}{dt} + 2y\frac{dy}{dt} = 0.$$

Hence

$$\frac{dy}{dt} = \frac{-x}{y}\frac{dx}{dt}.$$

When $x = 10$, $y = 24$, $dx/dt = 4$, this leads to $dy/dt = -\tfrac{5}{3}$. That is, y is *decreasing* (the top of the ladder is moving *down*) at the rate of $\tfrac{5}{3}$ ft/sec.

As a final example, consider the conical reservoir, Fig. 5–8, into which water runs at the constant rate of 2 ft³ per minute. How fast is the water level rising when it is 6 ft deep?

First, we must translate the problem into mathematical terms. To do this, we let

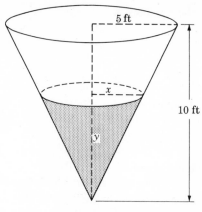

Figure 5-8

v = volume (ft^3) of water in the tank at time t (min),

x = radius (ft) of the section of the cone at the water line,

y = depth (ft) of water in the tank at time t.

Then, the statement that water runs into the tank at the rate of 2 ft^3/min becomes

$$\frac{dv}{dt} = 2.$$

The question we are to answer is

$$\frac{dy}{dt} = (?) \quad \text{when} \quad y = 6.$$

The relationship between the volume of water v and depth y is expressed by the equation

$$v = \tfrac{1}{3}\pi x^2 y.$$

But this involves the additional variable x as well as v and y. However, we may eliminate x since, by similar triangles, we have

$$\frac{x}{y} = \frac{5}{10} \quad \text{or} \quad x = \tfrac{1}{2}y.$$

Therefore

$$v = \tfrac{1}{12}\pi y^3,$$

and when we differentiate this with respect to t, we have

$$\frac{dv}{dt} = \frac{1}{4}\pi y^2 \frac{dy}{dt}.$$

Hence

$$\frac{dy}{dt} = \frac{4\,dv/dt}{\pi y^2},$$

and when

$$\frac{dv}{dt} = 2 \quad \text{and} \quad y = 6,$$

this gives

$$\frac{dy}{dt} = \frac{2}{9\pi} \approx 0.071 \text{ (ft/min)}.$$

PROBLEMS

1. Let A be the area of a circle of radius r. How is dA/dt related to dr/dt?

2. Let V be the volume of a sphere of radius r. How is dV/dt related to dr/dt?

3. Sand falls onto a conical pile at the rate of 10 ft^3/min. The radius of the base of the pile is always equal to one-half of its altitude. How fast is the altitude of the pile increasing when it is 5 ft deep?

4. Suppose that a raindrop is a perfect sphere. Assume that, through condensation, the raindrop accumulates moisture at a rate proportional to its surface area. Show that the radius increases at a constant rate.

5. Point A moves along the x-axis at the constant rate of a ft/sec while point B moves along the y-axis at the constant rate of b ft/sec. Find how fast the distance between them is changing when A is at the point $(x, 0)$ and B is at the point $(0, y)$.

6. A spherical balloon is inflated with gas at the rate of 100 ft^3/min. Assuming that the gas pressure remains constant, how fast is the radius of the balloon increasing at the instant when the radius is 3 ft?

7. A boat is pulled in to a dock by means of a rope with one end attached to the bow of the boat, the other end passing through a ring attached to the dock at a point 4 ft higher than the bow of the boat. If the rope is pulled in at the rate of 2 ft/sec, how fast is the boat approaching the dock when 10 ft of rope are out?

8. A balloon is 200 ft off the ground and rising vertically at the constant rate of 15 ft/sec. An automobile passes beneath it traveling along a straight road at the constant rate of 45 mi/hr = 66 ft/sec. How fast is the distance between them changing one second later?

9. Water is withdrawn from a conical reservoir 8 ft in diameter and 10 ft deep (vertex down) at the constant rate of 5 ft^3/min. How fast is the water level falling when the depth of water in the reservoir is 6 ft?

10. A particle moves around the circle $x^2 + y^2 = 1$ with an x-velocity component $dx/dt = y$. Find dy/dt. Does the particle travel in the clockwise or counterclockwise direction around the circle?

11. A man 6 ft tall walks at the rate of 5 ft/sec toward a street light that is 16 ft above the ground. At what rate is the tip of his shadow moving? At what rate is the length of his shadow changing when he is 10 ft from the base of the light?

12. When air expands adiabatically, the pressure p and volume v satisfy the relationship $pv^{1.4} = $ constant. At a certain instant the pressure is 50 lb/in^2

and the volume is 32 in^3 and is decreasing at the rate of 4 in^3/sec. How rapidly is the pressure changing at this instant?

13. A light is at the top of a pole 50 ft high. A ball is dropped from the same height from a point 30 ft away from the light. How fast is the shadow of the ball moving along the ground $\frac{1}{2}$ sec later? (Assume the ball falls a distance $s = 16t^2$ ft in t seconds.)

14. A boy flies a kite at a height of 300 ft, the wind carrying the kite horizontally away from the boy at a rate of 25 ft/sec. How fast must the boy pay out the string when the kite is 500 ft away from him?

15. A spherical iron ball 8 in. in diameter is coated with a layer of ice of uniform thickness. If the ice melts at the rate of 10 in^3 per minute, how fast is the thickness of the ice decreasing when it is 2 in. thick? How fast is the outer surface area of ice decreasing?

16. Two ships A and B are sailing away from the point O along routes such that the angle $AOB = 120°$. How fast is the distance between them changing if, at a certain instant $|OA| = 8$ mi, $|OB| = 6$ mi, ship A is sailing at the rate of 20 mi/hr, and ship B at the rate of 30 mi/hr? [*Hint:* Use the law of cosines.]

5–3 Significance of the sign of the second derivative. We have already seen how we may use the information given by dy/dx about the slope of the tangent to a curve to help in sketching it. We recall that in an interval where dy/dx is positive, the curve is rising to the right, while if dy/dx is negative the curve is falling to the right. Also it is evident that the regions of rise and fall are usually separated by high or low points where dy/dx is zero and the tangent is horizontal. However, it is possible for dy/dx to be zero at points which are neither high nor low points of the curve.

For example, if
$$y = (x - 2)^3 + 1,$$
then
$$\frac{dy}{dx} = 3(x - 2)^2;$$
and although
$$\frac{dy}{dx} = 0 \quad \text{at} \quad x = 2,$$

for all values of x other than 2, the slope is positive and y is an increasing function of x (Fig. 5–9).

The regions of rise and fall may also be separated by points where the derivative fails to exist.

For example, if $y = x^{2/3}$, then
$$\frac{dy}{dx} = \frac{2}{3}x^{-1/3} = \frac{2}{3\sqrt[3]{x}}$$

is positive when x is positive, and negative when x is negative. At the transition

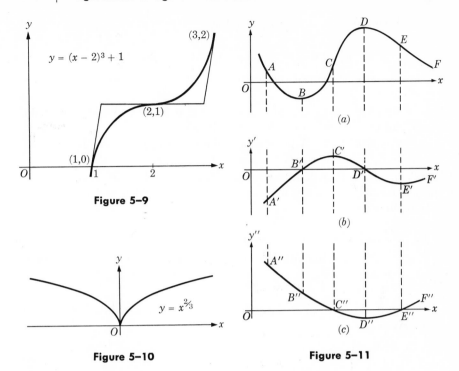

Figure 5–9

Figure 5–10

Figure 5–11

point $x = 0$, dy/dx does not exist, but $dx/dy = \frac{3}{2}x^{1/3}$ is zero, which means that the tangent to the curve at $(0,0)$ is vertical instead of horizontal (Fig. 5–10).

Next we shall see that the sign of the second derivative tells whether the graph of $y = f(x)$ is concave upward (y'' positive) or downward (y'' negative).

Consider, for example, the curve in Fig. 5–11(a). The first and second derivatives are represented by the curves in Fig. 5–11 (b) and (c). The arc ABC of the y-curve is concave upward; CDE is concave downward; EF is again concave upward. To focus attention, let us consider a section near A on arc ABC. Here y' is negative and the y-curve slopes downward to the right. But as we travel through A, moving from left to right, we find the slope becomes less negative. That is, y' is an *increasing* function of x. Therefore the y'-curve slopes upward at A'. Hence its slope (that is, y'') is positive there. The same kind of argument applies at all points along the arc ABC; namely, y' is an increasing function of x, so its derivative (that is, y'') is positive. This is indicated by drawing the arc $A''B''C''$ of the y''-curve above the x-axis.

Similarly, where the y-curve is concave downward (along CDE), the y'-curve is falling, so its slope (that is, y'') is negative.

The direction of concavity is, therefore,

upward if the second derivative is *positive,*

downward if the second derivative is *negative.*

In the first case we could also say the curve is cupped so as to "hold water"; in the second case it would "spill water."

Points of inflection. A point where the curve changes the direction of its concavity from downward to upward or vice versa is called a *point of inflection.* Inflection points occur at C and E in Fig. 5–11(a), and are characterized by a change in the sign of d^2y/dx^2. Such a change of sign may occur where

(a) $d^2y/dx^2 = 0$, or

(b) d^2y/dx^2 fails to exist (for example, it may become infinite at such a point).

In Fig. 5–11, case (a) is shown. Case (b) is shown in Fig. 5–12, where the curve is

$$y = x^{1/3},$$

from which we find

$$y' = \tfrac{1}{3}x^{-(2/3)},$$

$$y'' = -\tfrac{2}{9}x^{-(5/3)},$$

so that both y' and y'' become infinite when x approaches zero. On the other hand,

$$y' = \frac{1}{3x^{2/3}} = \frac{1}{3y^2}$$

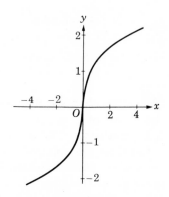

Figure 5–12

is always positive for both positive and negative values of x, so the curve is always rising and has a vertical tangent at $(0, 0)$. Also,

$$y'' = -\frac{2}{9}\left(\frac{1}{\sqrt[3]{x}}\right)^5 = \frac{-2}{9y^5}$$

is positive (the curve "holds water") when x is negative, and is negative (the curve "spills water") when x is positive, so that $(0, 0)$ is a point of inflection.

The example just given would have been much simpler to discuss if we had written the equation in the form $x = y^3$, and then

$$\frac{dx}{dy} = 3y^2, \qquad \frac{d^2x}{dy^2} = 6y,$$

so that we have

$$\frac{dx}{dy} = 0 \quad \text{and} \quad \frac{d^2x}{dy^2} = 0$$

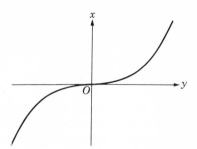

Figure 5–13

at $(0, 0)$. It is clear that dx/dy is positive for all y different from zero and d^2x/dy^2 has the same sign as y and therefore changes its sign at $y = 0$. If we interchange the x- and y-axes so as to take the x-axis to be vertical and the y-axis to be horizontal, the curve will be shown in Fig. 5–13.

5–4 Curve plotting. The discussion in Article 5–3 may be summarized and stated in the following outline of procedure to apply in sketching the graph of an equation $y = f(x)$.

A. Calculate dy/dx and d^2y/dx^2.

B. Find the values of x for which dy/dx is positive and for which it is negative. Calculate y and d^2y/dx^2 at the points of transition between positive and negative values of dy/dx. These may give maximum or minimum points on the curve. (See Figs. 5–4, 5–10, and 5–11a.)

C. Find the values of x for which d^2y/dx^2 is positive and for which it is negative. Calculate y and dy/dx at the points of transition between positive and negative values of d^2y/dx^2. These may give points of inflection of the curve. (See Figs. 5–11 and 5–12.)

D. Plot a few additional points. In particular, points which lie between the transition points already determined or points which lie to the left and to the right of all of them will ordinarily be useful. The nature of the curve for large values of $|x|$ should also be indicated.

E. Sketch a smooth curve through the points found above, unless there are discontinuities in the curve or its slope. Have the curve pass through its points rising or falling as indicated by the sign of dy/dx, and concave upward or downward as indicated by the sign of d^2y/dx^2.

We shall now apply this technique to a few examples.

EXAMPLE 1. (Fig. 5–14b)

$$y = \frac{1}{6}(x^3 - 6x^2 + 9x + 6).$$

Solution. $\qquad \dfrac{dy}{dx} = \dfrac{1}{6}(3x^2 - 12x + 9) = \dfrac{1}{2}(x^2 - 4x + 3),$

$$\frac{d^2y}{dx^2} = \frac{1}{2}(2x - 4) = x - 2.$$

In the factored form,

$$\frac{dy}{dx} = \frac{1}{2}(x - 1)(x - 3),$$

and the two factors change their signs at $x = 1$ and $x = 3$. (See Fig. 5–14a).

It is readily seen that $d^2y/dx^2 = x - 2$ is negative to the left of $x = 2$ and is positive to the right of $x = 2$, so that an inflection point occurs at $x = 2$. A fairly good sketch of the curve can now be made by using the information in the following table.

x	y	y'	y''	Remarks
-1	$-\frac{5}{3}$	$+$	$-$	Rising; concave down
0	1	$+\frac{3}{2}$	$-$	Rising; concave down
1	$\frac{5}{3}$	0	$-$	"Spills water"; max.
2	$\frac{4}{3}$	$-\frac{1}{2}$	0	Falling; point of inflection
3	1	0	$+$	"Holds water"; min.
4	$\frac{5}{3}$	$+\frac{3}{2}$	$+$	Rising; concave up

(a)

(b)

Figure 5–14

EXAMPLE 2. (Fig. 5–15b)

$$y = x + \frac{1}{x} = x + x^{-1}.$$

Solution.
$$\frac{dy}{dx} = 1 - x^{-2} = 1 - \frac{1}{x^2} = \frac{x^2 - 1}{x^2},$$

$$\frac{d^2y}{dx^2} = 2x^{-3} = \frac{2}{x^3}.$$

The sign of dy/dx will be the same as the sign of $x^2 - 1 = (x - 1)(x + 1)$. (See Fig. 5–15a.) But when x is near zero, $|y|$ will be large and y, dy/dx, d^2y/dx^2 all become infinite as x approaches zero. This curve is discontinuous at $x = 0$.

(a)

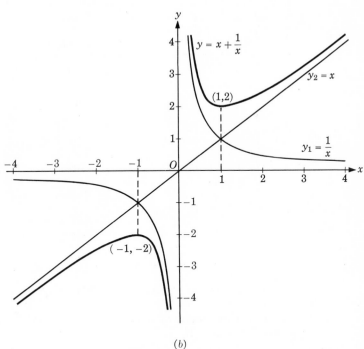

(b)

Figure 5–15

Also, for large values of x, the $1/x$ term becomes small and $y \approx x$. In fact,

$$\text{when } |x| \text{ is small,} \qquad y \approx \frac{1}{x},$$

$$\text{when } |x| \text{ is large,} \qquad y \approx x,$$

so that it is helpful to sketch (as can quickly be done) the curves

$$y_1 = \frac{1}{x}, \qquad y_2 = x,$$

as well as

$$y = x + \frac{1}{x} = y_1 + y_2.$$

Actually, replacing x by $-x$ merely changes the sign of y, so that it would suffice to sketch the portion of the curve in the first quadrant and then reflect the result with respect to the origin to get the portion in the third quadrant (Fig. 5–15b).

x	y_1	y_2	y	y'	y''	Remarks
-4	$-\frac{1}{4}$	-4	$-\frac{17}{4}$	$+$	$-$	Rising; concave down
-2	$-\frac{1}{2}$	-2	$-\frac{5}{2}$	$+$	$-$	Rising; concave down
-1	-1	-1	-2	0	-2	"Spills water"; max.
$-\frac{1}{2}$	-2	$-\frac{1}{2}$	$-\frac{5}{2}$	$-$	$-$	Falling; concave down
$-\frac{1}{4}$	-4	$-\frac{1}{4}$	$-\frac{17}{4}$	$-$	$-$	Falling; concave down
$+\frac{1}{4}$	4	$\frac{1}{4}$	$\frac{17}{4}$	$-$	$+$	Falling; concave up
$\frac{1}{2}$	2	$\frac{1}{2}$	$\frac{5}{2}$	$-$	$+$	Falling; concave up
1	1	1	2	0	$+2$	"Holds water"; min.
2	$\frac{1}{2}$	2	$\frac{5}{2}$	$+$	$+$	Rising; concave up
4	$\frac{1}{4}$	4	$\frac{17}{4}$	$+$	$+$	Rising; concave up

PROBLEMS

In each of the following problems (1 through 5), find intervals of values of x for which the curve is (a) rising, (b) falling, (c) concave upward, (d) concave downward. Sketch the curves, showing the high turning points M, low turning points m, and points of inflection I.

1. $y = x^2 - 4x + 3$ 2. $y = \dfrac{x}{x+1}$ 3. $y = 4 + 3x - x^3$

4. $y = \dfrac{x^3}{3} - \dfrac{x^2}{2} - 6x$ 5. $y = x + \dfrac{4}{x}$

6. Sketch a smooth curve $y = f(x)$ illustrating

   $f(1) = 0,$ $f'(x) < 0$ for $x < 1,$ $f'(x) > 0$ for $x > 1.$

7. Sketch a smooth curve $y = f(x)$ illustrating

   $f(1) = 0,$ $f''(x) < 0$ for $x < 1,$ $f''(x) > 0$ for $x > 1.$

Sketch each of the following curves (8 through 12), indicating high and low turning points and points of inflection

8. $y = 6 - 2x - x^2$ 9. $y = 2x^2 - 4x + 3$
10. $y = 12 - 12x + x^3$ 11. $y = x^4 - 32x + 48$
12. $y = x^3 - 3x^2 + 2$

For the following curves (13 through 16), find vertical tangents and sketch the curves.

13. $x = y^3 + 3y^2 + 3y + 2$ 14. $x = y^3 + 3y^2 - 9y - 11$

15. $x = y^4 - 2y^2 + 2$ 16. $x = y^2 + \dfrac{2}{y}$

17. Sketch a continuous curve $y = f(x)$ having the following characteristics:

   $f(-2) = 8,$ $f'(2) = f'(-2) = 0,$
   $f(0) = 4,$ $f'(x) < 0$ for $|x| < 2,$
   $f(2) = 0,$ $f''(x) < 0$ for $x < 0,$
   $f'(x) > 0$ for $|x| > 2,$ $f''(x) > 0$ for $x > 0.$

18. Sketch a continuous curve $y = f(x)$ having

   $f'(x) > 0$ for $x < 2,$ $f'(x) < 0$ for $x > 2,$

(a) if $f'(x)$ is continuous at $x = 2,$
(b) if $f'(x) \to 1$ as $x \to 2-$ and $f'(x) \to -1$ as $x \to 2+,$
(c) if $f'(x) = 1$ for all $x < 2$ and $f'(x) = -1$ for all $x > 2.$

19. Sketch a continuous curve $y = f(x)$ for $x > 0$ if

   $f(1) = 0$ and $f'(x) = 1/x$ for all $x > 0.$

Is such a curve necessarily concave upward or concave downward?

20. Show that the sum of any positive real number and its reciprocal is at least 2.

21. Sketch the curve

   $$y = 2x^3 + 2x^2 - 2x - 1$$

after locating its maximum, minimum, and inflection points. Then answer the following questions from your graph:

(a) How many times and approximately where does the curve cross the x-axis?

(b) How many times and approximately where would the curve cross the x-axis if $+3$ were added to all the y-values?

(c) How many times and approximately where would the curve cross the x-axis if -3 were added to all the y-values?

5–5   Maxima and minima. Theory.   A function f is said to have a relative, or local, *maximum* at $x = a$ if

$$f(a) \geq f(a + h)$$

for all positive and negative values of h sufficiently near zero. For a local *minimum* at $x = b$,

$$f(b) \leq f(b + h)$$

for values of h close to zero. The word *relative* or *local* is used to distinguish such a point from an *absolute* maximum or minimum that would occur if we could say, for example,

$$f(a) \geq f(x)$$

for all x and not just for all x close to a. In Fig. 5–15(b), for example, the point $(1, 2)$ is a *relative* minimum of the function

$$f(x) = x + \frac{1}{x}$$

because

$$x + \frac{1}{x} \geq 2$$

for all values of x close to 1. But certainly when x is negative, the inequality is no longer satisfied. Indeed, the function $f(x) = x + 1/x$ has no absolute minimum and no absolute maximum.

In Fig. 5–16 we indicate the graph of a function $y = f(x)$ defined only for the domain $0 \leq x \leq L$. This function has a relative minimum at C, which is also an absolute minimum. It also has relative maxima at A and at B, and an absolute maximum at B.

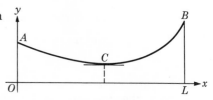

Figure 5–16

We have encountered relative maxima and minima in sketching curves and have observed that they occur at transition points between rising and falling portions of a curve. At such transition points we have also observed that dy/dx is usually zero, but may in exceptional cases become infinite (Fig. 5–10). We shall now prove the following theorem.

THEOREM. *Let the function f be defined for $a \leq x \leq b$ and have a relative maximum or minimum at $x = c$, where $a < c < b$. If the derivative $f'(x)$ exists as a finite number at $x = c$, then*

$$f'(c) = 0. \tag{1}$$

Proof. We shall give the proof for the case of a relative minimum at $x = c$; namely,

$$f(c) \leq f(c + h)$$

for all h close to zero (that is, when $c + h$ is close to c). By hypothesis,

$$f'(c) = \lim_{h \to 0} \frac{f(c + h) - f(c)}{h} \tag{2}$$

exists as a definite number which we want to prove is zero. In the ratio whose limit is $f'(c)$, when h is small, we have

$$\frac{f(c + h) - f(c)}{h} \geq 0 \quad \text{if} \quad h > 0$$

and

$$\frac{f(c + h) - f(c)}{h} \leq 0 \quad \text{if} \quad h < 0,$$

because in both cases the numerator is either positive or is zero. Hence if we let $h \to 0$ through positive values, we have

$$f'(c) \geq 0$$

from the first case; but if we let $h \to 0$ through negative values, we also have

$$f'(c) \leq 0$$

from the second case. Since the derivative is assumed to exist, we must have the same limit in both cases, so

$$0 \leq f'(c) \leq 0,$$

and the only way this can happen is to have

$$f'(c) = 0. \qquad \text{Q.E.D.}$$

The proof in case of a relative maximum at $x = c$ is similar.

Remark. The reader is cautioned not to read into the theorem more than it says. It does not say what happens if a maximum or minimum occurs

Figure 5–17

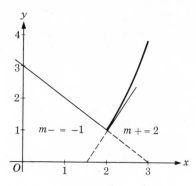

Figure 5–18

(a) at a point c where the derivative fails to exist, or

(b) at an end point of the interval of definition of the function. Neither does it say that the function necessarily does have a maximum or minimum at every place where the derivative is zero.

In Fig. 5–17, for example,

$$\lim_{h \to 0} \frac{f(c + h) - f(c)}{h} = m- \quad \text{or} \quad m+,$$

depending upon whether h approaches zero through negative or positive values respectively. Unless these two numbers $m-$ and $m+$ are equal, the derivative $f'(c)$ does not exist.

For example, if the function is given by

$$y = f(x) = \begin{cases} 3 - x, & \text{for} \quad x \le 2, \\ \frac{1}{2}x^2 - 1, & \text{for} \quad x > 2, \end{cases}$$

its graph is the continuous curve shown in Fig. 5–18. The slope is

$$\frac{dy}{dx} = \frac{d(3 - x)}{dx} = -1 \quad \text{for} \quad x < 2,$$

$$\frac{dy}{dx} = \frac{d(\frac{1}{2}x^2 - 1)}{dx} = x \quad \text{for} \quad x > 2,$$

and at the point $x = 2$, the left-hand tangent has slope $m- = -1$ and the right-hand tangent has slope $m+ = 2$. Clearly, the curve is falling before $x = 2$ and rising after $x = 2$, and has a minimum at $x = 2, y = 1$.

It is also easy to see from the proof of the theorem that when a maximum or minimum occurs at the end of a curve which exists only over a limited interval, the derivative need not vanish at such a point. For example, if the point $x = c$ is at the left end of such a curve, then in the limit in Eq. (2) it is not possible to take h to be negative, because $f(c + h)$ with h negative does not exist in this case. Strictly speaking, $f'(c)$ does not exist in these circumstances, although there may be a right-hand tangent at one end of the curve and a left-hand tangent at the other end (Fig. 5–16).

The point $(0, 0)$ on the curve $y = x^3$ is an example of a point where a curve has zero slope without having either a maximum or a minimum there.

It is customary to refer to a point on a curve $y = f(x)$ at which $f'(x) = 0$ as a "stationary point" on the curve. Values of x which satisfy the equation $f'(x) = 0$ are also called "critical values." In other words, a "critical value" of x corresponds to a "stationary point" on the curve $y = f(x)$.

5–6 Maxima and minima. Problems. The differential calculus is a powerful tool for solving problems that call for minimizing or maximizing a function. We shall illustrate how this is done in several instances, and then summarize the technique in a list of specific rules.

EXAMPLE 1. Find two positive numbers whose sum is 20 and such that their product is as large as possible.

Solution. If one of the numbers is x, the other is $(20 - x)$ and their product is

$$y = x(20 - x) = 20x - x^2. \tag{1}$$

Since both numbers are to be positive,

$$x > 0 \quad \text{and} \quad 20 - x > 0,$$

or

$$0 < x < 20.$$

From (1), we find

$$\frac{dy}{dx} = 20 - 2x = 2(10 - x),$$

which is

positive when $x < 10$,

negative when $x > 10$,

zero when $x = 10$.

Furthermore,

$$\frac{d^2y}{dx^2} = -2$$

is always negative and the curve representing (1) is concave downward at every point on it. The graph is the curve shown in Fig. 5–19, which has an absolute maximum at $x = 10$. The two numbers are thus $x = 10$, $20 - x = 10$.

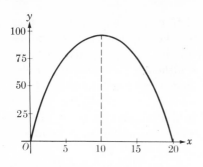

Figure 5–19   Figure 5–20

EXAMPLE 2. A square sheet of tin a inches on a side is to be used to make an open-top box by cutting a small square of tin from each corner and bending up the sides. How large a square should be cut from each corner in order that the box shall have as large a volume as possible?

Solution. We first draw a figure to illustrate the problem (Fig. 5–20). In the figure, the side of the square cut from each corner is taken to be x inches and the volume of the box in cubic inches is then given by

$$y = x(a - 2x)^2, \qquad 0 \le x \le a/2. \qquad (2)$$

The restrictions placed on x in (2) are clearly those imposed by the fact that one can neither cut a negative amount of material from a corner, nor can one cut away an amount which is more than the total amount present. It is also evident that $y = 0$ when $x = 0$ or when $x = a/2$, so that the maximum volume y must occur at some value of x between 0 and $a/2$. The function in (2) possesses a derivative at every such point, hence

when y is a maximum, dy/dx must be zero.

From (2), we find

$$y = a^2x - 4ax^2 + 4x^3,$$

$$\frac{dy}{dx} = a^2 - 8ax + 12x^2$$

$$= (a - 2x)(a - 6x),$$

so that

$$\frac{dy}{dx} = 0 \qquad \text{when} \qquad x = \frac{a}{2} \quad \text{or} \quad \frac{a}{6}.$$

We gain additional information about the shape of the curve representing (2) from

$$\frac{d^2y}{dx^2} = 24x - 8a = 24\left(x - \frac{a}{3}\right),$$

which shows that the curve is

$$\text{concave downward for } x < \frac{a}{3},$$

$$\text{concave upward} \quad \text{for } x > \frac{a}{3}.$$

In particular,

$$\text{at} \quad x = \frac{a}{6}: \quad \frac{dy}{dx} = 0, \quad \frac{d^2y}{dx^2} = -4a,$$

$$\text{at} \quad x = \frac{a}{2}: \quad \frac{dy}{dx} = 0, \quad \frac{d^2y}{dx^2} = +4a. \tag{3}$$

From (3) we see that if we were to draw the graph of the curve (2) it would "spill water" at $x = (a/6)$ and this is the only point between $x = 0$ and $x = (a/2)$ where a relative maximum of the volume y may occur (Fig. 5–21). Each corner square should thus have dimensions $a/6$ by $a/6$ to produce a box of maximum volume.

Figure 5–21   **Figure 5–22**

EXAMPLE 3. An oil can is to be made in the form of a right circular cylinder to contain one quart of oil. What dimensions of the can will require the least amount of material?

Solution. Again we start with a figure to illustrate the problem (Fig. 5–22). Clearly, the requirement that the can hold a quart of oil is the same as

$$V = \pi r^2 h = a^3, \tag{4a}$$

if the radius r and altitude h are in inches and a^3 is the number of cubic inches in a quart ($a^3 = 57.75$). How shall we interpret the phrase "least amount of material"? A reasonable interpretation arises from neglecting the thickness of the material and the waste due to the manufacturing process. Then we ask for dimensions r and h that make the total surface area

$$A = 2\pi r^2 + 2\pi rh \tag{4b}$$

as small as possible while still satisfying (4a).

We are not quite ready to apply the methods used in Examples 1 and 2, because Eq. (4b) expresses A as a function of *two* variables, r and h, and our methods call for A to be expressed as a function of just *one* variable. However, Eq. (4a) may be used to express one of the variables r or h in terms of the other; in fact, we find

$$h = \frac{a^3}{\pi r^2} \tag{4c}$$

or

$$r = \sqrt{\frac{a^3}{\pi h}}. \tag{4d}$$

The division in (4c) and (4d) is legitimate because neither r nor h can be zero, and only the positive square root is used in (4d) because the radius r can never be negative. If we substitute from (4c) into (4b), we have

$$A = 2\pi r^2 + \frac{2a^3}{r}, \qquad 0 < r < \infty, \tag{4e}$$

and now we may apply our previous methods. A minimum of A can occur only at a point where

$$\frac{dA}{dr} = 4\pi r - 2a^3 r^{-2} \tag{4f}$$

is zero, that is, where

$$4\pi r = \frac{2a^3}{r^2}, \qquad r = \frac{a}{\sqrt[3]{2\pi}}. \tag{4g}$$

At such a value of r, we shall have

$$\frac{d^2A}{dr^2} = 4\pi + 4a^3 r^{-3} = 12\pi > 0,$$

so the curve representing A as a function of r has $dA/dr = 0$ and d^2A/dr^2 positive ("holds water") at $r = a/\sqrt[3]{2\pi}$, which must therefore produce a relative minimum. Since the second derivative is *always positive* for $0 < r < \infty$, the curve is concave upward everywhere, and there can be no other relative minimum, so we have also found the absolute minimum. From (4g) and (4c), we find

$$r = a/\sqrt[3]{2\pi} = \sqrt[3]{V/2\pi},$$

$$h = 2a/\sqrt[3]{2\pi} = 2\sqrt[3]{V/2\pi}$$

as the dimensions of the can of volume V having minimum surface area. Figure 5–23 shows a curve representing A as a function of r as given by (4e).

There is an alternative method of solving problems of this type. Namely,

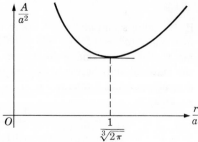

Figure 5-23

instead of solving (4a) for h in terms of r, say, we differentiate both (4a) and (4b) with respect to r, remembering that h is a function of r. Thus, we have

$$V = \pi r^2 h,$$

$$A = 2\pi r^2 + 2\pi rh,$$

and since

$$V \text{ is a constant,} \qquad dV/dr = 0,$$

and since we want to find when A will be a minimum, we put

$$\frac{dA}{dr} = 0$$

also. Hence

$$\frac{dV}{dr} = \pi\left(r^2\frac{dh}{dr} + 2rh\right) = 0, \qquad \frac{dh}{dr} = -\frac{2h}{r}, \qquad (4h)$$

$$\frac{dA}{dr} = 2\pi\left(2r + r\frac{dh}{dr} + h\right) = 2\pi(2r - h). \qquad (4i)$$

Therefore dA/dr is zero when

$$h = 2r. \qquad (4j)$$

When this is substituted into (4a), we have

$$V = \pi r^2 h = 2\pi r^3,$$

so that

$$r = \sqrt[3]{V/2\pi}, \qquad h = 2r = 2\sqrt[3]{V/2\pi}$$

give the critical dimensions for a cylindrical can of volume V.

We may use d^2A/dr^2 to test these critical values. We have

$$\frac{dA}{dr} = 2\pi(2r - h),$$

so that, if we take account of (4h), we find

$$\frac{d^2A}{dr^2} = 2\pi\left(2 - \frac{dh}{dr}\right) = 2\pi\left(2 + \frac{2h}{r}\right).$$

This is positive for all positive values of r and h, and hence A has a minimum at $r = r_{\text{crit}}$ where $dA/dr = 0$ and d^2A/dr^2 is positive.

EXAMPLE 4. A wire of length L is to be cut into two pieces, one of which is bent to form a circle and the other to form a square. How should the wire be cut if the sum of the areas enclosed by the two pieces is to be a maximum?

Solution. In the notation of Fig. 5–24, the sum of the combined areas is

$$A = \pi r^2 + x^2, \qquad (5a)$$

where r and x must satisfy the equation

$$L = 2\pi r + 4x. \qquad (5\text{b})$$

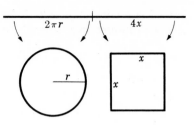

We could solve (5b) for x in terms of r, but instead we shall differentiate both (5a) and (5b), treating A and x as functions of r for $0 \le 2\pi r \le L$. Then

$$\frac{dA}{dr} = 2\pi r + 2x\frac{dx}{dr}, \qquad (5\text{c})$$

Figure 5–24

and

$$\frac{dL}{dr} = 2\pi + 4\frac{dx}{dr} = 0, \qquad \frac{dx}{dr} = -\frac{\pi}{2}, \qquad (5\text{d})$$

where dL/dr is zero because L is a constant. If we substitute dx/dr from (5d) into (5c), we get

$$\frac{dA}{dr} = \pi(2r - x) \qquad (5\text{e})$$

and, for future reference, we note that

$$\frac{d^2 A}{dr^2} = \pi\left(2 - \frac{dx}{dr}\right) = \pi\left(2 + \frac{\pi}{2}\right) \qquad (5\text{f})$$

is a positive constant, so that the curve which represents A as a function of r is always concave upward (Fig. 5–25).

    Now

$$\frac{dA}{dr} = 0 \qquad \text{when} \qquad x = 2r,$$

and when we substitute this into (5b),

$$L = 2\pi r + 4(2r) = (2\pi + 8)r,$$

we have

$$\frac{dA}{dr} = 0 \quad \text{when} \quad r = \frac{L}{2\pi + 8}, \qquad x = \frac{L}{\pi + 4}.$$

But the fact that the second derivative is positive means that this value of r gives a *minimum* for A. The problem asks for the *maximum* of A.

    Since r is limited to

$$0 \le r \le \frac{L}{2\pi},$$

we examine the values of A at the ends of this interval. When

$$r = 0: \qquad x = \frac{L}{4}, \qquad A = \frac{1}{16}L^2,$$

and when

$$r = \frac{L}{2\pi} : \qquad x = 0, \qquad A = \frac{1}{4\pi} L^2.$$

At the minimum,

$$r = \frac{1}{2} \frac{L}{\pi + 4}, \qquad x = \frac{L}{\pi + 4}, \qquad A = \frac{1}{4\pi + 16} L^2.$$

Using these values to make a rough sketch of A as a function of r (Fig. 5–25), it is readily seen that the maximum value of A occurs when $r = L/2\pi$, which means that the wire should not be cut at all, but all of it should be bent into the circle for maximum total area. Or, if we adopt the point of view that the wire *must* be cut, then there is no answer to the problem. For no matter how little of it is used for the square, we could always get a larger total area by using still less of it for the square.

Figure 5–25

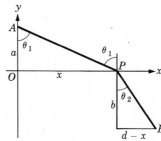

Figure 5–26

EXAMPLE 5. Fermat's principle in optics states that light travels from a point A to a point B along that path for which the time of travel is a minimum. Let us find the path that a ray of light will follow in going from a point A in a medium where the velocity of light is c_1 to a point B in a second medium where the velocity of light is c_2, when both points lie in the xy-plane and the x-axis separates the two media.

Solution. In either medium where the velocity of light remains constant, the light ray will follow a straight path, since then "shortest time" and "shortest distance" amount to the same thing. Hence the path will consist of a straight line segment from A to P in the first medium and another line segment $\overline{PB}$ in the second medium. The time required for the light to travel from A to P is

$$t_1 = \frac{\sqrt{a^2 + x^2}}{c_1},$$

and from P to B the time required is

$$t_2 = \frac{\sqrt{b^2 + (d - x)^2}}{c_2}.$$

We therefore seek to minimize

$$t = t_1 + t_2 = \frac{\sqrt{a^2 + x^2}}{c_1} + \frac{\sqrt{b^2 + (d - x)^2}}{c_2}. \tag{6a}$$

We find

$$\frac{dt}{dx} = \frac{x}{c_1\sqrt{a^2 + x^2}} - \frac{(d - x)}{c_2\sqrt{b^2 + (d - x)^2}} \tag{6b}$$

or

$$\frac{dt}{dx} = \frac{\sin\theta_1}{c_1} - \frac{\sin\theta_2}{c_2}, \tag{6c}$$

if we make use of the angles θ_1 and θ_2 in the figure.

If we restrict x to the interval $0 \leq x \leq d$, t has a negative derivative at $x = 0$ and a positive derivative at $x = d$, while at the value of x, say x_c, for which

$$\frac{\sin\theta_1}{c_1} = \frac{\sin\theta_2}{c_2}, \tag{6d}$$

dt/dx is zero. Figure 5–27 indicates the directions of the tangents to the curve giving t as a function of x at these three points, and suggests that t will indeed be a minimum at $x = x_c$. If we want further information on this point, by referring to Fig. 5–26 we see that a decrease in x will cause P to move to the left, making θ_1 smaller, and hence also $\sin\theta_1$ smaller, but will have the opposite effect on θ_2 and $\sin\theta_2$. Figure 5–28 shows that since $(\sin\theta_1)/c_1$ is an increasing function of x which is zero at $x = 0$, while $(\sin\theta_2)/c_2$ is a decreasing function of x which is zero at $x = d$, the two curves can cross at only one point, $x = x_c$, between 0 and d. To the right of x_c, the curve for $(\sin\theta_1)/c_1$ is above the curve for $(\sin\theta_2)/c_2$, but these roles are reversed to the left of x_c, so that

$$\frac{dt}{dx} = \frac{\sin\theta_1}{c_1} - \frac{\sin\theta_2}{c_2} \begin{cases} \text{is negative for } x < x_c, \\ \text{is zero for } x = x_c, \\ \text{is positive for } x > x_c, \end{cases}$$

and the minimum of t does indeed occur at $x = x_c$.

Instead of determining this value of x explicitly, it is customary to characterize the path followed by the ray of light by leaving the equation for $dt/dx = 0$ in the form (6d), which is known as the law of refraction or Snell's law. [See Sears, *Optics*, p. 27, Addison-Wesley (1949).]

Figure 5–27

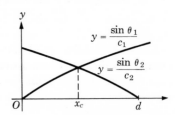

Figure 5–28

The reader will very likely have noticed in the above problems that the techniques summarized in the following rules have been used.

First. When possible, draw a figure to illustrate the problem and label those parts that are important in the problem. Constants and variables should be clearly distinguished.

Second. Write an equation for the quantity that is to be a maximum or a minimum. If this quantity is denoted by y, it is desirable to express it in terms of a single independent variable x. This may require some algebraic manipulation to make use of auxiliary conditions of the problem.

Third. If $y = f(x)$ is the quantity to be a maximum or a minimum, find those values of x for which

$$\frac{dy}{dx} = f'(x) = 0.$$

Fourth. Test each value of x for which $f'(x) = 0$ to determine whether it provides a maximum or minimum or neither. The usual tests are:

(a) If $\dfrac{d^2y}{dx^2}$ is positive when $\dfrac{dy}{dx} = 0$, y is a minimum.

If $\dfrac{d^2y}{dx^2}$ is negative when $\dfrac{dy}{dx} = 0$, y is a maximum.

If $\dfrac{d^2y}{dx^2} = 0$ when $\dfrac{dy}{dx} = 0$, the test fails.

(b) If

$$\frac{dy}{dx} \text{ is } \begin{cases} \text{positive for } x < x_c, \\ \text{zero for } x = x_c, \\ \text{negative for } x > x_c, \end{cases}$$

then a maximum occurs at x_c. But if dy/dx changes from negative to zero to positive as x advances through x_c, there is a minimum. If dy/dx does not change its sign, neither a maximum nor a minimum need occur.

Fifth. If the derivative fails to exist at some point, examine this point as possible maximum or minimum. (See Fig. 5–18.)

Sixth. If the function $y = f(x)$ is defined for only a limited range of values $a \leq x \leq b$, examine $x = a$ and $x = b$ for possible extreme values of y. (See Fig. 5–25.)

Remark. The following useful argument applies in many problems. It is often obvious from the formulas, or from physical conditions, that we have a continuous and everywhere-differentiable function that does not attain its maximum at an end point. Hence it has at least one maximum at an interior point, at which its derivative must be zero. So if we find just one zero for the derivative, we have the maximum without any appeal to second-derivative or other tests.

EXAMPLE 6. Suppose a manufacturer can sell x items per week at a price $P = 200 - 0.01x$ cents, and that it costs $y = 50x + 20{,}000$ cents to produce the x items. What is the production level for maximum profits?

Solution. The total revenue per week on x items is

$$xP = 200x - 0.01x^2.$$

The manufacturer's profit T is revenue minus cost:

$$T = xP - y = (200x - 0.01x^2) - (50x + 20{,}000)$$
$$= 150x - 0.01x^2 - 20{,}000.$$

To maximize T, we find

$$dT/dx = 150 - 0.02x,$$

which is zero when

$$x = 7500.$$

We know that this production level gives maximum profit, since the second derivative $d^2T/dx^2 = -0.02$ is negative, or by the argument in the "Remark" above. To sell the 7500 items, the manufacturer should charge \$1.25 per item.

PROBLEMS

1. Show that the rectangle that has maximum area for a given perimeter is a square.

2. Find the dimensions of the rectangle of greatest area that can be inscribed in a semicircle of radius r.

3. Find the area of the largest rectangle with lower base on the x-axis and upper vertices on the curve $y = 12 - x^2$.

4. An open rectangular box is to be made from a piece of cardboard 8 in. wide and 15 in. long by cutting a square from each corner and bending up the sides. Find the dimensions of the box of largest volume.

5. One side of an open field is bounded by a straight river. How would you put a fence around the other three sides of a rectangular plot in order to enclose as great an area as possible with a given length of fence?

6. An open storage bin with square base and vertical sides is to be constructed from a given amount of material. Determine its dimensions if its volume is a maximum. Neglect the thickness of the material and waste in construction.

7. A box with square base and open top is to hold 32 in^3. Find the dimensions that require the least amount of material. Neglect the thickness of the material and waste in construction.

8. A variable line through the point $(1, 2)$ intersects the x-axis at $A(a, 0)$ and the y-axis at $B(0, b)$. Find the area of the triangle AOB of least area if both a and b are positive.

9. A poster is to contain 50 in^2 of printed matter with margins of 4 in. each at top and bottom and 2 in. at each side. Find the over-all dimensions if the total area of the poster is a minimum.

10. A right triangle of given hypotenuse is rotated about one of its legs to generate a right circular cone. Find the cone of greatest volume.

11. It costs a manufacturer c dollars each to manufacture and distribute a certain item. If he sells it at x dollars each, he estimates that the number he can sell is given by $n = a/(x - c) + b(100 - x)$, where a and b are certain positive constants. What selling price will bring him a maximum profit?

12. A cantilever beam of length L has one end built into a wall, while the other end is simply supported. If the beam weighs w lb per unit length, its deflection y at distance x from the built-in end satisfies the equation

$$48EIy = w(2x^4 - 5Lx^3 + 3L^2x^2),$$

where E and I are constants depending upon the material of the beam and the shape of its cross section. How far from the built-in end does the maximum deflection occur?

13. Determine the constant a in order that the function

$$f(x) = x^2 + \frac{a}{x}$$

may have (a) a relative minimum at $x = 2$, (b) a relative minimum at $x = -3$, (c) a point of inflection at $x = 1$. (d) Show that the function cannot have a relative maximum for any value of a.

14. Determine the constants a and b in order that the function

$$f(x) = x^3 + ax^2 + bx + c$$

may have (a) a relative maximum at $x = -1$ and a relative minimum at $x = 3$, (b) a relative minimum at $x = 4$ and a point of inflection at $x = 1$.

15. A wire of length L is cut into two pieces, one being bent to form a square and the other to form an equilateral triangle. How should the wire be cut (a) if the sum of the two areas is a minimum, (b) if the sum of the areas is a maximum?

16. Find the points on the curve $5x^2 - 6xy + 5y^2 = 4$ that are nearest the origin.

17. The distance between the points (x_1, y_1) and (x_2, y_2) is

$$\sqrt{(x_2 - x_1)^2 + (y_2 - y_1)^2}.$$

Find the point on the curve $y = \sqrt{x}$ nearest the point $(c, 0)$, (a) if $c \geq \frac{1}{2}$, (b) if $c < \frac{1}{2}$.

18. Find the volume of the largest right circular cone that can be inscribed in a sphere of radius r.

19. Find the volume of the largest right circular cylinder that can be inscribed in a sphere of radius r.

20. Show that the volume of the largest right circular cylinder that can be inscribed in a given right circular cone is $\frac{4}{9}$ the volume of the cone.

21. The strength of a rectangular beam is proportional to the product of its width and the square of its depth. Find the dimensions of the strongest beam that can be cut from a circular cylindrical log of radius r.

22. The stiffness of a rectangular beam is proportional to the product of its breadth and the cube of its depth. Find the stiffest beam that can be cut from a log of given diameter.

23. The intensity of illumination at any point is proportional to the product of the strength of the light source and the inverse of the square of the distance from the source. If two sources of relative strengths a and b are a distance c apart, at what point on the line joining them will the intensity be a minimum? Assume the intensity at any point is the sum of intensities from the two sources.

24. A window is in the form of a rectangle surmounted by a semicircle. If the rectangle is of clear glass while the semicircle is of colored glass which transmits only half as much light per square foot as clear glass does, and the total perimeter is fixed, find the proportions of the window that will admit the most light.

25. Right circular cylindrical tin cans are to be manufactured to contain a given volume. There is no waste involved in cutting the tin that goes into the vertical sides of the can, but each end piece is to be cut from a square and the corners of the square wasted. Find the ratio of height to diameter for the most economical cans.

26. A silo is to be made in the form of a cylinder surmounted by a hemisphere. The cost of construction per square foot of surface area is twice as great for the hemisphere as for the cylinder. Determine the dimensions to be used if the volume is fixed and the cost of construction is to be a minimum. Neglect the thickness of the silo and waste in construction.

27. If the sum of the areas of a cube and a sphere is constant, what is the ratio of an edge of the cube to the diameter of the sphere when (a) the sum of their volumes is a minimum, (b) the sum of their volumes is a maximum?

28. Two towns, located on the same side of a straight river, agree to construct a pumping station and filtering plant at the river's edge, to be used jointly to supply the towns with water. If the distances of the two towns from the river are a and b and the distance between them is c, show that the sum of the lengths of the pipe lines joining them to the pumping station is at least as great as $\sqrt{c^2 + 4ab}$.

29. Light emanating from a source A is reflected to a point B by a plane mirror. If the time required for the light to travel from A to the mirror and then to B is a minimum, show that the angle of incidence is equal to the angle of reflection.

30. Show that a manufacturer's profit is maximized (or minimized) at a level of production where his marginal revenue equals marginal cost.

31. Suppose the government imposes a tax of ten cents, for each item sold, on the product of Example 6, but other features are unchanged. How much of the tax should the manufacturer absorb and how much should he pass on to the customer? Why? Compare his profits before and after the tax.

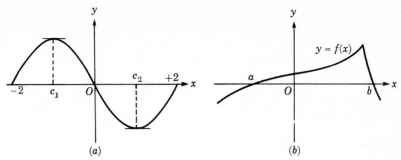

Figure 5–29

5–7 Rolle's Theorem. There is strong geometrical evidence to support the belief that between two points where a smooth curve $y = f(x)$ crosses the x-axis there must be at least one point where it has a horizontal tangent. But such is not the case if the curve has a corner, as in Fig. 5–29(b), where the derivative fails to exist. More precisely, we have the following theorem.

ROLLE'S THEOREM.* *Let the function f be defined and continuous on the closed interval $a \leq x \leq b$ and differentiable in the open interval $a < x < b$. Furthermore, let*

$$f(a) = f(b) = 0.$$

Then there is at least one number c between a and b where $f'(x)$ is zero; i.e.,

$$f'(c) = 0 \quad \text{for some } c \quad a < c < b.$$

Proof. Either $f(x)$ is identically equal to zero for all x, $a \leq x \leq b$, or else $f(x)$ is different from zero for some values of x in this interval. In the former case, $f'(x)$ is also identically zero and the theorem is true for this case.

But if $f(x)$ is not zero everywhere between a and b, then either it is positive some place, or negative some place, or both. In any case, the function will then have a maximum positive value or a minimum negative value, or both. That is, it has an extreme value at a point c where $f(c)$ is negative (in the case of a minimum) or $f(c)$ is positive (in the case of a maximum). In either case, c is neither a nor b, since

$$f(a) = f(b) = 0, \quad f(c) \neq 0.$$

---

* Published in 1691 in *Méthode pour Résoudre les Egalités* by the French mathematician Michel Rolle. See *Source Book in Mathematics* by D. E. Smith, p. 253.

Therefore c is between a and b and the theorem of Article 5–5 applies, showing that the derivative must be zero at $x = c$:

$$f'(c) = 0 \quad \text{for some } c \quad a < c < b. \qquad \text{Q.E.D.}$$

Remark 1. There may be more than one place between a and b where the derivative is zero. In Fig. 5–29(a), for example, dy/dx is zero at c_1 and at c_2 and they both lie between $a = -2$ and $b = +2$.

EXAMPLE. The polynomial

$$y = x^3 - 4x = f(x)$$

is continuous and differentiable for all x, $-\infty < x < +\infty$. If we take

$$a = -2, \quad b = +2,$$

the hypotheses of Rolle's Theorem are satisfied, since

$$f(-2) = f(+2) = 0.$$

Thus

$$f'(x) = 3x^2 - 4$$

must be zero at least once between -2 and $+2$. In fact, we find

$$3x^2 - 4 = 0$$

at

$$x = c_1 = -2\sqrt{3}/3 \quad \text{and} \quad x = c_2 = +2\sqrt{3}/3.$$

Remark 2. The reader may combine Rolle's Theorem with part (ii) of Theorem 3 of Article 4–8 to obtain the following criterion for isolating the real roots of an equation $f(x) = 0$. Suppose a and b are two real numbers such that

(a) $f(x)$ and its first derivative $f'(x)$ are continuous for $a \le x \le b$,
(b) $f(a)$ and $f(b)$ have opposite signs,
(c) $f'(x)$ is different from zero for all values of x between a and b.

Then there is one and only one real root of the equation $f(x) = 0$ between a and b.

To see the significance of this, suppose the equation is

$$f(x) = x^3 + 3x + 1 = 0.$$

Then

$$f'(x) = 3x^2 + 3$$

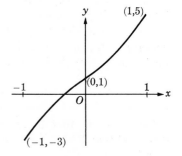

Figure 5–30

is always positive, so that the equation $f'(x) = 0$ can have no real roots. Hence the original equation $f(x) = 0$ cannot have as many as two real roots. It does, in fact, have exactly one real root, since the graph of

$$y = x^3 + 3x + 1$$

crosses the x-axis between $x = -1$ and $x = 0$ but can never cross the x-axis at any other point. (If it did, the derivative would have to be zero at some point between.)

PROBLEMS

Without trying to solve the equations exactly, show that the equation $f(x) = 0$ has one and only one real root between the given pair of numbers for each of the following functions $f(x)$.

1. $x^4 + 3x + 1$ $(-2, -1)$
2. $x^4 + 2x^3 - 2$ $(0, 1)$
3. $2x^3 - 3x^2 - 12x - 6$ $(-1, 0)$

4. Let $f(x)$, together with its first two derivatives $f'(x)$ and $f''(x)$, be continuous for $a \leq x \leq b$. Suppose the curve $y = f(x)$ intersects the x-axis in at least three different places between a and b inclusive. Using Rolle's Theorem, show that the equation $f''(x) = 0$ has at least one real root between a and b. Generalize this result.

5-8   The Mean Value Theorem.   In this article we shall prove the Mean Value Theorem, which is a generalization of Rolle's Theorem. Again we shall be concerned with a function $y = f(x)$ which is continuous for $a \leq x \leq b$ and which has a nonvertical tangent at each point between $A[a, f(a)]$ and $B[b, f(b)]$, although the tangent may be vertical at one or both of the end points A and B (Fig. 5–31). For example, the function might be

$$f(x) = \sqrt{a^2 - x^2}, \qquad -a \leq x \leq a,$$

which represents a semicircle that fulfills the requirements above.

Discussion.   Geometrically, the Mean Value Theorem states that if the function $y = f(x)$ is continuous for $a \leq x \leq b$ and has a derivative at each value of x for $a < x < b$, then there is at least one point c between a and b where the tangent to the curve will be parallel to the chord through the two points $A[a, f(a)]$ and $B[b, f(b)]$. This is intuitively plausible, for if we consider

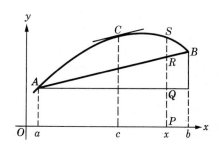

Figure 5–31

displacing the chord $\overline{AB}$ in Fig. 5–31 upward, keeping it parallel to $\overleftrightarrow{AB}$, there will be a transition between positions where it cuts the curve in two nearby points and where it will fail to touch the curve, and the transition will take place at a point C where the line will be tangent to this curve. This transition will occur where the vertical distance between the chord $\overline{AB}$ and the curve is a maximum.

The analytic proof of the Mean Value Theorem has its key idea in this last statement. The vertical distance between the chord and the curve is measured by RS in Fig. 5–31 and

$$RS = PS - PR.$$

Now PS is simply the ordinate y on the curve $y = f(x)$, so that

$$PS = f(x).$$

On the other hand, PR is the ordinate on the chord $\overline{AB}$ and may be found by using the equation

$$y - f(a) = m(x - a),$$

which is the equation of the straight line $\overleftrightarrow{AB}$ through the point $A[a, f(a)]$ with slope

$$m = \frac{f(b) - f(a)}{b - a}.$$

That is, the ordinate y of the point R on the line $\overleftrightarrow{AB}$ is

$$y = PR = f(a) + \frac{f(b) - f(a)}{b - a}(x - a).$$

Hence

$$RS = f(x) - f(a) - \frac{f(b) - f(a)}{b - a}(x - a) \tag{1}$$

and RS measures the vertical displacement from the chord $\overline{AB}$ to the curve $y = f(x)$ for any x between a and b.

Proof of the Mean Value Theorem. Denote the expression on the right side of Eq. (1) by $F(x)$, that is,

$$F(x) = f(x) - f(a) - \frac{f(b) - f(a)}{b - a}(x - a). \tag{2}$$

Then

$$F(a) = f(a) - f(a) - \frac{f(b) - f(a)}{b - a}(a - a) = 0$$

and

$$F(b) = f(b) - f(a) - \frac{f(b) - f(a)}{b - a}(b - a) = 0,$$

so that this function $F(x)$ is zero at both $x = a$ and $x = b$. But since $f(x)$ and $x - a$ in Eq. (2) are continuous for $a \leq x \leq b$ and differentiable for $a < x < b$, and the other expressions on the right side of the equation are constants, the function $F(x)$ satisfies all the hypotheses of Rolle's Theorem. Therefore its derivative must be zero at some place between a and b; that is,

$$F'(c) = 0 \quad \text{for some } c, \quad a < c < b. \tag{3a}$$

If we take the derivative of both sides of (2), we get

$$F'(x) = f'(x) - \frac{f(b) - f(a)}{b - a} \cdot \frac{d(x - a)}{dx}$$

and the result (3a) is equivalent to stating

$$f'(c) = \frac{f(b) - f(a)}{b - a} \tag{3b}$$

or

$$f(b) - f(a) = f'(c)(b - a) \quad \text{for some } c, \quad a < c < b. \tag{4}$$

These results are summarized in the following theorem.

THE MEAN VALUE THEOREM. *Let $y = f(x)$ be continuous for $a \leq x \leq b$, and possess a derivative at each x for $a < x < b$. Then there is at least one number c between a and b such that*

$$\boxed{f(b) - f(a) = f'(c)(b - a).}$$

We note that (3b) states that the slope $f'(c)$ of the curve at $C[c, f(c)]$ is the same as the slope $[f(b) - f(a)]/(b - a)$ of the chord joining the point $A[a, f(a)]$ and $B[b, f(b)]$; this is a form that is easily recalled.

Equation (4) contains a symbol c which is not very well defined except by this equation itself. For a specific function f and specific values of a and b, however, the equation can be used to find one or more values of c.

EXAMPLE 1. (Fig. 5-32) Let $f(x) = x^3$, $a = -2$, and $b = +2$. Then

$$f'(x) = 3x^2, \quad f'(c) = 3c^2,$$

$$f(b) = 2^3 = 8, \quad f(a) = (-2)^3 = -8,$$

$$\frac{f(b) - f(a)}{b - a} = \frac{8 - (-8)}{2 - (-2)} = \frac{16}{4} = 4,$$

so that

$$f'(c) = \frac{f(b) - f(a)}{b - a}$$

Figure 5-32

Figure 5-33

becomes

$$3c^2 = 4, \qquad c = \pm\tfrac{2}{3}\sqrt{3}.$$

There are thus two values of c, namely,

$$c_1 = -\tfrac{2}{3}\sqrt{3}, \qquad c_2 = +\tfrac{2}{3}\sqrt{3},$$

between $a = -2$ and $b = +2$, where the tangent to the curve $y = x^3$ is parallel to the chord through the points $(-2, -8)$ and $(+2, +8)$.

EXAMPLE 2. (Fig. 5-33) Let $f(x) = x^{2/3}$, $a = -8$, $b = +8$. Then

$$f'(x) = \frac{2}{3}x^{-1/3} = \frac{2}{3\sqrt[3]{x}}$$

exists everywhere between a and b *except* at $x = 0$. We find that

$$\frac{f(b) - f(a)}{b - a} = \frac{(8)^{2/3} - (-8)^{2/3}}{8 - (-8)} = \frac{4 - 4}{16} = 0,$$

and

$$f'(c) = \frac{2}{3\sqrt[3]{c}}$$

is not zero for any finite value of c. The result (3b) need not hold, and does not hold, in this case due to the failure of the derivative to exist at a point, namely $x = 0$, between $a = -8$ and $b = +8$.

Remark. The Mean Value Theorem has the following interesting interpretation when applied to an equation of motion $s = f(t)$. $\Delta s = f(b) - f(a)$ is the change in s corresponding to $\Delta t = b - a$ and the right side of Eq. (3b) is

$$\frac{\Delta s}{\Delta t} = \frac{f(b) - f(a)}{b - a} = \text{average velocity from } t = a \text{ to } t = b. \qquad (5)$$

The equation then tells us that there is an instant $t = c$ between a and b at which the instantaneous velocity $f'(c)$ is equal to the average velocity. The theorem may therefore be paraphrased as follows: If a motorist makes a trip in which his *average* velocity is 30 mi/hr, then at least once during the trip his speedometer must also have registered precisely 30 mi/hr.*

COROLLARY 1. *If a function F has a derivative which is equal to zero for all values of x in an interval $a < x < b$,*

$$F'(x) \equiv 0, \qquad a < x < b, \qquad (6a)$$

then the function is constant throughout the interval:

$$F(x) \equiv \text{constant}, \qquad a < x < b. \qquad (6b)$$

Proof. Suppose (6a) is satisfied. Let x_1 and x_2 be any two points in the interval with $a < x_1 < x_2 < b$. Then, since the function is differentiable for $x_1 \leq x \leq x_2$, it is also continuous in the same closed interval. Hence the Mean Value Theorem applies. That is, there is at least one number c, $x_1 < c < x_2$, such that

$$F(x_1) - F(x_2) = F'(c)(x_1 - x_2).$$

But $F'(c)$ is zero by hypothesis. Therefore

$$F(x_1) = F(x_2).$$

That is, the value of the function at any point x_1 is the same as its value at any other point x_2, for all x_1, x_2 in the interval (a, b). This is what is meant by Eq. (6b). Q.E.D.

COROLLARY 2. *If F_1 and F_2 are two functions each of which has its derivative equal to $f(x)$ for $a < x < b$, that is,*

$$\frac{dF_1(x)}{dx} = \frac{dF_2(x)}{dx} = f(x), \qquad a < x < b,$$

---

* The author wishes to thank Professor Raphael Salem for this interesting paraphrase.

then

$$F_1(x) - F_2(x) \equiv \text{constant}, \qquad a < x < b.$$

Proof. Apply Corollary 1, above, to the function $F(x) = F_1(x) - F_2(x)$.

PROBLEMS

In each of the following problems (1 through 5), a, b, and c refer to the equation $f(b) - f(a) = (b - a) f'(c)$, which expresses the Mean Value Theorem. Given $f(x)$, a, and b, find c.

1. $f(x) = x^2 + 2x - 1;$ $a = 0,$ $b = 1.$
2. $f(x) = x^3;$ $a = 0,$ $b = 3.$
3. $f(x) = x^{2/3};$ $a = 0,$ $b = 1.$
4. $f(x) = x + \dfrac{1}{x};$ $a = \frac{1}{2},$ $b = 2.$
5. $f(x) = \sqrt{x - 1};$ $a = 1,$ $b = 3.$

6. Suppose you know that $f'(x)$ always has a value between -1 and $+1$. Show that

$$|f(x) - f(a)| \le |x - a|.$$

7. The Mean Value Theorem gives the equation

$$f(b) = f(a) + (b - a)f'(c),$$

c between a and b. When all terms on the right side of this equation are known, the equation determines $f(b)$ for us. Usually, however, $f'(c)$ is not known unless $f(b)$ is known. But when b is near a, then c will also be near a, and the approximation

$$f'(c) \approx f'(a)$$

leads to the approximation

$$f(b) \approx f(a) + (b - a)f'(a).$$

Using this approximation, calculate

(a) $\sqrt{10}$ by taking $f(x) = \sqrt{x},$ $a = 9,$ $b = 10;$
(b) $(2.003)^2$ by taking $f(x) = x^2,$ $a = 2,$ $b = 2.003;$
(c) $1/99$ by taking $f(x) = 1/x,$ $a = 100,$ $b = 99.$

8. Let $P_1(x_1, y_1)$ and $P_2(x_2, y_2)$ be any two points on the parabola $y = ax^2 + bx + c$, and let $P_3(x_3, y_3)$ be the point on the arc P_1P_2 where the tangent is parallel to the chord $\overline{P_1P_2}$. Show that $x_3 = (x_1 + x_2)/2.$

REVIEW QUESTIONS AND EXERCISES FOR CHAPTER 5

1. Discuss the significance of the signs of the first and second derivatives. Sketch a small portion of a curve, illustrating how it looks near a point where:

(a) both y' and y'' are positive;

(b) $y' > 0, y'' < 0$;

(c) $y' < 0, y'' > 0$;

(d) $y' < 0, y'' < 0$.

2. Define: *point of inflection*. How do you find points of inflection from an equation of a curve?

3. How do you locate local maximum and minimum points of a curve? Discuss exceptional points, such as end points and points where the derivative fails to exist, in addition to the nonexceptional type. Illustrate with graphs.

4. Let n be a positive integer. For which values of n does the curve $y = x^n$ have (a) a local minimum at the origin, (b) a point of inflection at the origin?

5. Outline a general method of attack for solving "related rates" problems.

6. Outline a general method of attack for solving "max-min" problems.

7. What are the hypotheses of Rolle's theorem? What is the conclusion?

8. Is the converse of Rolle's theorem true?

9. With the book closed, state and prove the Mean Value Theorem. What is its geometrical interpretation?

10. We know that if $F(x) = x^2$, then $F'(x) = 2x$. If someone knows a function G such that $G'(x) = 2x$ but $G(x) \neq x^2$, what can be said about the difference $G(2) - G(1)$? Explain.

11. Read the article "Mathematics in Warfare" by F. W. Lanchester, *World of Mathematics*, Vol. 4, pp. 2138–2157, as a discussion of a practical problem in "related rates."

MISCELLANEOUS PROBLEMS FOR CHAPTER 5

In each of the following exercises (1 through 14) find y' and y''. Determine in each case the sets of values of x for which

(a) y is increasing (as x increases),
(b) y is decreasing (as x increases),
(c) the graph is concave upward,
(d) the graph is concave downward.

Also sketch the graph in each case, indicating *high* and *low* turning points and points of inflection.

1. $y = 9x - x^2$ 2. $y = x^3 - 5x^2 + 3x$

3. $y = 4x^3 - x^4$ 4. $y = 4x + x^{-1}$

5. $y = x^2 + 4x^{-1}$ 6. $y = x + 4x^{-2}$

7. $y = 5 - x^{2/3}$ 8. $y = \dfrac{x - 1}{x + 1}$

9. $y = x - \dfrac{4}{x}$ 10. $y = x^4 - 2x^2$

11. $y = \dfrac{x^2}{ax + b}$; $a > 0, b > 0$ 12. $y = 2x^3 - 9x^2 + 12x$

13. $y = (x - 1)(x + 1)^2$ 14. $y = x^2 - \frac{1}{6}x^3$

15. The slope of a curve at any point (x, y) is given by the equation

$$\frac{dy}{dx} = 6(x - 1)(x - 2)^2(x - 3)^3(x - 4)^4.$$

(a) For what value (or values) of x is y a maximum? Why?
(b) For what value (or values) of x is y a minimum? Why?

16. A particle moves along the x-axis with velocity $v = dx/dt = f(x)$. Show that its acceleration is $f(x)f'(x)$.

17. A meteorite entering the earth's atmosphere has velocity inversely proportional to $\sqrt{s}$ when at distance s from the center of the earth. Show that its acceleration is inversely proportional to s^2.

18. If the velocity of a falling body is $k\sqrt{s}$ at the instant when the body has fallen a distance s, find its acceleration.

19. The volume of a cube is increasing at a rate of 300 in^3/min at the instant when the edge is 20 in. Find the rate at which the edge is changing.

20. Sand falling at the rate of 3 ft^3/min forms a conical pile whose radius always equals twice the height. Find the rate at which the height is changing at the instant when the height is 10 ft.

21. At a certain instant airplane A is flying a level course at 500 mi/hr. At the same time, airplane B is straight above airplane A and flying at the rate of 700 mi/hr on a course that intercepts A's course at a point C that is 4 mi from B and 2 mi from A. (a) At the instant in question, how fast is the distance be-

tween the airplanes decreasing? (b) What is the minimum distance between the airplanes, if they continue on the present courses at constant speed?

22. A point moves along the curve $y^2 = x^3$ in such a way that its distance from the origin increases at the constant rate of 2 units per second. Find dx/dt at $(2, 2\sqrt{2})$.

23. Refer to the triangle in Fig. 5–7. How fast is its area changing when $x = 17\sqrt{2}$?

24. Suppose the cone in Fig. 5–8 has a small opening at the vertex through which the water escapes at the rate of $0.08\sqrt{y}$ ft³/min when its depth is y. Water is also running into the cone at a constant rate of c ft³/min. When the depth is $6\frac{1}{4}$ ft it is observed to be increasing at the rate 0.02 ft/min. Under these conditions, will the tank fill? Give a reason for your answer.

25. A particle projected vertically upward from the surface of the earth with initial velocity v_0 has velocity $\sqrt{v_0^2 - 2gR[1 - (R/s)]}$ when it reaches a distance s from the *center* of the earth. Here R is the radius of the earth. Show that the acceleration is inversely proportional to s^2.

26. Points A and B move along the x- and y-axes, respectively, in such a way that the perpendicular distance r (inches) from the origin to $\overleftrightarrow{AB}$ remains constant. How fast is $|OA|$ changing, and is it increasing or decreasing, when $|OB| = 2r$ and B is moving toward O at the rate of $0.3r$ in/sec?

27. Water is being poured into an inverted conical tank (vertex down) at the rate of 2 ft³/min. How fast is the water level rising when the depth of the water is 5 ft? The radius of the base of the cone is 3 ft and the altitude is 10 ft.

28. Divide 20 into two parts (not necessarily integers) such that the product of one part with the square of the other shall be a maximum.

29. Find the largest value of $f(x) = 4x^3 - 8x^2 + 5x$ for $0 \le x \le 2$. Give reasons for your answer.

30. Find two *positive* numbers whose sum is 36 and such that their product is as large as possible. Can the problem be solved if the product is to be as small as possible?

31. Determine the coefficients a, b, c, d so that the curve whose equation is $y = ax^3 + bx^2 + cx + d$ has a maximum at $(-1, 10)$ and an inflection point at $(1, -6)$.

32. Find that number which most exceeds its square.

33. The perimeter p and area A of a circular sector ("piece of pie") of radius r and arc length s are given by $p = 2r + s$; $A = \frac{1}{2}rs$. If the perimeter is known to be 100 ft, what value of r will produce a maximum area?

34. If a ball is thrown vertically upward with a velocity of 32 ft/sec, its height after t sec is given by the equation $s = 32t - 16t^2$. At what instant will the ball be at its highest point, and how high will it rise?

35. A right circular cone has altitude 12 ft and radius of base 6 ft. A cone is inscribed with its vertex at the center of the base of the given cone and its base parallel to the base of the given cone. Find the dimensions of the cone of maximum volume that can be so inscribed.

36. An oil can is to be made in the form of a right circular cylinder to contain 16π in³. What dimensions of the can will require the least amount of material?

37. An isosceles triangle is drawn with its vertex at the origin, its base parallel to and above the x-axis and the vertices of its base on the curve $12y = 36 - x^2$. Determine the area of the largest such triangle.

38. A tire manufacturer is able to make x (hundred) grade A tires and y (hundred) grade B tires per day, where $y = (40 - 10x)/(5 - x)$, $0 \le x \le 4$. If the profit on each grade A tire is twice the profit on a grade B tire, how many grade A tires per day should he make?

39. Find the points on the curve $x^2 - y^2 = 1$ which are nearest the point $P(a, 0)$ in case (a) $a = 4$, (b) $a = 2$, (c) $a = \sqrt{2}$.

40. A motorist is stranded in a desert 5 mi from a point A, which is the point on a long straight road nearest to him. He wishes to get to a point B on the road. If he can travel at 15 mi/hr on the desert and 39 mi/hr on the road, find the point at which he must meet the road to get to B in the shortest possible time if (a) B is 5 mi from A, (b) B is 10 mi from A, (c) B is 1 mi from A.

41. The base and the perimeter of a triangle are fixed. Determine the remaining two sides if the area is to be a maximum.

42. The base b and the area k of a triangle are fixed. Determine the base angles if the angle at the vertex opposite b is to be a maximum.

43. A line is drawn through a fixed point (a, b) to meet the axes $\overrightarrow{Ox}$, $\overrightarrow{Oy}$ in P and Q. Show that the minimum values of $|PQ|$ $|OP| + |OQ|$ and $|OP| \cdot |OQ|$ are respectively $(a^{2/3} + b^{2/3})^{3/2}$, $(\sqrt{a} + \sqrt{b})^2$, and $4ab$—where $a > 0$, $b > 0$, and P and Q are distinct.

44. Find the smallest value of the constant m if $mx - 1 + (1/x)$ is to be greater than or equal to zero for all positive values of x.

45. Let s be the distance from the fixed point $P_1(x_1, y_1)$ to a point $P(x, y)$ on the line L: $ax + by + c = 0$. Using calculus methods, (a) show that s^2 is a minimum when $\overleftrightarrow{P_1P}$ is perpendicular to L, and (b) show that the minimum distance is $|ax_1 + by_1 + c|/\sqrt{a^2 + b^2}$.

46. A playing field is to be built in the shape of a rectangle plus a semicircular area at each end. A 440-yd race track is to form the perimeter of the field. Find the dimensions of the field if the rectangular part is to have as large an area as possible.

47. If $ax + (b/x) \ge c$ for all positive values of x, where a, b, and c are positive constants, show that $ab \ge c^2/4$.

48. Prove that if $ax^2 + (b/x) \ge c$ for all positive values of x, where a, b, and c are positive constants, then $27ab^2 \ge 4c^3$.

49. Given $f(x) = ax^2 + 2bx + c$ with $a > 0$. By considering the minimum, prove that $f(x) \ge 0$ for all real x if, and only if, $b^2 - ac \le 0$.

50. In Problem 49, take

$$f(x) = (a_1x + b_1)^2 + (a_2x + b_2)^2 + \cdots + (a_nx + b_n)^2,$$

and deduce Schwarz's inequality:

$$(a_1b_1 + a_2b_2 + \cdots + a_nb_n)^2 \le (a_1^2 + a_2^2 + \cdots + a_n^2)(b_1^2 + b_2^2 + \cdots + b_n^2).$$

51. In Problem 50, prove that equality can hold only in case there is a real number x such that $b_i = -a_ix$ for every $i = 1, 2, \ldots, n$.

52. If x is positive and m is greater than one, prove that $x^m - 1 - m(x - 1)$ is not negative.

53. What are the dimensions of the rectangular plot of greatest area which can be laid out within a triangle of base 36 ft and altitude 12 ft? Assume that one side of the rectangle lies on the base of the triangle.

54. A fence h ft high runs parallel to and w ft from a vertical wall. Find the length of the shortest ladder which will reach from the ground across the top of the fence to the wall.

55. Assuming that the cost per hour of running the Queen Mary is $a + bv^n$, where a, b, and n are positive constants, $n > 1$, and v is the velocity through the water, find the speed for making the run from Liverpool to New York at minimum cost.

56. A flower bed is to be in the shape of a circular sector of radius r and central angle θ (i.e., like a piece of pie). Find r and θ if the area is fixed and the perimeter is a minimum.

57. A reservoir is to be built in the form of a right circular cone and the lateral area waterproofed. If the capacity of the reservoir is to be 72π ft^3 and one gallon of waterproofing material will cover 80 ft^2, how many gallons are required?

58. The motion of a particle in a straight line is given by $s = \lambda t - (1 + \lambda^4)t^2$. Show that the particle moves forward initially when λ is positive but ultimately retreats. Show also that for different values of λ the maximum possible distance that the particle can move forward is $\frac{1}{8}$.

59. Let $h(x) = f(x)g(x)$ be the product of two functions that have first and second derivatives and are positive; that is, $f(x) > 0, g(x) > 0$.

(a) Is it true, if f and g both have a relative maximum at $x = a$, that h has a relative maximum at $x = a$?

(b) Is it true, if f and g both have a point of inflection at $x = a$, that h has a point of inflection at $x = a$?

For both (a) and (b) either give a proof or construct a numerical example showing that the statement is false.

60. The 4 points $(-2, -\frac{1}{2})$, $(0, 1)$, $(1, 2)$, and $(3, 3)$ are observed to lie more or less close to a straight line of equation $y = mx + 1$. Find m if the sum

$$(y_1 - mx_1 - 1)^2 + (y_2 - mx_2 - 1)^2 + (y_3 - mx_3 - 1)^2 + (y_4 - mx_4 - 1)^2$$

is to be a minimum, where $(x_1, y_1), \ldots, (x_4, y_4)$ are the coordinates of the given points.

61. The curve $(y + 1)^3 = x^2$ passes through the points $(1, 0)$ and $(-1, 0)$. Does Rolle's Theorem justify the conclusion that dy/dx vanishes for some value of x in the interval $-1 \leq x \leq 1$? Give reasons for your answer.

62. If $a < 0 < b$ and $f(x) = x^{-1/3}$, show that there is no c that satisfies Eq. (4), Article 5–8. Illustrate with a sketch of the graph.

63. If $a < 0 < b$ and $f(x) = x^{1/3}$, show that there is a value of c that satisfies Eq. (4), Article 5–8, even though the function fails to have a derivative at $x = 0$. Illustrate with a sketch of the graph.

64. Show that the equation $f(x) = 2x^3 - 3x^2 + 6x + 6 = 0$ has exactly one real root and find its value accurate to two significant figures. [*Hint:* $f(-1) = -5, f(0) = +6$, and $f'(x) > 0$ for all real x.]

Integration

6–1   Introduction. In the preceding chapters we have pursued one of the two main branches of the calculus, namely, *differential calculus.* We shall now turn our attention to the other main branch of the subject, *integral calculus.* Today, "to integrate" has two meanings when used in connection with calculus. The deeper and more fundamental meaning is nearly the same as the nontechnical definition: "to indicate the whole of; to give the sum or total of" (Webster). The mathematical meaning of the word in this sense will be amply illustrated in finding areas bounded by curves, volumes of various solids, lengths of curves, centers of gravity, and other applications.

The second mathematical meaning of the verb "to integrate" is "to find a function whose derivative is given." This is the aspect of integration that we shall discuss in the next two articles.

The two kinds of integration are called respectively *definite* and *indefinite,* and the connection between the two is given by a theorem which is called the *fundamental theorem* of integral calculus.

6–2   The indefinite integral. Suppose that we are given the derivative dy/dx as a function

$$\frac{dy}{dx} = f(x), \qquad a < x < b, \tag{1}$$

and are asked to find $y = F(x)$.

For example, we might be asked to find y as a function of x if

$$\frac{dy}{dx} = 2x.$$

From our experience with derivatives, we can find one answer, namely,

$$y = x^2.$$

On the other hand, we realize that this is not the only answer, since

$$y = x^2 + 1, \qquad y = x^2 - \sqrt{2}, \qquad y = x^2 + 5\pi$$

are also valid answers. Indeed,

$$y = x^2 + C$$

is an answer if C is any constant.

DEFINITION 1. *An equation such as* (1), *which specifies the derivative as a function of x (or as a function of x and y), is called a* differential equation.

For example,

$$\frac{dy}{dx} = 2xy^2$$

is a differential equation. Second, third, and higher order derivatives may also occur in differential equations, such as

$$\frac{d^2y}{dx^2} + 6xy\frac{dy}{dx} + 3x^2y^3 = 0,$$

and so on. For the time being we shall restrict attention to the special type of differential equation considered in Eq. (1). Differential equations of more general types will be considered in Chapter 19.

DEFINITION 2. *A function $y = F(x)$ is called a* solution *of the differential equation* (1) *if, over the domain $a < x < b$, $F(x)$ is differentiable and*

$$\frac{dF(x)}{dx} = f(x). \tag{2}$$

We also say, in these circumstances, that $F(x)$ is an integral of $f(x)$ with respect to x.

Remark. It is clear from this definition that if $F(x)$ is an integral of $f(x)$ with respect to x, then $F(x) + C$ is also such an integral when C is any constant whatever. For if Eq. (2) is satisfied, then we also have

$$\frac{d}{dx}[F(x) + C] = \frac{dF(x)}{dx} + \frac{dC}{dx}$$

$$= f(x) + 0 = f(x).$$

What is not clear, however, is whether there are other integrals of $f(x)$ not contained in this collection given by the formula $F(x) + C$.

Specifically, we know that $y = x^2 + C$ is a solution, for any constant C, of the differential equation $dy/dx = 2x$. But are there any other solutions?

This question is answered by the second corollary of the Mean Value Theorem, Article 5–8. For if both $F_1(x)$ and $F_2(x)$ are integrals of $f(x)$, then

$$\frac{dF_1(x)}{dx} = \frac{dF_2(x)}{dx} = f(x)$$

or

$$\frac{d[F_1(x) - F_2(x)]}{dx} = 0,$$

and hence
$$F_1(x) - F_2(x) = C,$$

where C is a constant. Hence, if we take $F_2(x) = F(x)$, we have $F_1(x) = F(x) + C$.

Therefore, if
$$y = F(x)$$

is any solution whatever of Eq. (1), then *all* solutions are contained in the formula
$$y = F(x) + C,$$

where C is an arbitrary constant. This is indicated by writing
$$\int f(x)\, dx = F(x) + C, \tag{3}$$

where the symbol $\int$ is called an "integral sign" and Eq. (3) is read "The integral of $f(x)\, dx$ is $F(x)$ plus C." This is a standard notation. We may interpret it in either of two ways:

1. We may think of the symbol
$$\int \ldots dx \tag{4}$$

as meaning "integral, with respect to x, of . . ." The symbol (4) is then interpreted as the inverse of the symbol
$$\frac{d}{dx} \ldots ,$$

which means "derivative, with respect to x, of . . ." In this interpretation the integral sign and the dx go together; the integral sign specifies the operation of integration, and the dx tells us that the "variable of integration" is x.

2. Or, we may think of Eq. (2) as written in *differential* form:
$$dF(x) = f(x)\, dx, \tag{5}$$

before the operation indicated by the integral sign is performed. Then, when we introduce the integral sign in Eq. (5) (that is, when we "integrate" both sides of the equation), we get
$$\int dF(x) = \int f(x)\, dx.$$

If we compare this with Eq. (3), we have
$$\int dF(x) = F(x) + C. \tag{6}$$

In other words, when we integrate the *differential* of a function we get that function plus an arbitrary constant. In this interpretation, we therefore think of the symbol $\int$ for integration (without absorbing the dx as part of the symbol) as meaning the operation which is the inverse of the operation denoted by the symbol d for differentiation. This is the interpretation which we shall adopt in this book.

Thus, if we want to solve the differential equation

$$\frac{dy}{dx} = 3x^2,$$

we use the definition of the differential

$$dy = \frac{dy}{dx}\, dx$$

to change it to the differential form

$$dy = 3x^2\, dx.$$

Now we know, from past experience, that

$$d(x^3) = 3x^2\, dx.$$

Hence we have

$$y = \int 3x^2\, dx = \int d(x^3) = x^3 + C.$$

If both x and y occur in the differential equation, but in such a way that we can separate the variables so as to combine all y terms with dy and all x terms with dx, we then integrate as in the following example.

EXAMPLE. Solve the differential equation

$$\frac{dy}{dx} = x^2\sqrt{y}, \qquad y > 0. \tag{7}$$

Solution. We change to differentials

$$dy = x^2\sqrt{y}\, dx$$

and then divide by $\sqrt{y}$ to obtain

$$y^{-(1/2)}\, dy = x^2\, dx,$$

in which the variables have been separated. The left side of this equation is

$$d(2y^{1/2}) = y^{-(1/2)}\, dy,$$

while the right side is

$$d(x^3/3) = x^2\, dx.$$

Therefore

$$d(2y^{1/2}) = d(x^3/3).$$

When we integrate this equation, we may write

$$2y^{1/2} + C_1 = \frac{x^3}{3} + C_2$$

or

$$2y^{1/2} = \frac{x^3}{3} + C,$$

where we have combined the two constants C_1 and C_2 into a single constant

$$C = C_2 - C_1.$$

In fact, when we integrate the two sides of a differential equation, it always suffices to add the arbitrary constant C to just one side of the equation since, in any case, if we add constants to both sides of the equation they may always be combined into a single constant.

Integration, as defined above, requires the ability to guess the answer. But the following formulas help to reduce the amount of guesswork in many cases. In these formulas, u and v denote differentiable functions of some independent variable (say of x) and a, n, and C are constants.

$$\int du = u + C, \tag{a}$$

$$\int a\,du = a \int du, \tag{b}$$

$$\int (du + dv) = \int du + \int dv, \tag{c}$$

$$\int u^n \, du = \frac{u^{n+1}}{n+1} + C, \qquad (n \neq -1). \tag{d}$$

In words, these formulas say that:

(a) The integral of the differential of a function u is u plus an arbitrary constant C.

(b) A constant may be moved across the integral sign. [*Caution:* Variables must *not* be moved across the integral sign.]

(c) The integral of the sum of two differentials is the sum of their integrals. This may be extended to the sum of any *finite* number of differentials:

$$\int (du_1 + du_2 + \cdots + du_n) = \int du_1 + \int du_2 + \cdots + \int du_n.$$

(d) If n is not equal to minus one, the integral of $u^n\,du$ is obtained by adding one to the exponent and dividing by the new exponent. For example:

$$\int x^{1/2}\,dx = \frac{x^{3/2}}{3/2} + C = \tfrac{2}{3}x^{3/2} + C.$$

Caution: One *must* have precisely du as well as u^n in order to use this formula. For example,

$$\int \sqrt{2x+1}\,dx$$

does not fit the formula if we let

$$u = 2x+1, \qquad n = \tfrac{1}{2},$$

because then

$$du = \frac{du}{dx}\cdot dx = 2\,dx$$

is *not* present precisely. But only the constant factor 2 is missing, and this factor can be introduced after the integral sign provided we compensate for it by a factor of $\tfrac{1}{2}$ in front of the integral sign [by(b)]. Thus we write

$$\int \sqrt{2x+1}\,dx = \frac{1}{2}\int \sqrt{2x+1}\cdot 2\,dx$$

$$= \frac{1}{2}\int u^{1/2}\,du \qquad [u = 2x+1, \quad du = 2\,dx]$$

$$= \frac{1}{2}\frac{u^{3/2}}{3/2} + C$$

$$= \frac{1}{3}(2x+1)^{3/2} + C.$$

PROBLEMS

Solve the following differential equations.

1. $\dfrac{dy}{dx} = x^2 + 1$

2. $\dfrac{dy}{dx} = \dfrac{1}{x^2} + x, \quad x > 0$

3. $\dfrac{dy}{dx} = \dfrac{x}{y}, \quad y > 0$

4. $\dfrac{dy}{dx} = \sqrt{xy}, \quad x > 0, \; y > 0$

5. $\dfrac{dy}{dx} = \sqrt[3]{y/x}, \quad x > 0, \; y > 0$

6. $\dfrac{dy}{dx} = 2xy^2, \quad y > 0$

7. $\dfrac{dy}{dx} = 3x^2 - 2x + 5$

8. $\dfrac{ds}{dt} = 3t^2 + 4t - 6$

9. $\dfrac{dr}{dz} = (2z+1)^3$

10. $\dfrac{du}{dv} = 2u^2(4v^3 + 4v^{-3}), \quad v > 0, \quad u > 0$

11. $\dfrac{dx}{dt} = 8\sqrt{x}, \quad x > 0$

12. $\dfrac{dy}{dt} = (2t + t^{-1})^2, \quad t > 0$

13. $\dfrac{dy}{dz} = \sqrt{(z^2 - z^{-2})^2 + 4}, \quad z > 0$

Evaluate the following integrals:

14. $\displaystyle\int (2x + 3)\, dx$

15. $\displaystyle\int (x^2 - \sqrt{x})\, dx$

16. $\displaystyle\int (3x - 1)^{234}\, dx$

17. $\displaystyle\int (2 - 7t)^{2/3}\, dt$

18. $\displaystyle\int \sqrt{2 + 5y}\, dy$

19. $\displaystyle\int \dfrac{dx}{(3x + 2)^2}$

20. $\displaystyle\int \dfrac{3r\, dr}{\sqrt{1 - r^2}}$

21. $\displaystyle\int \sqrt{2x^2 + 1}\, x\, dx$

22. $\displaystyle\int t^2(1 + 2t^3)^{-(2/3)}\, dt$

23. $\displaystyle\int \dfrac{y\, dy}{\sqrt{2y^2 + 1}}$

24. $\displaystyle\int \left(\sqrt{x} + \dfrac{1}{\sqrt{x}}\right) dx$

25. $\displaystyle\int \dfrac{(z + 1)\, dz}{\sqrt[3]{z^2 + 2z + 2}}$

6-3 Applications of indefinite integration. Differential equations, such as Eq. (1) or (7) of Article 6-2, arise in chemistry, physics, mathematics, and all branches of engineering. Some of these applications will be illustrated in the examples that follow. Before proceeding with these, however, let us consider the meaning of the arbitrary constant C, which always enters when we integrate a differential equation. If we draw one of the integral curves $y = F(x)$ (corresponding to taking $C = 0$), then any other integral curve $y = F(x) + C$ is obtained by simply shifting this curve through a vertical displacement C. Thus we obtain, as in Fig. 6-1, a family of "parallel" curves. They are parallel in the sense that the slope of the tangent to any one of them, at the point of abscissa x, is $f(x)$, the same for all curves $y = F(x) + C$. Now clearly this family of parallel curves

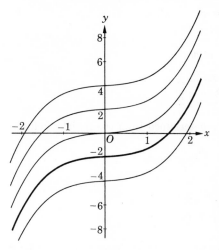

Figure 6-1

has the property that, given any point (x_0, y_0) with x_0 in the allowed domain of the independent variable x, there is one and only one curve of the family that passes through this particular point. For in order that the curve shall pass through the point, the equation must be satisfied by these particular coordinates. This uniquely specifies the value of C, namely,

$$C = y_0 - F(x_0).$$

With C thus determined, we get a definite function expressing y in terms of x.

The condition imposed that $y = y_0$ when $x = x_0$ is often referred to as an "initial condition." This terminology is particularly appropriate in connection with mechanical problems, where time is the independent variable and initial velocities or initial positions of moving bodies are specified.

EXAMPLE 1. The velocity, at time t, of a moving body is given by

$$v = at,$$

where a is a constant. If the body's coordinate is s_0 at time $t = 0$, find the distance s as a function of t.

Solution. The velocity v is the same as the derivative ds/dt. Hence we want to solve the problem that consists of

$$\text{the differential equation:} \frac{ds}{dt} = at \tag{1}$$

and

$$\text{the initial condition:} \ s = s_0 \quad \text{when} \quad t = 0. \tag{2}$$

From Eq. (1), we have

$$ds = at \, dt,$$

$$s = \int at \, dt = a\frac{t^2}{2} + C.$$

The constant of integration may now be determined from the initial condition, which requires that

$$s_0 = C.$$

Hence, the solution of the problem is

$$s = a\frac{t^2}{2} + s_0.$$

EXAMPLE 2. (Fig. 6–1) Find the curve whose slope at the point (x, y) is $3x^2$ if the curve is also required to pass through the point $(1, -1)$.

Solution. In mathematical language, we have the following problem:

$$\text{differential equation}: \frac{dy}{dx} = 3x^2$$

$$\text{initial condition}: y = -1 \quad \text{when} \quad x = 1.$$

First, we integrate the differential equation:

$$dy = 3x^2\, dx,$$

$$y = \int 3x^2\, dx = x^3 + C.$$

Then we impose the initial condition to evaluate the constant C:

$$-1 = 1^3 + C; \quad C = -2.$$

We substitute the value of C into the solution of the differential equation, and obtain the particular integral curve that passes through the given point, namely,

$$y = x^3 - 2.$$

PROBLEMS

In each of the following problems (1 through 6), find the position s as a function of t from the given velocity $v = ds/dt$. Evaluate the constant of integration so as to have $s = s_0$ when $t = 0$.

1. $v = 3t^2$
3. $v = (t + 1)^2$
5. $v = (t + 1)^{-2}$
2. $v = 2t + 1$
4. $v = (t^2 + 1)^2$
6. $v = \sqrt{2gs}$ $(g = \text{constant})$

In each of the following problems (7 through 11), find the velocity v and position s as functions of t from the given acceleration $a = dv/dt$. Evaluate the constants of integration so as to have $v = v_0$ and $s = s_0$ when $t = 0$.

7. $a = g$ (constant)
9. $a = \sqrt[3]{2t + 1}$
11. $a = (t^2 + 1)^2$
8. $a = t$
10. $a = (2t + 1)^{-3}$

12. The gravitational attraction exerted by the earth on a particle of mass m at distance s from the center is given by $F = -mgR^2s^{-2}$, where R is the radius of the earth and F is negative because the force acts in opposition to increasing s. If a particle is projected vertically upward from the surface of the earth with initial velocity $v_0 = \sqrt{2gR}$, apply Newton's second law $F = ma$ with $a = v(dv/ds)$ to show that $v = v_0\sqrt{R/s}$ and that $s^{3/2} = R^{3/2}[1 + (3v_0t/2R)]$.

Remark. The initial velocity $v_0 = \sqrt{2gR}$ (approximately 7 miles per second) is known as the "velocity of escape," since the displacement s tends to infinity with increasing t provided the initial velocity is this large. Actually, a somewhat larger initial velocity is required for escape from the earth's gravitational attraction, due to the retardation effect of air resistance, which we have here neglected for the sake of simplicity.

Solve the following differential equations subject to the prescribed initial conditions.

13. $\dfrac{dy}{dx} = x\sqrt{y};$ $x = 0, \quad y = 1.$

14. $\dfrac{dy}{dx} = 2xy^2;$ $x = 1, \quad y = 1.$

15. $\dfrac{dy}{dx} = x\sqrt{1 + x^2};$ $x = 0, \quad y = -3.$

16. $\dfrac{dy}{dx} = \dfrac{4\sqrt{(1 + y^2)^3}}{y};$ $x = 0, \quad y = 1.$

6–4   Brief review of trigonometry.   Many natural phenomena are periodic; that is, they repeat after definite periods of time. Such phenomena are most readily studied through the use of the trigonometric functions, particularly sines and cosines. Our object in this article is to apply the operations of the calculus to these functions, but before we do so, we shall review some of their properties.

When the angle θ is placed in standard position at the center of a circle of radius r, the trigonometric functions of θ are defined by the equations

$$\sin \theta = \frac{y}{r} = \frac{1}{\csc \theta}, \quad \cos \theta = \frac{x}{r} = \frac{1}{\sec \theta}, \quad \tan \theta = \frac{y}{x} = \frac{1}{\cot \theta}. \tag{1}$$

Since, by the theorem of Pythagoras, we have

$$x^2 + y^2 = r^2,$$

it follows that

$$\cos^2 \theta + \sin^2 \theta = 1. \tag{2}$$

It is also useful to express the coordinates of P in terms of r and θ as follows:

$$x = r \cos \theta, \quad y = r \sin \theta. \tag{3}$$

When $\theta = 0$ in Fig. 6–2, we have $y = 0$ and $x = r$; hence, from the definitions (1), we obtain

$$\sin 0 = 0, \quad \cos 0 = 1.$$

Similarly, when $\theta = 90°$ we have $x = 0$, $y = r$; hence

$$\sin 90° = 1, \quad \cos 90° = 0.$$

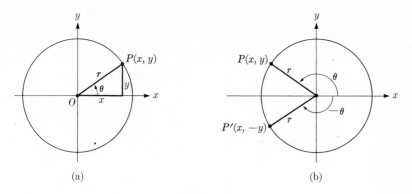

(a)   (b)

Figure 6–2

Figure 6–2(b) shows two angles of opposite sign and equal in magnitude. By symmetry, the points $P(x, y)$ and $P'(x, -y)$, where the two rays θ and $-\theta$ intersect the circle, have equal abscissas and ordinates that differ only in sign. Hence we have

$$\sin(-\theta) = \frac{-y}{r} = -\sin\theta,$$

$$\cos(-\theta) = \frac{x}{r} = \cos\theta.$$

In particular,

$$\sin(-90°) = -\sin 90° = -1,$$

$$\cos(-90°) = \cos 90° = 0.$$

Both $\sin\theta$ and $\cos\theta$ are continuous functions of the angle θ, since a small change in θ produces a corresponding small change in both x and y. However, $\tan\theta$ is discontinuous at angles θ for which $x = 0$, that is, for θ equal to an odd integral multiple of $\pm 90°$. Likewise, $\sec\theta$ is discontinuous when $x = 0$, while $\cot\theta$ and $\csc\theta$ are discontinuous when $y = 0$ in Eqs. (1).

It will be helpful, for reasons which will soon be made apparent, to review the formulas

$$\sin(A + B) = \sin A \cos B + \cos A \sin B, \qquad (4a)$$

and

$$\cos(A + B) = \cos A \cos B - \sin A \sin B, \qquad (4b)$$

together with two formulas obtained from these by replacing B by $-B$ and recalling that

$$\sin(-B) = -\sin B, \quad \cos(-B) = \cos B, \qquad (4c)$$

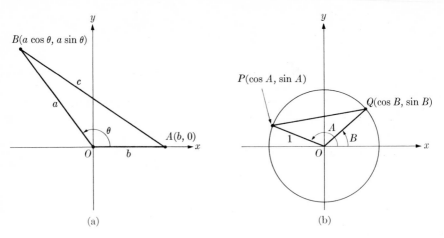

Figure 6–3

namely,

$$\sin (A - B) = \sin A \cos B - \cos A \sin B, \tag{4d}$$

$$\cos (A - B) = \cos A \cos B + \sin A \sin B. \tag{4e}$$

Equation (4e) may easily be established for all angles A and B by two applications of the formula for the distance between two points:

$$d = \sqrt{(x_2 - x_1)^2 + (y_2 - y_1)^2}.$$

The first application gives the law of cosines. The second then yields the identity (4e). The other formulas (4a, b, d) can be derived from (4e) as shown below.

Law of cosines. In Fig. 6–3(a), triangle OAB has been placed with one vertex O at the origin, a second vertex A on the x-axis at $A(b, 0)$. The third vertex B has coordinates

$$x = a \cos \theta, \qquad y = a \sin \theta,$$

as given by Eq. (3) with $r = a$. The angle included between sides $\overline{OA}$ and $\overline{OB}$ is θ. By the formula for the distance between two points, the square of the distance c from A to B is

$$c^2 = (a \cos \theta - b)^2 + (a \sin \theta)^2$$
$$= a^2 (\cos^2 \theta + \sin^2 \theta) + b^2 - 2ab \cos \theta,$$

or

$$\boxed{c^2 = a^2 + b^2 - 2ab \cos \theta.} \tag{5}$$

In words: "the square of any side of a triangle is equal to the sum of the squares of the other two sides minus twice the product of those two sides and the cosine of their included angle." When the angle θ is a right angle, its cosine is zero, and Eq. (5) reduces to the theorem of Pythagoras. Equation (5) holds for a general angle θ, since it is based solely on the distance formula and on Eqs. (3) for the coordinates of a point.

Addition formulas. Equation (4e) follows from the law of cosines applied to the triangle OPQ in Fig. 6–3(b). We take $|OP| = |OQ| = r = 1$. Then the coordinates of P are

$$x_P = \cos A, \qquad y_P = \sin A$$

and of Q,

$$x_Q = \cos B, \qquad y_Q = \sin B.$$

Hence the square of the distance between P and Q is

$$
\begin{aligned}
(PQ)^2 &= (x_Q - x_P)^2 + (y_Q - y_P)^2 \\
&= (x_Q^2 + y_Q^2) + (x_P^2 + y_P^2) - 2(x_Q x_P + y_Q y_P) \\
&= 2 - 2\,(\cos A \cos B + \sin A \sin B).
\end{aligned}
$$

But angle $QOP = A - B$, and the law of cosines gives

$$
\begin{aligned}
(PQ)^2 &= (OP)^2 + (OQ)^2 - 2(OP)(OQ) \cos\,(A - B) \\
&= 2 - 2 \cos\,(A - B).
\end{aligned}
$$

When we equate these two expressions for $(PQ)^2$, we obtain

$$\cos\,(A - B) = \cos A \cos B + \sin A \sin B. \tag{4e}$$

We now deduce Eqs. (4a, b, c, d) from Eq. (4e) and the results

$$
\begin{aligned}
\sin 0° = 0, \quad & \sin 90° = 1, \quad \sin\,(-90°) = -1, \\
\cos 0° = 1, \quad & \cos 90° = 0, \quad \cos\,(-90°) = 0,
\end{aligned} \tag{6}
$$

which follow at once from the definitions in Eqs. (1).

1. Since (4e) is an identity, it is true when we replace A by $0°$ and use (6). The result is

$$\cos\,(-B) = \cos B. \tag{7a}$$

2. Next replace A by $90°$ in (4e), and use (6). The result is

$$\cos\,(90° - B) = \sin B. \tag{7b}$$

This expresses the familiar result that the sine of an angle is the cosine of the complementary angle. The companion result

$$\cos B = \sin\,(90° - B) \tag{7c}$$

follows from Eq. (7b) by replacing B by $90° - B$ and $90° - B$ by $90° - (90° - B) = B$.

3. We next put $B = -90°$ in (4e), and use (6) to get

$$\cos(A + 90°) = -\sin A. \tag{7d}$$

In (7b) we may replace B by $-A$ to obtain

$$\cos(90° + A) = \sin(-A).$$

When we compare this with (7d) above, we find

$$\sin(-A) = -\sin A. \tag{7e}$$

4. Notice that Eqs. (7a, e) agree with Eqs. (4c) and have been derived from the fundamental identity for $\cos(A - B)$. In it, we now replace B by $-B$ and make use of (4c) to get

$$\cos(A + B) = \cos A \cos B - \sin A \sin B. \tag{4b}$$

5. To derive formulas for $\sin(A \pm B)$, we use the identity (7b) with B replaced by $A + B$ or by $A - B$. Thus we have

$$\begin{aligned}
\sin(A + B) &= \cos(90° - (A + B)) \\
&= \cos(90° - A - B) \\
&= \cos(90° - A)\cos B + \sin(90° - A)\sin B \\
&= \sin A \cos B + \cos A \sin B. \tag{4a}
\end{aligned}$$

And Eq. (4d) follows from this if we replace B by $-B$.

These are the key results of analytic trigonometry, and all have been derived simply from the distance formula and the definitions of sine and cosine. The most important formulas to remember are:

$$\sin(A + B) = \sin A \cos B + \cos A \sin B, \tag{4a}$$

$$\cos(A + B) = \cos A \cos B - \sin A \sin B, \tag{4b}$$

$$\sin(-B) = -\sin B, \quad \cos(-B) = \cos B. \tag{4c}$$

If we let

$$\alpha = A + B \quad \text{and} \quad \beta = A - B,$$

so that

$$A = \tfrac{1}{2}(\alpha + \beta), \quad B = \tfrac{1}{2}(\alpha - \beta),$$

and subtract Eq. (4d) from Eq. (4a), we obtain the further useful identity

$$\sin \alpha - \sin \beta = 2 \cos \frac{\alpha + \beta}{2} \sin \frac{\alpha - \beta}{2}. \tag{8}$$

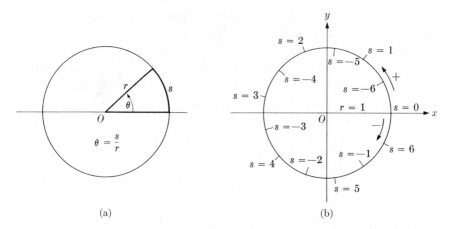

Figure 6–4

Radian measure. In all work with the trigonometric functions in the calculus, it is desirable to measure the angle in *radians*. The number of radians in the angle θ in Fig. 6–4(a) is defined as the number of "radius units" contained in the arc s subtended by the central angle θ; that is

$$\theta \text{ (in radians)} = \frac{s}{r}. \tag{9a}$$

This also implies that

$$s = r\theta \quad (\theta \text{ in radians}). \tag{9b}$$

Another useful interpretation of radian measure is easy to get if we take $r = 1$ in (9b). Then the central angle θ, in radians, is just equal to the arc s subtended by θ. We may imagine the circumference of the circle marked off with a scale from which we may read θ. We think of a number scale, like the y-axis shifted one unit to the right, as having been wrapped around the circle. The unit on this number scale is the same as the unit radius. We put the zero of the scale at the place where the initial ray crosses the circle, and wrap the positive end of the scale around the circle in the counterclockwise direction, negative in the opposite direction (see Fig. 6–4b). Then θ can be read from this curved s-"axis." A unit of arc length, $s = 1$ radius, subtends a central angle of $57°18'$ (approximately); so

$$1 \text{ radian} \approx 57°18'. \tag{10}$$

We find this, and other relations between degree measure and radian measure, by using the fact that the full circumference has arc length $s = 2\pi r$ and central angle $360°$.   Therefore

$$\boxed{360° = 2\pi \text{ radians,}} \tag{11a}$$

$$180° = \pi = 3.14159\ldots \text{ radians,} \tag{11b}$$

$$\left(\frac{360}{2\pi}\right)^° = 1 \text{ radian} = 57°17'44.8'', \tag{11c}$$

$$1° = \frac{2\pi}{360} = \frac{\pi}{180} \approx 0.01745 \text{ radian.} \tag{11d}$$

It should be emphasized, however, that the radian measure of an angle is dimensionless, since r and s in Eqs. (9a, b) both represent lengths measured in identical units, for instance feet, inches, centimeters, or light years. Thus $\theta = 2.7$ is to be interpreted as a pure number.   The sine and cosine of 2.7 are the ordinate and abscissa, respectively, of the point $P(x, y)$ on a circle of radius r at the end of an arc of length 2.7 radii.   For practical purposes we would convert 2.7 radians to 2.7 $(360/2\pi)$ degrees and say

$$\sin 2.7 = \sin\left[2.7\left(\frac{360}{2\pi}\right)^°\right] \approx \sin\left[154°41'55''\right] \approx 0.42738.$$

We include here a short table of the angles most frequently used, their radian measures, and their sines and cosines.

Degrees	0°	30°	45°	60°	90°	180°	270°	360°
Radians	0	$\pi/6$	$\pi/4$	$\pi/3$	$\pi/2$	π	$3\pi/2$	2π
Sines	0	1/2	$\sqrt{2}/2$	$\sqrt{3}/2$	1	0	-1	0
Cosines	1	$\sqrt{3}/2$	$\sqrt{2}/2$	1/2	0	-1	0	1

Figure 6–5

Figures 6–5(a), (b) show graphs of the curves $y = \sin x$ and $y = \cos x$. The portion of either curve between 0 and 2π is repeated endlessly to the left and to the right. It should also be noted that the cosine curve is the same as the sine curve shifted to the left an amount $\pi/2$.

PROBLEMS

In Problems 1 through 6, sketch the graph of the given equation.

1. $y = 2 \sin x$ 2. $y = 3 \sin 2x$

3. $y = A \sin (Bx + C)$, A, B, C constants $\neq 0$ 4. $y = 2 \cos 3x$

5. $y = 3 \cos (2x + \pi/4)$ 6. $y = 2 \tan x/3$

7. Show that the area of a sector of a circle having central angle θ and radius r is $\frac{1}{2}r^2\theta$, if θ is measured in radians.

8. Let $A(r, 0)$ be the point where the positive x-axis cuts a circle of radius r, center at the origin O. Let $P(r \cos \theta, r \sin \theta)$ be a point on the circle in the first quadrant, with angle $AOP = \theta$ radians. Let $\overleftrightarrow{AT}$ be tangent to the circle at A and suppose it intersects the line $\overleftrightarrow{OP}$ at T. By considering the areas of triangle AOP, sector AOP, and triangle AOT, prove the following inequality:

$$\sin \theta < \theta < \tan \theta, \quad \text{if} \quad 0 < \theta < \pi/2.$$

9. In Eq. (4e) take $B = A$. Does the result agree with something else you know?

10. In Eq. (4d) take $B = A$. Does the result agree with something you already know?

11. Derive a formula for tan $(A - B)$ from Eqs. (4d, e).

12. Derive a formula for tan $(A + B)$ from Eqs. (4a, b).

13. Express all of the trigonometric functions of a general angle θ in terms of $\sin \theta$ and $\cos \theta$.

14. A function $f(\theta)$ is said to be

$$\text{an even function of } \theta \text{ if } f(-\theta) = f(\theta),$$
$$\text{an odd function of } \theta \text{ if } f(-\theta) = -f(\theta).$$

Which of the six trigonometric functions are even, and which are odd?

15. Deduce formulas for cos $2A$ and sin $2A$ from Eqs. (4a, b).

16. Let P and Q be points on a circle with radius $r = 1$, center at the origin O, and such that $\overline{OP}$ makes an angle $-B$ with the positive x-axis, $\overline{OQ}$ an angle A. Use the law of cosines to derive a formula for cos $(A + B)$ directly from this configuration.

6–5 Differentiation and integration of sines and cosines. We shall now apply the operations of the calculus to the sine and cosine functions. We need the result given by the following theorem.

THEOREM. *Let θ be measured in radians. Then*

$$\lim_{\theta \to 0} \frac{\sin \theta}{\theta} = 1. \tag{1}$$

Proof. First we shall suppose that θ is a small positive angle at the center of a circle of radius $r = 1$ (Fig. 6–6). In the figure, $\overline{OP}$ and $\overline{OQ}$ are sides of the angle, $\overline{PT}$ is tangent to the circle at P and intersects the side $\overline{OQ}$ at T. We observe that

$$\text{area } \triangle OPQ < \text{area sector } OPQ < \text{area } \triangle OPT. \tag{2}$$

These areas may be expressed in terms of θ as follows:

$$\text{area } \triangle OPQ = \tfrac{1}{2}|OP| \cdot |OQ| \cdot \sin \theta = \tfrac{1}{2} \sin \theta, \tag{3a}$$

$$\text{area sector } OPQ = \tfrac{1}{2}r^2\theta = \tfrac{1}{2}\theta, \tag{3b}$$

$$\text{area } \triangle OPT = \tfrac{1}{2}|OP| \cdot |PT| = \tfrac{1}{2} \tan \theta. \tag{3c}$$

We substitute from Eqs. (3a, b, c) into (2) and obtain

$$\tfrac{1}{2} \sin \theta < \tfrac{1}{2}\theta < \tfrac{1}{2} \tan \theta, \qquad \text{when} \qquad 0 < \theta < \pi/2. \tag{4}$$

Since $\sin \theta$ is positive in (4), the inequality signs will go the same way if we divide all three terms by $\tfrac{1}{2} \sin \theta$. Therefore,

$$1 < \frac{\theta}{\sin \theta} < \frac{1}{\cos \theta}, \qquad \text{when} \qquad 0 < \theta < \pi/2. \tag{5a}$$

We next take reciprocals in (5a), which requires that we reverse the inequality signs:

$$1 > \frac{\sin \theta}{\theta} > \cos \theta, \qquad \text{when} \qquad 0 < \theta < \pi/2. \tag{5b}$$

This quickly brings us to our goal. Since $\cos \theta$ approaches 1 as θ approaches zero, the difference between 1 and $\cos \theta$ tends to zero, while (5b) shows that the difference between 1 and $(\sin \theta)/\theta$ is even smaller:

$$\left| 1 - \frac{\sin \theta}{\theta} \right| < |1 - \cos \theta|.$$

Therefore,

$$\lim_{\theta \to 0} \frac{\sin \theta}{\theta} = 1. \qquad \text{Q.E.D.}$$

Although the geometrical argument leading to Eq. (1) is based on the assumption that θ is positive, the same limit is obtained if θ approaches zero through negative values. For if $\theta = -\alpha$ and α is positive, then when α approaches zero, we have

$$\frac{\sin \theta}{\theta} = \frac{\sin (-\alpha)}{-\alpha} = \frac{-\sin \alpha}{-\alpha} = \frac{\sin \alpha}{\alpha} \rightarrow 1.$$

If θ were not measured in radians but in degrees, the limit that we would obtain in place of Eq. (1) would be

$$\lim_{\theta \to 0} \frac{\sin \theta°}{\theta°} = \frac{\pi}{180}.$$

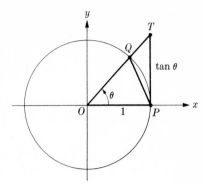

Figure 6–6

It is the contrast between the simplicity of the result in Eq. (1) and the factor $\pi/180$ in this equation that makes it desirable to use radian measure in all calculus operations with the trigonometric functions.

The following table shows $\sin \theta$ and $(\sin \theta)/\theta$ for a few selected values of θ near zero. To get the effect of $(\sin \theta)/\theta$ approaching 1, we read the last column upward from the bottom.

Degrees	θ (radians)	$\sin \theta$	$\dfrac{\sin \theta}{\theta}$
0°	0	0	undefined
1°	0.017453	0.017452	0.99994
2°	0.034907	0.034900	0.9998
5°	0.08727	0.08716	0.9987
10°	0.17453	0.17365	0.995

Derivative of sin u. We now consider a function defined by

$$y = \sin u$$

and calculate the derivative from the definition

$$\frac{dy}{du} = \lim_{\Delta u \to 0} \frac{\Delta y}{\Delta u}.$$

Let u be given an increment Δu and y a corresponding increment Δy. Then

$$y + \Delta y = \sin (u + \Delta u),$$

and hence

$$\Delta y = \sin (u + \Delta u) - \sin u \qquad \text{(a)}$$

$$= 2 \cos \left(u + \frac{\Delta u}{2} \right) \sin \frac{\Delta u}{2}, \qquad \text{(b)}$$

where we have made use of Eq. (8) of Article 6–4, with $\alpha = u + \Delta u$ and $\beta = u$, in going from (a) to (b). If we divide (b) by Δu, we have

$$\frac{\Delta y}{\Delta u} = 2 \cos \left(u + \frac{\Delta u}{2} \right) \frac{\sin (\Delta u/2)}{\Delta u} = \cos (u + \theta) \frac{\sin \theta}{\theta},$$

where $\theta = \Delta u/2$. We now let θ approach zero and make use of Eq. (1), and obtain

$$\lim_{\Delta u \to 0} \frac{\Delta y}{\Delta u} = \lim_{\theta \to 0} \left[\cos (u + \theta) \frac{\sin \theta}{\theta} \right] = \cos u.$$

But since $y = \sin u$, this means that

$$\frac{dy}{du} = \frac{d (\sin u)}{du} = \cos u.$$

If u is a differentiable function of x, we may apply the chain rule

$$\frac{dy}{dx} = \frac{dy}{du} \frac{du}{dx}$$

to this, with the result that we obtain

$$\boxed{\frac{d (\sin u)}{dx} = \cos u \cdot \frac{du}{dx}.} \qquad \text{VII}$$

Thus to find the derivative of the sine of a function, we take the cosine of the same function and multiply it by the derivative of the function.

For example, if

$$y = \sin 2x,$$

then

$$\frac{dy}{dx} = \cos 2x \cdot \frac{d(2x)}{dx} = 2 \cos 2x.$$

Derivative of cos u. To obtain a formula for the derivative of $\cos u$, we make use of the identities

$$\cos u = \sin \left(\frac{\pi}{2} - u \right), \qquad \sin u = \cos \left(\frac{\pi}{2} - u \right).$$

Thus

$$\frac{d\,(\cos u)}{dx} = \frac{d\sin\left(\frac{\pi}{2} - u\right)}{dx}$$

$$= \cos\left(\frac{\pi}{2} - u\right) \cdot \frac{d\left(\frac{\pi}{2} - u\right)}{dx}$$

$$= \sin u \cdot -\frac{du}{dx},$$

or

$$\boxed{\frac{d\,(\cos u)}{dx} = -\sin u \cdot \frac{du}{dx}.}$$ VIII

This equation tells us that the derivative of the cosine of a function is minus the sine of the same function, times the derivative of the function.

For example, let

$$y = \cos(x^2),$$

then

$$\frac{dy}{dx} = -\sin(x^2)\frac{d(x^2)}{dx} = -2x\sin(x^2).$$

The formulas VII and VIII may be combined with the formulas given previously, as in the following examples.

EXAMPLE 1. Let

$$y = \sin^2(3x) = u^2 \qquad \text{with} \qquad u = \sin 3x.$$

Solution.
$$\frac{dy}{dx} = 2u\frac{du}{dx} = 2\sin 3x\frac{d(\sin 3x)}{dx}$$

$$= 2\sin 3x \cdot \cos 3x\frac{d(3x)}{dx}$$

$$= 6\sin 3x\cos 3x.$$

EXAMPLE 2. Let

$$y = \sec^2 5x = (\cos 5x)^{-2}.$$

Solution. First we must apply the formula for the derivative of a function to a power,

$$\frac{d(u^n)}{dx} = nu^{n-1}\frac{du}{dx}.$$

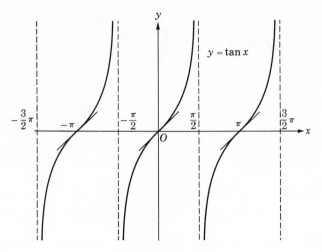

Figure 6–7

We then have
$$\frac{dy}{dx} = -2 \left(\cos 5x\right)^{-3} \frac{d \left(\cos 5x\right)}{dx}$$

$$= \left(-2 \sec^3 5x\right) \left(-\sin 5x \frac{d(5x)}{dx}\right)$$

$$= +10 \sec^3 5x \sin 5x.$$

EXAMPLE 3. Show that the function

$$f(x) = \tan x$$

is an increasing function of x at any point where $\cos x \neq 0$.

Solution. To show this (Fig. 6–7), we let

$$y = f(x) = \tan x \qquad \text{or} \qquad y = \frac{\sin x}{\cos x}.$$

Then
$$\frac{dy}{dx} = \frac{\cos x \dfrac{d \left(\sin x\right)}{dx} - \sin x \dfrac{d \left(\cos x\right)}{dx}}{\cos^2 x}$$

$$= \frac{\cos x \cdot \cos x \dfrac{dx}{dx} - \sin x \left(-\sin x \dfrac{dx}{dx}\right)}{\cos^2 x}$$

$$= \frac{\cos^2 x + \sin^2 x}{\cos^2 x} = \frac{1}{\cos^2 x} = f'(x)$$

exists and is positive at any point where $\cos x \neq 0$. Since $f'(x)$ is positive, $f(x)$ is an increasing function of x. In fact, since $\cos^2 x \leq 1$, we observe that $dy/dx \geq 1$ at every point on the curve $y = \tan x$. (When $\cos x = 0$, $\tan x$ does not exist.)

EXAMPLE 4. Find the velocity and acceleration of a particle moving in a circle of radius r with constant angular velocity ω, $\omega > 0$.

Solution. In Fig. 6–8, if the position of the particle at time t is $P(x, y)$, then

$$x = r \cos \theta, \qquad y = r \sin \theta, \qquad (6a)$$

and it is given that the angular velocity

$$\frac{d\theta}{dt} = \omega \qquad (6b$$

is constant. The velocity is a vector with components

$$v_x = \frac{dx}{dt} = \frac{dx}{d\theta} \frac{d\theta}{dt},$$

$$v_y = \frac{dy}{dt} = \frac{dy}{d\theta} \frac{d\theta}{dt} \qquad (6c)$$

parallel to the x- and y-axes respectively. Also, the acceleration is a vector with components

$$a_x = \frac{dv_x}{dt}, \qquad a_y = \frac{dv_y}{dt} \qquad (6d)$$

parallel to the coordinate axes. From (6a) and (6b), we find

$$v_x = \frac{dx}{dt} = -r \sin \theta \frac{d\theta}{dt}$$

$$= -\omega r \sin \theta = -\omega y,$$

$$v_y = \frac{dy}{dt} = r \cos \theta \frac{d\theta}{dt} \qquad (6e)$$

$$= \omega r \cos \theta = \omega x,$$

and from these we find in turn

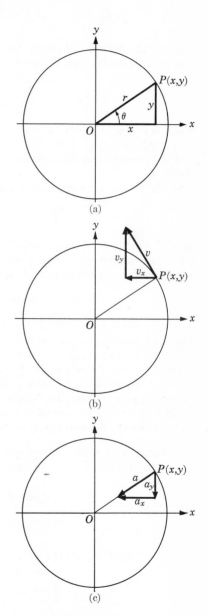

(a)

(b)

(c)

Figure 6–8

$$a_x = \frac{dv_x}{dt} = -\omega\frac{dy}{dt} = -\omega^2 x, \qquad a_y = \frac{dv_y}{dt} = \omega\frac{dx}{dt} = -\omega^2 y. \qquad (6f)$$

The velocity vector has both magnitude and direction. Its magnitude is

$$\sqrt{v_x^2 + v_y^2} = \sqrt{\omega^2 y^2 + \omega^2 x^2} = \omega\sqrt{y^2 + x^2} = \omega r,$$

which is the angular velocity ω times the radius of the circle. Its direction is specified, except for sense, by its slope, which is given by

$$\frac{v_y}{v_x} = \frac{dy/dt}{dx/dt} = \frac{dy}{dx},$$

which is the same as the slope of the tangent to the curve at P. The sense is seen graphically (Fig. 6–8b) to be in the counterclockwise direction, since from (6e) the x-component has a sign opposite to the sign of y if, as we assume, ω is positive.

Similarly, the acceleration vector has magnitude

$$\sqrt{a_x^2 + a_y^2} = \omega^2\sqrt{x^2 + y^2} = \omega^2 r,$$

and its direction will be opposite to that of the vector from O to P, since the latter has components x and y, while (6f) shows that the acceleration has its corresponding components just $(-\omega^2)$ times these; that is,

the acceleration vector $\mathbf{a} = -\omega^2 \overrightarrow{OP}.$

This shows that the acceleration is toward the center of the circle at each instant and has a constant magnitude $\omega^2 r$.

To summarize: If a particle moves in a circle of radius r with constant angular velocity ω, then its velocity vector is tangent to the circle and has magnitude ωr, while its acceleration vector points toward the center of the circle and has magnitude $\omega^2 r$. Hence (by Newton's second law) the force needed to keep a particle of mass m moving at constant speed ωr in a circle of radius r is $m\omega^2 r$, directed toward the center of the circle.

Integration of sines and cosines. Corresponding to the derivative formulas VII and VIII, we also have the differential formulas

$$d\,(\sin u) = \cos u\,du, \qquad\qquad \text{VII}'$$

$$d\,(\cos u) = -\sin u\,du, \qquad\qquad \text{VIII}'$$

and the integration formulas

$$\int \cos u\,du = \sin u + C,$$

$$\int \sin u\,du = -\cos u + C. \qquad\qquad (7)$$

EXAMPLE 5. $\int \cos 2t\, dt = \frac{1}{2} \int \cos 2t \cdot 2dt$

$$= \frac{1}{2} \int \cos u\, du \quad (u = 2t)$$

$$= \frac{1}{2} \sin 2t + C.$$

EXAMPLE 6. Evaluate the integral

$$\int \frac{\cos 2x}{\sin^3 2x}\, dx.$$

Solution. Since

$$d\,(\sin 2x) = 2 \cos 2x\, dx,$$

we recognize the numerator as being

$$\tfrac{1}{2} d\,(\sin 2x).$$

Hence we have

$$\int \frac{\cos 2x\, dx}{\sin^3 2x} = \int (\sin 2x)^{-3} \cdot \tfrac{1}{2} d\,(\sin 2x)$$

$$= \frac{1}{2} \int u^{-3}\, du \quad (u = \sin 2x)$$

$$= \frac{1}{2} \frac{u^{-2}}{-2} + C$$

$$= \frac{-1}{4 \sin^2 2x} + C.$$

PROBLEMS

Evaluate the following limits (1 through 20) by making use of Eq. (1) together with appropriate trigonometric identities and theorems on limits:

1. $\lim\limits_{\theta \to 0} \dfrac{\tan \theta}{\theta}$

2. $\lim\limits_{\theta \to \pi} \dfrac{\sin \theta}{\pi - \theta}$ [*Hint:* let $x = \pi - \theta$.]

3. $\lim\limits_{\theta \to 0} \dfrac{\sin 2\theta}{\theta}$

4. $\lim\limits_{x \to 0} \dfrac{\sin x}{3x}$

5. $\lim\limits_{x \to 0} \dfrac{\sin 5x}{\sin 3x}$

6. $\lim\limits_{x \to 0} \tan 2x \csc 4x$

7. $\lim\limits_{\theta \to 0} \dfrac{\sin^2 \theta}{\theta}$

8. $\lim\limits_{\theta \to 0} \dfrac{1 - \cos \theta}{\theta}$ $\left[Hint\text{: If } |\theta| < \pi, 1 - \cos \theta = \dfrac{\sin^2 \theta}{1 + \cos \theta}. \right]$

9. $\lim\limits_{\theta \to 0} \dfrac{1 - \cos \theta}{\theta^2}$

10. $\lim\limits_{y \to 0} \dfrac{\tan 2y}{3y}$

11. $\lim\limits_{u \to 0} \dfrac{3u}{\sin 5u}$

12. $\lim\limits_{x \to \infty} x \sin \dfrac{1}{x}$ $\left[\textit{Hint:} \text{ Let } \dfrac{1}{x} = u. \right]$

13. $\lim\limits_{y \to \infty} 2y \tan \dfrac{\pi}{y}$

14. $\lim\limits_{x \to \pi/2} \dfrac{2x - \pi}{\cos x}$

15. $\lim\limits_{\theta \to 0} \theta \cot 2\theta$

16. $\lim\limits_{x \to 0} \dfrac{x^2 + 2x}{\sin 2x}$

17. $\lim\limits_{x \to 0} \dfrac{\sin 2x}{2x^2 + x}$

18. $\lim\limits_{h \to 0} \dfrac{\sin (a + h) - \sin a}{h}$

19. $\lim\limits_{h \to 0} \dfrac{\cos (a + h) - \cos a}{h}$

20. $\lim\limits_{h \to 2} \dfrac{\cos (\pi/h)}{h - 2}$

In each of the following problems (21 through 36), find dy/dx.

21. $y = \sin (3x + 4)$

22. $y = x \sin x$

23. $y = \dfrac{\sin x}{x}$

24. $y = \cos 5x$

25. $y = x^2 \sin 3x$

26. $y = \sqrt{2 + \cos 2x}$

27. $y = \sin^2 x + \cos^2 x$

28. $y = \dfrac{2}{\cos 3x}$

29. $y = 3 \sin 2x - 4 \cos 2x$

30. $y = 3 \cos^2 2x - 3 \sin^2 2x$

31. $y = 2 \sin x \cos x$

32. $y = \dfrac{1}{\sin x}$

33. $y = \cos^2 3x$

34. $y = \cot x$

35. $x \sin 2y = y \cos 2x$

36. $y^2 = \sin^4 2x + \cos^4 2x$

37. Using the Mean Value Theorem, prove that

$$|\sin b - \sin a| \le |b - a|.$$

38. Show that the curve

$$y = x + \sin x$$

has no relative maxima or minima even though it does have points where dy/dx is zero. Sketch the curve.

39. A particle moves on the curve

$$x = a \cos \omega t, \qquad y = b \sin \omega t,$$

where a, b, and ω are constants. Show that the acceleration components are

$$a_x = -\omega^2 x \qquad \text{and} \qquad a_y = -\omega^2 y.$$

Evaluate the following integrals, Problems 40 through 60.

40. $\displaystyle\int \sin 3x \, dx$

41. $\displaystyle\int \cos (2x + 4) \, dx$

42. $\displaystyle\int x \sin (2x^2) \, dx$

43. $\displaystyle\int (\cos \sqrt{x}) \, \frac{dx}{\sqrt{x}}$

44. $\displaystyle\int \sin 2t \, dt$

45. $\displaystyle\int \cos (3\theta - 1) \, d\theta$

46. $\displaystyle\int 4 \cos 3y \, dy$

47. $\displaystyle\int 2 \sin z \cos z \, dz$

48. $\displaystyle\int \sin^2 x \cos x \, dx$

49. $\displaystyle\int \cos^2 2y \sin 2y \, dy$

50. $\displaystyle\int (1 - \sin^2 3t) \cos 3t \, dt$

51. $\displaystyle\int \frac{\sin x \, dx}{\cos^2 x}$

52. $\displaystyle\int \frac{\cos x \, dx}{\sin^2 x}$

53. $\displaystyle\int \sqrt{2 + \sin 3t} \cos 3t \, dt$

54. $\displaystyle\int \frac{\sin 2t \, dt}{\sqrt{2 - \cos 2t}}$

55. $\displaystyle\int \sin^3 \frac{y}{2} \cos \frac{y}{2} \, dy$

56. $\displaystyle\int \frac{\sin \dfrac{z - 1}{3} \, dz}{\cos^2 \dfrac{z - 1}{3}}$

57. $\displaystyle\int \cos^2 \frac{2x}{3} \sin \frac{2x}{3} \, dx$

58. $\displaystyle\int (1 + \sin 2t)^{3/2} \cos 2t \, dt$

59. $\displaystyle\int (3 \sin 2x + 4 \cos 3x) \, dx$

60. $\displaystyle\int \sin t \cos t \, (\sin t + \cos t) \, dt$

6–6   Area under a curve.   In geometry we learned how to find areas of certain polygons: rectangles, triangles, parallelograms, trapezoids.   Indeed, the area of any polygon can be found by cutting it into triangles.

The area of a circle is easily computed from the familiar formula $A = \pi r^2$.   But the idea behind this simple formula isn't so simple.   In fact, it is the subtle concept of a *limit*, the area of the circle being *defined* as the limit of areas of inscribed (or circumscribed) regular polygons as the number of sides increases without bound.   A similar idea is involved in the definition we now introduce for other plane areas.

Let $y = f(x)$ define a continuous function of x on the closed interval $a \leq x \leq b$.   For simplicity, we shall also suppose that $f(x)$ is positive for $a \leq x \leq b$.   We consider the problem of calculating the area bounded

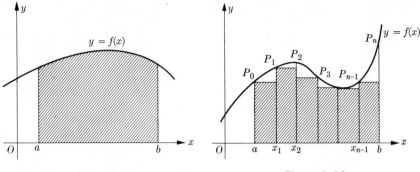

Figure 6–9   Figure 6–10

above by the graph of the function, on the sides by vertical lines through $x = a$ and $x = b$, and below by the x-axis (Fig. 6–9).

We divide the area into n thin strips of uniform width $\Delta x = (b - a)/n$ by lines perpendicular to the x-axis through the end points $x = a$ and $x = b$ and many intermediate points, which we number as $x_1, x_2, \ldots,$ x_{n-1} (Fig. 6–10). We use an inscribed rectangle to approximate the area in each strip. For instance, in the figure, we approximate the area of the strip $aP_0P_1x_1$ by the shaded rectangle of altitude $\overline{aP_0}$ and base $\overline{a \ldots x_1}$. The area of this rectangle is

$$f(a) \cdot (x_1 - a) = f(a) \cdot \Delta x,$$

since the length of the altitude $\overline{aP_0}$ is the value of f at $x = a$, and the length of the base is $x_1 - a = \Delta x$. Similarly, the inscribed rectangle in the second strip has area

$$f(x_1) \cdot \Delta x.$$

Continuing in this fashion, we inscribe a rectangle in each strip.

In the special case where the function increases with x as in Fig. 6–11, we always use the ordinate at the left edge of the strip as the altitude of the corresponding rectangle. Then we have

$$
\begin{aligned}
\text{area of first rectangle} &= f(a) \cdot \Delta x, \\
\text{area of second rectangle} &= f(x_1) \cdot \Delta x, \\
\text{area of third rectangle} &= f(x_2) \cdot \Delta x, \\
&\ \ \vdots \\
\text{area of nth and last rectangle} &= f(x_{n-1}) \cdot \Delta x.
\end{aligned}
$$

EXAMPLE. Suppose $f(x) = 1 + x^2$; $a = 0$, $b = 1$, and $n = 4$. There are $n - 1 = 3$ intermediate points $x_1 = \frac{1}{4}$, $x_2 = \frac{1}{2}$, and $x_3 = \frac{3}{4}$, which divide the

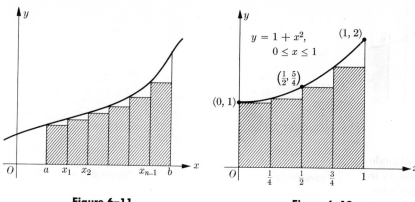

Figure 6-11   Figure 6-12

interval $0 \le x \le 1$ into $n = 4$ subintervals, each of length $\Delta x = \frac{1}{4}$. The inscribed rectangles (Fig. 6–12) have areas

$$f(0) \cdot \Delta x = 1 \cdot \frac{1}{4} = \frac{16}{64}$$
$$f(\tfrac{1}{4}) \cdot \Delta x = \frac{17}{16} \cdot \frac{1}{4} = \frac{17}{64}$$
$$f(\tfrac{1}{2}) \cdot \Delta x = \frac{5}{4} \cdot \frac{1}{4} = \frac{20}{64}$$
$$f(\tfrac{3}{4}) \cdot \Delta x = \frac{25}{16} \cdot \frac{1}{4} = \frac{25}{64}$$
$$\text{Sum} \quad = \frac{78}{64} = 1.21875.$$

Since the area under the curve is larger than the sum of the areas of these inscribed rectangles, we may expect it to be somewhat larger than 1.22. In fact, by using methods we shall soon develop, we shall find that the area is exactly $\frac{4}{3}$. Thus our estimate of 1.22 is about 8% too small. There are easy ways of improving the accuracy, for example by using trapezoids in place of rectangles to approximate each strip, but we defer that to a later time.

If the curve slopes downward as in Fig. 6–13, the inscribed rectangles have areas as follows:

first rectangle $f(x_1) \cdot \Delta x$,
second rectangle $f(x_2) \cdot \Delta x$,
third rectangle $f(x_3) \cdot \Delta x$,

$\vdots$

nth and last $f(b) \quad \cdot \Delta x$.

More generally, the curve may rise and fall between $x = a$ and $x = b$, as in Fig. 6–14. But there is a number c_1 between a and x_1 inclusive such that the first inscribed rectangle has area $f(c_1) \cdot \Delta x$; and a number c_2 in the second closed subinterval such that the area of the second inscribed

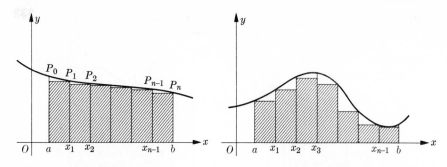

Figure 6–13   Figure 6–14

rectangle is $f(c_2) \cdot \Delta x$; and so on. The number c_1 is the place between a and x_1 inclusive where f is minimized for the first subinterval. Similarly, the minimum value of f for x in the second subinterval is attained at c_2, and so on.

The sum of the areas of these inscribed rectangles is

$$S_n = f(c_1) \cdot \Delta x + f(c_2) \cdot \Delta x + \cdots + f(c_n) \cdot \Delta x. \tag{1}$$

We may also write this in more abbreviated form by using the sigma notation,

$$S_n = \sum_{k=1}^{n} f(c_k) \cdot \Delta x. \tag{2}$$

The Greek letter Σ (capital sigma) is used this way in mathematics to denote a sum. Note that each term of the sum in (1) is of the form $f(c_k) \cdot \Delta x$, with only the subscript on c changing from one term to another. We have indicated the subscript by k, but we could equally well have used i or j or any other symbol except a letter which is already in use for something else. In the first term in the sum on the right side of Eq. (1) the subscript is $k = 1$; in the second, $k = 2$; and so on to the last, or nth in which $k = n$. We indicate this by writing $k = 1$ below the Σ in (2), to say that the sum is to *start* with the term we get by replacing k in the expression that follows by 1. The n above the sigma tells us where to *stop*. For instance, if $n = 4$, we have

$$\sum_{k=1}^{4} f(c_k) \cdot \Delta x = f(c_1) \cdot \Delta x + f(c_2) \cdot \Delta x + f(c_3) \cdot \Delta x + f(c_4) \cdot \Delta x.$$

The only thing that changes from one summand to the next is the numeral in the place indicated by k. First we replace k by 1, then by 2, then 3, then 4. And we add.

Here are a few other examples of $\sum$ notation:

(a) $\displaystyle\sum_{k=1}^{5} k^2 = 1^2 + 2^2 + 3^2 + 4^2 + 5^2,$

(b) $\displaystyle\sum_{k=1}^{3} \frac{k}{k+1} = \frac{1}{1+1} + \frac{2}{2+1} + \frac{3}{3+1},$

(c) $\displaystyle\sum_{j=0}^{2} \frac{j+1}{j+2} = \frac{0+1}{0+2} + \frac{1+1}{1+2} + \frac{2+1}{2+2},$

(d) $\displaystyle\sum_{i=1}^{4} x_i = x_1 + x_2 + x_3 + x_4,$

(e) $\displaystyle\sum_{k=1}^{4} x^k = x + x^2 + x^3 + x^4.$

We turn our attention once more to the area under a curve. We *define* it to be **the limit of the sums of the areas of inscribed rectangles as their number increases without bound. In symbols,**

$$A = \lim_{n\to\infty} [f(c_1)\,\Delta x + f(c_2)\,\Delta x + \cdots + f(c_n)\,\Delta x]$$
$$= \lim_{n\to\infty} \sum_{k=1}^{n} f(c_k)\,\Delta x. \tag{3}$$

Remark 1. The limit indicated in Eq. (3) exists, provided f is continuous. That is, by taking larger and larger values of n and computing the sum of the areas of inscribed rectangles for each n, we get answers which differ from one another (and from what we would intuitively call the area under the curve) by amounts which become arbitrarily small as n increases.

Remark 2. We could have used circumscribed instead of inscribed rectangles. We would then replace the c_k in Eq. (3) by other numbers, say e_k. These would be the places in the subintervals where the function takes on its *maximum* instead of minimum values. The corresponding sums would tend to overestimate the exact area, but in the limit we would get the same answer whether we used inscribed or circumscribed rectangles. The fact that the two kinds of sums of areas of rectangles give the same limit is a consequence of the *uniform continuity* of the function f over the domain $a \leq x \leq b$. It is a theorem which is usually proved in more advanced courses in mathematical analysis. (It is also implied by the inequalities and equations (10) through (14) of Article 6-9.)

Remark 3. Just as we use the simple formula $A = \pi r^2$ to find the area of a circle, rather than resorting to a calculation of the limit of areas of inscribed polygons, so with the area under a curve. We shall not actually compute many areas directly from the definition in Eq. (3). Rather we shall develop from it a method for getting answers very quickly and simply. But first we need the definition of area, as given above, as a starting place.

PROBLEMS

In each of the following problems (1 through 5), sketch the graph of the given equation over the interval $a \leq x \leq b$. Divide the interval into $n = 4$ subintervals each of length $\Delta x = (b - a)/4$. (a) Sketch the inscribed rectangles and compute the sum of their areas. (b) Do the same using the circumscribed in place of the inscribed rectangle in each subinterval.

1. $y = 2x + 1$, $a = 0$, $b = 1$.   2. $y = x^2$, $a = -1$, $b = 1$.

3. $y = \sin x$, $a = 0$, $b = \pi$.   4. $y = 1/x$, $a = 1$, $b = 2$.

5. $y = \sqrt{x}$, $a = 0$, $b = 4$.

6–7   Computation of areas as limits. In Article 6–6 we defined the area under the graph of $y = f(x)$ over the interval $a \leq x \leq b$ as the *limit* of sums of areas of inscribed rectangles. We computed a few sums, but no limits. To compute the limits we need some algebraic formulas. We now develop these. Then we compute some areas as limits to show how it can be done. In Article 6–8 we show how much easier it is using calculus.

We need the following formulas:

$$\sum_{k=1}^{n} k = 1 + 2 + 3 + \cdots + n = \frac{n(n + 1)}{2}$$

$$\sum_{k=1}^{n} k^2 = 1^2 + 2^2 + 3^2 + \cdots + n^2 = \frac{n(n + 1)(2n + 1)}{6},$$

which we shall prove by the method of mathematical induction. This consists in showing that each formula is true when $n = 1$, and that if the formula is true for any integer n, then it is also true for the next integer, $n + 1$. We shall also show how such formulas might be discovered.

First, consider the sum of first powers:

$$F(n) = 1 + 2 + 3 + \cdots + n.$$

Here is a short table that shows how $F(n)$ increases with n. The last column exhibits $F(n)/n$, the ratio of $F(n)$ to n.

n	$F(n)$	$F(n)/n$
1	1	$1 = \frac{2}{2}$
2	$1 + 2 = 3$	$\frac{3}{2} = \frac{3}{2}$
3	$1 + 2 + 3 = 6$	$\frac{6}{3} = \frac{4}{2}$
4	$1 + 2 + 3 + 4 = 10$	$\frac{10}{4} = \frac{5}{2}$
5	$1 + 2 + 3 + 4 + 5 = 15$	$\frac{15}{5} = \frac{6}{2}$
6	$1 + 2 + 3 + 4 + 5 + 6 = 21$	$\frac{21}{6} = \frac{7}{2}$

The last column seems to indicate that the ratio $F(n)/n$ is equal to $(n + 1)/2$. At least such is the case for all the entries in the table ($n = 1, 2, 3, 4, 5, 6$). In other words, the formula

$$\frac{F(n)}{n} = \frac{n + 1}{2}$$

or

$$1 + 2 + 3 + \cdots + n = \frac{n(n + 1)}{2} \qquad (1)$$

is true for $n = 1, 2, 3, 4, 5, 6$. Suppose now that n is any integer for which (1) is known to be true (at the moment, n could be any integer from 1 through 6). Then if $(n + 1)$ were added to both sides of the equation, the new equation

$$1 + 2 + 3 + \cdots + n + (n + 1) = \frac{n(n + 1)}{2} + (n + 1) \qquad (2)$$

would also be true for that same n. But the right side of (2) is

$$\frac{n(n + 1)}{2} + (n + 1) = \frac{(n + 1)}{2}(n + 2) = \frac{(n + 1)(n + 2)}{2},$$

so that (2) becomes

$$1 + 2 + 3 + \cdots + n + (n + 1) = \frac{(n + 1)((n + 1) + 1)}{2},$$

which is just like Eq. (1) except that n is replaced by $n + 1$. Thus if Eq. (1) is true for an integer n, it is also true for the next integer $n + 1$. Hence we now know that it is true for $n + 1 = 7$, since it was true for $n = 6$. Then we can say it is true for $n + 1 = 8$, since it is true for $n = 7$. By the principle of mathematical induction, then, it is true for every positive integer n.

Now let's consider the squares. Let

$$Q(n) = 1^2 + 2^2 + 3^2 + \cdots + n^2$$

be the sum of the squares of the first n positive integers. Obviously this grows faster than the sum of first powers, but let us look at the ratio to compare them.

n	$F(n)$	$Q(n)$	$Q(n)/F(n)$
1	1	$1^2 = 1$	$\frac{1}{1} = \frac{3}{3}$
2	3	$1^2 + 2^2 = 5$	$\frac{5}{3} = \frac{5}{3}$
3	6	$1^2 + 2^2 + 3^2 = 14$	$\frac{14}{6} = \frac{7}{3}$
4	10	$1^2 + 2^2 + 3^2 + 4^2 = 30$	$\frac{30}{10} = \frac{9}{3}$
5	15	$1^2 + 2^2 + 3^2 + 4^2 + 5^2 = 55$	$\frac{55}{15} = \frac{11}{3}$
6	21	$1^2 + 2^2 + 3^2 + 4^2 + 5^2 + 6^2 = 91$	$\frac{91}{21} = \frac{13}{3}$

We note how regular the last column is: $\frac{3}{3}$, $\frac{5}{3}$, $\frac{7}{3}$, and so on. In fact it is just $(2n + 1)/3$ for $n = 1, 2, 3, 4, 5, 6$; that is,

$$Q(n) = F(n) \cdot \frac{2n + 1}{3}.$$

But from Eq. (1), $F(n) = n(n + 1)/2$, and hence

$$Q(n) = 1^2 + 2^2 + 3^2 + \cdots + n^2 = \frac{n(n + 1)(2n + 1)}{6} \qquad (3)$$

is true for the integers n from 1 through 6. To establish it for all other positive integers, we proceed as before. Start with any n for which (3) is true and add $(n + 1)^2$. Then

$$1^2 + 2^2 + 3^2 + \cdots + n^2 + (n + 1)^2 = \frac{n(n + 1)(2n + 1)}{6} + (n + 1)^2$$

$$= \frac{(n + 1)}{6} [n(2n + 1) + 6(n + 1)]$$

$$= \frac{(n + 1)}{6} (2n^2 + 7n + 6)$$

$$= \frac{(n + 1)(n + 2)(2n + 3)}{6}. \qquad (4)$$

We note that the last expression in (4) is the same as the last expression in (3) with n replaced by $n + 1$. In other words, if the formula in (3) is true for any integer n, we have just shown that it is true for $n + 1$. Since we know it is true for $n = 6$, it is also true for $n + 1 = 7$. And now that we know it is true for $n = 7$, it follows that it is true for $n + 1 = 8$, and so on. It is true for every positive integer n by the principle of mathematical induction.

We now apply these formulas to find areas under two graphs.

EXAMPLE 1. Consider the line $y = mx$ (Fig. 6–15). Let b and a be any positive numbers, $b > a$. Let n be a positive integer and divide the interval $a \ldots b$ into n subintervals each of length $\Delta x = (b - a)/n$, by inserting the points

$$x_1 = a + \Delta x,$$
$$x_2 = a + 2\,\Delta x,$$
$$x_3 = a + 3\,\Delta x,$$
$$\vdots$$
$$x_{n-1} = a + (n - 1)\,\Delta x.$$

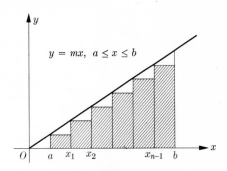

$y = mx, \ a \le x \le b$

Figure 6–15

The inscribed rectangles have areas

$$f(a)\,\Delta x = ma \cdot \Delta x,$$
$$f(x_1)\,\Delta x = m(a + \Delta x) \cdot \Delta x,$$
$$f(x_2)\,\Delta x = m(a + 2\,\Delta x) \cdot \Delta x,$$
$$\vdots$$
$$f(x_{n-1})\,\Delta x = m[a + (n - 1)\,\Delta x] \cdot \Delta x,$$

whose sum is

$$
\begin{aligned}
S_n &= m[a + (a + \Delta x) + (a + 2\,\Delta x) + \cdots + (a + (n - 1)\,\Delta x)] \cdot \Delta x \\
&= m[na + (1 + 2 + \cdots + (n - 1))\,\Delta x]\,\Delta x \\
&= m\left[na + \frac{(n - 1)n}{2}\,\Delta x \right]\Delta x \\
&= m\left[a + \frac{n - 1}{2}\,\Delta x \right] n\,\Delta x \qquad \left(\Delta x = \frac{b - a}{n}\right) \\
&= m\left[a + \frac{b - a}{2}\cdot\frac{n - 1}{n} \right] \cdot (b - a).
\end{aligned}
$$

The area under the graph is defined to be the limit of S_n as $n \to \infty$. In the final form, the only place n appears is in the fraction

$$\frac{n - 1}{n} = 1 - \frac{1}{n},$$

and $1/n \to 0$ as $n \to \infty$, so

$$\lim \frac{n - 1}{n} = 1.$$

Therefore,

$$\lim S_n = m\left(a + \frac{b - a}{2}\right) \cdot (b - a)$$

$$= \frac{ma + mb}{2} \cdot (b - a).$$

This is easily interpreted as the area of a trapezoid, with "bases" (in this case vertical) ma and mb and with altitude $(b - a)$.

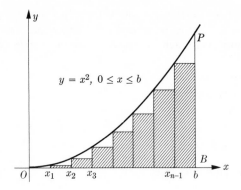

Figure 6–16

EXAMPLE 2. Consider the graph of $y = x^2$, $0 \leq x \leq b$, Fig. 6–16. Let n be a positive integer; divide the interval $0 \leq x \leq b$ into n subintervals each of length $\Delta x = b/n$, by inserting the points

$$x_1 = \Delta x, \quad x_2 = 2\,\Delta x, \quad x_3 = 3\,\Delta x, \quad \ldots, \quad x_{n-1} = (n-1)\,\Delta x.$$

The inscribed rectangles have areas

$$f(0)\,\Delta x = 0,$$
$$f(x_1)\,\Delta x = (\Delta x)^2\,\Delta x,$$
$$f(x_2)\,\Delta x = (2\,\Delta x)^2\,\Delta x,$$
$$f(x_3)\,\Delta x = (3\,\Delta x)^2\,\Delta x,$$
$$\vdots$$
$$f(x_{n-1})\,\Delta x = ((n-1)\,\Delta x)^2\,\Delta x.$$

The sum of these areas is

$$S_n = (1^2 + 2^2 + 3^2 + \cdots + (n-1)^2)(\Delta x)^3$$

$$= \frac{(n-1)n(2n-1)}{6} \cdot \left(\frac{b}{n}\right)^3$$

$$= \frac{b^3}{6} \cdot \frac{n-1}{n} \cdot \frac{n}{n} \cdot \frac{2n-1}{n}$$

$$= \frac{b^3}{6} \cdot \left(1 - \frac{1}{n}\right) \cdot \left(2 - \frac{1}{n}\right).$$

To find the area under the graph, we let n increase without bound and get

$$A = \lim S_n = \frac{b^3}{3}.$$

Therefore the area under the curve is $\frac{1}{3}$ the base b times the "altitude" b^2. The triangle OBP, Fig. 6–16, has area $\frac{1}{2}b \cdot b^2 = b^3/2$, and the area under the curve turns out to be somewhat smaller, as we should expect.

PROBLEMS

1. Verify the formula

$$\sum_{k=1}^{n} k^3 = 1^3 + 2^3 + \cdots + n^3 = \left(\frac{n(n+1)}{2}\right)^2$$

for $n = 1, 2, 3$. Then add $(n+1)^3$ and thereby prove by mathematical induction (as in the text) that the formula is true for all positive integers n.

2. Using the result of Problem 1 and the method of Example 2 in the text, show that the area under the graph of $y = x^3$ over the interval $0 \le x \le b$ is $b^4/4$.

3. Find the area under the graph of $y = mx$ over the interval $a \le x \le b$ by using *circumscribed* rectangles in place of the inscribed rectangles of Example 1 in the text.

4. Find the area under the curve $y = x^2$ over the interval $0 \le x \le b$ by using circumscribed rectangles in place of the inscribed rectangles of Example 2 in the text.

5. Do Problem 2 above by using circumscribed rectangles instead of inscribed rectangles.

6. Establish the formulas given below, for every positive integer n, by showing (a) that the formula is correct for $n = 1$, and (b) if true for n, the formula is also true for $n + 1$.

$$\sum_{k=1}^{n} (2k - 1) = 1 + 3 + 5 + \cdots + (2n - 1) = n^2,$$

$$\sum_{k=1}^{n} \frac{1}{k(k+1)} = \frac{1}{1 \cdot 2} + \frac{1}{2 \cdot 3} + \cdots + \frac{1}{n \cdot (n+1)} = \frac{n}{n+1}.$$

6–8 Areas by calculus. In Article 6–6 we defined the area under a curve and showed how we could estimate it by computing sums of areas of rectangles. Nothing more than arithmetic is involved in these calculations, but we pay the price of getting only an estimate of the true area. On the other hand, in Article 6–7 we used algebraic techniques and actually computed *limits*, thus getting exact areas at the cost of fairly extensive algebraic preliminaries. In this article we shall follow the path blazed by Leibniz and Newton to show how exact areas can be easily computed by using calculus.

To begin we need some preliminary results. We consider a function f which is positive-valued and continuous over the domain $a \leq x \leq b$. Let A_a^c, A_c^b, A_a^b denote the areas under the graph and above the x-axis from a to c, from c to b, and from a to b, respectively (Fig. 6–17). If c is between a and b, we have

$$A_a^c + A_c^b = A_a^b. \tag{1}$$

And this is also true when $c = a$ if we define the area from a to a to be zero,

$$A_a^a = 0. \tag{2}$$

Equation (1) is also true if c is beyond b, provided we adopt some conventions about signed areas. Let us say that area above the x-axis is positive if we go from left to right, and negative if we go from right to left. Thus in Fig. 6–17 A_a^c, A_c^b, and A_a^b are all positive, while

$$A_c^a = -A_a^c, \qquad A_b^c = -A_c^b, \qquad A_b^a = -A_a^b \tag{3}$$

are negative. So formula (1) is also true in the form

$$A_a^b + A_b^c = A_a^c, \tag{4}$$

because adding A_b^c to A_a^b just subtracts A_c^b from the latter, leaving A_a^c (Fig. 6–17).

The following theorem will also be used.

THE INTERMEDIATE VALUE THEOREM. *Let f be a positive-valued continuous function over the domain $a \leq x \leq b$. Let A_a^b denote the area under the graph of f over the domain. Then there is at least one number c between a and b such that*

$$A_a^b = f(c) \cdot (b - a). \tag{5}$$

Proof. Suppose m and M are respectively the minimum and maximum values of f over the domain $a \ldots b$. Then

$$m(b - a) \leq A_a^b \leq M(b - a),$$

and therefore

$$m \leq \frac{A_a^b}{b - a} \leq M.$$

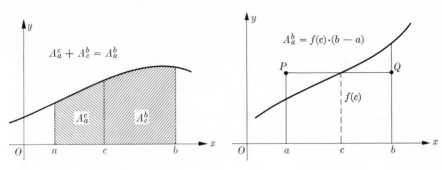

Figure 6-17   Figure 6-18

Since $A_a^b/(b-a)$ lies between the minimum and maximum values of $f(x)$ for $a \le x \le b$, there is at least one place c between a and b where $f(c)$ is equal to this number:

$$f(c) = \frac{A_a^b}{b-a}, \qquad \text{[Article 4-8, Theorem 3].}$$

Equation (5) follows.

Remark. The geometric interpretation of the Intermediate Value Theorem is this. A line drawn parallel to the x-axis at the right place between m and M units above the x-axis will serve as upper boundary of a rectangle having the same area as that under the curve, and it will surely cut the curve at least once between $x = a$ and $x = b$. The abscissa of that cut is a suitable value of c in Eq. (5) (See Fig. 6-18).

To compute the area A_a^b, we now consider any abscissa x between a and b, the area A_a^x, and the area $A_a^{x+\Delta x}$, where $\Delta x \ne 0$ (Fig. 6-19). We shall derive a differential equation for the area function A_a^x. The solution of this differential equation, with the initial condition

$$A_a^a = 0,$$

will enable us to compute the area from a to any x and, in particular, from a to b.

From Eq. (1) we have

$$A_a^x + A_x^{x+\Delta x} = A_a^{x+\Delta x},$$

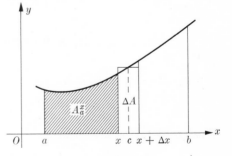

Figure 6-19

so that

$$\Delta(A_a^x) = A_a^{x+\Delta x} - A_a^x = A_x^{x+\Delta x}. \tag{6a}$$

Then, by Eq. (5),

$$A_x^{x+\Delta x} = f(c) \cdot \Delta x, \tag{6b}$$

where c is a number between x and $x + \Delta x$, which must therefore approach x as Δx approaches zero. Combining (6a) and (6b) and dividing by Δx, we get

$$\frac{\Delta A_a^x}{\Delta x} = f(c), \tag{7}$$

and therefore

$$\frac{d A_a^x}{dx} = \lim_{\Delta x \to 0} \frac{\Delta A_a^x}{\Delta x}$$

$$= \lim_{c \to x} f(c)$$

$$= f(x),$$

where the last line follows from the fact that f is continuous.

Therefore the area function A_a^x satisfies the differential equation

$$\boxed{\frac{d A_a^x}{dx} = f(x)} \tag{8a}$$

and the initial condition

$$\boxed{A_a^a = 0.} \tag{8b}$$

Thus if $F(x)$ is any integral of $f(x)\, dx$, we have

$$A_a^x = \int f(x)\, dx = F(x) + C \tag{9a}$$

and

$$A_a^a = 0 = F(a) + C.$$

Hence

$$C = -F(a)$$

and

$$A_a^x = F(x) - F(a).$$

Finally, by taking $x = b$ we get

$$A_a^b = F(b) - F(a). \tag{9b}$$

Equations (9a) and (9b) summarize the method for finding the area under a curve by integration. If the equation of the curve is $y = f(x)$, we integrate this function f to find

$$F(x) + C = \int f(x)\, dx. \tag{10a}$$

If the interval is $a \le x \le b$, we then compute

$$A_a^b = F(x)]_a^b = F(b) - F(a). \tag{10b}$$

The standard notation $F(x)]_a^b$ in Eq. (10b) simply means: first replace x by the upper value b to calculate $F(b)$ and from this subtract the value $F(a)$ obtained by setting $x = a$. For example,

$$2x + 3\Big]_1^5 = 13 - 5 = 8.$$

It is worth noting that the constant of integration may be omitted in evaluating Eq. (10b). For if we use $F(x) + C$ in place of $F(x)$ in (10b), we find

$$F(x) + C\Big]_a^b = [F(b) + C] - [F(a) + C]$$

$$= F(b) - F(a)$$

$$= F(x)\Big]_a^b.$$

EXAMPLE 1. The area under the graph of $y = mx$, $a \le x \le b$, Fig. 6–15, is

$$\int mx\, dx\Big]_a^b = \frac{mx^2}{2}\Big]_a^b = \frac{mb^2}{2} - \frac{ma^2}{2}$$

$$= \frac{mb + ma}{2} \cdot (b - a).$$

EXAMPLE 2. The area under the graph of $y = x^2$, $0 \le x \le b$, Fig. 6–16, is

$$\int x^2\, dx\Big]_0^b = \frac{x^3}{3}\Big]_0^b = \frac{b^3}{3}.$$

Compare both the results and the methods with Examples 1 and 2 of Article 6–7.

EXAMPLE 3. As another illustration of the method of finding areas, let us calculate the area bounded by the parabola $y = 6 - x - x^2$ and the x-axis.

Solution. We find where the curve crosses the x-axis by setting

$$y = 0 = 6 - x - x^2 = (3 + x)(2 - x),$$

Figure 6–20

which gives

$$x = -3 \quad \text{or} \quad x = 2.$$

The curve is sketched in Fig. 6–20.

According to Eqs. (10a, b), the area is

$$A^2_{-3} = \int (6 - x - x^2)\, dx \Big]^2_{-3} = 6x - \frac{x^2}{2} - \frac{x^3}{3} \Big]^2_{-3}$$

$$= (12 - 2 - \tfrac{8}{3}) - (-18 - \tfrac{9}{2} + \tfrac{27}{3}) = 20\tfrac{5}{6}.$$

The curve in Fig. 6–20 is an arch of a parabola, and it is interesting to note that the area is exactly equal to two-thirds the base times the altitude:

$$\tfrac{2}{3}(5)(\tfrac{25}{4}) = \tfrac{125}{6} = 20\tfrac{5}{6}.$$

EXAMPLE 4. Show that the area under one arch of the curve $y = \sin x$ is 2.

Solution. One arch of the sine curve extends from $x = 0$ to $x = \pi$ (Fig. 6–5a). Therefore the area is

$$A^\pi_0 = \int \sin x\, dx \Big]^\pi_0 = -\cos x \Big]^\pi_0$$

$$= -\cos \pi + \cos 0.$$

Since $\cos \pi = -1$ while $\cos 0 = +1$, this gives

$$A^\pi_0 = 2.$$

PROBLEMS

In Problems 1 through 10, find the area bounded by the x-axis, the given curve $y = f(x)$, and the given vertical lines:

1. $y = x^2 + 1$; $x = 0$, $x = 3$.

2. $y = 2x + 3$; $x = 0$, $x = 1$.

3. $y = \sqrt{2x + 1}$; $x = 0$, $x = 4$.

4. $y = \dfrac{1}{\sqrt{2x + 1}}$; $x = 0$, $x = 4$.

5. $y = \dfrac{1}{(2x+1)^2}$; $x = 1$, $x = 2$.   6. $y = (2x+1)^2$; $x = -1$, $x = 3$.

7. $y = x^3 + 2x + 1$; $x = 0$, $x = 2$.   8. $y = x\sqrt{2x^2 + 1}$; $x = 0$, $x = 2$.

9. $y = \dfrac{x}{\sqrt{2x^2 + 1}}$; $x = 0$, $x = 2$.   10. $y = \dfrac{x}{(2x^2 + 1)^2}$; $x = 0$, $x = 2$.

11. Find the area bounded by the coordinate axes and the line $x + y = 1$.

12. Find the area between the curve $y = 4 - x^2$ and the x-axis.

13. Find the area between the curve $y = 1/\sqrt{x}$, the x-axis, and the lines $x = 1$, $x = 4$.

14. Find the area between the curve $y = \sqrt{1 - x}$ and the coordinate axes.

15. Find the area between the curve $x = 1 - y^2$ and the y-axis.

16. Find the area contained between the x-axis and one arch of the curve $y = \cos 3x$.

*17. Take $B = A$ in Eq. (4b), Article 6–4, and show that

$$\cos 2A = \cos^2 A - \sin^2 A.$$

Combine this with the identity

$$1 = \cos^2 A + \sin^2 A$$

to show that

$$\cos^2 A = \tfrac{1}{2}(1 + \cos 2A), \qquad \sin^2 A = \tfrac{1}{2}(1 - \cos 2A).$$

Make use of the last of these identities to find the area contained between the x-axis and one arch of the curve $y = \sin^2 3x$.

18. The graph of $y = \sqrt{a^2 - x^2}$ over $-a \le x \le a$ is a semicircle of radius a. (a) Using this fact, explain why it is true that

$$\int \sqrt{a^2 - x^2} \, dx \bigg]_{-a}^{a} = \frac{1}{2} \pi a^2.$$

(b) Evaluate $\int \sqrt{a^2 - x^2} \, dx]_0^a$.

19. The integral in Problem 18 above can be evaluated by using the substitution

$$x = a \cos \theta, \qquad \pi \ge \theta \ge 0$$

to replace $\sqrt{a^2 - x^2} \, dx$ by $-a^2 \cos^2 \theta \, d\theta$. Combine this with Problem 17 above to show that

$$\int \sqrt{a^2 - x^2} \, dx \bigg]_{-a}^{a} = \int - a^2 \cos^2 \theta \, d\theta \bigg]_{\pi}^{0} = -\frac{a^2}{2} \int (1 + \cos 2\theta) \, d\theta \bigg]_{\pi}^{0},$$

and thus verify the result given in Problem 18(a), by evaluating this final integral.

* The method used in this problem should be used in several later problems involving integration of squares of sines and cosines.

6–9   The definite integral and the Fundamental Theorem of integral calculus. In Articles 6–6, 6–7, and 6–8, we made a systematic study of the area problem. We have arrived at the following result.

If the function f is positive and continuous over the domain $a \leq x \leq b$, then the area under its graph is

$$A_a^b = \lim \sum f(c_k)\, \Delta x = \int f(x)\, dx]_a^b = F(x)]_a^b = F(b) - F(a). \quad (1)$$

The first part of this equation is just the definition of the area as the limit of the sum of areas of inscribed rectangles. The last part of the equation gives a short way of evaluating this limit, that is, by calculus. Therein lies one of the most powerful ideas of "modern" mathematics ("modern" in the sense of post-Renaissance); for the key idea is this: the limit can be evaluated by integration.   This, essentially, is what is known as the *Fundamental Theorem* of integral calculus.   It ties together the summation process (which Archimedes used over two thousand years ago for finding areas, volumes, and centers of gravity) and the differentiation process, from which one may find the tangent to a curve. It is a remarkable fact that the inverse of the "tangent problem" (that is, the inverse of differentiation) provides a ready tool for solving the summation problem. And its applications, as we shall see, extend far beyond the finding of areas.   They include volumes of solids, lengths of curves, areas of surfaces of revolution, centers of gravity, work done by a variable force, and gravitational and electrical potential.

While Eq. (1) above is expressed in terms of area, and up until now has been restricted to positive-valued functions, the Fundamental Theorem is less restrictive.

FUNDAMENTAL THEOREM OF INTEGRAL CALCULUS. *Let f be a function which is continuous over the domain $a \leq x \leq b$. Let*

$$a, x_1, x_2, \ldots, x_{n-1}, b \qquad\qquad (2)$$

be a set of numbers $a < x_1 < x_2 < \ldots < x_{n-1} < b$ which partition the interval $a \ldots b$ into n equal subintervals each of length

$$\Delta x = (b - a)/n. \qquad\qquad (3)$$

Let $c_1, c_2, \ldots, c_n$ be a set of n numbers, one in each subinterval,

$$a \leq c_1 \leq x_1, \qquad x_1 \leq c_2 \leq x_2, \qquad \ldots, \qquad x_{n-1} \leq c_n \leq b. \qquad (4)$$

Let

$$S_n = f(c_1)\, \Delta x + f(c_2)\, \Delta x + \cdots + f(c_n)\, \Delta x$$

$$= \sum_{k=1}^{n} f(c_k)\, \Delta x. \qquad\qquad (5)$$

Finally, let $F(x)$ be any integral of $f(x)\,dx$,

$$F(x) = \int f(x)\,dx. \tag{6}$$

Then, as $n \to \infty$,

$$\lim S_n = \lim \sum f(c_k)\,\Delta x = F(b) - F(a). \tag{7}$$

Proof. We shall first prove (7) for the special set of numbers $c_1, c_2, \ldots, c_n$ that we get by applying the Mean Value Theorem of Article 5–8 to the function F in each subinterval. We can do this because F is differentiable and continuous. Thus, remembering that $F'(x) = f(x)$, we have

$$F(x_1) - F(a) = F'(c_1) \cdot (x_1 - a) = f(c_1)\,\Delta x,$$

$$F(x_2) - F(x_1) = F'(c_2) \cdot (x_2 - x_1) = f(c_2)\,\Delta x,$$

$$F(x_3) - F(x_2) = F'(c_3) \cdot (x_3 - x_2) = f(c_3)\,\Delta x, \tag{8}$$

$$\vdots$$

$$F(x_{n-1}) - F(x_{n-2}) = F'(c_{n-1}) \cdot (x_{n-1} - x_{n-2}) = f(c_{n-1})\,\Delta x,$$

$$F(b) - F(x_{n-1}) = F'(c_n) \cdot (b - x_{n-1}) = f(c_n)\,\Delta x.$$

We add Eqs. (8), and note that $F(x_1)$, $F(x_2)$, $\ldots$, $F(x_{n-1})$ all appear twice on the left side, once positive and once negative. Hence these terms cancel out, leaving only $F(b) - F(a)$ in the sum. Thus we get

$$F(b) - F(a) = f(c_1)\,\Delta x + f(c_2)\,\Delta x + \cdots + f(c_n)\,\Delta x. \tag{9}$$

Since the left side of this equation does not in any way involve n, it remains fixed as we let $n \to \infty$, thus establishing Eq. (7), for this particular way of choosing the numbers $c_1, c_2, \ldots, c_n$.

But the theorem states that the same answer is obtained no matter how the c's are chosen in the subintervals, so long as there is one c in each subinterval. To establish this final result, we recall that the function f is continuous on the closed interval $a \le x \le b$, and therefore is *uniformly continuous* there [Article 4–8, Theorem 3 (iii)]. Hence, if ϵ is any positive number, there exists a positive number δ, depending only upon ϵ, such that

$$|f(c_k) - f(c'_k)| < \epsilon \tag{10}$$

whenever

$$|c_k - c'_k| < \delta. \tag{11}$$

And we can make $\Delta x = (b - a)/n < \delta$ by making

$$n > (b - a)/\delta. \tag{12}$$

For all sufficiently large n, (12) is satisfied. Now let c_1, c_1' be two numbers in the first subinterval, c_2, c_2' in the second, and so on. Form the sums

$$S_n = \sum_{k=1}^{n} f(c_k)\,\Delta x,$$

$$S_n' = \sum_{k=1}^{n} f(c_k')\,\Delta x.$$

Their difference is less than or equal to

$$|f(c_1) - f(c_1')|\,\Delta x + |f(c_2) - f(c_2')|\,\Delta x + \cdots + |f(c_n) - f(c_n')|\,\Delta x. \quad (13)$$

Every term in (13) is less than $\epsilon \cdot \Delta x$, by (10), and there are n terms. Therefore

$$|S_n - S_n'| < n \cdot (\epsilon \cdot \Delta x) = \epsilon \cdot (n\,\Delta x) = \epsilon \cdot (b - a), \quad (14)$$

provided condition (12) is satisfied. This inequality, (14), says that the sums S_n and S_n' that we get from two different choices of the c's in the subintervals can be made to differ by as little as we please [no more than $\epsilon \cdot (b - a)$] by making n sufficiently large. But for the particular choice of the c's in Eqs. (8), we have

$$S_n = F(b) - F(a).$$

Therefore S_n' differs arbitrarily little from $F(b) - F(a)$ when n is sufficiently large. This means that

$$\lim S_n' = F(b) - F(a). \quad (15)$$

Equation (15) completes the proof.

Remark 1. The integral sign, $\int$, is a modified capital S (for sum), intended to remind us of the close connection between integration and summation.

Remark 2. The limit in Eq. (7),

$$\lim \sum f(c_k)\,\Delta x,$$

is called the *definite integral* of f from a to b. It is denoted by the symbol $\int_a^b f(x)\,dx$. The Fundamental Theorem tells us how to evaluate this definite integral provided we know any indefinite integral of the integrand $f(x)\,dx$. We just subtract the value of the indefinite integral F at a (the *lower limit* of integration) from its value at b (the *upper limit*).

Remark 3. If the function has only nonnegative (that is, positive or

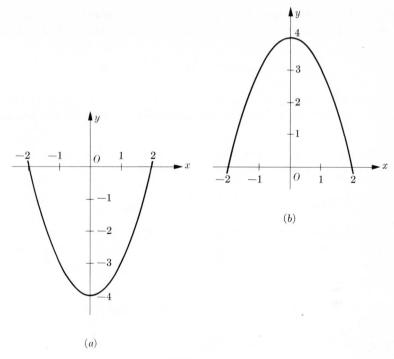

Figure 6–21

zero) values over $a \leq x \leq b$, then the definite integral

$$\int_a^b f(x) \, dx = F(x) \Big]_a^b = F(b) - F(a) \qquad (16)$$

represents the area under its graph, above the x-axis, between the ordinates at $x = a$ and $x = b$. If, on the other hand, the function f were everywhere negative between a and b, the summands $f(c_k) \, \Delta x$ would all be negative (assuming $b > a$ and $\Delta x = (b - a)/n$ is positive) and the integral, (16), would be negative.

EXAMPLE 1. For $|x| < 2$, $f(x) = x^2 - 4$ is negative (Fig. 6–21a).

$$\int_{-2}^{2} f(x) \, dx = \frac{x^3}{3} - 4x \Big]_{-2}^{2} = (\tfrac{8}{3} - 8) - (-\tfrac{8}{3} + 8) = -\tfrac{32}{3}.$$

The area between the curve and the x-axis, from $x = -2$ to $x = +2$, contains $\tfrac{32}{3}$ units of area. The sign is negative because the area is below the x-axis. Clearly, the graph (Fig. 6–21b) of

$$y = g(x) = -f(x) = 4 - x^2, \qquad -2 \leq x \leq 2$$

is just the mirror image, with respect to the x-axis as mirror, of the curve in Fig. 6–21(a). The area between the graph of $y = g(x)$ and the x-axis is

$$\int_{-2}^{2} g(x)\, dx = 4x - \frac{x^3}{3}\Big]_{-2}^{2} = \tfrac{32}{3}.$$

The absolute value is the same as for the integral of $f(x)\, dx$ between the same limits. For $g(x)\, dx$ the sign is positive, since the area between the g-curve and the x-axis is above the axis.

Remark 4. If the graph of $y = f(x)$, $a \le x \le b$, is partly below and partly above the x-axis, as in Fig. 6–22, then

$$\lim \sum f(c_k)\, \Delta x = \int_{a}^{b} f(x)\, dx = F(x)\Big]_{a}^{b} = F(b) - F(a)$$

is the algebraic sum of *signed* areas, positive areas above the x-axis, negative areas below. For example, if the absolute values of the areas between the curve and the x-axis in Fig. 6–22, are A_1, A_2, A_3, A_4, then the definite integral of f from a to b is equal to

$$\int_{a}^{b} f(x)\, dx = -A_1 + A_2 - A_3 + A_4.$$

Thus if we wanted the sum of the absolute values of these signed areas, that is

$$A = |-A_1| + A_2 + |-A_3| + A_4,$$

we should need to find the abscissas s_1, s_2, s_3 of the points P_1, P_2, P_3 where the curve crosses the x-axis. We would then compute, separately,

$$-A_1 = \int_{a}^{s_1} f(x)\, dx, \qquad A_2 = \int_{s_1}^{s_2} f(x)\, dx,$$

$$-A_3 = \int_{s_2}^{s_3} f(x)\, dx, \qquad A_4 = \int_{s_3}^{b} f(x)\, dx,$$

and add their absolute values.

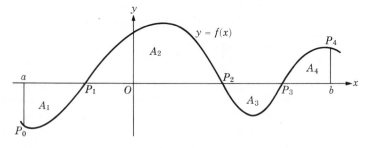

Figure 6–22

EXAMPLE 2. Find the total area bounded by the curve $y = x^3 - 4x$ and the x-axis.

Solution. The graph, Fig. 6–23, lies above the x-axis from -2 to 0, below from 0 to $+2$. (The polynomial $x^3 - 4x$ factors as

$$x^3 - 4x = x(x - 2)(x + 2).$$

It is easy to determine the sign of the product from the signs of the three factors.)

$$A_1 = \int_{-2}^{0} (x^3 - 4x)\, dx = \frac{x^4}{4} - 2x^2 \Big]_{-2}^{0} = 0 - (4 - 8) = +4,$$

$$-A_2 = \int_{0}^{2} (x^3 - 4x)\, dx = \frac{x^4}{4} - 2x^2 \Big]_{0}^{2} = (4 - 8) - 0 = -4,$$

$$A_1 + |-A_2| = 4 + |-4| = 8.$$

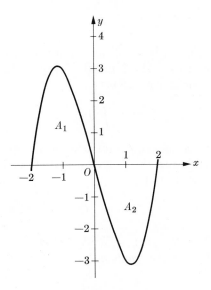

Figure 6–23

Remark 5. The variable of integration in a definite integral plays no essential role. For example, if $f(x) = x^2$, then

$$\int_{a}^{b} f(x)\, dx = \frac{x^3}{3} \Big]_{a}^{b} = \frac{1}{3}(b^3 - a^3).$$

The answer is a number that depends upon the function f, and upon the numbers a and b. But it does *not* depend upon the variable x. We would get the same result if we were to use a different letter, say t, for the variable of integration:

$$\int_a^b f(t)\ dt = \int_a^b t^2\ dt = \frac{t^3}{3}\Big]_a^b = \frac{1}{3}\ (b^3 - a^3).$$

More generally, for any function f that is continuous on $[a, b]$, the variable of integration might be called x, or t, or u, and we have the equalities

$$\int_a^b f(x)\ dx = \int_a^b f(t)\ dt = \int_a^b f(u)\ du.$$

In fact, the variable of integration is often called a "dummy" variable. Sometimes the definite integral is written as

$$\int_a^b f.$$

Remark 6. The definite integral, as a limit of sums, provides a new way of defining functions. The integral of any continuous function $f(t)$ from $t = a$ to $t = x$ defines a number

$$F(x) = \int_a^x f(t)\ dt, \tag{17a}$$

which can be computed as a limit (at least in theory). The function F defined by this formula has the property that its derivative at any x is the value of the integrand f at x:

$$F'(x) = f(x). \tag{17b}$$

THEOREM. *Let f be continuous on the interval $[a, b]$. Let x be a number in (a, b) and define $F(x)$ by the equation*

$$F(x) = \int_a^x f(t)\ dt.$$

Then, F is differentiable at x and

$$F'(x) = f(x).$$

Proof. (We assume $a < x < b$ so that, if h is sufficiently small, $x + h$ is also between a and b).

We use the definition of the derivative

$$F'(x) = \lim_{h \to 0} \frac{F(x + h) - F(x)}{h}$$

$$= \lim_{h \to 0} \frac{1}{h} \int_x^{x+h} f(t)\, dt.$$

By the Intermediate Value Theorem, Article 6-8, Eq. (5), we have

$$\int_x^{x+h} f(t)\, dt = f(c)h$$

for some c between x and $x + h$. When we divide both sides of this equation by h, and then let h approach zero, c approaches x and $f(c)$ approaches $f(x)$. (Why?) Hence

$$F'(x) = \lim_{h \to 0} \left[\frac{1}{h} f(c) \cdot h \right] = \lim_{c \to x} f(c) = f(x).$$

EXAMPLE 3. Suppose $F(x) = \int_0^x \sqrt{1 - t^2}\, dt$, $0 < x < 1$. Then $F'(x) = \sqrt{1 - x^2}$.

Remark 7. The Fundamental Theorem is sometimes used as a tool for approximating sums. This is the reverse of what we did in Article 6-7. There we found formulas for sums of first powers, and of squares, of the positive integers 1 through n. Then we used these formulas to compute limits of sums of areas of inscribed rectangles for the graphs of $y = mx$, $a \le x \le b$, and of $y = x^2$, $0 \le x \le b$. In the following example, we work back from the definite integral (or, what amounts to the same thing, the area under the graph) to an approximation for the sum of the square roots of the integers 1 through n. The process is not completely reversible. We can go from exact formulas for sums to definite integrals by way of limits, but we cannot go back from the definite integral to an exact formula for the sum, because we don't know which terms went to zero in the limit process, and hence we cannot recover them.

EXAMPLE 4. Consider the function defined by $f(x) = \sqrt{x}$, $0 \le x \le 1$. Let n be a positive integer, and $\Delta x = 1/n$. In Eq. (7) take $c_1 = x_1 = \Delta x$, $c_2 = x_2 = 2\,\Delta x, \ldots, c_n = b = 1 = n\,\Delta x$. Then

$$S_n = \sqrt{c_1}\, \Delta x + \sqrt{c_2}\, \Delta x + \cdots + \sqrt{c_n}\, \Delta x$$

$$= \frac{\sqrt{1} + \sqrt{2} + \cdots + \sqrt{n}}{n^{3/2}}$$

$$\to \int \sqrt{x}\, dx \Big]_0^1 = \frac{x^{3/2}}{3/2} \Big]_0^1 = \frac{2}{3}, \quad \text{as } n \to \infty.$$

When n is large, S_n will be close to its limit $\frac{2}{3}$. This means that the numerator

$$\sqrt{1} + \sqrt{2} + \cdots + \sqrt{n} \text{ is approximately equal to } \frac{2}{3}n^{3/2}.$$

For $n = 10$, the sum of the square roots is 22.5^-, while $\frac{2}{3}n^{3/2}$ is 21.1^-, so that the approximation is in error by about 6%.

PROBLEMS

1. For each of the following cases, integrate the given function f to find a new function F, defined by $F(x) = \int f(x)\ dx$. Apply the Mean Value Theorem to this new function F to find an expression for c_k in terms of x_k and x_{k-1} such that

$$F(x_k) - F(x_{k-1}) = F'(c_k)(x_k - x_{k-1}).$$

(a) $f(x) = x$,   (b) $f(x) = x^2$,   (c) $f(x) = x^3$,   (d) $f(x) = 1/\sqrt{x}$.

2. Consider the function defined by $f(x) = x$ and take $a = 0, b > 0$. Show that by taking

$$c_k = \tfrac{1}{2}(x_k + x_{k-1})$$

in Eq. (5), the resulting sum has the constant value

$$S_n = \tfrac{1}{2}b^2,$$

independent of the value of n. (Let $a = x_0$ and $b = x_n$.)

3. Take $f(x) = x^2$, $a = 0, b > 0$ and form S_n, Eq. (5), using

$$c_k = \sqrt{\frac{x_k^2 + x_k x_{k-1} + x_{k-1}^2}{3}}.$$

Show that no matter what value n has, the resulting sum S_n has the constant value

$$S_n = \tfrac{1}{3}b^3.$$

(Let $a = x_0$ and $b = x_n$.) What is the limit of S_n as $n \to \infty$? Note that one should substitute $x_k - x_{k-1}$ for Δx and recognize that

$$\left(\frac{x_k^2 + x_k x_{k-1} + x_{k-1}^2}{3} \right) \Delta x = \frac{x_k^3 - x_{k-1}^3}{3}.$$

4. Take $f(x) = x^3$, $a = 0, b > 0$, and calculate S_n, Eq. (5), taking

$$c_k = \sqrt[3]{\frac{x_k^3 + x_k^2 x_{k-1} + x_k x_{k-1}^2 + x_{k-1}^3}{4}}.$$

Express the result in a form which is independent of the number of subdivisions n. (Let $a = x_0$ and $b = x_n$.)

5. Take $f(x) = 1/\sqrt{x}$, $a = 1$, $b > 1$. Use the intermediate values

$$c_k = \left(\frac{\sqrt{x_{k-1}} + \sqrt{x_k}}{2} \right)^2$$

and calculate S_n, Eq. (5). Express the result in a form which is independent of the number of subdivisions. (Let $a = x_0$, and $b = x_n$.)

Evaluate each of the following definite integrals (6 through 16).

6. $\displaystyle\int_1^2 (2x + 5)\, dx$

7. $\displaystyle\int_0^1 (x^2 - 2x + 3)\, dx$

8. $\displaystyle\int_{-1}^1 (x + 1)^2\, dx$

9. $\displaystyle\int_0^2 \sqrt{4x + 1}\, dx$

10. $\displaystyle\int_0^\pi \sin x\, dx$

11. $\displaystyle\int_0^\pi \cos x\, dx$

12. $\displaystyle\int_{\pi/4}^{\pi/2} \frac{\cos x\, dx}{\sin^2 x}$ (Let $u = \sin x$.)

13. $\displaystyle\int_0^{\pi/6} \frac{\sin 2x}{\cos^2 2x}\, dx$

*14. $\displaystyle\int_0^\pi \sin^2 x\, dx$

*15. $\displaystyle\int_0^{2\pi/\omega} \cos^2(\omega t)\, dt$ (ω constant)

16. $\displaystyle\int_0^1 \frac{dx}{(2x + 1)^3}$

17. (a) Express the area between the curves $y = x^2$, $y = 18 - x^2$ as a *limit of a sum* of areas of rectangles. (b) Evaluate the area of part (a) by Eq. (7).

18. Approximate the area under the curve $y = 1/x$ between $x = 1$ and $x = 2$ by five rectangles, each of base $\Delta x = 0.2$. Use the ordinate of the curve at the *midpoint* of each subinterval as the altitude of the approximating rectangle. The following short table of reciprocals may be used for convenience:

x	1.1	1.3	1.5	1.7	1.9
$1/x$	0.909	0.769	0.667	0.588	0.526

(Compare your answer with 0.693, which is the value of $\int_1^2 dx/x$ to 3 decimals.)

In each of the following problems (19 through 25), use Eqs. (17a, b) to find $F'(x)$ for the given functions F:

19. $F(x) = \displaystyle\int_0^x \sqrt{1 + t^2}\, dt$

20. $F(x) = \displaystyle\int_1^x \frac{dt}{t}$

21. $F(x) = \displaystyle\int_x^1 \sqrt{1 - t^2}\, dt$

22. $F(x) = \displaystyle\int_0^x \frac{dt}{1 + t^2}$

23. $F(x) = \displaystyle\int_1^{2x} \cos(t^2)\, dt$ [*Hint:* Use the chain rule with $u = 2x$.]

24. $F(x) = \displaystyle\int_1^{x^2} \frac{dt}{1 + \sqrt{1 - t}}$

25. $F(x) = \displaystyle\int_{\sin x}^0 \frac{dt}{2 + t}$

* See Problem 17, Article 6–8.

6–10   The trapezoidal rule for approximating an integral. Any definite integral may be thought of as an area, or an algebraic sum of signed areas, as discussed in Article 6–9. We know how to evaluate a definite integral when an indefinite integral of the integrand is known.   But there are simple integrands, for example $(\sin x)/x$, for which no simple indefinite integral is known. In such instances, as long as the integrand is continuous, the definite integral still exists and we may wish to evaluate it numerically. We can often obtain good accuracy by using numerical methods for approximating a definite integral.   These methods are also important for computations done by machines. One of the simplest of these numerical methods is the *trapezoidal rule*, which we shall now derive. (See Fig. 6–24.)

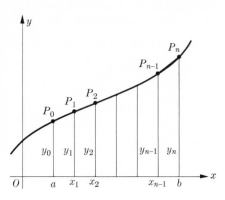

Figure 6–24

Suppose that the definite integral $\int_a^b f(x)\,dx$ is to be evaluated. We divide the interval $a \le x \le b$ into n subintervals, each of length $\Delta x = (b-a)/n$, in the usual way by inserting the points

$$x_1 = a + \Delta x, \qquad x_2 = a + 2\,\Delta x, \qquad \ldots, \qquad x_{n-1} = a + (n-1)\,\Delta x$$

between

$$x_0 = a \qquad \text{and} \qquad x_n = b.$$

The integral from a to b is just the sum of the integrals from a to x_1, from x_1 to x_2, etc., and finally, the integral from x_{n-1} to b;

$$\int_a^b f(x)\,dx = \int_a^{x_1} f(x)\,dx + \int_{x_1}^{x_2} f(x)\,dx + \cdots + \int_{x_{n-1}}^b f(x)\,dx$$

$$= \sum_{k=1}^{n} \int_{x_{k-1}}^{x_k} f(x)\,dx.$$

The integral over the first subinterval is now *approximated* by the area of the trapezoid $aP_0P_1x_1$, which equals $\frac{1}{2}\,(y_0 + y_1)\,\Delta x$; over the second subinterval by the area of the trapezoid $x_1P_1P_2x_2$, which is $\frac{1}{2}\,(y_1 + y_2)\Delta x$; and so on.   The *trapezoidal rule* is: To estimate the definite integral $\int_a^b f(x)\,dx$, use the *trapezoidal approximation* T given by

$$T = \tfrac{1}{2}(y_0 + y_1)\,\Delta x + \tfrac{1}{2}(y_1 + y_2)\,\Delta x + \cdots$$
$$+ \tfrac{1}{2}(y_{n-2} + y_{n-1})\,\Delta x + \tfrac{1}{2}(y_{n-1} + y_n)\,\Delta x \qquad (1a)$$
$$= (\tfrac{1}{2}y_0 + y_1 + y_2 + \cdots + y_{n-1} + \tfrac{1}{2}y_n)\,\Delta x,$$

where

$$y_0 = f(x_0), \quad y_1 = f(x_1), \quad \ldots, \quad y_{n-1} = f(x_{n-1}), \quad y_n = f(x_n). \qquad (1b)$$

EXAMPLE 1. Use the trapezoidal rule with $n = 4$ to estimate $\int_1^2 x^2\,dx$ and compare this approximation with the exact value of the integral.

Solution. The exact value of this integral is

$$\int_1^2 x^2\,dx = \frac{x^3}{3}\Big]_1^2 = \frac{7}{3}.$$

For the trapezoidal approximation we have

$$x_0 = a = 1, \quad x_n = b = 2, \quad n = 4,$$
$$\Delta x = (b - a)/n = (2 - 1)/4 = \tfrac{1}{4},$$

so that

$x_0 = a$	$= 1,$	$y_0 = f(x_0) = 1^2 = \frac{16}{16}$
$x_1 = a + \Delta x = \frac{5}{4},$		$y_1 = f(x_1) = (\frac{5}{4})^2 = \frac{25}{16}$
$x_2 = a + 2\,\Delta x = \frac{6}{4},$		$y_2 = f(x_2) = (\frac{6}{4})^2 = \frac{36}{16}$
$x_3 = a + 3\,\Delta x = \frac{7}{4},$		$y_3 = f(x_3) = (\frac{7}{4})^2 = \frac{49}{16}$
$x_4 = b$	$= 2,$	$y_4 = f(x_4) = (\frac{8}{4})^2 = \frac{64}{16}$

and

$$T = (\tfrac{1}{2}y_0 + y_1 + y_2 + y_3 + \tfrac{1}{2}y_4)\,\Delta x$$
$$= (\tfrac{75}{8})\,\Delta x = \tfrac{75}{32} = 2.34375.$$

Thus the approximation is too large by about 1 part in 233, or less than one-half of one percent.

The graph in Fig. 6–25 shows clearly that each approximating trapezoid contains slightly more area than the corresponding strip of area under the curve. But the polygonal line $P_0P_1P_2P_3P_4$ lies very close to the curve, so we would expect the area under the curve to be quite close to the area of the polygon $AP_0P_1P_2P_3P_4BA$, which is the trapezoidal approximation.

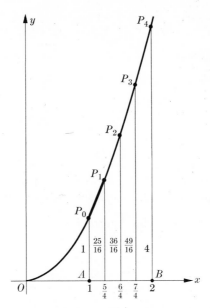

Fig. 6–25. Trapezoidal approximation to area under graph of y = x², 1 ≤ x ≤ 2.

Accuracy of the trapezoidal approximation. It is easy to prove that as n increases and Δx approaches zero the trapezoidal approximation approaches the exact value of the definite integral as limit. For we have

$$T = (y_1 + y_2 + \cdots + y_n)\,\Delta x + \tfrac{1}{2}(y_0 - y_n)\,\Delta x$$

$$= \sum_{k=1}^{n} f(x_k)\,\Delta x + \tfrac{1}{2}[f(a) - f(b)]\,\Delta x. \tag{2}$$

When n increases without bound and Δx approaches zero, the sum indicated by the sigma approaches $\int_a^b f(x)\,dx$ as limit, and the last term in (2) approaches zero. Therefore,

$$\lim T = \int_a^b f(x)\,dx.$$

This means, of course, that by taking n sufficiently large the difference between T and the integral can be made as small as desired.

By methods studied in more advanced calculus (an extension of the Mean Value Theorem), it is possible to prove* that, if f is continuous on $a \le x \le b$, and twice differentiable on $a < x < b$, then there is a number e between a and b such that

---

    * See, for example, J. M. H. Olmsted, *Intermediate Analysis* (Appleton-Century-Crofts, 1956), p. 145.

$$\int_a^b f(x)\, dx = T - \frac{b-a}{12} f''(e) \cdot (\Delta x)^2. \qquad (3)$$

Thus as Δx approaches zero the "error," that is, the difference between the integral and the trapezoidal approximation, approaches zero as the *square* of Δx. By estimating the size of the second derivative of f between a and b, we can get a good estimate of how accurate T is as an approximation to the integral.

EXAMPLE 2. In Example 1 above, $f(x) = x^2$, $f''(x) = 2$, and the predicted error in (3) is

$$-\frac{b-a}{12} f''(e) \cdot (\Delta x)^2 = -\frac{2-1}{12} \cdot 2 \cdot \frac{1}{16} = -\frac{1}{96}.$$

This is precisely what we find when we subtract $T = \frac{75}{32}$ from $\int_1^2 x^2\, dx = \frac{7}{3}$, since $\frac{7}{3} - \frac{75}{32} = -\frac{1}{96}$. Here we are able to give the error *exactly*, since the second derivative of $f(x) = x^2$ is a constant and we have no uncertainty caused by not knowing e in the term $f''(e)$. Of course we are not always this lucky, and in most cases the best we can do is to *estimate* the difference between the integral and T.

EXAMPLE 3. Suppose the trapezoidal rule, with $n = 5$, is used to approximate $\int_1^2 (1/x)\, dx$. Estimate the error.

Solution. Here

$$f(x) = x^{-1}, \qquad f'(x) = -x^{-2}, \qquad f''(x) = 2x^{-3} = 2/x^3.$$

Since $f''(x)$ steadily decreases from

$$f''(1) = 2 \qquad \text{to} \qquad f''(2) = \tfrac{1}{4},$$

we can estimate the error only as lying between

$$-\tfrac{1}{12} \cdot 2 \cdot \tfrac{1}{25} = -\tfrac{1}{150} \approx -0.0067$$

and

$$-\tfrac{1}{12} \cdot \tfrac{1}{4} \cdot \tfrac{1}{25} = -\tfrac{1}{1200} \approx -0.0008.$$

Therefore the integral lies between $T - \frac{1}{150}$ and $T - \frac{1}{1200}$, so that it is slightly about two-decimal place accuracy for the integral by using the trapezoidal rule with $n = 5$, $\Delta x = \frac{1}{5}$. By taking $n = 10$, $\Delta x = \frac{1}{10}$, the error is cut by approximately a factor of 4 (the e of $f''(e)$ in the error may change when n does, and hence we cannot say that the error is cut precisely by a factor of 4).

PROBLEMS

1. Interpret the meaning of the sign of the correction term in Eq. (3) in case the graph of $y = f(x)$ is: (a) concave upward over $a < x < b$, (b) concave downward. Illustrate both cases with sketches.

Test the accuracy of the trapezoidal approximation to the definite integral $\int_a^b f(x)\, dx$ in each of the following problems (2 through 5).

2. $f(x) = x;$ $a = 0,$ $b = 2,$ $n = 4.$
3. $f(x) = x^3;$ $a = 0,$ $b = 2,$ $n = 4.$
4. $f(x) = \sqrt{x};$ $a = 0,$ $b = 2,$ $n = 4.$
5. $f(x) = 1/x^2;$ $a = 1,$ $b = 2,$ $n = 2.$

6–11   Some comments on notation. In each application of the definite integral it is reasonably easy to set up sums which approximate the answer to some physical problem. In general, it will even be possible (though not necessary) to find *particular* choices of the points c_k such that the *particular* sums

$$S_n = \sum_{k=1}^{n} f(c_k)\, \Delta x$$

give the *exact* value. Then

$$\lim_{n \to \infty} S_n = \int_a^b f(x)\, dx = F(x) \Big]_a^b = F(b) - F(a)$$

also gives the *exact* value. But since all sums S_n give the *same* answer in the limit (provided the function $f(x)$ is continuous for $a \le x \le b$, and this condition will usually be satisfied by the functions we shall encounter), we could get the same limit from

$$S_n = \sum_{k=1}^{n} f(x_k)\, \Delta x. \tag{1a}$$

Finally, we modify this notation slightly by dropping the subscript k entirely and writing simply

$$S_a^b = \sum_{a}^{b} f(x)\, \Delta x, \tag{1b}$$

where we write a and b to indicate that we have a sum of expressions, each of the form $f(x)\, \Delta x$, extending over a set of subintervals from $x = a$ to $x = b$. Of course it is not the *sum* (1b) that we are interested in, but rather the *limit* of the sum as given by the definite integral, and the notation (1b) is most suggestive of the final form, namely,

$$\lim_{\Delta x \to 0} S_a^b = \lim_{\Delta x \to 0} \sum_{a}^{b} f(x)\, \Delta x = \int_a^b f(x)\, dx = F(x) \Big]_a^b. \tag{2}$$

As remarked in Article 6–9, it was the close relationship between sums and integrals which led to the adoption of the symbol $\int$ (a modified S) to denote integration.

It should also be noted that *since it is the integral* which gives the *exact* answer in (2), and since the expression $f(x)\, dx$ after the integral sign is the same as the differential of $F(x)$,

$$\frac{dF(x)}{dx} = f(x), \tag{3a}$$

$$dF(x) = f(x)\, dx, \tag{3b}$$

we would arrive at the *correct final result* for the area under the curve $y = f(x)$ between $x = a$ and $x = b$, say, if we were to write

$$dA = f(x)\, dx, \qquad A = \int_a^b f(x)\, dx. \tag{4}$$

It is easy to attach a geometric interpretation to (4), but it is also easy to be misled by this interpretation into feeling that the integral in (4) gives only an approximation to the area, rather than giving its exact value. Enough has already been said on this latter point, however, so that the careful reader need not be a victim of this delusion. If we accept the interpretation simply as a short-cut for setting up the *integral whose value gives the exact result*, we may thereby gain from its simplicity. Namely, if we again think of the area from the left boundary a to a right boundary x, this area is a function of x, with derivative $dA/dx = y = f(x)$, as we found in Article 6–8. When we multiply both sides of this equation by dx, we get the result $dA = f(x)\, dx$, as in (4). But if we think of dx as a small increment in x, we may also interpret this as the area of a small rectangle with base extending along the x-axis from x to $x + dx$, and with altitude $f(x) = y$ equal to the ordinate of the curve (see Fig. 6–26). Then this rectangle gives an approximation to that portion of the area under the curve lying between x and $x + dx$, and we think of the integral

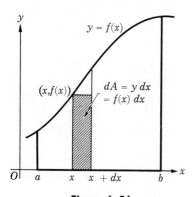

Figure 6–26

$$A = \int_a^b f(x)\, dx$$

as adding together all of these small rectangles from $x = a$ to $x = b$ and then taking the *limit* of the sum so as to give the *exact value*.

It should be borne in mind that what has just been discussed should in no way obscure the fact that a *precise* formulation of the problem would involve a process of

(a) subdividing the interval $a \leq x \leq b$,

(b) forming a sum $\sum\limits_{a}^{b} f(x) \, \Delta x$,

(c) taking the limit, $\lim\limits_{\Delta x \to 0} \sum\limits_{a}^{b} f(x) \, \Delta x$, and

(d) applying the fundamental theorem to evaluate this limit,

$$\lim_{\Delta x \to 0} \sum_{a}^{b} f(x) \, \Delta x = \int_{a}^{b} f(x) \, dx = F(x) \Big]_{a}^{b}.$$

Insofar as the short-cut described above leads to the same final answer, without leading to confusion or feelings of misgiving, it may be helpful and time-saving. But whenever there is doubt that the final answer may only be an approximation instead of a mathematically exact answer, a reconsideration, along the lines which led up to the fundamental theorem, should be made. It is probably desirable, at least in the beginning, to go through the precise formulation first, and then it is but a matter of seconds to repeat the setup of the problem by the short-cut method.

6–12 Summary. Much that we have done in this chapter is related to area. This is useful and gives us a way of interpreting sums like those in Eq. (5), Article 6–9, and Eq. (1a) in Article 6–11. But it is also good to express the main results in ways that don't depend upon area. In this article we shall summarize six results of major importance. Although we have appealed to the notion of area in presenting them in earlier sections, they can all be proved by purely analytical methods, with no reference to area. (See, for example, Apostol, *Modern Mathematical Analysis*, or Buck, *Advanced Calculus*, or Rudin, *Principles of Analysis*.)

Once again we start with a function f defined on an interval $a \leq x \leq b$. We partition the interval into n subintervals by inserting points x_1, $x_2, \ldots, x_{n-1}$ between $a = x_0$ and $b = x_n$. We do not require that the points be uniformly spaced. The kth subinterval has length $\Delta x_k = x_k - x_{k-1}$, which may vary with k. In the kth subinterval a number c_k is chosen arbitrarily, for each k from 1 through n. Then we form the sum

$$\sum_{k=1}^{n} f(c_k) \cdot (x_k - x_{k-1}). \tag{1}$$

This sum depends upon the function f, the points $x_0, x_1, x_2, \ldots, x_n$ and upon the c's. However, for a given function f and interval $[a, b]$ it may happen that all sums like (1) are nearly equal to some constant, provided the subintervals are all sufficiently short. If this is true, then that constant is called the *Riemann integral* of f from a to b, and is variously denoted by $R_a^b(f)$, or $\int_a^b f$, or $\int_a^b f(x)\,dx$, or $\int_a^b f(t)\,dt$, or $\int_a^b f(u)\,du$, and so on.

DEFINITION OF RIEMANN INTEGRAL. *Let f be a function whose domain includes the interval $[a, b]$, $a < b$. Let f have the property that there exists a number $R_a^b(f)$ so related to f that to each positive number ϵ there corresponds a positive number δ such that every sum (1) differs from $R_a^b(f)$ by less than ϵ whenever all subintervals have lengths Δx_k less than δ. Then:*

  (a) *f is said to be* Riemann-integrable (*or, more briefly, integrable*) *over $[a, b]$, and*

  (b) *$R_a^b(f)$ is called the* Riemann integral (*or, more briefly, the integral*) *of f from a to b.*

THEOREM 1. *If f is Riemann integrable over an interval $[a, b]$, then it is also integrable over any subinterval contained in $[a, b]$.*

THEOREM 2. *Every function that is continuous on a closed bounded interval $[a, b]$ is Riemann integrable there.*

Remark. Although we are mainly interested in continuous functions, they are not the only ones that are integrable. All bounded functions that are *piecewise* continuous are also integrable. "Piecewise continuous" means that the interval can be divided into a finite number of nonoverlapping open subintervals over each of which the function is continuous. "Bounded" means that, for some finite constant M, $|f(x)| \leq M$ for all values of x in the interval. Figure 6–27 shows the graph of a bounded piecewise-continuous function over $[a, b]$. For this example, the integral $R_a^b(f)$ would be computed as the sum

$$R_a^b(f) = R_a^u(f) + R_u^v(f) + R_v^w(f) + R_w^z(f) + R_z^b(f).$$

If $b < a$ and $R_b^a(f)$ exists, then we define $R_a^b(f)$ to be its negative:

$$R_a^b(f) = -R_b^a(f). \tag{2}$$

If $a = b$, we define $R_a^a(f)$ to be zero.

THEOREM 3. *Let a, b, c be three numbers belonging to an interval over which the Riemann integral of f exists. Then*

$$R_a^c(f) = R_a^b(f) + R_b^c(f). \tag{3}$$

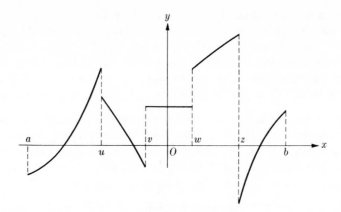

Figure 6–27

THEOREM 4. *Let f be Riemann integrable over* [a, b]. *Let x be any number between a and b at which f is continuous. Then* $R_a^x(f)$ *is differentiable at x and its derivative there is f(x):*

$$\frac{d}{dx} R_a^x(f) = f(x). \tag{4}$$

THEOREM 5. THE MEAN VALUE THEOREM FOR INTEGRALS. *Let f be continuous on* [a, b]. *Then there exists at least one number c between a and b such that*

$$R_a^b(f) = f(c) \cdot (b - a). \tag{5}$$

THEOREM 6. FUNDAMENTAL THEOREM OF INTEGRAL CALCULUS. *Let f be Riemann integrable over* [a, b]. *Let F be any continuous indefinite integral of f, that is,*

$$F'(x) = f(x) \quad for \quad a < x < b.$$

Then

$$R_a^b(f) = F(b) - F(a). \tag{6}$$

PROBLEMS

1. Rewrite Equations (2) through (6), Article 6–12, using the notation $\int_a^b f(t)\, dt$ in place of $R_a^b(f)$ for the Riemann integral of f from a to b.

2. Sketch graphs of each of the following piecewise-continuous functions on $(0, 2)$ and compute $\int_0^2 f(x)\, dx$:

(a) $f(x) = \begin{cases} x, \text{ for } 0 \leq x < 1 \\ \sin(\pi x), \text{ for } 1 \leq x \leq 2. \end{cases}$

(b) $f(x) = \begin{cases} \sqrt{1 - x}, & \text{ for } 0 \leq x \leq 1 \\ (7x - 6)^{-1/3}, & \text{ for } 1 < x \leq 2. \end{cases}$

3. Find $F'(x)$ for $x = \frac{1}{2}$ and for $x = \frac{3}{2}$ if $F(x) = \int_0^x f(t)\, dt$ and (a) f is defined as in Problem 2(a) above, (b) f is defined as in Problem 2(b) above, (c) $f(t) = \dfrac{\sin (\pi t)}{1 + t}$.

REVIEW QUESTIONS AND EXERCISES FOR CHAPTER 6

1. The process of "indefinite integration" is sometimes called "antidifferentiation." Explain why the two terms should be synonymous.

2. Can there be more than one indefinite integral of a given function? If more than one exist, how are they related? What theorem of Chapter 5 is the key to this relationship?

3. If the acceleration of a moving body is given as a function of time (t), what further information do you need in order to find the law of motion, $s = f(t)$? How is s found?

4. Develop the law of cosines from the formula for the distance between two points.

5. Develop the formula for $\cos (A - B)$ from the law of cosines.

6. Write expressions for $\sin (A + B)$ and $\sin (A - B)$. Set $\alpha = A + B$, $\beta = A - B$ and develop a formula for $\sin \alpha - \sin \beta$.

7. Under what assumptions is it true that $\lim \dfrac{\sin \theta}{\theta} = 1$? Prove the result.

8. Write expressions for $\cos (A + B)$ and $\cos (A - B)$. Set $\alpha = A + B$, $\beta = A - B$, and develop a formula for $\cos \alpha - \cos \beta$. Use the result to develop a formula for the derivative of $\cos x$, from the definition

$$\frac{d(\cos x)}{dx} = \lim_{\Delta x \to 0} \frac{\cos (x + \Delta x) - \cos x}{\Delta x}.$$

9. Let A_n be the area bounded by a regular n-sided polygon inscribed in a circle of radius r. Show that $A_n = (n/2)r^2 \sin (2\pi/n)$. Find $\lim A_n$ as $n \to \infty$. Does the result agree with what you know about the area of a circle?

10. Write a formula for the area bounded above by the semicircle $y = \sqrt{r^2 - t^2}$, below by the t-axis, on the left by the y-axis, and on the right by the line $t = x$. Without making any calculations, what do you know must be the derivative, with respect to x, of this expression? Explain.

11. What property of continuous functions is used in the proof of the Intermediate Value Theorem?

12. Is every Riemann-integrable function also differentiable? Give a reason for your answer.

13. Is the function f defined on the domain $0 \le x \le 1$ by

$$f(x) = \begin{cases} 0 \text{ when } x \text{ is rational} \\ 1 \text{ when } x \text{ is irrational} \end{cases}$$

Riemann-integrable over $(0, 1)$? Give a reason for your answer.

14. If you could not find an indefinite integral of $f(x)\, dx$, how could you still calculate $\int_a^b f(x)\, dx$ to any specified number of decimal places of accuracy, assuming f is continuous over $a \le x \le b$? Illustrate for $f(x) = 1/x$, $a = 1$, $b = 2$, and one-decimal-place accuracy.

Solve the differential equations in Problems 1–5.

1. $\dfrac{dy}{dx} = xy^2$

2. $\dfrac{dy}{dx} = \sqrt{1 + x + y + xy}$

3. $\dfrac{dy}{dx} = \dfrac{x^2 - 1}{y^2 + 1}$

4. $\dfrac{dx}{dy} = \dfrac{y - \sqrt{y}}{x + \sqrt{x}}$

5. $\dfrac{dx}{dy} = \left(\dfrac{2 + x}{3 - y}\right)^2$

6. Solve each of the following differential equations subject to the prescribed initial conditions:

(a) $\dfrac{dy}{dx} = x\sqrt{x^2 - 4};\quad x = 2,\ y = 3.$ (b) $\dfrac{dy}{dx} = xy^3;\quad x = 0,\ y = 1.$

7. Can there be a curve satisfying the following conditions? d^2y/dx^2 is everywhere equal to zero and, when $x = 0$, $y = 0$ and $dy/dx = 1$. Give a reason for your answer.

8. Find an equation of the curve whose slope at the point (x, y) is $3x^2 + 2$, if the curve is required to pass through the point $(1, -1)$.

9. A particle moves along the x-axis. Its acceleration is $a = -t^2$. At $t = 0$, the particle is at the origin. In the course of its motion, it reaches the point $x = b$, where $b > 0$, but no point beyond b. Determine its velocity at $t = 0$.

10. A particle moves with acceleration $a = \sqrt{t} - (1/\sqrt{t})$. Assuming that the velocity $v = 2$ and the distance $s = 5$ when $t = 0$, find (a) the velocity v in terms of t, (b) the distance s in terms of t.

11. A particle is accelerated with acceleration $3 + 2t$, where t is the time. At $t = 0$, the velocity is 4. Find the velocity as a function of time and the distance between the position of the particle at time zero and at time 4.

12. The acceleration of a particle moving along the x-axis is given by $d^2x/dt^2 = -4x$. If the particle starts from rest at $x = 5$, find the velocity when it first reaches $x = 3$.

13. Let $f(x)$, $g(x)$ be two continuously differentiable functions satisfying the relationships $f'(x) = g(x)$; $f''(x) = -f(x)$. Let $h(x) = f^2(x) + g^2(x)$. If $h(0) = 5$, find $h(10)$.

14. The family of straight lines $y = ax + b$ (a, b arbitrary constants) can be characterized by the relation $y'' = 0$. Find a similar relation satisfied by the family of all circles $(x - h)^2 + (y - h)^2 = r^2$, where h and r are arbitrary constants. [*Hint:* Eliminate h and r from the set of three equations including the given one and two obtained by successive differentiation.]

15. Assume that the brakes of an automobile produce a constant deceleration of k ft/sec². (a) Determine what k must be to bring an automobile traveling 60 mi/hr (88 ft/sec) to rest in a distance of 100 ft from the point where the brakes

* These problems can be taken up during, or after, the study of Chapter 9.

are applied. (b) With the same k, how far would a car traveling 30 mi/hr travel before being brought to a stop?

16. Solve the differential equation $dy/dx = x\sqrt{1 + x^2}$ subject to the condition that $y = -2$ when $x = 0$.

17. The acceleration due to gravity is -32 ft/sec^2. A stone is thrown upward from the ground with a speed of 96 ft/sec. Find the height to which the stone rises in t sec. What is the maximum height reached by the stone?

18. (*Amer. Math. Monthly*, 1955, M. S. Klamkin.) Show that the following procedure will produce a continuous polygonal "curve" whose slope at the point (x_k, y_k) will be $f(x_k)$. First, sketch the auxiliary curve $C:y = xf(x)$. Then through the point $P_0(x_0, y_0)$, draw the ordinate $x = x_0$ intersecting C in $Q_0(x_0, x_0 f(x_0))$. Through P_0 draw a line segment $\overline{P_0 P_1}$ parallel to $\overrightarrow{OQ_0}$. Then the slope of $\overrightarrow{P_0 P_1}$ is $f(x_0)$. Now take $P_1(x_1, y_1)$ on this segment to lie close to P_0. For example, take $x_1 = x_0 + h$, where h is small. Then find $Q_1(x_1, x_1 f(x_1))$ on C and through P_1 draw a line segment $\overline{P_1 P_2}$ parallel to $\overrightarrow{OQ_1}$. Continue the process by taking $P_2(x_2, y_2)$ close to P_1, with $x_2 = x_1 + h$; then find $Q_2(x_2, x_2 f(x_2))$ on C and through P_2 draw a line segment $\overline{P_2 P_3}$ parallel to $\overrightarrow{OQ_2}$; and so on.

19. (a) Apply the procedure of Problem 18 to the case $f(x) = 1/x$ with $x_0 = 1$, $y_0 = 1$, and $h = \frac{1}{4}$. Continue the process until you reach the point $P_4(x_4, y_4)$. What is your value of y_4? (b) Repeat the construction of part (a), but with $h = \frac{1}{8}$, and continue until you reach $x_8 = 2$. What is your value of y_8?

20. A body is moving with velocity 16 ft/sec when it is suddenly subjected to a deceleration. If the deceleration is proportional to the square root of the velocity, and the body comes to rest in 4 sec, (a) how fast is the body moving 2 sec after it begins decelerating, and (b) how far does the body travel before coming to rest?

Evaluate the integrals in Problems 21 through 33:

21. $\displaystyle \int \frac{x^3 + 1}{x^2}\, dx$

22. $\displaystyle \int y\sqrt{1 + y^2}\, dy$

23. $\displaystyle \int t^{1/3}(1 + t^{4/3})^{-7}\, dt$

24. $\displaystyle \int \frac{(1 + \sqrt{u})^{1/2}}{\sqrt{u}}\, du$

25. $\displaystyle \int \frac{dr}{\sqrt[3]{(7 - 5r)^2}}$

26. $\displaystyle \int \cos 4x\, dx$

27. $\displaystyle \int \sin^2 3x \cos 3x\, dx$

28. $\displaystyle \int \frac{\cos x\, dx}{\sqrt{\sin x}}$

29. $\displaystyle \int \cos (2x - 1)\, dx$

30. $\displaystyle \int \frac{y\, dy}{\sqrt{25 - 4y^2}}$

31. $\displaystyle \int \frac{dt}{t\sqrt{2t}}$

32. $\displaystyle \int (x^2 - \sqrt{x})\, dx$

33. $\displaystyle \int \frac{dx}{(2 - 3x)^2}$

Find dy/dx in Problems 34 through 38:

34. $y = \cos(1 - 2x)$

35. $y = \dfrac{\cos x}{\sin x}$

36. $y = \sec^2(5x)$

37. $y = \sin^4 5x$

38. $y^3 = \sin^3 x + \cos^3 x$

39. Given $y = 3 \sin 2x$ and $x = u^2 + \pi$, find the value of dy/du when $u = 0$.

40. If $0 < x < \pi/2$, prove that $x > \sin x > 2x/\pi$.

41. If one side and the opposite angle of a triangle are fixed, prove that the area is a maximum when the triangle is isosceles.

42. A light hangs above the center of a table of radius r ft. The illumination at any point on the table is directly proportional to the cosine of the angle of incidence (i.e., the angle a ray of light makes with the normal) and is inversely proportional to the square of the distance from the light. How far should the light be above the table in order to give the strongest illumination at the edge of the table?

43. If A, B, C are constants, $AB \neq 0$, prove that the graph of the curve $y = A \sin(Bx + C)$ is always concave toward the x-axis and that its points of inflection coincide with its points of intersection with the x-axis.

44. Two particles move on the same straight line so that their distances from a fixed point O, at any time t, are $x_1 = a \sin bt$ and $x_2 = a \sin[bt + (\pi/3)]$, where a and b are constants, $ab \neq 0$. Find the greatest distance between them.

45. If the identity $\sin(x + a) = \sin x \cos a + \cos x \sin a$ is differentiated with respect to x, is the resulting equation also an identity? Does this principle apply to the equation $x^2 - 2x - 8 = 0$? Explain.

46. A revolving beacon light in a lighthouse $\frac{1}{2}$ mile offshore makes two revolutions per minute. If the shoreline is a straight line, how fast is the ray of light moving along the shore when it passes a point one mile from the lighthouse?

47. The coordinates of a moving particle are $x = a \cos^3 \theta$, $y = a \sin^3 \theta$. If a is a positive constant and θ increases at the constant rate of ω rad/sec, find the magnitude of the velocity vector.

48. The area bounded by the x-axis, the curve $y = f(x)$, and the lines $x = a$, $x = b$ is equal to $\sqrt{b^2 - a^2}$ for all $b > a$. Find $f(x)$.

49. Evaluate the following limits:

(a) $\lim\limits_{x \to 0} \dfrac{2 \sin 5x}{3x}$;

(b) $\lim\limits_{x \to 0} \sin 5x \cot 3x$;

(c) $\lim\limits_{x \to 0} x \csc^2 \sqrt{2x}$.

50. Find dy/dx and d^2y/dx^2 if $x = \cos 3t$ and $y = \sin^2 3t$.

51. Let $f(x)$ be a continuous function. Express

$$\lim_{n \to \infty} \frac{1}{n}\left[f\left(\frac{1}{n}\right) + f\left(\frac{2}{n}\right) + \cdots + f\left(\frac{n}{n}\right) \right]$$

as a definite integral.

52. Use the result of Problem 51 to evaluate:

(a) $\lim\limits_{n \to \infty} \dfrac{1}{n^{16}} [1^{15} + 2^{15} + 3^{15} + \cdots + n^{15}]$,

(b) $\lim\limits_{n\to\infty} \dfrac{\sqrt{1}+\sqrt{2}+\sqrt{3}+\cdots+\sqrt{n}}{n^{3/2}}$,

(c) $\lim\limits_{n\to\infty} \dfrac{1}{n}\left[\sin\dfrac{\pi}{n}+\sin\dfrac{2\pi}{n}+\sin\dfrac{3\pi}{n}+\cdots+\sin\dfrac{n\pi}{n}\right]$.

Find:

(d) $\lim\limits_{h\to 0} \dfrac{1}{h}\displaystyle\int_x^{x+h} \dfrac{du}{u+\sqrt{u^2+1}}$,   (e) $\lim\limits_{x\to x_1}\left[\dfrac{x}{x-x_1}\displaystyle\int_{x_1}^x f(t)\,dt\right]$.

53. Variables x and y are related by the equation

$$x = \int_0^y \frac{1}{\sqrt{1+4t^2}}\,dt.$$

Show that d^2y/dx^2 is proportional to y and find the constant of proportionality.

CHAPTER **7**

Applications of the Definite Integral

7–1 Introduction. In Chapter 6 we discovered a close connection between sums of the form

$$S_a^b = \sum_a^b f(x)\,\Delta x \tag{1}$$

and integration, the inverse of differentiation. When f is continuous on $a \leq x \leq b$, we found that the *limit* of S_a^b as Δx approaches zero is just $F(b) - F(a)$, where F is any integral of f:

$$F(x) = \int f(x)\,dx. \tag{2}$$

We applied this to the problem of computing the area between the x-axis and the graph of $y = f(x)$, $a \leq x \leq b$. In this chapter we shall extend the applications to the following topics: area between two curves, distance, volumes, lengths of curves, areas of surfaces of revolution, average value of a function, center of mass, centroid, and work.

7–2 Area between two curves. Suppose that

$$y_1 = f_1(x), \qquad y_2 = f_2(x)$$

define two functions of x that are continuous for $a \leq x \leq b$, and furthermore, suppose that

$$f_1(x) \geq f_2(x) \qquad \text{for} \qquad a \leq x \leq b.$$

Then the y_1 curve is above the y_2 curve from a to b (Fig. 7–1) and we consider the problem of finding the area bounded above by the y_1 curve, below by the y_2 curve, and on the sides by the vertical lines $x = a$, $x = b$. If the x-interval from a to b is divided into n equal subintervals, each of width $\Delta x = (b - a)/n$, and a rectangle of width Δx and altitude extending from the y_2 curve to the y_1 curve is used to approximate that portion of the area between the curves that lies between x and $x + \Delta x$, we find the area of such a rectangle is

$$(y_1 - y_2)\,\Delta x = [f_1(x) - f_2(x)]\,\Delta x.$$

273

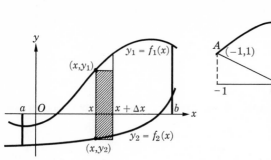

Figure 7–1   Figure 7–2

The total area in question is *approximated* by adding together the areas
of all such rectangles

$$A \approx \sum_{a}^{b} [f_1(x) - f_2(x)] \, \Delta x.$$

Finally, if we let $\Delta x \to 0$, we obtain the exact area:

$$A = \lim_{\Delta x \to 0} \sum_{a}^{b} [f_1(x) - f_2(x)] \, \Delta x = \int_{a}^{b} [f_1(x) - f_2(x)] \, dx. \qquad (1)$$

EXAMPLE. Find the area (Fig. 7–2) bounded by the parabola

$$y = 2 - x^2$$

and the straight line

$$y = -x.$$

Solution. We first find where the curves intersect by finding points that
satisfy both equations simultaneously. That is, we solve

$$2 - x^2 = -x$$

or
$$x^2 - x - 2 = 0, \qquad (x - 2)(x + 1) = 0, \qquad x = -1, \, 2.$$

The points of intersection are thus $A(-1, 1)$ and $B(2, -2)$. For all values of x
between -1 and $+2$, the curve

$$y_1 = 2 - x^2$$

is above the line

$$y_2 = -x$$

by an amount

$$y_1 - y_2 = (2 - x^2) - (-x) = 2 - x^2 + x.$$

This is the altitude of a typical rectangle used to approximate that portion of the area lying between x and $x + \Delta x$. The total area is approximated by

$$A^2_{-1} \approx \sum_{-1}^{2} (y_1 - y_2) \, \Delta x = \sum_{-1}^{2} (2 - x^2 + x) \, \Delta x$$

and is given exactly by

$$A^2_{-1} = \lim_{\Delta x \to 0} \sum_{-1}^{2} (2 - x^2 + x) \, \Delta x = \int_{-1}^{2} (2 - x^2 + x) \, dx = 4\tfrac{1}{2}.$$

PROBLEMS

1. Make a sketch to represent a region that is bounded on the right by a continuous curve $x = f(y)$, on the left by a continuous curve $x = g(y)$, below by the line $y = a$, and above by the line $y = b$. Divide the region into n horizontal strips each of altitude $\Delta y = (b - a)/n$ and express the area of the region (a) as a limit of a sum of areas of rectangles, and (b) as an appropriate definite integral.

2. Find the area bounded by the x-axis and the curve $y = 2x - x^2$.

3. Find the area bounded by the y-axis and the curve $x = y^2 - y^3$.

4. Find the area bounded by the curve $y^2 = x$ and the line $x = 4$.

5. Find the area bounded by the curve $y = 2x - x^2$ and the line $y = -3$.

6. Find the area bounded by the curve $y = x^2$ and the line $y = x$.

7. Find the area bounded by the curve $x = 3y - y^2$ and the line $x + y = 3$.

8. Find the area bounded by the curves $y = x^4 - 2x^2$ and $y = 2x^2$.

9. Find the area of the "triangular" shaped region in the first quadrant bounded by the y-axis and the curves $y = \sin x$, $y = \cos x$.

10. The area bounded by the curve $y = x^2$ and the line $y = 4$ is divided into two equal portions by the line $y = c$. Find c.

11. Find the area bounded by the curve $\sqrt{x} + \sqrt{y} = 1$ and the coordinate axes.

7-3 **Distance.** As a second application of the basic principles involved in the use of the Fundamental Theorem of the calculus, we shall calculate the distance traveled by a body moving with velocity

$$v = f(t). \tag{1}$$

To simplify the discussion we shall assume that $f(t)$ is positive, as well as being continuous, for $a \leq t \leq b$. This means that the body moves only in one direction and does no backing up.

Now there are two ways in which we can calculate the distance traveled by the body between $t = a$ and $t = b$.

First method. If we can integrate the differential equation

$$ds = f(t) \, dt, \tag{2}$$

which we get by substituting ds/dt for v in Eq. (1), then we can determine the position s of the body as a function of t, say

$$s = F(t) + C. \tag{3}$$

The distance traveled by the body between $t = a$ and $t = b$ is then given by

$$s \Big]_{t=a}^{t=b} = F(t) + C \Big]_a^b = F(b) - F(a).$$

We recognize this, of course, as saying that the distance is given by the definite integral

$$\boxed{\; s \Big]_{t=a}^{t=b} = \int_a^b f(t)\, dt = F(t) \Big]_a^b = F(b) - F(a). \;} \tag{4}$$

Second method. In this method, we imagine the total time interval $a \le t \le b$ as divided into n subintervals, each of duration $\Delta t = (b - a)/n$. The velocity at the beginning of the first subinterval is

$$v_1 = f(t_1) = f(a).$$

If Δt is small, the velocity remains nearly constant throughout the time from a to $a + \Delta t$. Hence during the first subinterval of time, the body travels a distance Δs_1 which is approximately equal to $v_1\, \Delta t$:

$$\Delta s_1 \approx v_1\, \Delta t = f(t_1)\, \Delta t. \tag{5}$$

If, instead of using the velocity v_1 at time t_1, we were to use the *average* velocity

$$\overline{v_1} = \frac{\Delta s_1}{\Delta t}, \tag{6a}$$

we could write

$$\Delta s_1 = \overline{v_1}\, \Delta t \tag{6b}$$

exactly. Now by the Mean Value Theorem, we know that there is some instant, say T_1, between t_1 and $t_1 + \Delta t$ where the instantaneous velocity is equal to the average velocity $\overline{v_1}$. In other words,

$$f(T_1) = \overline{v_1} \text{ for some } T_1, \qquad t_1 < T_1 < t_1 + \Delta t, \tag{6c}$$

and therefore

$$\Delta s_1 = f(T_1)\, \Delta t$$

exactly. By reasoning in the same manner for the second, third, $\dots$, nth subintervals, we conclude that there are instants of time $T_2, T_3, \dots, T_n$

in these respective intervals such that

$$\Delta s_2 = f(T_2)\, \Delta t,$$

$$\Delta s_3 = f(T_3)\, \Delta t,$$

$$\vdots$$

$$\Delta s_n = f(T_n)\, \Delta t,$$

where $\Delta s_2,\ \Delta s_3,\ \ldots,\ \Delta s_n$ represent the distances traveled during these respective time subintervals. Therefore the total distance traveled between $t = a$ and $t = b$ is

$$
\begin{aligned}
s\Big]_{t=a}^{t=b} &= \Delta s_1 + \Delta s_2 + \Delta s_3 + \cdots + \Delta s_n \\
&= f(T_1)\, \Delta t + f(T_2)\, \Delta t + \cdots + f(T_n)\, \Delta t \\
&= \sum_{k=1}^{n} f(T_k)\, \Delta t.
\end{aligned}
\tag{7}
$$

Let us now take finer and finer subdivisions Δt and let n increase without limit. For each n we select the appropriate instants of time $T_1,\ T_2,\ \ldots,$ T_n according to the method described above. Then the particular sums used in Eq. (7) tend to the definite integral

$$\lim_{n \to \infty} \sum_{k=1}^{n} f(T_k)\, \Delta t = \int_a^b f(t)\, dt \tag{8}$$

as limit, by virtue of the Fundamental Theorem. On the other hand, these sums all give the distance traveled by the body. Therefore the distance traveled is equal to the integral in Eq. (8) [or Eq. (4)].

Remark 1. If, instead of using the velocities at the instants of time $T_1,\ T_2,\ \ldots,\ T_n$ described above, we had used the velocities

$$v_1 = f(t_1), \qquad v_2 = f(t_2), \qquad \ldots, \qquad v_n = f(t_n)$$

at the beginnings of the various subintervals, then we would have had *n approximations* like (5) with subscripts 1, 2, ..., n. Then we would have obtained an *approximation*

$$\Delta s_1 + \Delta s_2 + \cdots + \Delta s_n \approx f(t_1)\, \Delta t + f(t_2)\, \Delta t + \cdots + f(t_n)\, \Delta t,$$

or

$$s\Big]_{t=a}^{t=b} \approx \sum_{k=1}^{n} f(t_k)\, \Delta t. \tag{9}$$

Now since $f(t)$ is continuous, the sums (7) and (9) have the same *limit* as $n \to \infty$. In other words, the approximation (9) gets better as n increases, and the *limit* again gives the exact value, namely, the integral in Eq. (8).

Remark 2. Of course, the two methods give the same result, Eqs. (4) and (8). The second method is useful primarily (a) because it shows how the simple formula

$$\text{distance} = \text{velocity} \times \text{time},$$

which applies only to the case of *constant* velocity, can be extended to the case of variable velocity, provided we apply it to short subintervals Δt; and (b) because it can be used [in the form of the approximation (9)] to estimate the distance in cases where the velocity is given empirically by a table of values or a graph instead of by a formula $f(t)$ with known indefinite integral $F(t)$.

Remark 3. If the velocity changes sign during the interval (a, b), then the integral in Eq. (4) gives only the *net* change in s. This permits cancellation of distances traveled forwards and backwards. For example, it would give an answer of 2 miles if the body traveled forward 7 miles and backed up 5 miles. If we want to determine the actual total distance traveled, we should calculate the integral of the *absolute value* of the velocity,

$$\int_a^b |f(t)| \, dt. \tag{10}$$

This would be done by integrating separately over the intervals where v is positive and where v is negative and adding the absolute values of the results.

Remark 4. The preceding discussion shows that the distance traveled is given by precisely the same expression as that for the area bounded

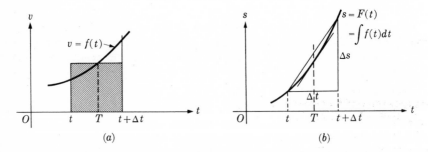

(a)   (b)

Figure 7-3

by the curve

$$v = f(t)$$

and the t-axis from a to b. All of the discussion above can be interpreted geometrically. For example, T is chosen between t and $t + \Delta t$ in such a way that the area of the rectangle of base Δt and altitude $f(T)$ (Fig. 7–3a) is precisely equal to the area under the velocity curve between t and $t + \Delta t$. This is also the place where the slope of the curve $s = F(t)$ (Fig. 7–3b) is equal to the slope of the chord.

PROBLEMS

In each of the following problems (1 through 8), the function $v = f(t)$ represents the velocity v (ft/sec) of a moving body as a function of the time t (sec). Sketch the graph of v versus t and find that portion of the given time interval $a \le t \le b$ in which the velocity is (a) positive, and (b) negative. Then find the total distance traveled by the body between $t = a$ and $t = b$.

1. $v = 2t + 1; \; 0 \le t \le 2$　　　　2. $v = t^2 - t - 2; \; 0 \le t \le 3$

3. $v = t - \dfrac{8}{t^2}; \;\; 1 \le t \le 3$　　　4. $v = |t - 1|; \;\; 0 \le t \le 2$

5. $v = 6 \sin 3t; \;\; 0 \le t \le \dfrac{\pi}{2}$　　6. $v = 4 \cos 2t; \;\; 0 \le t \le \pi$

7. $v = \sin t + \cos t; \;\; 0 \le t \le \pi$

8. $v = \sin t \sqrt{2 + 2 \cos t}; \;\; 0 \le t \le \pi$

In each of the following problems (9 through 13), the function $a = f(t)$ represents the acceleration (ft/sec^2) of a moving body and v_0 is its velocity at time $t = 0$. Find the *distance* traveled by the body between time $t = 0$ and $t = 2$.

9. $a = \sin t; \; v_0 = 2$　　　　　10. $a = 1 - \cos t; \; v_0 = 0$

11. $a = g \text{ (const.)}; \;\; v_0 = 0$　　　12. $a = \sqrt{4t + 1}; \;\; v_0 = -4\frac{1}{3}$

13. $a = \dfrac{1}{\sqrt{4t + 1}}; \; v_0 = 1$

14. Suppose water flows into a tank at the rate of $f(t)$ (gal/min), where f is a given, positive, continuous function of t. Let the amount of water in the tank at time $t = 0$ be Q_0 (gal). Apply the Fundamental Theorem to show that the amount of water in the tank at any later time $t = b$ is

$$Q = Q_0 + \int_0^b f(t) \, dt.$$

15. Use the trapezoidal rule, Article 6–10, to find (approximately) the distance traveled between $t = 0$ and $t = 2$ by a body whose velocity is given by the following table of values.

v (ft/sec)	2.2	2.5	3.0	3.8	5.0
t (sec)	0	0.5	1.0	1.5	2.0

Also find (approximately) the average velocity during the time $t = 0$ to $t = 2$.

7-4   Volume.   The volumes of many solids can be found by an application of the "method of slicing." Suppose, for example, that the solid is bounded by two parallel planes perpendicular to the x-axis at $x = a$ and $x = b$. Imagine the solid cut into thin slices of thickness Δx by planes perpendicular to the x-axis. Then the total volume V of the solid is the sum of the volumes of these slices.

Let ΔV be the volume of the representative slice between x and $x + \Delta x$. Then if A' and A'' are respectively the smallest and largest cross-sectional areas of the solid between x and $x + \Delta x$, it will be seen at once that

$$A' \, \Delta x \le \Delta V \le A'' \, \Delta x$$

or

$$\Delta V = A(\bar{x}) \, \Delta x,$$

where $A(\bar{x})$ denotes an appropriate intermediate cross-sectional area of the solid at some $\bar{x}$ between x and $x + \Delta x$. Then

$$V = \sum_{a}^{b} A(\bar{x}) \, \Delta x$$

will give the total volume of the solid exactly. If, instead of choosing the exactly appropriate intermediate point $\bar{x}$ in the typical subinterval, we use the area $A(x)$ of the cross section at x, we have only an approximation,

$$V \approx \sum_{a}^{b} A(x) \, \Delta x.$$

But now let $\Delta x \to 0$. Then, if the cross-sectional area is a continuous function of x, all these sums will approach the same limit. Since one se-

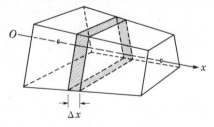

Figure 7-4

quence of sums always gives the value V, it will have this value as its limit. Hence the other sums will also give the value V in the limit,

that is,
$$V = \lim_{\Delta x \to 0} \sum_a^b A(x)\, \Delta x = \int_a^b A(x)\, dx. \tag{1}$$

Volume of a solid of revolution. The solid generated by rotating a plane area about an axis in its plane is called a solid of revolution. To find the volume of a solid such as shown in Fig. 7–5, we need only observe that the cross-sectional area $A(x)$ in Eq. (1) is the area of a circle of radius $r = y = f(x)$, so that

$$A(x) = \pi r^2 = \pi[f(x)]^2. \tag{2}$$

EXAMPLE 1. Suppose the curve in Fig. 7–5 represents the graph of

$$y = \sqrt{x}$$

from $(0, 0)$ to $(4, 2)$. Then the volume of the representative slice is

$$\Delta V \approx \pi y^2\, \Delta x = \pi(\sqrt{x})^2\, \Delta x,$$

and the total volume is approximately

$$V \approx \sum_0^4 \pi x\, \Delta x.$$

Exactly, we have

$$V = \lim_{\Delta x \to 0} \sum_0^4 \pi x\, \Delta x = \int_0^4 \pi x\, dx = \pi \frac{x^2}{2}\Big]_0^4 = 8\pi.$$

Method of cylindrical shells. Suppose the area $PQRS$ in Fig. 7–6 is revolved around the y-axis. We can compute the volume generated in the

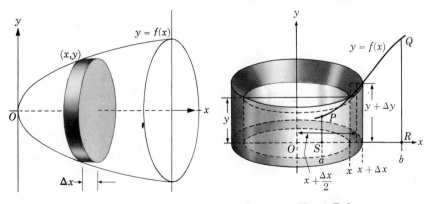

Figure 7–5   Figure 7–6

following way. Consider a strip of area between the ordinate at x and the ordinate at $x + \Delta x$. When this strip is revolved around the y-axis, it generates a hollow, thin-walled shell of inner radius x, outer radius $x + \Delta x$, and volume ΔV. The base of this shell is a ring bounded by two concentric circles. The inner radius is

$$r_1 = x$$

and the outer radius is

$$r_2 = x + \Delta x.$$

The area of the ring is

$$\Delta A = \pi(r_2^2 - r_1^2) = 2\pi \left(\frac{r_2 + r_1}{2}\right)(r_2 - r_1) = 2\pi r\, \Delta x.$$

Here

$$r = \frac{r_2 + r_1}{2} = x + \frac{\Delta x}{2}$$

is the radius of the circle midway between the inner and outer boundaries of the ring, and $2\pi r$ is its circumference.

Now if we had a cylindrical shell of constant altitude y standing on this base, its volume would be

$$\text{altitude} \times \text{base} = y\, \Delta A.$$

In the present case, the altitude of the shell varies between y and $y + \Delta y$. Its volume therefore lies between $y\, \Delta A$ and $(y + \Delta y)\, \Delta A$. That is,

$$y\, \Delta A \leq \Delta V \leq (y + \Delta y)\, \Delta A$$

or

$$y \cdot 2\pi r\, \Delta x \leq \Delta V \leq (y + \Delta y) \cdot 2\pi r\, \Delta x.$$

The total volume V is contained between the "lower" sum

$$s = \sum_a^b y \cdot 2\pi \left(x + \frac{\Delta x}{2}\right) \Delta x$$

and the "upper" sum

$$S = \sum_a^b (y + \Delta y) \cdot 2\pi \left(x + \frac{\Delta x}{2}\right) \Delta x.$$

As Δx approaches zero, both of these sums approach the following integral as limit (see Article 7–5). Hence this limit must also be equal to the volume V, namely,

$$V = \lim_{\Delta x \to 0} s = \lim_{\Delta x \to 0} S = \int_a^b y \cdot 2\pi x\, dx = \int_a^b 2\pi x f(x)\, dx.$$

Remark. An easy way to visualize this result is to imagine that the volume element ΔV has been cut along a generator of the cylinder and that the shell has been rolled out flat like a thin sheet of tin. The sheet then has dimensions very nearly equal to $2\pi x$ by $y = f(x)$ by Δx. Hence

$$\Delta V \approx 2\pi x \cdot f(x) \cdot \Delta x,$$

and the total volume is given approximately by

$$V \approx \sum_a^b 2\pi x \cdot f(x) \cdot \Delta x.$$

As Δx approaches zero, we obtain a limit that is equal to the exact volume:

$$V = \lim_{\Delta x \to 0} \sum_a^b 2\pi x \cdot f(x) \cdot \Delta x$$

$$= \int_a^b 2\pi x f(x) \, dx.$$

EXAMPLE 2. In Example 1 above, where the area under the curve $y = \sqrt{x}$ is revolved around the x-axis, we may take a horizontal strip of area between the lines at distances y and $y + \Delta y$ above the x-axis. The volume generated by revolving this strip around the x-axis is a hollow cylindrical shell of inner circumference $2\pi y$, inner length $4 - x$, and wall thickness Δy. Hence, the total volume V is approximately

$$V \approx \sum_{y=0}^{2} 2\pi y(4 - x)\, \Delta y$$

and is exactly equal to the limit of this sum as Δy approaches zero:

$$V = \lim_{\Delta y \to 0} \sum_{y=0}^{2} 2\pi y(4 - x)\, \Delta y$$

$$= \int_0^2 2\pi y(4 - y^2)\, dy$$

$$= 2\pi \left[2y^2 - \frac{y^4}{4} \right]_0^2 = 8\pi.$$

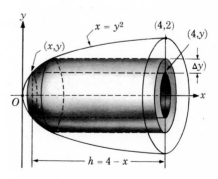

Figure 7–7

Various methods for finding volumes are illustrated in the following examples.

EXAMPLE 3. The circle

$$x^2 + y^2 = a^2$$

is rotated about the x-axis to generate a sphere. Find its volume.

Solution. We imagine the sphere cut into thin slices by planes perpendicular to the x-axis (Fig. 7–8). The volume of a typical slice between two planes at x and $x + \Delta x$ is approximately

$$\pi y^2\, \Delta x = \pi(a^2 - x^2)\, \Delta x,$$

and the sum of all slices is approximately

$$V_{-a}^{a} \approx \sum_{-a}^{a} \pi(a^2 - x^2)\, \Delta x.$$

The exact volume is given by

$$V_{-a}^{a} = \lim_{\Delta x \to 0} \sum_{-a}^{a} \pi(a^2 - x^2)\, \Delta x$$

$$= \int_{-a}^{a} \pi(a^2 - x^2)\, dx$$

$$= \pi\left[a^2 x - \frac{x^3}{3} \right]_{-a}^{a} = \tfrac{4}{3}\pi a^3.$$

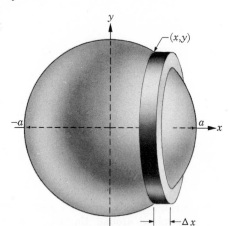

Figure 7–8

EXAMPLE 4. A hole of diameter a is bored through the center of the sphere in Example 3 above. Find the remaining volume.

The volume in question could be generated by rotating about the y-axis the area inside the circle $x^2 + y^2 = a^2$ lying to the right of the line $x = a/2$ (Fig. 7–9a). The line and the circle intersect at the points $(a/2, \pm a\sqrt{3}/2)$. There are at least three methods for finding the required volume.

Method 1. The volume is

$$V = V_1 - V_2,$$

where V_1 (Fig. 7–9b) is the volume of the segment of the sphere contained between the two planes perpendicular to the y-axis at $y = \pm a\sqrt{3}/2$, and V_2 is the volume of a right circular cylinder of radius $a/2$ and altitude $2(a\sqrt{3}/2) = a\sqrt{3}$, so that

$$V_2 = \frac{\sqrt{3}}{4}\pi a^3.$$

To find V_1, imagine the solid as being cut into thin slices by planes perpendicular

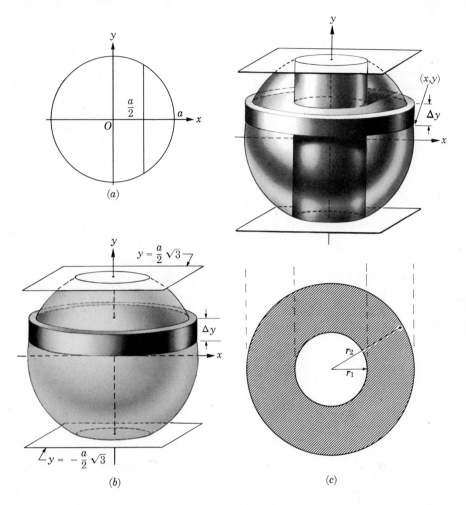

Figure 7–9(a), (b), (c)

to the y-axis. The slice between y and $y + \Delta y$ is approximated by a cylinder of altitude Δy and cross-sectional area $\pi x^2 = \pi(a^2 - y^2)$, so that we have the approximation

$$V_1 \approx \sum_{-a\sqrt{3}/2}^{a\sqrt{3}/2} \pi(a^2 - y^2)\,\Delta y$$

and the exact value

$$V_1 = \int_{-a\sqrt{3}/2}^{a\sqrt{3}/2} \pi(a^2 - y^2)\,dy = \frac{3\sqrt{3}}{4}\pi a^3.$$

Thus

$$V = V_1 - V_2 = \frac{3\sqrt{3}}{4}\pi a^3 - \frac{\sqrt{3}}{4}\pi a^3 = \frac{\sqrt{3}}{2}\pi a^3.$$

Method 2. Instead of subtracting volumes, we may work directly with the volume required. Again we imagine the solid to be cut into thin slices by planes perpendicular to the y-axis. Each slice (Fig. 7–9c) is now like a washer of thickness Δy, inner radius

$$r_1 = \frac{a}{2},$$

and outer radius

$$r_2 = x = \sqrt{a^2 - y^2}.$$

The area of a face of such a washer is

$$\pi r_2^2 - \pi r_1^2 = \pi(\tfrac{3}{4}a^2 - y^2)$$

and the volume of the solid is approximately

$$V \approx \sum_{-a\sqrt{3}/2}^{a\sqrt{3}/2} \pi(\tfrac{3}{4}a^2 - y^2)\,\Delta y,$$

while its exact value is

$$V = \lim_{\Delta y \to 0} \sum_{-a\sqrt{3}/2}^{a\sqrt{3}/2} \pi(\tfrac{3}{4}a^2 - y^2)\,\Delta y$$

$$= \int_{-a\sqrt{3}/2}^{a\sqrt{3}/2} \pi(\tfrac{3}{4}a^2 - y^2)\,dy$$

$$= \frac{\sqrt{3}}{2}\pi a^3.$$

(d)

Figure 7–9(d)

Method 3. This time we imagine the solid to be cut into a number of hollow cylindrical shells (Fig. 7–9d) by cylinders having the y-axis as their common axis and having radii

$$x_1 = \frac{a}{2}, \quad x_2, \quad x_3, \quad \ldots, \quad x_n, \quad x_{n+1} = a.$$

The first shell has inner radius x_1 and outer radius x_2, the second shell has inner radius x_2 and outer radius x_3, and so on, the kth shell having inner radius x_k and outer radius x_{k+1}. The volume of the kth shell is approximately

$$2\pi x_k^* \cdot \Delta x_k \cdot 2y_k^* = 4\pi x_k^* \sqrt{a^2 - (x_k^*)^2}\,\Delta x_k,$$

where (x_k^*, y_k^*), Fig. 7–9(f), is the point of abscissa

$$x_k^* = \tfrac{1}{2}(x_k + x_{k+1})$$

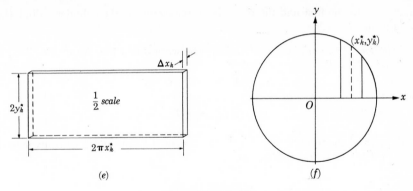

Figure 7–9(e), (f)

on the circle in the first quadrant. (Imagine the kth cylindrical shell to have been cut along a generator and flattened into a sheet of length $2\pi x_k^*$, altitude $2y_k^*$, and thickness Δx_k, Fig. 7–9e.) Then the entire volume will be approximated by

$$V \approx \sum_{k=1}^{n} 4\pi x_k^* \sqrt{a^2 - (x_k^*)^2}\, \Delta x_k$$

$$\approx \sum_{a/2}^{a} 4\pi x \sqrt{a^2 - x^2}\, \Delta x.$$

The exact value will be the *limit* of this sum, namely,

$$V = \lim_{\Delta x \to 0} \sum_{a/2}^{a} 4\pi x \sqrt{a^2 - x^2}\, \Delta x$$

$$= \int_{a/2}^{a} 4\pi x \sqrt{a^2 - x^2}\, dx.$$

To evaluate this integral, we let

$$u = a^2 - x^2,$$

then

$$V = 4\pi \int_{a/2}^{a} \sqrt{a^2 - x^2}\,(x\, dx)$$

$$= 4\pi \int u^{1/2}(-\tfrac{1}{2}\, du) = -\frac{4\pi}{3}\left[(a^2 - x^2)^{3/2}\right]_{a/2}^{a} = \frac{\sqrt{3}}{2}\pi a^3.$$

EXAMPLE 5. A wedge is cut from a right circular cylinder of radius r by two planes, one perpendicular to the axis of the cylinder while the second makes an angle α with the first and intersects it at the center of the cylinder. Find the volume of the wedge.

Solution. The volume ΔV of the slice between y and $y + \Delta y$ in Fig. 7–10 is approximately

$$\Delta V \approx A(y)\,\Delta y,$$

where

$$A(y) = \tfrac{1}{2}xh$$

is the area of the triangle that forms one face of the slice and is to be expressed as a function of y. By trigonometry,

$$h = x \tan \alpha,$$

and by the theorem of Pythagoras,

$$x^2 + y^2 = r^2$$

or

$$x^2 = r^2 - y^2.$$

Hence

$$A(y) = \tfrac{1}{2}x^2 \tan \alpha = \tfrac{1}{2}\tan \alpha\,(r^2 - y^2).$$

(a)

(b)

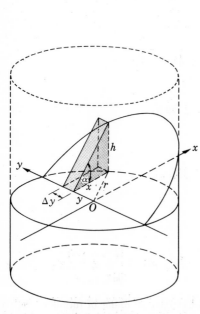

Figure 7–10   Figure 7–11

The total volume is given by

$$V = \lim_{\Delta y \to 0} \sum_{-r}^{r} A(y)\,\Delta y$$

$$= \int_{-r}^{r} \frac{1}{2} \tan \alpha (r^2 - y^2)\,dy.$$

Remembering that the factor $\frac{1}{2} \tan \alpha$ is a constant, we find

$$V = \tfrac{2}{3} r^3 \tan \alpha.$$

EXAMPLE 6. The base of a certain solid is an equilateral triangle of side s, with one vertex at the origin and an altitude along the x-axis. Each plane section perpendicular to the x-axis is a square, one side of which lies in the base of the solid. Find the volume of the solid.

Solution. Figure 7–11(a) represents the base of the solid with a strip of width Δx, which corresponds to a slice of the solid of volume

$$\Delta V \approx A(x)\,\Delta x,$$

where

$$A(x) = (2y)^2 = 4y^2$$

is the area of a face of the slice. The slice extends upward from the plane of the paper in Fig. 7–11(a). It is possible to find the required volume from the statement of the problem by reference to this figure and without visualizing the actual solid. A perspective view of the solid is, however, given in Fig. 7–11(b). It is required to find y in terms of x so that the area $A(x)$ will be given as a function of x. Since the base triangle is equilateral, its altitude h is given by

$$h^2 = s^2 - (s/2)^2 = \tfrac{3}{4}s^2$$

or

$$h = \frac{s}{2}\sqrt{3}.$$

Then, by similar triangles, we find

$$\frac{2y}{x} = \frac{s}{h} = \frac{2}{\sqrt{3}}$$

or

$$y = \frac{x}{\sqrt{3}}.$$

Then

$$V = \int_0^h A(x)\,dx$$

$$= \int_0^{s\sqrt{3}/2} \frac{4}{3} x^2\,dx = \frac{s^3}{2\sqrt{3}} = \frac{1}{3} hs^2.$$

PROBLEMS

In Problems 1 through 8, find the volumes generated when the areas bounded by the given curves and lines are rotated about the x-axis. [*Note:* $x = 0$ is the y-axis and $y = 0$ is the x-axis.]

1. $x + y = 2$; $x = 0$, $y = 0$ 2. $y = \sin x$; $y = 0$ $(0 \leq x \leq \pi)$
                                              [See Problem 17, Article 6–8.]

3. $y = x - x^2$; $y = 0$ 4. $y = 3x - x^2$; $y = x$
5. $x = 2y - y^2$; $x = 0$ 6. $y = x$, $y = 1$; $x = 0$
   (Use cylindrical shells.)
7. $y = x^2$; $y = 4$ 8. $y = 3 + x^2$; $y = 4$

9. By integration find the volume generated by the triangle with vertices at $(0, 0)$, $(h, 0)$, (h, r) when it is rotated (a) about the x-axis, (b) about the y-axis.

10. (a) The area bounded by the curve $y = x^2$ and the line $y = x$ is revolved around the y-axis. Find the volume generated. (b) Find the volume generated if the area is revolved around the x-axis.

11. The area bounded by the curve $y = x^2$ and the line $y = 4$ generates various solids of revolution when rotated as follows:

(a) about the y-axis,   (b) about the line $y = 4$,

(c) about the x-axis,   (d) about the line $y = -1$,

(e) about the line $x = 2$.

Find the volume generated in each case.

12. (a) A hemispherical bowl of radius a contains water to a depth h. Find the volume of water in the bowl. (b) (Review problem on related rates.) Water runs into a hemispherical bowl of radius 5 ft at the rate of 0.2 ft^3/sec. How fast is the water level in the bowl rising when the water is 4 ft deep?

13. A football has a volume that is approximately the same as the volume generated by rotating the area inside the ellipse $b^2x^2 + a^2y^2 = a^2b^2$ (where a and b are constants) about the x-axis. Find the volume so generated.

14. The cross sections of a certain solid by planes perpendicular to the x-axis are circles with diameters extending from the curve $y = x^2$ to the curve $y = 8 - x^2$. The solid lies between the points of intersection of these two curves. Find its volume.

15. The base of a certain solid is the circle $x^2 + y^2 = a^2$. Each plane section of the solid cut out by a plane perpendicular to the x-axis is a square with one edge of the square in the base of the solid. Find the volume of the solid.

16. Two great circles, lying in planes that are perpendicular to each other, are marked on a sphere of radius a. A portion of the sphere is then shaved off in such a manner that any plane section of the remaining solid, perpendicular to the common diameter of the two great circles, is a square with vertices on these circles. Find the volume of the solid that remains.

17. The base of a certain solid is the circle $x^2 + y^2 = a^2$. Each plane section of the solid cut out by a plane perpendicular to the y-axis is an isosceles right triangle with one leg in the base of the solid. Find the volume.

18. The base of a certain solid is the region between the x-axis and the curve $y = \sin x$ between $x = 0$ and $x = \pi/2$. Each plane section of the solid perpendicular to the x-axis is an equilateral triangle with one side in the base of the solid. Find the volume.

19. A rectangular swimming pool is 30 ft wide and 50 ft long. The depth of water h(ft) at distance x (ft) from one end of the pool is measured at 5-ft intervals and found to be as follows:

x (ft)	0	5	10	15	20	25	30	35	40	45	50
h (ft)	6.0	8.2	9.1	9.9	10.5	11.0	11.5	11.9	12.3	12.7	13.0

Use the trapezoidal rule to find (approximately) the volume of water in the pool.

20. The circle $x^2 + y^2 = a^2$ is rotated about the line $x = b$ ($b > a$) to generate a torus. Find the volume generated. [*Hint:* $\int_{-a}^{a} \sqrt{a^2 - x^2}\, dx = \pi a^2/2$, since it is the area of a semicircle of radius a.]

7–5 Approximations. By now it is apparent that each application of the Fundamental Theorem that we have so far made has involved the following steps:

1. Select an independent variable, say x, such that the quantity U to be computed can be represented as a sum of pieces ΔU, where ΔU is that part of U that is associated with the subinterval $(x, x + \Delta x)$ of the domain $a \le x \le b$ of the variable x.

2. Subdivide the domain (a, b) into n subintervals. For the sake of simplicity we usually take the lengths all to be the same, namely, equal to $\Delta x = (b - a)/n$.

3. Approximate that portion ΔU of U that is associated with the subinterval $(x, x + \Delta x)$ by an expression of the form

$$\Delta U \approx f(X)\, \Delta x. \tag{1}$$

In this expression, X is to be some point in the subinterval $(x, x + \Delta x)$ and the function f is to be continuous over the entire domain $a \le x \le b$.

4. Then the total quantity U is given *approximately* by

$$U \approx \sum_{a}^{b} f(X)\, \Delta x. \tag{2}$$

5. Take the limit, as Δx approaches zero, of the sum in Eq. (2). This limit is the definite integral

$$\lim_{\Delta x \to 0} \sum_{a}^{b} f(X)\, \Delta x = \int_{a}^{b} f(x)\, dx. \tag{3}$$

Is this limit also an approximation to U or does it give U exactly?

In the case of area, distance, and volume we have seen that the *limit* in (3) does give U exactly. In order for us to be able to apply these methods to new situations as they arise, we need an answer to the following question.

Question: How accurate must the approximations in (1) and (2) be in order to say that all of the error is squeezed out in going to the limit, (3), with the result that the exact value of U is given by the limit

$$U = \lim_{\Delta x \to 0} \sum_a^b f(X)\, \Delta x = \int_a^b f(x)\, dx? \tag{4}$$

Answer: Denote by $\alpha\, \Delta x$ the correction that must be added to the right side of Eq. (1) to give ΔU exactly. That is, suppose that

$$\Delta U = f(X)\, \Delta x + \alpha\, \Delta x, \tag{5}$$

exactly.

First case. Suppose these correction terms are no larger than a constant K times $(\Delta x)^2$,

$$|\alpha\, \Delta x| \le K\, (\Delta x)^2,$$

where K is a constant the same for all subintervals and all methods of subdivision. Then we have

$$\Delta U = f(X)\, \Delta x + \alpha\, \Delta x,$$

$$U = \sum_a^b f(X)\, \Delta x + \sum_a^b \alpha\, \Delta x$$

and

$$\left| U - \sum_a^b f(X)\, \Delta x \right| = \left| \sum_a^b \alpha\, \Delta x \right| \le \sum_a^b K\, (\Delta x)^2. \tag{6}$$

This last sum consists of n terms each of which is equal to $K(\Delta x)^2$, where $\Delta x = (b-a)/n$. Therefore

$$\sum_a^b K\, (\Delta x)^2 = nK(b-a)^2/n^2 = K(b-a)^2/n = K(b-a)\, \Delta x,$$

and (6) becomes

$$\left| U - \sum_a^b f(X)\, \Delta x \right| \le K(b-a)\, \Delta x. \tag{7}$$

In other words, if the error in the approximation (1) to each individual ΔU is no more than a constant times the *square* of Δx, then the error in the approximation (2) to the *total* U is no more than a constant times the *first power* of Δx. Now let Δx approach zero in (7). The sum on the left becomes the definite integral (3), and the term on the right becomes zero. In other words, U is exactly equal to the definite integral in this case.

Second case. Suppose the correction terms are numerically no larger than a constant K' times Δx times δy:

$$|\alpha \, \Delta x| \leq K' \, \Delta x \, \delta y,$$

where K' is the same for all subintervals and all methods of subdivision, and where δy is the oscillation in the interval $(x, x + \Delta x)$ of a function $y = \phi(x)$ that is continuous over the closed interval (a, b). Then one finds in this case that the total error in the approximation (2) is no larger than

$$K'(b - a) \text{ times (max. } \delta y).$$

But the maximum δy also approaches zero when Δx does, so again we find that U is given exactly by the definite integral.

We have given criteria such as

$$|\alpha \, \Delta x| \leq K \, (\Delta x)^2 \qquad \text{or} \qquad |\alpha \, \Delta x| \leq K' \, \Delta x \, \delta y,$$

where K and K' are constants. Usually, in an application, we have a function of x in place of K or K' in these inequalities. But a function of x that is continuous over the closed interval $a \leq x \leq b$ has a maximum absolute value M on that interval, and we could take K (or K') equal to M in such a case. Also, the correction terms $\alpha \, \Delta x$ could involve finite combinations of the two cases discussed above, provided the inequality

$$|\alpha \, \Delta x| \leq K \, (\Delta x)^2 + K' \, \Delta x \, \delta y$$

is satisfied for some choice of the constants K and K'.

Roughly speaking, we may say that in the approximation

$$\Delta U \approx f(X) \, \Delta x$$

we must include all first power Δx terms but we may omit higher power terms like $(\Delta x)^2$, $(\Delta x)^3$, and so on, or we may omit such mixed terms as $(\Delta x)(\Delta y)$, $(\Delta x)^2(\Delta y)$, $(\Delta x) \, (\Delta y)^2$, and so on. If each separate piece ΔU is estimated to this degree of accuracy, then the total quantity U which is given approximately by the sum (2) will be given exactly by the limit of the sum, namely, by the integral (4).

In discussing the cylindrical shell method of finding a volume of revolution, Article 7–4, we found that we could estimate the volume ΔV in a hollow shell as follows:

$$2\pi \left(x + \frac{\Delta x}{2} \right) \cdot y \cdot \Delta x \le \Delta V \le 2\pi \left(x + \frac{\Delta x}{2} \right) (y + \Delta y) \, \Delta x. \qquad (8)$$

Multiplied out, this becomes

$$2\pi xy \, \Delta x + \pi y \, (\Delta x)^2 \le \Delta V \le 2\pi xy \, \Delta x + \pi y \, (\Delta x)^2 + 2\pi x \, \Delta x \Delta y + \pi \Delta y (\Delta x)^2.$$

If we ignore all except the first power terms in Δx, we have the approximation

$$\Delta V \approx 2\pi xy \, \Delta x,$$

with an error that involves combinations like $\pi y \, (\Delta x)^2$, $2\pi x \, \Delta y \, \Delta x$, $\pi \Delta y (\Delta x)^2$. All such terms may be safely ignored when we go to the *limit* of the sum:

$$V = \lim_{\Delta x \to 0} \sum_a^b 2\pi xy \, \Delta x = \int_a^b 2\pi xy \, dx = \int_a^b 2\pi x f(x) \, dx.$$

Infinitesimals. A variable, such as Δx above, that approaches zero as a limit is called an infinitesimal. Terms that approach zero as the first power of Δx are said to be of the *same order* as Δx, but terms which approach zero as $(\Delta x)^2$ or as $\Delta y \, \Delta x$ are called infinitesimals of *higher order* than Δx. In setting up a definite integral, we must retain those infinitesimals that are of the same order as Δx, but we may omit those infinitesimals that are of higher order than Δx. Thus we may omit the term $\alpha \, \Delta x$, Eq. (5), if α is an infinitesimal of the same order as Δx (or higher order) or of the same order as δy (or higher order), and the *limit* in (4) will give the exact value of U.

PROBLEMS

1. In Fig. 7–6, Article 7–4, let V_a^x denote the volume generated by rotating about the y-axis the area under the curve $y = f(x)$ between the ordinate at a and the ordinate at x, $(x > a)$. By making use of the inequality (8) in this section, show that

$$\frac{dV_a^x}{dx} = \lim_{\Delta x \to 0} \frac{\Delta V_a^x}{\Delta x} = 2\pi x f(x).$$

From this, deduce that

$$V_a^b = \int_a^b 2\pi x f(x) \, dx.$$

2. Let U_a^x denote the amount of the quantity U associated with the interval

(a, x) and let ΔU in Eq. (5) represent $U_a^{x+\Delta x} - U_a^x = U_x^{x+\Delta x}$. If the function $f(x)$ in Eq. (5) is continuous over the closed interval $a \leq x \leq b$ and $|\alpha \Delta x| \leq K(\Delta x)^2$, where K is a constant, show that

$$\frac{dU_a^x}{dx} = \lim_{\Delta x \to 0} \frac{\Delta U}{\Delta x} = f(x).$$

From this, deduce that $U_a^b = \int_a^b f(x)\, dx$.

3. In Problem 2, replace the condition $|\alpha \Delta x| \leq K(\Delta x)^2$ by the condition

$$|\alpha \Delta x| \leq |K' \Delta x\ \delta y|,$$

where K' is a constant and δy is the oscillation over the interval $(x, x + \Delta x)$ of a function $y = g(x)$ that is continuous over the closed interval $a \leq x \leq b$, and derive the same conclusion as in Problem 2.

7-6   Length of a plane curve. Divide the arc AB, Fig. 7–12, into n pieces and join the successive points of division by straight lines. A representative line, such as $\overline{PQ}$, will have length

$$|PQ| = \sqrt{(\Delta x_k)^2 + (\Delta y_k)^2}.$$

The length of the curve AB is approximately

$$L_A^B \approx \sum_{k=1}^{n} \sqrt{(\Delta x_k)^2 + (\Delta y_k)^2}.$$

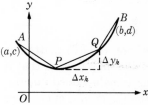

Figure 7–12

When the number of division points is increased indefinitely while the lengths of the individual segments tend to zero, we obtain

$$L_A^B = \lim_{n \to \infty} \sum_{k=1}^{n} \sqrt{(\Delta x_k)^2 + (\Delta y_k)^2}, \tag{1}$$

provided the limit exists.* The sum on the right side of (1) is not in the standard form to which we can apply the Fundamental Theorem of the integral calculus, but it can be put into such a form as follows.

Suppose that the function $y = f(x)$ is continuous and possesses a continuous derivative at each point of the curve from $A[a, f(a)]$ to $B[b, f(b)]$. Then, by the Mean Value Theorem, there is some point $P^*(x_k^*, y_k^*)$ be-

---

* For most smooth curves encountered in practice, the limit does exist. Such curves are called rectifiable. An example of a continuous curve that is not rectifiable is given by the curve

$$y = \begin{cases} x \sin 1/x & \text{when} \quad x \neq 0, \\ 0 & \text{when} \quad x = 0, \end{cases} \qquad \frac{-\pi}{2} \leq x \leq \frac{\pi}{2}.$$

tween P and Q on the curve where the tangent to the curve is parallel to the chord $\overline{PQ}$. That is,

$$f'(x_k^*) = \frac{\Delta y_k}{\Delta x_k}$$

or

$$\Delta y_k = f'(x_k^*)\,\Delta x_k.$$

Hence (1) may also be written in the form

$$L_A^B = \lim_{n \to \infty} \sum_{k=1}^{n} \sqrt{(\Delta x_k)^2 + (f'(x_k^*)\,\Delta x_k)^2}$$

$$= \lim_{\Delta x \to 0} \left(\sum_a^b \sqrt{1 + (f'(x^*))^2}\,\Delta x \right)$$

or

$$\boxed{L_A^B = \int_a^b \sqrt{1 + \left(\frac{dy}{dx}\right)^2}\,dx,} \qquad (2a)$$

where we have written dy/dx for $f'(x)$.

We may remark that it is sometimes convenient, if x may be expressed as a single-valued function of y, to interchange the roles of x and y (indeed, the *length* of a curve does not depend upon the particular axes used) and the length is also given by

$$\boxed{L_A^B = \int_c^d \sqrt{1 + \left(\frac{dx}{dy}\right)^2}\,dy.} \qquad (2b)$$

In many applications, the curve is traced by a moving particle whose coordinates x and y are given as functions of some third variable, such as the time t. Let the equations of motion be

$$x = g(t), \qquad y = h(t), \qquad (3)$$

and let t_k, t_{k+1} be the values of t at P and Q respectively. Suppose the arc AB is described just once by $P(x, y)$ as t goes from t_a at A to t_b at B. If the functions $g(t)$ and $h(t)$ are continuously differentiable for t between t_a and t_b inclusive, the Mean Value Theorem may be applied to Eq. (3) to give

$$\Delta x_k = x_{k+1} - x_k = g(t_{k+1}) - g(t_k) = g'(t_k')\,\Delta t_k,$$

$$\Delta y_k = y_{k+1} - y_k = h(t_{k+1}) - h(t_k) = h'(t_k'')\,\Delta t_k,$$

where t'_k and t''_k are two suitably chosen values of t between t_k and t_{k+1}. Then (1) becomes

$$
\begin{aligned}
L_A^B &= \lim_{n \to \infty} \sum_{k=1}^{n} \sqrt{(g'(t'_k))^2 + (h'(t''_k))^2}\, \Delta t_k \\
&= \int_{t_a}^{t_b} \sqrt{\left(\frac{dx}{dt}\right)^2 + \left(\frac{dy}{dt}\right)^2}\, dt.
\end{aligned}
\tag{4}
$$

Clearly, there is nothing inherently dependent upon the fact that t stands for time in Eqs. (3) and (4). Any other variable could serve as well, and if θ is used instead of t in (3) in representing the curve, then we need only replace t by θ in (4) as well.

EXAMPLE 1. The coordinates (x, y) of a point on a circle of radius r can be expressed in terms of the central angle θ, Fig. 5-13, as follows:

$$x = r \cos \theta, \qquad y = r \sin \theta.$$

The point $P(x, y)$ moves once around the circle as θ varies from 0 to 2π, so that the circumference of the circle is given by

$$C = \int_0^{2\pi} \sqrt{\left(\frac{dx}{d\theta}\right)^2 + \left(\frac{dy}{d\theta}\right)^2}\, d\theta.$$

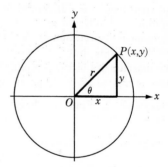

Figure 7-13

We find

$$\frac{dx}{d\theta} = -r \sin \theta, \qquad \frac{dy}{d\theta} = r \cos \theta,$$

so that

$$\left(\frac{dx}{d\theta}\right)^2 + \left(\frac{dy}{d\theta}\right)^2 = r^2(\sin^2 \theta + \cos^2 \theta) = r^2,$$

and hence

$$C = \int_0^{2\pi} r\, d\theta = r[\theta]_0^{2\pi} = 2\pi r.$$

It should be remarked that Eq. (4) is frequently written in terms of differentials in place of derivatives. This is done formally by writing $(dt)^2$ under the radical in place of the dt outside the radical, and then writing

$$(dx)^2 = \left(\frac{dx}{dt}\, dt\right)^2 = \left(\frac{dx}{dt}\right)^2 (dt)^2$$

and

$$(dy)^2 = \left(\frac{dy}{dt}\,dt\right)^2 = \left(\frac{dy}{dt}\right)^2 (dt)^2.$$

It is also customary to eliminate the parentheses in $(dx)^2$ and write dx^2 instead, so that Eq. (4) is written

$$L = \int \sqrt{dx^2 + dy^2}. \qquad (5)$$

Of course, dx and dy must both be expressed in terms of one and the same variable, and appropriate limits must be supplied in (5) before the integration can be performed

A useful mnemonic device is also associated with (5). Namely, it is customary to write

$$ds = \sqrt{dx^2 + dy^2} \qquad (6)$$

and treat ds as the differential of arc length, which can be integrated (between appropriate limits) to give the total length of a curve. Figure 7–14(a) gives the exact interpretation of ds corresponding to Eq. (6). Figure 7–14(b) is not strictly accurate, but is to be thought of as a simplified version of Fig. 7–14(a). The inaccuracies in this simplified version will be compensated if the arc of the curve is treated as the hypotenuse ds of a right triangle of sides dx and dy.

EXAMPLE 2. Find the length of the curve $y = x^{2/3}$ between $x = -1$ and $x = 8$.

Solution. From the equation of the curve, we find

$$\frac{dy}{dx} = \frac{2}{3}x^{-1/3}.$$

Since this becomes infinite at the origin (see Fig. 7–15), we use Eq. (2b) instead of (2a) to find the length of the curve. Then we need to find dx/dy. Since the

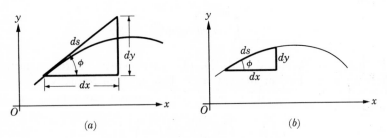

Figure 7–14

equation of the curve,

$$y = x^{2/3},$$

can also be written as

$$x = \pm\, y^{3/2},$$

we find

$$\frac{dx}{dy} = \pm\frac{3}{2} y^{1/2},$$

or

$$dx = \pm\frac{3}{2} y^{1/2}\, dy.$$

Then

$$ds^2 = dx^2 + dy^2 = (\tfrac{9}{4}y + 1)\, dy^2,$$

so that

$$ds = \sqrt{\tfrac{9}{4}y + 1}\; dy.$$

The portion of the curve between $A(-1, 1)$ and the origin has length

$$L_1 = \int_0^1 \sqrt{\tfrac{9}{4}y + 1}\; dy,$$

while the rest of the curve from the origin to $B(8, 4)$ has length

$$L_2 = \int_0^4 \sqrt{\tfrac{9}{4}y + 1}\; dy,$$

and the total length is

$$L = L_1 + L_2.$$

It is necessary to calculate the two lengths L_1 and L_2 as separate integrals, since $x = \pm\, y^{3/2}$ needs to be separated into two distinct functions of y. For the portion AO of the curve, we have $x = -y^{3/2}$, $0 \le y \le 1$; while on the arc OB, we have $x = +y^{3/2}$, $0 \le y \le 4$.

To evaluate the given integrals, we let

$$u = \tfrac{9}{4}y + 1,$$

then

$$du = \tfrac{9}{4}dy, \qquad dy = \tfrac{4}{9}du,$$

and

$$\int (\tfrac{9}{4}y + 1)^{1/2}\, dy = \tfrac{4}{9}\int u^{1/2}\, du = \tfrac{8}{27}u^{3/2}.$$

Therefore,

$$L = \tfrac{8}{27}\left\{ (\tfrac{9}{4}y + 1)^{3/2}\Big]_0^1 + (\tfrac{9}{4}y + 1)^{3/2}\Big]_0^4 \right\}$$

$$= \tfrac{1}{27}(13\sqrt{13} + 80\sqrt{10} - 16) = 10.5.$$

As a check against gross errors, we calculate the sum of the lengths of the two inscribed chords:

$$|AO| + |OB| = \sqrt{2} + \sqrt{80} = 10.4.$$

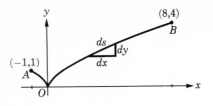

The check appears to be satisfactory.

The curve in Fig. 7–15 has a cusp at $(0,0)$ where the slope becomes infinite. If we were to reconstruct the derivation of Eq. (2) for this particular curve, we would see that the crucial step that re-

Figure 7–15

quired an application of the Mean Value Theorem could not have been taken for the case of a chord $\overline{PQ}$ from a point P to the left of the cusp to a point Q to its right. For this reason, if for no other, when one or more cusps occur between the ends of a portion of a curve whose length is to be calculated, it is best to calculate the lengths of portions of the curve between cusps and add the results. We recall that the Mean Value Theorem is still valid even when the derivative becomes infinite at an extremity of the interval where it is to be applied, so that the derivation of Eq. (2) would be valid for the separate portions of a curve lying *between* cusps (or other discontinuities of dy/dx, such as occur at corners). Thus in the example just worked, we find the lengths L_1 from $A(-1, 1)$ to O (up to the cusp) and L_2 from O to $B(8, 4)$, then add the results to obtain $L = L_1 + L_2$. This was done by the sum of the two integrals. Had there been no point of discontinuity of dy/dx, it would not have been necessary to take two separate integrals, and Eq. (2a) could have been used.

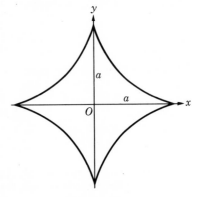

Figure 7–16

EXAMPLE 3. The coordinates of the point $P(x, y)$ on the four-cusped hypocycloid are given by

$$x = a \cos^3 \theta, \qquad y = a \sin^3 \theta.$$

Find the total length of the curve (Fig. 7–16).

Solution. When θ varies from 0 to $\pi/2$, P traces out the portion of the curve in the first quadrant. Also, from the fact that

$$x^{2/3} + y^{2/3} = a^{2/3} (\cos^2 \theta + \sin^2 \theta) = a^{2/3}$$

it will be seen that for every point (x, y) on the curve in the first quadrant, the corresponding points $(-x, y)$, $(-x, -y)$, and $(x, -y)$ in the other three quadrants are also on the curve, which is therefore symmetrical about both axes.

The portion of the curve in the first quadrant lies *between* two cusps and is one-quarter of the total length of the curve. Therefore

$$L = 4 \int_{\theta=0}^{\theta=\pi/2} \sqrt{dx^2 + dy^2}.$$

From the equation of the curve, we find

$$\frac{dx}{d\theta} = -3a \cos^2 \theta \sin \theta, \qquad dx = 3a \cos \theta \sin \theta \, (-\cos \theta) \, d\theta,$$

$$\frac{dy}{d\theta} = 3a \sin^2 \theta \cos \theta, \qquad dy = 3a \cos \theta \sin \theta \, (\sin \theta) \, d\theta,$$

and hence

$$ds^2 = dx^2 + dy^2 = (3a \cos \theta \sin \theta)^2 \, (\cos^2 \theta + \sin^2 \theta) \, (d\theta)^2$$

or

$$ds^2 = (3a \cos \theta \sin \theta \, d\theta)^2.$$

Hence, for θ between 0 and $\pi/2$,

$$ds = 3a \cos \theta \sin \theta \, d\theta$$

and

$$L = 4 \int_0^{\pi/2} 3a \cos \theta \sin \theta \, d\theta.$$

To evaluate this integral, we let

$$u = \sin \theta, \qquad du = \cos \theta \, d\theta,$$

and

$$\int \cos \theta \sin \theta \, d\theta = \int u \, du = \tfrac{1}{2}u^2 = \tfrac{1}{2} \sin^2 \theta,$$

so that

$$L = (12a) \left(\tfrac{1}{2} \sin^2 \theta \right) \Big]_0^{\pi/2} = 6a.$$

PROBLEMS

1. Find the length of the curve $y = \tfrac{1}{3}(x^2 + 2)^{3/2}$ from $x = 0$ to $x = 3$.

2. Find the length of the curve $y = x^{3/2}$ from $(0, 0)$ to $(4, 8)$.

3. Find the length of the curve $9x^2 = 4y^3$ from $(0, 0)$ to $(2\sqrt{3}, 3)$.

4. Find the length of the curve $y = x^3/3 + 1/(4x)$ from $x = 1$ to $x = 3$.

5. Find the length of the curve $x = y^4/4 + 1/(8y^2)$ from $y = 1$ to $y = 2$.

6. Find the length of the curve $(y + 1)^2 = 4x^3$ from $x = 0$ to $x = 1$.

7. Find the distance traveled between $t = 0$ and $t = \pi/2$ by a particle $P(x, y)$

whose position at time t is given by

$$x = a \cos t + at \sin t, \qquad y = a \sin t - at \cos t,$$

where a is a positive constant.

8. Find the distance traveled by the particle $P(x, y)$ between $t = 0$ and $t = 4$ if the position at time t is given by

$$x = \frac{t^2}{2}, \qquad y = \tfrac{1}{3}(2t + 1)^{3/2}.$$

9. The position of a particle $P(x, y)$ at time t is given by

$$x = \tfrac{1}{3}(2t + 3)^{3/2}, \qquad y = \frac{t^2}{2} + t.$$

Find the distance it travels between $t = 0$ and $t = 3$.

7–7   Area of a surface of revolution. Suppose that the curve in Fig. 7–17 is rotated about the x-axis. It will generate a surface in space. The inscribed polygonal line segments will generate inscribed frustums of cones. The sum of the lateral areas of these frustums will be an approximation to the area of the surface. To obtain an analytic expression for

Figure 7–17

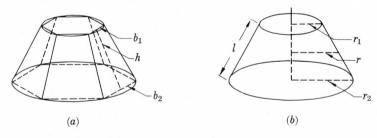

(a)   (b)

Figure 7–18

this approximation, we require the formula

$$A = \pi(r_1 + r_2)l \tag{1}$$

for the lateral area A of a frustum of slant height l, where r_1 and r_2 are the radii of its bases.

To establish Eq. (1), we may imagine the frustum of a cone to be the limit of inscribed frustums of pyramids (see Fig. 7–18a). If each base of an inscribed frustum of a pyramid is a regular polygon of n sides, and b_1 is the length of one side in the upper face, while b_2 is the length of a side in the lower face, then the lateral area will consist of n trapezoids each having an area

$$\tfrac{1}{2}(b_1 + b_2)h.$$

Hence the n trapezoids have area

$$\tfrac{1}{2}(nb_1 + nb_2)h.$$

As n increases indefinitely, we have

$$\lim_{n\to\infty} nb_1 = 2\pi r_1, \qquad \lim_{n\to\infty} nb_2 = 2\pi r_2,$$

and

$$\lim_{n\to\infty} h = l,$$

so that

$$A = \lim_{n\to\infty} \tfrac{1}{2}(nb_1 + nb_2)h = \tfrac{1}{2}(2\pi r_1 + 2\pi r_2)l = \pi(r_1 + r_2)l,$$

which establishes Eq. (1). Note that if $r_1 = r_2$, Eq. (1) reduces to the correct formula for the lateral area of a cylinder, and if $r_1 = 0$, it gives the correct result for the lateral area of a cone. It can also be put into the form

$$A = 2\pi rl$$

where

$$r = \tfrac{1}{2}(r_1 + r_2)$$

is the radius of the mid-section of the frustum. In this form, (1) says that the lateral area of a frustum of a cone = (circumference of mid-section) $\times$ (slant height).

We now consider the portion of the surface ΔS generated by the arc PQ, and its inscribed frustum of a cone generated by the chord $\overline{PQ}$. Call the coordinates of P: (x, y), and of Q: $(x + \Delta x, y + \Delta y)$, and take

$$r_1 = y, \qquad r_2 = y + \Delta y, \qquad l = \sqrt{(\Delta x)^2 + (\Delta y)^2}$$

in Eq. (1). Then we have the approximation

$$S \approx \sum_{x=a}^{b} \pi(2y + \Delta y)\sqrt{(\Delta x)^2 + (\Delta y)^2}$$

or

$$S \approx \sum_{a}^{b} 2\pi\left(y + \frac{1}{2}\Delta y\right)\sqrt{1 + \left(\frac{\Delta y}{\Delta x}\right)^2}\,\Delta x.$$

If y and dy/dx are continuous functions of x and we omit products like $(\Delta y)(\Delta x)$ and higher powers of Δx in this approximation, we have

$$S \approx \sum_{a}^{b} 2\pi y\sqrt{1 + \left(\frac{dy}{dx}\right)^2}\,\Delta x.$$

Then taking the limit as Δx tends to zero, we get

$$S = \lim_{\Delta x \to 0} \sum_{a}^{b} 2\pi y\sqrt{1 + \left(\frac{dy}{dx}\right)^2}\,\Delta x$$

or

$$S = \int_{a}^{b} 2\pi y\sqrt{1 + \left(\frac{dy}{dx}\right)^2}\,dx. \tag{2}$$

Our end result, Eq. (2), is easily remembered if we write

$$\sqrt{1 + \left(\frac{dy}{dx}\right)^2}\,dx = ds$$

and take

$$S = \int 2\pi y\,ds. \tag{3}$$

If we let

$$dS = 2\pi y\,ds,$$

so that

$$S = \int dS,$$

we may interpret dS as the product of a

$$\text{circumference} = 2\pi y$$

and a

$$\text{slant height} = ds.$$

Thus dS gives the lateral area of a frustum of a cone of slant height ds if the point (x, y) is the mid-point of the element of arc length ds (Fig. 7–19).

A question which often occurs to the alert student is the following. Why not approximate the surface area S by inscribed *cylinders* and arrive at a result

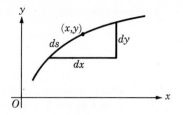

Figure 7–19

$$S = \int 2\pi y \, dx,$$

having dx instead of ds, to replace Eq. (3)? This is a reasonable question. Since we know from our discussion on volume that inscribed cylinders work perfectly well for *volumes* of revolution, why not use them for *surfaces* of revolution also? The answer hinges on the fact that the approximation.

$$\Delta V \approx \pi y^2 \, \Delta x$$

for the volume of a slice involves, at worst, terms which are products like (Δx) (Δy) and higher powers of Δx and these contribute zero to the *limit* of the sum of volumes of the inscribed cylinders. (See Article 7–5.) But the approximations

$$\text{(a) } \Delta S \approx 2\pi y \, \Delta x$$

and

$$\text{(b) } \Delta S \approx 2\pi y \sqrt{(\Delta x)^2 + (\Delta y)^2}$$

for the surface area of a slice cannot *both* be this accurate. For their ratio is

$$\frac{2\pi y \sqrt{(\Delta x)^2 + (\Delta y)^2}}{2\pi y \, \Delta x} = \sqrt{1 + \left(\frac{\Delta y}{\Delta x}\right)^2},$$

which has the limiting value

$$\lim_{\Delta x \to 0} \sqrt{1 + \left(\frac{\Delta y}{\Delta x}\right)^2} = \sqrt{1 + \left(\frac{dy}{dx}\right)^2},$$

and this will be different from one (unless $dy/dx = 0$, which would not be generally true), whereas two approximations that differ only by terms involving products like $(\Delta y)(\Delta x)$ and higher powers of Δx have a ratio whose limiting value is unity. Since the approximations (a) and (b) above will usually lead to different answers when we pass to the corresponding definite integrals, they cannot both be correct, and we must abandon one or both of them. But the approximation (b) is clearly the one which corresponds to a natural way of defining the surface area of a surface of revolution and it leads to (3).

If the axis of revolution is the y-axis, the corresponding formula that replaces (3) is

$$S = \int 2\pi x \, ds,$$

while, more generally, we may write

$$S = \int 2\pi\rho \, ds \qquad\qquad (4)$$

if ρ is the distance from the axis of revolution to the element of arc length ds. Both ρ and ds need to be expressed in terms of some one variable and proper limits must be supplied to (4) in any particular problem.

EXAMPLE 1. The circle

$$x^2 + y^2 = r^2$$

is revolved about the x-axis (Fig. 7–20). Find the area of the sphere generated.

Solution. We write

$$dS = 2\pi y \, ds,$$

$$ds = \sqrt{dx^2 + dy^2},$$

and use

$$x = r \cos \theta, \qquad y = r \sin \theta$$

to represent the circle. Then

$$dx = -r \sin \theta \, d\theta, \qquad dy = r \cos \theta \, d\theta,$$

so that

$$ds = r \, d\theta$$

and

$$dS = 2\pi y \, ds = 2\pi(r \sin \theta) \, r \, d\theta$$

$$= 2\pi r^2 \sin \theta \, d\theta.$$

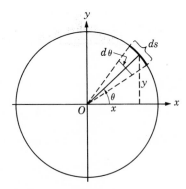

Figure 7–20

The top half of the circle generates the entire sphere, and the representative point (x, y) traces out this upper semicircle as θ varies from 0 to π. Hence

$$S = \int_0^\pi 2\pi r^2 \sin \theta \, d\theta$$

$$= 2\pi r^2 \left[-\cos \theta \right]_0^\pi = 4\pi r^2.$$

EXAMPLE 2. The circle in Example 1 is revolved about the line $y = -r$, which is tangent to the circle at the point $(0, -r)$ (Fig. 7–21). Find the area of the surface generated.

Solution. Here it takes the whole circle to generate the surface, and in terms of the previous example, this means that we must let θ vary from 0 to 2π. The radius of rotation now becomes

$$\rho = y + r,$$

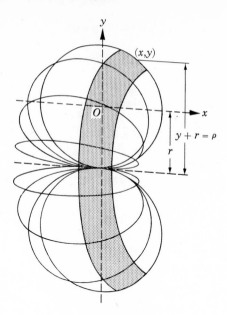

Figure 7–21

and we have

$$dS = 2\pi\rho \, ds = 2\pi(y + r)r \, d\theta = 2\pi(r \sin \theta + r)r \, d\theta.$$

Hence

$$S = \int_0^{2\pi} 2\pi \, (\sin \theta + 1)r^2 \, d\theta = 2\pi r^2 \left[-\cos \theta + \theta\right]_0^{2\pi} = 4\pi^2 r^2.$$

PROBLEMS

1. Find the area of the surface generated by rotating the hypocycloid $x = a \cos^3 \theta$, $y = a \sin^3 \theta$ about the x-axis.

2. Find the area of the surface generated by rotating the portion of the curve $y = \frac{1}{3}(x^2 + 2)^{3/2}$ between $x = 0$ and $x = 3$ about the y-axis.

3. Find the area of the surface generated by rotating about the x-axis the arc of the curve $y = x^3$ between $x = 0$ and $x = 1$.

4. Find the area of the surface generated by rotating about the y-axis the arc of the curve $y = x^2$ between $(0, 0)$ and $(2, 4)$.

5. The arc of the curve $y = x^3/3 + 1/(4x)$ from $x = 1$ to $x = 3$ is rotated about the line $y = -1$. Find the surface area generated.

6. The arc of the curve $x = y^4/4 + 1/(8y^2)$ from $y = 1$ to $y = 2$ is rotated about the x-axis. Find the surface area generated.

7. The curve described by the particle $P(x, y)$,

$$x = t + 1, \qquad y = \frac{t^2}{2} + t,$$

from $t = 0$ to $t = 4$, is rotated about the y-axis. Find the surface area that is generated.

8. The loop of the curve $9x^2 = y(3 - y)^2$ is rotated about the x-axis. Find the surface area generated.

7–8   Average value of a function. The process of finding the average value of a finite number of data is familiar to all students. For example, if $y_1, y_2, \ldots, y_n$ are the grades of a class of n students on a certain calculus quiz, then the class average on that quiz is

$$y_{av} = \frac{y_1 + y_2 + \cdots + y_n}{n}. \tag{1}$$

When the number of data is infinite, it is not feasible to use Eq. (1) (since it is likely to take on the meaningless form ∞/∞). This situation arises, in particular, when the data y are given by a continuous function

$$y = f(x), \qquad a \le x \le b.$$

In this case, the average value of y, with respect to x, is defined to be

$$(y_{av})_x = \frac{1}{b - a} \int_a^b f(x) \, dx. \tag{2}$$

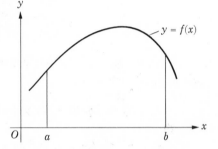

Figure 7–22

The curve in Fig. 7–22, for example, might represent temperature as a function of time over a twenty-four hour period. Equation (2) would then give the "average temperature" for the day.

Remark 1. It may be possible to express y as a function of x, or, alternatively, as a function of u. Then $(y_{av})_x$ and $(y_{av})_u$ need not be equal. For example, for a freely falling body starting from rest,

$$s = \tfrac{1}{2}gt^2, \qquad v = gt, \qquad v = \sqrt{2gs}.$$

Suppose we calculate the average velocity, first with respect to t and second with respect to s, from $t_1 = 0$, $s_1 = 0$ to $t_2 > 0$, $s_2 = \tfrac{1}{2}gt_2^2$. Then, by definition,

$$(v_{av})_t = \frac{1}{t_2 - 0} \int_0^{t_2} gt \, dt = \tfrac{1}{2}gt_2 = \tfrac{1}{2}v_2,$$

$$(v_{av})_s = \frac{1}{s_2 - 0} \int_0^{s_2} \sqrt{2gs} \, ds = \tfrac{2}{3}\sqrt{2gs_2} = \tfrac{2}{3}v_2.$$

Remark 2. If both sides of Eq. (2) are multiplied by $b - a$, we have

$$(y_{\text{av}})_x \cdot (b - a) = \int_a^b f(x)\, dx. \tag{3}$$

The right side of Eq. (3) represents the area bounded above by the curve $y = f(x)$, below by the x-axis, and on the sides by the ordinates $x = a$, $x = b$. The left side of the equation can be interpreted as the area of a rectangle of altitude $(y_{\text{av}})_x$ and of base $b - a$. Hence, Eq. (3) provides a geometric interpretation of $(y_{\text{av}})_x$ as that ordinate of the curve $y = f(x)$ that should be used as altitude if one wishes to construct a rectangle whose base is the interval $a \le x \le b$ and whose area is equal to the area under the curve (Fig. 7–23). In the narrower sense of area, this statement is only valid when the curve lies above the x-axis. In case the curve lies partly or entirely

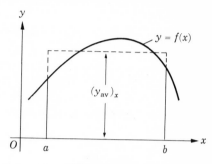

Figure 7–23

below the x-axis, we would count areas below the x-axis as negative. In such a case there might well be a certain amount of canceling of positive and negative areas.

Remark 3. Equation (2) is a *definition*, and hence is not subject to proof. Nevertheless, some discussion may help to explain why this particular formula is used to define the average. One might arrive at it as follows. From the total "population" of x-values, $a \le x \le b$, we select a representative "sample," $x_1, x_2, \ldots, x_n$, uniformly distributed between a and b. Then, using Eq. (1), we calculate the average of the functional values

$$y_1 = f(x_1), \qquad y_2 = f(x_2), \qquad \ldots, \qquad y_n = f(x_n)$$

associated with these representative x's. This gives us

$$\frac{y_1 + y_2 + \cdots + y_n}{n} = \frac{f(x_1) + f(x_2) + \cdots + f(x_n)}{n}. \tag{4}$$

Since we require that the x's be uniformly distributed between a and b, let us take the spacing to be Δx, with

$$x_2 - x_1 = x_3 - x_2 = \cdots = x_n - x_{n-1} = \Delta x$$

and

$$\Delta x = \frac{b - a}{n}.$$

Then, in (4), let us replace the n in the denominator by $(b - a)/\Delta x$, thus obtaining

$$\frac{f(x_1) + f(x_2) + \cdots + f(x_n)}{(b - a)/\Delta x} = \frac{f(x_1)\,\Delta x + f(x_2)\,\Delta x + \cdots + f(x_n)\,\Delta x}{b - a}.$$

If, now, n is very large (Δx small), the expression

$$f(x_1)\,\Delta x + f(x_2)\,\Delta x + \cdots + f(x_n)\,\Delta x = \sum_{k=1}^{n} f(x_k)\,\Delta x$$

is very nearly equal to $\int_a^b f(x)\,dx$. In fact, if we take limits, letting $n \to \infty$, we obtain precisely

$$\lim_{n \to \infty} \frac{f(x_1)\,\Delta x + f(x_2)\,\Delta x + \cdots + f(x_n)\,\Delta x}{b - a} = \frac{1}{b - a} \int_a^b f(x)\,dx.$$

This is the expression used to define the average value of y in Eq. (2).

PROBLEMS

In each of the following problems (1 through 5), find the average value with respect to x, over the given domain, of the given function $f(x)$. In each case, draw a graph of the curve $y = f(x)$, and sketch a rectangle whose altitude is the average ordinate.

1. (a) $\sin x$, $\quad 0 \le x \le \pi/2$
   (b) $\sin x$, $\quad 0 \le x \le 2\pi$

2. (a) $\sin^2 x$, $\quad 0 \le x \le \pi/2$
   (b) $\sin^2 x$, $\quad \pi \le x \le 2\pi$

3. $\sqrt{2x + 1}$, $\quad 4 \le x \le 12$

4. $\frac{1}{2} + \frac{1}{2}\cos 2x$, $\quad 0 \le x \le \pi$

5. $\alpha x + \beta$; $\quad a \le x \le b$ $\quad [\alpha, \beta, a, b, \text{constants}]$

6. Given a circle C of radius a, and a diameter $\overline{AB}$ of C, chords are drawn perpendicular to $\overline{AB}$, intercepting equal segments along $\overline{AB}$. Find the limit of the average of the lengths of these chords, as the number of chords tends to infinity. [*Hint:* $\int_{-a}^{a} \sqrt{a^2 - x^2}\,dx$ is $\frac{1}{2}\pi a^2$, since it is the area of a semicircle of radius a.]

7. Solve Problem 6 under the modified assumption that the chords intercept equal arcs along the circumference of C.

8. Solve Problem 6 using the *squares* of the lengths, in place of the lengths of the chords.

9. Solve Problem 7 using the *squares* of the lengths, in place of the lengths of the chords.

7–9 Moments and center of mass. If several masses $m_1, m_2, \ldots, m_n$ are placed along the x-axis at distances $x_1, x_2, \ldots, x_n$ respectively from the origin (Fig. 7–24), then their moment about the origin is defined to be

$$x_1 m_1 + x_2 m_2 + \cdots + x_n m_n = \sum_{k=1}^{n} x_k m_k. \tag{1}$$

If all the mass

Figure 7-24

$$m_1 + m_2 + \cdots + m_n = \sum_{k=1}^{n} m_k \quad (2)$$

is concentrated at one point of abscissa $\bar{x}$, the total moment is

$$\bar{x} \left(\sum_{k=1}^{n} m_k \right).$$

The position of $\bar{x}$ for which this is the same as the total moment in (1) is called the *center of mass*. The condition

$$\bar{x} \sum_{k=1}^{n} m_k = \sum_{k=1}^{n} x_k m_k$$

thus determines

$$\bar{x} = \frac{\displaystyle\sum_{k=1}^{n} x_k m_k}{\displaystyle\sum_{k=1}^{n} m_k}. \quad (3)$$

EXAMPLE 1. The principle of a moment underlies the simple seesaw. For instance (Fig. 7-25), suppose one child weighs 80 lb and sits 5 ft from the point O, while the other child weighs 100 lb and is 4 ft from O. Then the child at the left end of the seesaw produces a moment of $80 \times 5 = 400$ (lb-ft), which tends to rotate the plank counterclockwise about O. The child at the right end of the plank produces a moment of $100 \times 4 = 400$ (lb-ft), which tends to rotate the plank clockwise around O. If we introduce coordinates $x_1 = -5$ and $x_2 = +4$, we find

$$x_1 m_1 + x_2 m_2 = (-5)(80) + (4)(100)$$

$$= -400 + 400 = 0$$

as the resultant moment about O. The same moment, zero, would be obtained if both children were at O, which is the center of their mass.

Figure 7-25

If, instead of being placed on the x-axis, the masses are located in the xy-plane at points $(x_1, y_1,)$ (x_2, y_2), ..., (x_n, y_n), in that order, then we define their moments with respect to the y-axis and with respect to the x-axis as

$$M_y = x_1 m_1 + x_2 m_2 + \cdots + x_n m_n = \sum_{k=1}^{n} x_k m_k,$$

$$M_x = y_1 m_1 + y_2 m_2 + \cdots + y_n m_n = \sum_{k=1}^{n} y_k m_k.$$

The center of mass is the point $(\bar{x}, \bar{y})$,

$$\bar{x} = \frac{\sum x_k m_k}{\sum m_k}, \qquad \bar{y} = \frac{\sum y_k m_k}{\sum m_k}, \tag{4}$$

where the total mass could be concentrated and still give the same total moments M_y and M_x.

In space, three coordinates are needed to specify the position of a point. If the masses are located at the points (x_1, y_1, z_1), (x_2, y_2, z_2), ..., (x_n, y_n, z_n), we define their moments with respect to the various coordinate planes as

$$M_{yz} = x_1 m_1 + x_2 m_2 + \cdots + x_n m_n = \sum_{k=1}^{n} x_k m_k,$$

$$M_{zx} = y_1 m_1 + y_2 m_2 + \cdots + y_n m_n = \sum_{k=1}^{n} y_k m_k,$$

$$M_{xy} = z_1 m_1 + z_2 m_2 + \cdots + z_n m_n = \sum_{k=1}^{n} z_k m_k.$$

$(M_{yz} = $ moment with respect to the yz-plane, etc.)

The center of mass $(\bar{x}, \bar{y}, \bar{z})$ is the point where the total mass could be concentrated without altering these moments. Its coordinates therefore are given by

$$\bar{x} = \frac{\sum x_k m_k}{\sum m_k}, \qquad \bar{y} = \frac{\sum y_k m_k}{\sum m_k}, \qquad \bar{z} = \frac{\sum z_k m_k}{\sum m_k}. \tag{5}$$

Now most physical objects with which we deal are composed of enormously large numbers of molecules. It would be extremely difficult, and in most cases unnecessary, for us to concern ourselves with the molecular structure of a physical object, such as a pendulum, whose motion as a whole is to be studied. Instead, we make certain simplifying assumptions which we recognize as being only approximately correct. One such assumption is that the matter in a given solid is continuously distributed throughout the solid. Furthermore, if P is a point in the solid and ΔV is an element of volume which contains P, and if Δm is the mass of ΔV, then we assume that the ratio $\Delta m/\Delta V$ tends to a definite limit

$$\delta = \lim_{\Delta V \to 0} \frac{\Delta m}{\Delta V}, \tag{6}$$

as the largest dimension of ΔV approaches zero. The limit δ is called the *density* of the solid at the point P. It is customary to write Eq. (6) in the alternative forms

$$\delta = dm/dV, \qquad dm = \delta\, dV. \tag{7}$$

If now a solid is divided into small pieces ΔV of mass Δm and if $P(\tilde{x}, \tilde{y}, \tilde{z})$ is a point in ΔV and δ is the density at P, then

$$\Delta m \approx \delta\, \Delta V.$$

The moments of Δm with respect to the coordinate planes are not defined by what we have done thus far. But now we may think of replacing the Δm that fills the volume ΔV by an equal mass all concentrated at the point P. The moments of this concentrated mass with respect to the coordinate planes are

$$\tilde{x}\, \Delta m, \qquad \tilde{y}\, \Delta m, \qquad \tilde{z}\, \Delta m.$$

Now we add the moments of all the concentrated masses in all the volume elements ΔV and take the limit as the ΔV's approach zero. This leads us to the following *definitions* of the moments M_{yz}, etc., for the mass as a whole:

$$M_{yz} = \lim_{\Delta m \to 0} \sum \tilde{x}\, \Delta m = \int \tilde{x}\, dm,$$

$$M_{zx} = \lim_{\Delta m \to 0} \sum \tilde{y}\, \Delta m = \int \tilde{y}\, dm,$$

$$M_{xy} = \lim_{\Delta m \to 0} \sum \tilde{z}\, \Delta m = \int \tilde{z}\, dm.$$

From these, we then deduce the equations

$$\bar{x} = \frac{\int \tilde{x}\, dm}{\int dm}, \qquad \bar{y} = \frac{\int \tilde{y}\, dm}{\int dm}, \qquad \bar{z} = \frac{\int \tilde{z}\, dm}{\int dm} \tag{8}$$

for the center of mass of the solid as a whole.

In theory, the element dm is approximately the mass in a volume element dV which has three small dimensions as in Fig. 7–26. In a later chapter we shall see how to evaluate the integrals (8) which arise when this is done. In practice, however, we can usually take

$$dm = \delta \, dV$$

with a volume element dV which has only one small dimension. Then we must interpret $\bar{x}, \bar{y}, \bar{z}$ in the integrands in (8) as the coordinates of the **center of mass** of the **element** dm.

In many problems of practical importance the density δ is constant and the solid possesses a plane of symmetry. Then it is easy to see that the center of mass lies in this plane of symmetry. For we may, with no loss of generality, choose our coordinate reference frame in such a way that the yz-plane is the plane of symmetry. Then for every element of mass Δm with a positive $\bar{x}$ there is a symmetrically located element of mass with a corresponding negative $\bar{x}$. These two elements have moments which are equal in magnitude and of opposite signs. The whole mass is made up of such symmetric pairs of elements and the sum of their moments about the yz-plane is zero. Therefore $\bar{x} = 0$; that is, the center of mass lies in the plane of symmetry. If there are two planes of symmetry, their intersection is an axis of symmetry and the center of mass must lie on this axis, since it lies in both planes of symmetry.

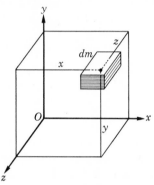

Figure 7–26

The most frequently encountered distributions of mass are

(a) along a thin wire or filament: $dm = \delta_1 \, ds$,
(b) in a thin plate or shell: $dm = \delta_2 \, dA$ or $\delta_2 \, dS$,
(c) in a solid: $dm = \delta_3 \, dV$,

where

$$ds = \text{element of arc length},$$
$$\delta_1 = \text{mass per unit length of the wire},$$
$$dA \text{ or } dS = \text{element of area},$$
$$\delta_2 = \text{mass per unit area of the plate or shell},$$
$$dV = \text{element of volume},$$
$$\delta_3 = \text{mass per unit volume of the solid}.$$

EXAMPLE 1. Find the center of mass of a thin homogeneous triangular plate of base b and altitude h.

Solution. Divide the triangle into strips of width dy parallel to the x-axis. A representative strip is shown in Fig. 7–27. The mass of the strip is approximately

$$dm = \delta_2 \, dA,$$

where

$$dA = l \, dy$$

and l is the width of the triangle at distance y above its base. By similar triangles,

$$\frac{l}{b} = \frac{h - y}{h}$$

or

$$l = \frac{b}{h} (h - y),$$

so that

$$dm = \delta_2 \frac{b}{h} (h - y) \, dy.$$

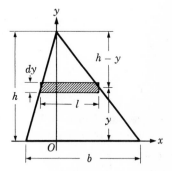

Figure 7–27

For the y-coordinate of the center of mass of the element dm, we have $\tilde{y} = y$. For the entire plate,

$$\bar{y} = \frac{\int y \, dm}{\int dm} = \frac{\int_0^h \delta_2 \frac{b}{h} y(h - y) \, dy}{\int_0^h \delta_2 \frac{b}{h} (h - y) \, dy} = \frac{1}{3} h.$$

Thus the center of mass lies above the base of the triangle at a distance one-third of the way toward the opposite vertex. By considering each side in turn as being a base of the triangle, this result shows that the center of gravity lies at the intersection of the medians.

EXAMPLE 2. A thin homogeneous wire is bent to form a semicircle of radius r (Fig. 7–28). Find its center of mass.

Solution. Here we take

$$dm = \delta_1 \, ds,$$

where ds is an element of arc length of the wire and

$$\delta_1 = \frac{M}{L} = \frac{M}{\pi r}$$

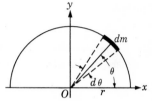

Figure 7–28

is the mass per unit length of the wire. In terms of the central angle θ measured in radians (as usual), we have

$$ds = r\, d\theta$$

and

$$\tilde{x} = r\cos\theta, \qquad \tilde{y} = r\sin\theta.$$

Hence

$$\bar{x} = \frac{\displaystyle\int_0^\pi r\cos\theta\, \delta_1\, r\, d\theta}{\displaystyle\int_0^\pi \delta_1\, r\, d\theta} = \frac{\delta_1 r^2 \Big[\sin\theta\Big]_0^\pi}{\delta_1 r \Big[\theta\Big]_0^\pi} = 0,$$

$$\bar{y} = \frac{\displaystyle\int_0^\pi r\sin\theta\, \delta_1\, r\, d\theta}{\displaystyle\int_0^\pi \delta_1\, r\, d\theta} = \frac{\delta_1 r^2 \Big[-\cos\theta\Big]_0^\pi}{\delta_1 r \Big[\theta\Big]_0^\pi} = \frac{2}{\pi} r.$$

The center of mass is therefore on the y-axis at a distance $2/\pi$ (roughly $\frac{2}{3}$) of the way up from the origin toward the intercept $(0, r)$.

EXAMPLE 3. Find the center of mass of a solid hemisphere of radius r if its density at any point P is proportional to the distance of P from the base of the hemisphere.

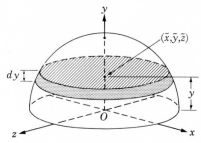

Figure 7–29

Solution. Imagine the solid cut into slices of thickness dy by planes perpendicular to the y-axis (Fig. 7–29), and take

$$dm = \delta_3\, dV,$$

where

$$dV = A(y)\, dy$$

is the volume of the representative slice at distance y above the base of the hemisphere, which is in the xz-plane, and where

$$\delta_3 = ky \qquad (k = \text{constant})$$

is the density of the solid in this slice. The area of a face of the slice dV is

$A(y) = \pi x^2$, where $x^2 + y^2 = r^2$, that is,

$$dV = A(y)\,dy = \pi(r^2 - y^2)\,dy,$$

so that

$$dm = k\pi(r^2 - y^2)y\,dy.$$

The center of mass of the slice may be taken at its geometrical center, that is

$$(\bar{x}, \bar{y}, \bar{z}) = (0, y, 0),$$

so that

$$\bar{x} = \bar{z} = 0$$

and

$$
\bar{y} = \frac{\displaystyle\int y\,dm}{\displaystyle\int dm}
$$

$$
= \frac{\displaystyle\int_0^r k\pi(r^2 - y^2)y^2\,dy}{\displaystyle\int_0^r k\pi(r^2 - y^2)y\,dy} = \frac{k\pi\left[\dfrac{r^2 y^3}{3} - \dfrac{y^5}{5}\right]_0^r}{k\pi\left[\dfrac{r^2 y^2}{2} - \dfrac{y^4}{4}\right]_0^r}
$$

$$
= \frac{8}{15}r.
$$

PROBLEMS

In each of the following problems (1 through 5), find the center of mass of a thin homogeneous plate covering the given portion of the xy-plane.

1. The first quadrant of the circle $x^2 + y^2 = a^2$.
2. The area bounded by the parabola $y = h^2 - x^2$ and the x-axis.
3. The "triangular" shaped area in the first quadrant between the circle $x^2 + y^2 = a^2$ and the lines $x = a$, $y = a$.
4. The area between the x-axis and the curve $y = \sin x$ between $x = 0$ and $x = \pi$. [*Hint:* Take $dA = y\,dx$ and $\bar{y} = \frac{1}{2}y$.]
5. The area between the y-axis and the curve $x = 2y - y^2$.
6. Find the distance, from the base, of the center of mass of a thin triangular plate of base b and altitude h if its density varies as the square root of the distance from the base.
7. In Problem 6, suppose that the density varies as the square of the distance.
8. Find the center of mass of a homogeneous solid right circular cone.
9. Find the center of mass of a solid right circular cone if the density varies as the distance from the base.
10. In Problem 9 suppose that the density varies as the square of the distance.
11. In Example 2 (see Fig. 7–28) suppose that the density is $\delta_1 = k\sin\theta$, k being constant. Find the center of mass.

7–10   Centroid and center of gravity.   In the case of a mass having uniform density, Eqs. (8), Article 7–9, reduce to

$$
\bar{x} = \frac{\int \bar{x}\delta_3 \, dV}{\int \delta_3 \, dV} = \frac{\delta_3 \int \bar{x} \, dV}{\delta_3 \int dV} = \frac{\int \bar{x} \, dV}{\int dV},
$$

$$
\bar{y} = \frac{\int \bar{y} \, dV}{\int dV}, \qquad \bar{z} = \frac{\int \bar{z} \, dV}{\int dV}.
$$

$$(1)$$

for a solid, with similar equations having dA or ds in place of dV in the case of a plate or a wire. Since these expressions involve only the geometric objects, namely volumes, areas, and curves, we speak of the point $(\bar{x}, \bar{y}, \bar{z})$ in such cases as the *centroid* of the object. The term *center of gravity* is also used, since the line of action of the forces due to gravity acting on the elements of the object pass through this point. (See Sears, *Mechanics, Heat, and Sound*, Chapters 3 and 7, for a discussion of physical concepts involved.)

EXAMPLE 1. Find the center of gravity of a solid hemisphere of radius r.

Solution. As in Example 3, Article 7–9, imagine the solid (Fig. 7–29) cut into slices of thickness dy by planes perpendicular to the y-axis. The centroid of a slice is its geometrical center, on the y-axis, at $(0, y, 0)$. Its moment with respect to the xz-plane is

$$
dM_{zz} = y \, dV
$$

$$
= y\pi(r^2 - y^2) \, dy.
$$

Hence

$$
M_{zz} = \pi \int_0^r (r^2 y - y^3) \, dy = \frac{\pi r^4}{4}.
$$

Since the volume of the hemisphere is

$$
V = \frac{2}{3}\pi r^3,
$$

we have

$$
\bar{y} = \frac{M_{zz}}{V} = \frac{3}{8}r.
$$

EXAMPLE 2. Find the center of gravity of a thin hemispherical shell of inner radius r and thickness t.

Solution. We shall solve this problem, (a) exactly, by using the results of the preceding example, then (b) we shall see how the position of the center of gravity changes as we hold r fixed and let $t \to 0$. Finally, (c) we shall solve the problem approximately without using the results of Example 1, by considering the center of mass of an imaginary distribution of mass over the surface of the hemisphere of radius r, assuming that the thickness t is negligible in comparison with r. (As, for example, the gold leaf covering the dome of the State House in Boston.)

(a) Let M_1, M_2, and M; V_1, V_2, and V denote respectively the moments with respect to the xz-plane and the volumes of the solid hemisphere of radius r, the solid hemisphere of radius $(r + t)$, and the hemispherical shell of thickness t and inner radius r. Since the moment of the sum of two masses is the sum of their moments and

$$V_1 + V = V_2,$$

we also have

$$M_1 + M = M_2,$$

that is

$$M = M_2 - M_1.$$

But by Example 1,

$$M_2 = \frac{\pi}{4}(r + t)^4, \qquad M_1 = \frac{\pi}{4}r^4,$$

so that

$$M = \frac{\pi}{4}[(r + t)^4 - r^4]$$

$$= \frac{\pi}{4}[4r^3 t + 6r^2 t^2 + 4rt^3 + t^4],$$

while

$$V = V_2 - V_1 = \tfrac{2}{3}\pi[(r + t)^3 - r^3]$$

$$= \tfrac{2}{3}\pi(3r^2 t + 3rt^2 + t^3);$$

hence

$$\bar{y} = \frac{M}{V} = \frac{1}{2}\frac{[r^3 + \frac{3}{2}r^2 t + rt^2 + \frac{1}{4}t^3]}{[r^2 + rt + \frac{1}{3}t^2]}.$$

(b) In the case of a shell where the thickness t is negligible in comparison with r, this reduces to $\bar{y} = \frac{1}{2}r$, by writing

$$\bar{y} = \frac{1}{2}\frac{r^3\left[1 + \frac{3}{2}\left(\frac{t}{r}\right) + \left(\frac{t}{r}\right)^2 + \frac{1}{4}\left(\frac{t}{r}\right)^3\right]}{r^2\left[1 + \left(\frac{t}{r}\right) + \frac{1}{3}\left(\frac{t}{r}\right)^2\right]},$$

and then letting $(t/r) \to 0$.

(c) To solve the problem directly, without reference to Example 1, consider the mass of the shell as being uniformly distributed over its surface so that the mass of any portion cut from the shell will be proportional to its (inner) surface area. The proportionality factor,

$$\sigma = \delta t,$$

where δ is the volume density and t the thickness of the shell, is frequently referred to as a surface density factor. (Thus in working with sheet metal stock, say aluminum of uniform thickness and density, we might speak of it as weighing so many pounds *per square foot*. This would be our σ, and A square feet of this particular stock would weigh σA pounds.) Then the slice of shell between planes perpendicular to the y-axis at distances y and $y + \Delta y$ respectively above the xz-plane has mass

$$\Delta m = \sigma \, \Delta S,$$

where ΔS is the surface area of the slice (see Fig. 7–30). The moment of this slice with respect to the xz-plane then lies between

$$y \, \Delta m \qquad \text{and} \qquad (y + \Delta y) \, \Delta m,$$

and hence differs from $y \, \Delta m$ by at most $\Delta y \, \Delta m$. The sum of the moments of the slices has a limit, as Δy approaches zero, equal to $\int y \, dm$. We are thus led to

$$\bar{y} = \frac{\int y \, dm}{\int dm} = \frac{\int \sigma y \, dS}{\int \sigma \, dS} = \frac{\sigma \int y \, dS}{\sigma \int dS},$$

since σ is constant by our hypotheses. Here

$$dS = 2\pi x \, ds = 2\pi (r \cos \theta) r \, d\theta$$

if we use

$$x = r \cos \theta, \qquad y = r \sin \theta$$

to represent the circle $x^2 + y^2 = r^2$. Hence

$$\bar{y} = \frac{\displaystyle\int_0^{\pi/2} r \sin \theta \cdot 2\pi (r \cos \theta) \cdot r \, d\theta}{\displaystyle\int_0^{\pi/2} 2\pi (r \cos \theta) r \, d\theta}$$

$$= \frac{2\pi r^3 \displaystyle\int_0^{\pi/2} \sin \theta \cos \theta \, d\theta}{2\pi r^2 \displaystyle\int_0^{\pi/2} \cos \theta \, d\theta} = r \frac{\left[\frac{1}{2} \sin^2 \theta\right]_0^{\pi/2}}{\left[\sin \theta\right]_0^{\pi/2}} = \frac{1}{2} r.$$

Figure 7-30

Observe that the element of arc ds which, when rotated about the y-axis, generates dS, need only move along the arc of the circle in the first quadrant, namely, $0 \le \theta \le \pi/2$, in order to give us the entire hemisphere.

By the symmetry of the shell, the center of gravity lies on the y-axis, that is,

$$(\bar{x}, \bar{y}, \bar{z},) = (0, \tfrac{1}{2}r, 0).$$

PROBLEMS

In Problems 1 through 5 find the center of gravity of the areas bounded by the given curves and lines.

1. The x-axis and the curve $y = c^2 - x^2$.

2. The y-axis and the curve $x = y - y^3$, $0 \le y \le 1$.

3. The curve $y = x^2$ and the line $y = 4$.

4. The curve $y = x - x^2$ and the line $x + y = 0$.

5. The curve $x = y^2 - y$ and the line $y = x$.

6. Find the center of gravity of a solid right circular cone of altitude h and base-radius r.

7. Find the center of gravity of the solid generated by rotating, about the y-axis, the area bounded by the curve $y = x^2$ and the line $y = 4$.

8. The area bounded by the curve $x = y^2 - y$ and the line $y = x$ is rotated about the x-axis. Find the center of gravity of the solid thus generated.

9. Find the center of gravity of a very thin right circular conical shell of base-radius r and altitude h.

10. Find the center of gravity of the surface area generated by rotating about the line $x = -r$, the arc of the circle $x^2 + y^2 = r^2$ that lies in the first quadrant. (Use $x = r \cos \theta$, $y = r \sin \theta$ to represent the circle.)

11. Find the moment, about the x-axis, of the arc of the parabola $y = \sqrt{x}$ lying between $(0, 0)$ and $(4, 2)$.

12. Find the center of gravity of the arc length of one quadrant of a circle.

7-11   Work. When a constant force F (pounds) acts throughout a distance s (feet), the *work* done (in foot-pounds) is the product of force and distance,

$$W = Fs. \tag{1}$$

When the force is not constant, as for instance in stretching or compressing a spring, then Eq. (1) cannot be used directly to give the work done. The law in (1) can be used, however, to find approximately the work done over a *short* interval Δs if the force is a continuous function of s. The integral process then enables us to extend the law in (1) to find the total work done.

To illustrate, suppose we consider the work done in compressing a spring from its natural unstressed length L to a length $\frac{3}{4}L$ (Fig. 7-31) if the force required to hold it under compression is

$$F = cx, \tag{2}$$

where x is the amount it has been compressed and c is a proportionality

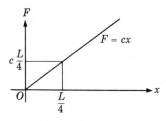

Figure 7–31   **Figure 7–3 2**

factor (called the "spring constant"). Thus to compress the spring by
an amount $L/4$, the force must be increased from

$$F_0 = c \times 0 = 0$$

to

$$F_1 = c\frac{L}{4},$$

and as it does so the point of application of the force will move from
$x = 0$ to $x = L/4$ in Fig. 7–31. How, then, shall we find the *work* done
during the process? We imagine the x-interval from 0 to $L/4$ to be
divided into a large number of subintervals, each of length Δx. As the
spring is compressed an amount Δx, so that its left end moves across
the representative subinterval from x to $x + \Delta x$, the *force* will vary from
cx to $c(x + \Delta x)$, and since it acts through a *distance* Δx, the work done
for this small compression will lie between

$$cx\ \Delta x \qquad \text{and} \qquad c(x + \Delta x)\ \Delta x,$$

so that the total work will be given approximately by

$$W \approx \sum_{x=0}^{L/4} cx\ \Delta x,$$

or

$$W = \sum_{x=0}^{L/4} c\tilde{x}\ \Delta x$$

for appropriate choices of the $\tilde{x}$ between x and $x + \Delta x$. In the limit as
Δx tends to zero, we have

$$W = \lim_{\Delta x \to 0} \sum_{x=0}^{L/4} cx\ \Delta x = \int_0^{L/4} cx\ dx = \frac{cL^2}{32}$$

or

$$W = \tfrac{1}{2}(cL/4)(L/4).$$

In this last form, the factor $\frac{1}{2}c(L/4)$ is one-half the final value reached by F when the spring has been compressed to $\frac{3}{4}$ of its original length, and the factor $L/4$ is the total distance through which the variable force has acted. This suggests

$$W = \bar{F}s \tag{3}$$

as a suitable modification of Eq. (1) when the force is variable, where $\bar{F}$ represents the *average* value of the variable force throughout the total displacement. However, the determination of $\bar{F}$ itself involves an integration in the general case, so that it is usually as easy to apply the principles illustrated in the example just considered as it is to apply Eq. (3). In fact, Eq. (3) may be interpreted as *defining* $\bar{F}$.

In a manner entirely analogous to that in the above example, it is easily seen that

$$\boxed{W = \int_a^b F \, ds} \tag{4}$$

gives the work done by a variable force (which, however, always acts along a given direction) as the point of application undergoes a displacement from $s = a$ to $s = b$. This leads to the following interesting theorem of mechanics.

THEOREM. *Let F denote the resultant of all forces acting on a particle of mass m. Let the direction of F remain constant. Then whether the magnitude of F is constant or variable, the work done on the particle by the force F is equal to the change in the kinetic energy of the particle.*

The ingredients required for a proof of this theorem are:

(a) Eq. (4), which gives the work,
(b) the definition of kinetic energy, K.E. $= \frac{1}{2}mv^2$, and
(c) Newton's second law: $F = m(dv/dt)$.

The fact that

$$v = \frac{ds}{dt}$$

and

$$\frac{dv}{dt} = \frac{dv}{ds}\frac{ds}{dt} = \frac{dv}{ds}v$$

and Newton's second law enable us to write Eq. (4) in the form

$$W = \int_{s=a}^{s=b} mv \frac{dv}{ds} \, ds = \int_{v=v_a}^{v=v_b} mv \, dv,$$

which leads to

$$W = \frac{1}{2} mv^2 \Big]_{v_a}^{v_b} = \frac{1}{2} mv_b^2 - \frac{1}{2} mv_a^2.$$

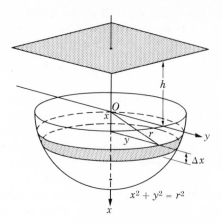

$$x^2 + y^2 = r^2$$

Figure 7–33

That is, the work done by the force F is the kinetic energy at b minus the kinetic energy at a or, more simply, the change in kinetic energy:

$$W = \Delta(\text{K.E.}).$$

As a second example of work in a situation where the simple Eq. (1) cannot be applied to the *total* but can be applied to a *small piece*, we consider the problem of pumping all the water from a full hemispherical bowl of radius r (feet) to a distance h (feet) above the top of the bowl (see Fig. 7–33).

We introduce coordinate axes as shown in Fig. 7–33 and imagine the bowl to be divided into a large number of thin slices by planes perpendicular to the x-axis between $x = 0$ and $x = r$. The representative slice between the planes at x and $x + \Delta x$ has volume ΔV which, if we neglect only infinitesimals of higher order than Δx, is given approximately by

$$\Delta V \approx \pi y^2 \, \Delta x = \pi(r^2 - x^2) \, \Delta x.$$

To the same order of approximation, the force F required to lift *this slice* is equal to its weight:

$$w \, \Delta V \approx \pi w(r^2 - x^2) \, \Delta x,$$

where w is the weight of a cubic foot of water. Finally, the *distance* through which this force must act lies between

$$h + x \qquad \text{and} \qquad h + x + \Delta x,$$

so that the work ΔW done in *lifting this one slice* is approximately

$$\Delta W \approx \pi w(r^2 - x^2)(h + x) \, \Delta x,$$

where we again have suppressed all higher powers of Δx. This is justified in the *limit* of the sum, and the total work is

$$W = \lim_{\Delta x \to 0} \sum_0^r \pi w(r^2 - x^2)(h + x)\,\Delta x$$

$$= \int_0^r \pi w(h + x)(r^2 - x^2)\,dx$$

$$= hw\int_0^r \pi(r^2 - x^2)\,dx + w\int_0^r \pi x(r^2 - x^2)\,dx$$

$$= hwV + \bar{x}wV.$$

Here (wV) is the weight of the whole bowlful of water of volume V, and the second integral may be interpreted physically as giving the work required in pumping *all* the water from the depth of the center of gravity of the bowl to the level $x = 0$, while the first integral gives the work done in pumping the whole bowlful of water from the level $x = 0$ up a distance of h feet. The actual evaluation of the integrals leads to

$$W = \tfrac{2}{3}\pi r^3 w(h + \tfrac{3}{8}r).$$

Can you prove for yourself that no matter what the shape of the container in Fig. 7–33, the total work is the sum of two terms, one of which is

$$W_1 = hw\int dV$$

and represents the total work done in lifting a bowlful of water a distance h, while the other is

$$W_2 = w\int x\,dV$$

and represents the work done in lifting a bowlful of water a distance equal to the depth of the center of gravity of the bowl?

PROBLEMS

1. If the spring in Fig. 7–31 has natural length $L = 18$ in., and a force of 10 lb is sufficient to compress it to a length of 16 in., what is the value of the "spring constant" c for the particular spring in question? How much work is done in compressing it from a length of 16 in. to a length of 12 in.?

2. Answer the questions of Problem 1 if the law of force is $F = c \sin (\pi x/2L)$ in place of Eq. (2).

3. Two electrons repel each other with a force inversely proportional to the square of the distance between them. Suppose one electron is held fixed at the point $(1, 0)$ on the x-axis. Find the work required to move a second electron along the x-axis from the point $(-1, 0)$ to the origin.

4. If two electrons are held stationary at the points $(-1, 0)$ and $(1, 0)$ on the x-axis, find the work done in moving a third electron from $(5, 0)$ to $(3, 0)$ along the x-axis.

5. If a straight hole could be bored through the center of the earth, a particle of mass m falling in this hole would be attracted toward the center of the earth with a force $mg\, r/R$ when it is at distance r from the center. (R is the radius of earth; g is the acceleration due to gravity at the surface of the earth.) How much work is done on the particle as it falls from the surface to the center of the earth?

6. A bag of sand originally weighing 144 lb is lifted at a constant rate of 3 ft/min. The sand leaks out uniformly at such a rate that half of the sand is lost when the bag has been lifted 18 ft. Find the work done in lifting the bag this distance.

7. Gas in a cylinder of constant cross-sectional area A expands or is compressed by the motion of a piston. If p is the pressure of the gas in pounds per square inch and v is its volume in cubic inches, show that the work done by the gas as it goes from an initial state (p_1, v_1) to a second state (p_2, v_2) is

$$W = \int_{(p_1, v_1)}^{(p_2, v_2)} p\, dv \text{ (inch-pounds).}$$

[*Hint:* Take the x-axis perpendicular to the face of the piston. Then $dv = A\, dx$ and $F = pA$.]

8. Use the result of Problem 7 to find the work done on the gas in compressing it from $v_1 = 243$ in^3 to $v_2 = 32$ in^3 if the initial pressure $p_1 = 50$ lb/in^2 and the pressure and volume satisfy the law for adiabatic change of state, $pv^{1.4} = $ constant.

9. Find the work done in pumping all the water out of a conical reservoir of radius 10 ft at the top, altitude 8 ft, to a height of 6 ft above the top of the reservoir.

10. Find the work done in Problem 9 if at the beginning the reservoir is filled to a depth of 5 ft and the water is pumped just to the top of the reservoir.

REVIEW QUESTIONS AND EXERCISES FOR CHAPTER 7

1. List nine applications of the definite integral presented in this chapter.
2. How do you define the area bounded above by a curve $y = f_1(x)$, below by a curve $y = f_2(x)$, and on the sides by $x = a$ and $x = b$, $a < b$?
3. How do you define the volume generated by rotating a plane area about an axis in its plane and not intersecting the area?
4. How do you define the length of a plane curve? Can you extend this to a curve in three-dimensional space?
5. How do you define the surface area of a sphere? Of other surfaces of revolution?
6. How do you define the average value of a function over an interval?
7. How do you define center of mass?
8. How do you define work done by a variable force?

MISCELLANEOUS PROBLEMS FOR CHAPTER 7

1. Sketch the graphs of the equations $y = 2 - x^2$ and $x + y = 0$ in one diagram, and find the area bounded by them.

2. Find the maximum and minimum points of the curve $y = x^3 - 3x^2$ and find the total area bounded by this curve and the x-axis. Sketch.

In the following problems (3–15), find the area bounded by the given curves and lines. Use the trapezoidal rule, Article 6–10, to approximate any integral you cannot evaluate by the Fundamental Theorem. A sketch is usually helpful.

3. $y = x$, $y = \dfrac{1}{x^2}$, $x = 2$ 4. $y = x$, $y = \dfrac{1}{\sqrt{x}}$, $x = 2$

5. $y = x + 1$, $y = 3 - x^2$ 6. $y = 2x^2$, $y = x^2 + 2x + 3$

7. $x = 2y^2$, $x = 0$, $y = 3$ 8. $4x = y^2 - 4$, $4x = y + 16$

9. $x^{1/2} + y^{1/2} = a^{1/2}$, $x = 0$, $y = 0$

10. $y = \sqrt{9 + x^2}$, $y = 0$, $x = 0$, $x = 4$

11. $y^2 = 9x$, $y = \dfrac{3x^2}{8}$

12. $y = \dfrac{1}{1 + x^2}$, $y = 0$, $x = 0$, $x = 1$

13. $y = x\sqrt{2x^2 + 1}$, $x = 0$, $x = 2$

14. $y^2 = 4x$ and $y = 4x - 2$ 15. $y = 2 - x^2$ and $y = x^2 - 6$

16. The function $v = 3t^2 - 15t + 18$ represents the velocity v (ft/sec) of a moving body as a function of the time t (sec). (a) Find that portion of the time interval $0 \le t \le 3$ in which the velocity is positive. (b) Find that portion where v is negative. (c) Find the total distance traveled by the body from $t = 0$ to $t = 3$.

17. The area from 0 to x under a certain graph is given to be

$$A = (1 + 3x)^{1/2} - 1, \quad x \ge 0.$$

(a) Find the *average* rate of change of A with respect to x as x increases from 1 to 8. (b) Find the *instantaneous* rate of change of A with respect to x at $x = 5$. (c) Find the ordinate (height) y of the graph as a function of x. (d) Find the average value of the ordinate (height) y, with respect to x, as x increases from 1 to 8.

18. A solid is generated by rotating, about the x-axis, the area bounded by the curve $y = f(x)$, the x-axis, and the lines $x = a$, $x = b$. Its volume, for all $b > a$, is $b^2 - ab$. Find $f(x)$.

19. Find the volume generated by rotating the area bounded by the given curves and lines about the line indicated:

(a) $y = x^2$, $y = 0$, $x = 3$; about the x-axis.
(b) $y = x^2$, $y = 0$, $x = 3$; about the line $x = -3$.

327

(c) $y = x^2$, $y = 0$, $x = 3$; about the y-axis, first integrating with respect to x and then integrating with respect to y.

(d) $x = 4y - y^2$, $x = 0$; about the y-axis.

(e) $x = 4y - y^2$, $x = 0$; about the x-axis.

20. A solid is generated by rotating $f(x)$, $(0 \le x \le a)$, about the x-axis. Its volume for all a is $a^2 + a$; find $f(x)$.

21. The area bounded by the curve $y^2 = 4x$ and the straight line $y = x$ is rotated about the x-axis. Find the volume generated.

22. Sketch the area bounded by the curve $y^2 = 4ax$, the line $x = a$, and the x-axis. Find the respective volumes generated by rotating this area in the following ways: (a) about the x-axis, (b) about the line $x = a$, (c) about the y-axis.

23. The area bounded by the curve $y = x/\sqrt{x^3 + 8}$, the x-axis, and the line $x = 2$ is rotated about the y-axis, generating a certain volume. Set up the integral that should be used to evaluate the volume and then evaluate the integral.

24. Find the volume of the solid generated by rotating the larger area bounded by $y^2 = x - 1$, $x = 3$, and $y = 1$ about the y-axis.

25. The area bounded by the curve $y^2 = 4ax$ and the line $x = a$ is rotated about the line $x = 2a$. Find the volume generated.

26. Two circles have a common diameter and lie in perpendicular planes. A square moves in such a way that its plane is perpendicular to this diameter and its diagonals are chords of the circles. Find the volume generated.

27. Find the volume generated by rotating about the x-axis the area bounded by the x-axis and one arch of the curve $y = \sin 2x$.

28. A round hole of radius $\sqrt{3}$ ft is bored through the center of a solid sphere of radius 2 ft. Find the volume cut out.

29. The base of a solid is the area bounded by $y^2 = 4ax$ and $x = a$. Each cross section perpendicular to the x-axis is an equilateral triangle. Find the volume of the solid.

30. Find the length of the curve $x = (\frac{3}{5})y^{5/3} - (\frac{3}{4})y^{1/3}$ from $y = 0$ to $y = 1$.

31. Find the surface area generated when the curve of Problem 30 is rotated about the line $y = -1$.

32. Find the length of the curve $y = (2x^{3/2}/3) - (x^{1/2}/2)$ from $x = 0$ to $x = 4$ and the surface area generated when the curve is rotated about the y-axis.

33. Find the average value of y with respect to x for that part of the curve $y = \sqrt{ax}$ between $x = a$ and $x = 3a$.

34. Find the average value of y^2 with respect to x for the curve $ay = b\sqrt{a^2 - x^2}$ between $x = 0$ and $x = a$. Also find the average value of y with respect to x^2 for $0 \le x \le a$.

35. Consider the curve $y = f(x)$, $x \ge 0$ such that $f(0) = a$. Let $s(x)$ denote the arc length along the curve from $(0, a)$ to $(x, f(x))$. Find $f(x)$ if (a) $s(x) = Ax$.

(What are the permissible values of A?) (b) Is it possible for $s(x) = x^n$, $n > 1$? Give a reason for your answer.

36. A point moves in a straight line during the time from $t = 0$ to $t = 3$ according to the law $s = 120t - 16t^2$. (a) Find the average value of the velocity, with respect to time, for these three seconds. [Compare with the "average velocity," Article 1–9, Eq. (6).] (b) Find the average value of the velocity with respect to the distance s during the three seconds.

37. Sketch a smooth curve through the points $A(1, 3)$, $B(3, 5)$, $C(5, 6)$, $D(7, 6)$, $E(9, 7)$, $F(11, 10)$. The area bounded by this curve, the x-axis, and the lines $x = 1$, $x = 11$ is rotated about the x-axis to generate a solid. Use the trapezoidal rule to approximate the volume generated. Also determine approximately the average value of the circular cross-sectional area (with respect to x).

38. Determine the center of mass of a thin homogeneous plate covering the area enclosed by the curves $y^2 = 8x$ and $y = x^2$.

39. Find the center of mass of a homogeneous plate covering the area in the first quadrant bounded by the curve $4y = x^2$, the y-axis, and the line $y = 4$.

40. Find the center of gravity of the area bounded by the curve $y = 4x - x^2$ and the line $2x - y = 0$.

41. Find the center of mass of a thin homogeneous plate covering the portion of the xy-plane, in the first quadrant, bounded by the curve $y = x^2$, the x-axis, and the line $x = 1$.

42. Consider a thin metal plate of area A and constant density and thickness. Show that if its first moment about the y-axis is M, its moment about the line $x = b$ is $M - bA$. Indicate why this result actually shows that the center of gravity is a physical property of the body, independent of the coordinate system used for finding its location.

43. Find the center of mass of a thin plate covering the region bounded by the curve $y^2 = 4ax$ and the line $x = a$, a = positive constant, if the density at (x, y) is directly proportional to (a) x, (b) $|y|$.

44. A particle of mass M starts from rest at time $t = 0$ and is moved with constant acceleration a from $x = 0$ to $x = h$ against a variable force $F(t) = t^2$. Find the work done.

45. Below the surface of the earth the force of its gravitational attraction is directly proportional to the distance from its center. Find the work done in lifting an object, whose weight at the surface is w lb, from a distance r ft below the earth's surface to the surface.

46. A storage tank is a right circular cylinder 20 ft long and 8 ft in diameter with its axis horizontal. If the tank is half full of oil weighing w lb/ft³, find the work done in emptying it through a pipe that runs from the bottom of the tank to an outlet that is 6 ft above the top of the tank.

Transcendental Functions

8–1 The trigonometric functions. We have learned how to differentiate and integrate polynomials, and certain other algebraic functions including some rational functions and fractional powers. By definition, y is an *algebraic* function of x if it is a function that satisfies an irreducible algebraic equation of the form

$$P_0(x)y^n + P_1(x)y^{n-1} + \cdots + P_{n-1}(x)y + P_n(x) = 0,$$

with n a positive integer and with coefficients $P_0(x)$, $P_1(x)$,...that are polynomials in x. For instance, $y = \sqrt{x}, x > 0$, defines an algebraic function whose elements (x, y) satisfy the irreducible equation

$$y^2 - x = 0.$$

Sums, products, quotients, powers, and roots of algebraic functions are in turn algebraic functions.

A function that is not algebraic is called *transcendental*. The class of transcendental functions includes the trigonometric, logarithmic, exponential, and inverse trigonometric functions, and many more which are less familiar.

We have learned how to differentiate and integrate two transcendental functions—the sine and cosine. In this chapter we shall add to this list the derivatives of the remaining trigonometric functions, their inverse functions, and the logarithmic and exponential functions.

At this stage it is well to recall the following formulas for derivatives and differentials:

Derivatives	*Differentials*
I. $\dfrac{dc}{dx} = 0.$	I′. $dc = 0.$
II. $\dfrac{d(cu)}{dx} = c\,\dfrac{du}{dx}.$	II′. $d(cu) = c\,du.$
III. $\dfrac{d(u+v)}{dx} = \dfrac{du}{dx} + \dfrac{dv}{dx}.$	III′. $d(u+v) = du + dv.$
IV. $\dfrac{d(uv)}{dx} = u\,\dfrac{dv}{dx} + v\,\dfrac{du}{dx}.$	IV′. $d(uv) = u\,dv + v\,du.$

V. $\dfrac{d\left(\dfrac{u}{v}\right)}{dx} = \dfrac{v\,\dfrac{du}{dx} - u\,\dfrac{dv}{dx}}{v^2}.$ V'. $d\left(\dfrac{u}{v}\right) = \dfrac{v\,du - u\,dv}{v^2}.$

VI. $\dfrac{d(u^n)}{dx} = n\,u^{n-1}\,\dfrac{du}{dx}.$ VI'. $d(u^n) = n\,u^{n-1}\,du.$

VII. $\dfrac{d\,(\sin u)}{dx} = \cos u\,\dfrac{du}{dx}.$ VII'. $d\,(\sin u) = \cos u\,du.$

VIII. $\dfrac{d\,(\cos u)}{dx} = -\sin u\,\dfrac{du}{dx}.$ VIII'. $d\,(\cos u) = -\sin u\,du.$

The first six of these by themselves enable us to differentiate the *algebraic* functions, which include polynomials, ratios of polynomials, and roots or powers of either of these types. VII, VII', VIII, and VIII' are discussed in Article 6–5.

When we combine formulas V, VII, and VIII and apply them to the trigonometric identities

$$\tan u = \frac{\sin u}{\cos u}, \qquad \cot u = \frac{\cos u}{\sin u},$$

$$\sec u = \frac{1}{\cos u}, \qquad \csc u = \frac{1}{\sin u}, \tag{1}$$

it is a simple matter to complete the list of formulas for differentiating the trigonometric functions and, doing so, we obtain:

IX. $\dfrac{d\,(\tan u)}{dx} = \sec^2 u\,\dfrac{du}{dx}.$ IX'. $d\,(\tan u) = \sec^2 u\,du.$

X. $\dfrac{d\,(\cot u)}{dx} = -\csc^2 u\,\dfrac{du}{dx}.$ X'. $d\,(\cot u) = -\csc^2 u\,du.$

XI. $\dfrac{d\,(\sec u)}{dx} = \sec u \tan u\,\dfrac{du}{dx}.$ XI'. $d\,(\sec u) = \sec u \tan u\,du.$

XII. $\dfrac{d\,(\csc u)}{dx} = -\csc u \cot u\,\dfrac{du}{dx}.$ XII'. $d\,(\csc u) = -\csc u \cot u\,du.$

The proofs of the formulas given above should be carried through by the reader.

These are the forms which are customarily used, though there are alternate forms such as

$$\frac{d\,(\sec u)}{dx} = \frac{\sin u}{\cos^2 u}\frac{du}{dx}$$

which are obtained from the expressions given by using some trigonometric identities. One reason for preferring the forms above is that they are quite easy to remember if we note that *the derivative of every cofunction* (i.e., cos, cot, csc) *can be obtained from the derivative of the corresponding function* (i.e., sin, tan, sec) by

(a) *introducing a minus sign,* and
(b) *replacing each function by its cofunction.*

Apply this, for example, to the formula

$$\frac{d\,(\sec u)}{dx} = \sec u \tan u \frac{du}{dx}.$$

Replace sec u and tan u by their *co*functions on *both sides* of the equation and put in a *minus* sign; the result is

$$\frac{d\,(\csc u)}{dx} = -\csc u \cot u \frac{du}{dx}.$$

Thus it is really only necessary to "memorize" the two new formulas

$$\frac{d\,(\tan u)}{dx} = \sec^2 u \frac{du}{dx},$$

$$\frac{d\,(\sec u)}{dx} = \sec u \tan u \frac{du}{dx},$$

and the above rule produces the other two.

The formulas IX′–XII′ for differentials immediately produce the four new integration formulas:

$$\boxed{\begin{aligned} &\int \sec^2 u\,du = \tan u + C, \qquad \int \sec u \tan u\,du = \sec u + C, \\ &\int \csc^2 u\,du = -\cot u + C, \qquad \int \csc u \cot u\,du = -\csc u + C. \end{aligned}}$$ (2)

EXAMPLE 1. Find dy/dx if $y = \tan^2 3x$.
First we apply the power formula VI,

$$\frac{dy}{dx} = 2 \tan 3x \frac{d\,(\tan 3x)}{dx}$$

and then IX,

$$\frac{d\,(\tan 3x)}{dx} = \sec^2 3x \frac{d(3x)}{dx},$$

and then II,

$$\frac{d(3x)}{dx} = 3\frac{dx}{dx} = 3.$$

When these are combined, we get

$$\frac{dy}{dx} = 6 \tan 3x \sec^2 3x.$$

EXAMPLE 2. Integrate $\int \tan^2 3x \, dx$.

At first sight, this seems to be impossible with the formulas we have for integration. But the trigonometric identity

$$\sin^2 3x + \cos^2 3x = 1$$

becomes

$$\tan^2 3x + 1 = \sec^2 3x$$

when we divide both sides by $\cos^2 3x$. Hence,

$$\tan^2 3x = \sec^2 3x - 1$$

and

$$\int \tan^2 3x \, dx = \int (\sec^2 3x - 1) \, dx = \int \sec^2 3x \, dx - \int 1 \, dx$$

$$= \tfrac{1}{3} \int \sec^2 3x \, d(3x) - \int 1 \, dx = \tfrac{1}{3} \tan 3x - x + C.$$

PROBLEMS

Sketch the graphs of the following equations, Problems 1–10.

1. $y = \sin x$
2. $y = \cos x$
3. $y = \tan x$
4. $y = \cot x$
5. $y = \sec x$
6. $y = \csc x$
7. $y = 3 \sin 2x$
8. $y = 4 \cos (x/3)$
9. $y = \sin^2 x$
10. $y = \tfrac{1}{2} + \tfrac{1}{2} \cos 2x$
11. (a) Derive formula IX
    (b) Derive formula XI
12. (a) Derive formula X
    (b) Derive formula XII

Find dy/dx in each of the following problems (13 through 33):

13. $y = \tan (3x^2)$
14. $y = \tan^2 (\cos x)$
15. $y = \cot (3x + 5)$
16. $y = \sqrt{\cot x}$
17. $y = \sec^2 x - \tan^2 x$
18. $y = \tfrac{1}{3} \sec^3 x$
19. $y = 3x + \tan 3x$
20. $y = 3 \tan 2x$
21. $y = x - \tan x$
22. $y = \sec^4 x - \tan^4 x$
23. $y = (\csc x + \cot x)^2$
24. $y = 2 \sin^2 3x$

25. $y = \frac{1}{2}x - \frac{1}{4}\sin 2x$

26. $y = \frac{1}{2}x + \frac{1}{4}\sin 2x$

27. $y = \sin^3\dfrac{x}{3} - 3\sin\dfrac{x}{3}$

28. $y = 3\cos^2\dfrac{x}{2}$

29. $y = 2\sin\frac{1}{2}x - x\cos\frac{1}{2}x$

30. $x^2 = \sin y + \sin 2y$

31. $y = \sin^3 x - \sin 3x$

32. $y = \frac{1}{3}\sin^3 5x - \sin 5x$

33. $x + \tan(xy) = 0$

34. Find the maximum height of the curve $y = 6\cos x - 8\sin x$ above the x-axis.

35. Find the maximum and minimum values of the function $y = 2\sin x + \cos 2x$ for $0 \le x \le \pi/2$.

36. Show that the function $f(x) = x + \sin x$ has no relative maxima or minima.

37. Show that the curve $y = x\sin x$ is tangent to the line $y = x$ whenever $\sin x = 1$, and is tangent to the line $y = -x$ whenever $\sin x = -1$.

38. A revolving light 3 miles from a straight shoreline makes 8 revolutions per minute. Find the velocity of the beam of light along the shore at the instant when it makes an angle of 45° with the shoreline.

39. A rope with a ring in one end is looped over two pegs in a horizontal line. The free end, after being passed through the ring, has a weight suspended from it, so that the rope hangs taut. If the rope slips freely through the ring, the weight will descend as far as possible. Find the angle formed at the bottom of the loop. (Assume that the length of the rope is at least four times as great as the distance between the pegs.)

Evaluate the following integrals:

40. $\displaystyle\int \sin 3t\, dt$

41. $\displaystyle\int \sec^2 2\theta\, d\theta$

42. $\displaystyle\int \tan^3 x\sec^2 x\, dx$

43. $\displaystyle\int \sec^3 x\tan x\, dx$

44. $\displaystyle\int \sec\dfrac{x}{2}\tan\dfrac{x}{2}\, dx$

45. $\displaystyle\int \cos^2 y\, dy$

46. $\displaystyle\int \dfrac{d\theta}{\cos^2\theta}$

47. $\displaystyle\int \dfrac{d\theta}{\sin^2(\theta/3)}$

48. Find the area bounded by the curve $y = \tan x\sec^2 x$, the x-axis, and the line $x = \pi/3$.

49. The area bounded above by the curve $y = \tan x$, below by the x-axis, and on the right by the line $x = \pi/4$ is revolved about the x-axis. Find the volume generated.

8-2   The inverse trigonometric functions.   The equation

$$x = \sin y \tag{1}$$

determines infinitely many real values of y for each x in the range $-1 \le x \le 1$.

For example, if $x = \frac{1}{2}$ then we ask for all angles y such that $\sin y = \frac{1}{2}$. The two angles 30° and 150° in the first and second quadrants occur to us immediately. But any whole multiple of 360° may be either added to or subtracted from these and the sine of the resulting angle will still be $\frac{1}{2}$. Expressing these facts in mathematical language and using radian measure for the angles, we have $\sin y = \frac{1}{2}$ if

$$y = \begin{cases} \dfrac{\pi}{6} + 2n\pi \\[2mm] \dfrac{5\pi}{6} + 2n\pi \end{cases} \qquad n = 0, \pm 1, \pm 2, \cdots$$

Similarly, we find that $\sin y = -\frac{1}{2}$ if

$$y = \begin{cases} -\dfrac{\pi}{6} + 2n\pi \\[2mm] -\dfrac{5\pi}{6} + 2n\pi \end{cases} \qquad n = 0, \pm 1, \pm 2, \cdots$$

Now it is desirable, for some of our later applications, to adopt a rule for picking a *principal value* of y. We shall require that the rule (a) produce one and only one value of y for each x, $-1 \le x \le 1$, such that $\sin y = x$; and (b) give two "nearly equal" values of y for two "nearly equal" values of x.

To state requirement (b) more specifically, we require that if x_1 and x_2 are two values of x both between -1 and $+1$, and y_1 and y_2 are the corresponding values of y such that $\sin y = x$, then $y_2 - y_1$ should tend to zero if $x_2 - x_1$ does. The portion of the curve AOB shown heavily marked in Fig. 8–2 fulfills these requirements. For any x between -1 and $+1$ there is one and only one corresponding point (x, y) on this portion of the curve, and the y-value satisfies $\sin y = x$. Furthermore, this is a continuous curve, so that if (x_1, y_1) and (x_2, y_2) are two points on it and $(x_2 - x_1) \to 0$, then also $(y_2 - y_1) \to 0$.

To be sure that the point (x, y) stays on the portion AOB of Fig. 8–2, we need only restrict y:

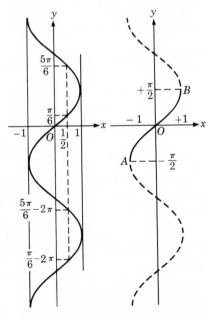

Figure 8–1   **Figure 8–2**

$$\sin y = x, \qquad -\frac{\pi}{2} \le y \le \frac{\pi}{2}. \tag{2}$$

The restrictions placed on y give a continuous function

$$y = \sin^{-1} x, \qquad -\frac{\pi}{2} \le y \le \frac{\pi}{2}, \tag{3}$$

called the "inverse sine of x" which is defined on the domain $-1 \le x \le 1$ and has values on the range $-\pi/2 \le y \le +\pi/2$. Note that the minus one in Eq. (3), although written as an exponent, does *not* mean

$$(\sin x)^{-1} = \frac{1}{\sin x} = \csc x.$$

Actually, Eq. (3) merely gives a name to a new function that is defined implicitly by Eq. (2). The symbol $f^{-1}(x)$ is often used to denote the function y defined implicitly by $f(y) = x$, that is,

$$y = f^{-1}(x).$$

The notation arcsin x is also used to represent the function that we have denoted by $\sin^{-1} x$, but the latter notation is now more commonly used. Thus,

$$\sin^{-1}\left(\frac{1}{2}\right) = \frac{\pi}{6}, \qquad \sin^{-1}\left(-\frac{1}{2}\right) = -\frac{\pi}{6}.$$

In terms of angles referred to standard position in the various quadrants, Eq. (2) and the restriction $-\pi/2 \le y \le \pi/2$ mean that the answer to the question: "What is the angle y whose sine is x?" is always an angle in the *first* or *fourth* quadrant, but if it is in the *fourth* quadrant, it is to be expressed as the *negative* of an angle between 0 and $\pi/2$ and not as a positive angle $\ge 3\pi/2$, since the latter would violate the restriction in (2).

At the risk of appearing to labor a point which is already clear, we also note that the inverse sine is an *odd* function of x. This means that

$$\sin^{-1}(-x) = -\sin^{-1}(x).$$

Keeping this fact firmly in mind will prevent us from using values of y corresponding to points on the discontinuous curve composed of the portions OB and CD on the curve in Fig. 8–3. The objection to using these is that for a small positive value of x, say $x_1 = +0.01$,

Figure 8–3

the point is near O and $y_1 \approx 0.01$; while for a small negative value of x, say $x_2 = -0.01$, the point is near D and $y_2 \approx 2\pi - 0.01$. The difference $y_2 - y_1$ is nearly $2\pi = 6.28+$, whereas the difference $x_1 - x_2$ is, in this case, only 0.02. This difficulty is not encountered if we restrict the value of y as in (3), which confines us to the *continuous* curve AOB of Fig. 8–2.

To each of the other trigonometric functions there also corresponds an *inverse* trigonometric function. In each case, we restrict the angle in such a way that the function is *single-valued*.

The same reasoning that led us to adopt the particular range

$$-\frac{\pi}{2} \le y \le \frac{\pi}{2}$$

for the principal value of $y = \sin^{-1} x$ prompts us to adopt a similar range for the principal value of y satisfying the equation $x = \tan y$ (see Fig. 8–4). Thus we write

$$y = \tan^{-1} x, \qquad -\frac{\pi}{2} < y < \frac{\pi}{2} \qquad (4)$$

to mean the same as

$$\tan y = x, \qquad -\frac{\pi}{2} < y < \frac{\pi}{2}. \qquad (5)$$

The inverse tangent function, (4), is defined on the *domain* $-\infty < x < +\infty$, that is, for all real x. Its *range* is $-\pi/2 < y < +\pi/2$. The values $y = \pm\pi/2$ are to be excluded, since the tangent becomes infinite as the angle approaches $\pm\pi/2$.

When we come to the inverse cosine function, we simply *define* it by the equation

$$\cos^{-1} x = \frac{\pi}{2} - \sin^{-1} x. \qquad (6)$$

Since

$$-\frac{\pi}{2} \le \sin^{-1} x \le \frac{\pi}{2},$$

the range of principal values for (6) is

$$0 \le \cos^{-1} x \le \pi. \qquad (7)$$

Figure 8-4

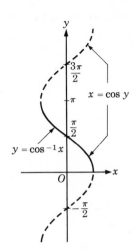

Figure 8-5

The *domain* of the inverse cosine function is $-1 \leq x \leq 1$. Its *range* is $0 \leq y \leq \pi$. The principal value is thus represented by the heavily marked portion of the curve

$$x = \cos y$$

shown in Fig. 8–5.

The reason for defining $\cos^{-1} x$ by Eq. (6) is as follows. In the right triangle in Fig. 8–6, the acute angles α and β are complementary, that is

$$\alpha + \beta = \frac{\pi}{2}.$$

But we also have

$$\sin \alpha = x = \cos \beta,$$

Figure 8-6

so that

$$\alpha = \sin^{-1} x, \qquad \beta = \cos^{-1} x,$$

and the relation $\alpha + \beta = \pi/2$ is the same as $\beta = \pi/2 - \alpha$; that is,

$$\cos^{-1} x = \frac{\pi}{2} - \sin^{-1} x.$$

Thus Eq. (6) expresses the fact that the angle whose cosine is x is the complement of the angle whose sine is x.

For exactly analogous reasons, we also define the inverse cotangent to be

$$\cot^{-1} x = \frac{\pi}{2} - \tan^{-1} x, \tag{8}$$

and we thus restrict the principal value to

$$0 < \cot^{-1} x < \pi. \tag{9}$$

The inverse secant and inverse cosecant functions will be single-valued functions of x on the domain $|x| \geq 1$ if we adopt the definitions

$$\sec^{-1} x = \cos^{-1}\left(\frac{1}{x}\right), \tag{10a}$$

$$\csc^{-1} x = \sin^{-1}\left(\frac{1}{x}\right), \tag{10b}$$

with their principal values confined to the ranges

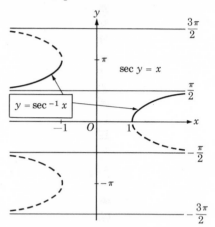

Figure 8–7

$$0 \leq \sec^{-1} x \leq \pi, \tag{11a}$$

$$-\frac{\pi}{2} \leq \csc^{-1} x \leq \frac{\pi}{2}. \tag{11b}$$

The reason for adopting the definitions above is based on the following considerations. If $\sec y = x$, then $\cos y = 1/x$, and we simply ask that the principal values of y be the same in these two cases, that is

$$y = \sec^{-1} x = \cos^{-1}\left(\frac{1}{x}\right).$$

It should be noted, however, that some writers choose the principal value of the inverse secant of x to lie between 0 and $\pi/2$ when x is positive, and between $-\pi$ and $-\pi/2$ (hence, as a negative angle in the third quadrant) when x is negative. This latter method has the advantage of simplifying the formula for the derivative of $\sec^{-1} x$, but has the disadvantage of failing to satisfy the relationship expressed in Eq. (10a) when x is negative. Either method leads to a function which is discontinuous, as is inherent in the nature of the secant function itself, since to pass from a point where the secant is negative to a point where the secant is positive requires crossing one of the discontinuities of the curve.

PROBLEMS

1. Given that $\alpha = \sin^{-1} \frac{1}{2}$, find $\cos \alpha$, $\tan \alpha$, $\sec \alpha$, $\csc \alpha$.
2. Given that $\alpha = \cos^{-1}\left(-\frac{1}{2}\right)$, find $\sin \alpha$, $\tan \alpha$, $\sec \alpha$, $\csc \alpha$.

3. Evaluate $\sin^{-1}(1) - \sin^{-1}(-1)$.   4. Evaluate $\tan^{-1}(1) - \tan^{-1}(-1)$.

5. Evaluate $\sec^{-1}(2) - \sec^{-1}(-2)$.

6. A picture a feet high is placed on a wall with its base b feet above the level of an observer's eye. If the observer stands x feet from the wall, show that the angle of vision α subtended by the picture is given by

$$\alpha = \cot^{-1}\frac{x}{a+b} - \cot^{-1}\frac{x}{b}.$$

7. Prove:

(a) $\tan^{-1}(-x) = -\tan^{-1}x,$ (b) $\cos^{-1}(-x) = \pi - \cos^{-1}x,$

(c) $\sec^{-1}(-x) = \pi - \sec^{-1}(x).$

8. Simplify each of the following expressions:

(a) $\sin(\sin^{-1}0.735),$ (b) $\cos(\sin^{-1}0.8),$ (c) $\sin(2\sin^{-1}0.8),$

(d) $\tan^{-1}(\tan \pi/3),$ (e) $\cos^{-1}(-\sin \pi/6),$ (f) $\sec^{-1}(\sec(-30°)).$

8-3   Derivatives of the inverse trigonometric functions.   The following formulas may now be derived.

$$\text{XIII.} \quad \frac{d(\sin^{-1}u)}{dx} = \frac{du/dx}{\sqrt{1-u^2}}. \qquad \text{XIII'.} \quad d(\sin^{-1}u) = \frac{du}{\sqrt{1-u^2}}.$$

$$\text{XIV.} \quad \frac{d(\cos^{-1}u)}{dx} = -\frac{du/dx}{\sqrt{1-u^2}}. \qquad \text{XIV'.} \quad d(\cos^{-1}u) = -\frac{du}{\sqrt{1-u^2}}.$$

$$\text{XV.} \quad \frac{d(\tan^{-1}u)}{dx} = \frac{du/dx}{1+u^2}. \qquad \text{XV'.} \quad d(\tan^{-1}u) = \frac{du}{1+u^2}.$$

$$\text{XVI.} \quad \frac{d(\cot^{-1}u)}{dx} = -\frac{du/dx}{1+u^2}. \qquad \text{XVI'.} \quad d(\cot^{-1}u) = -\frac{du}{1+u^2}.$$

$$\text{XVII.} \quad \frac{d(\sec^{-1}u)}{dx} = \frac{du/dx}{|u|\sqrt{u^2-1}}. \qquad \text{XVII'.} \quad d(\sec^{-1}u) = \frac{du}{|u|\sqrt{u^2-1}}.$$

$$\text{XVIII.} \quad \frac{d(\csc^{-1}u)}{dx} = \frac{-du/dx}{|u|\sqrt{u^2-1}}. \qquad \text{XVIII'.} \quad d(\csc^{-1}u) = \frac{-du}{|u|\sqrt{u^2-1}}.$$

To illustrate how these are derived, we shall prove formulas XIII and XVII. Let

$$y = \sin^{-1}u, \qquad -\frac{\pi}{2} \le y \le \frac{\pi}{2}.$$

Then
$$\sin y = u,$$

$$\cos y \frac{dy}{dx} = \frac{du}{dx}, \qquad \frac{dy}{dx} = \frac{1}{\cos y}\frac{du}{dx}.$$

To express the right side in terms of u, we use the fact that

$$\cos y = \pm\sqrt{1 - \sin^2 y} = \pm\sqrt{1 - u^2}.$$

When $-\pi/2 \le y \le \pi/2$, $\cos y$ is not negative; hence

$$\cos y = +\sqrt{1 - u^2}$$

and

$$\frac{dy}{dx} = \frac{1}{\sqrt{1 - u^2}}\frac{du}{dx},$$

which establishes XIII.

Next, let

$$y = \sec^{-1} u, \qquad 0 \le y \le \pi.$$

Then

$$\sec y = u, \qquad \sec y \tan y \frac{dy}{dx} = \frac{du}{dx},$$

$$\frac{dy}{dx} = \frac{1}{\sec y \tan y}\frac{du}{dx}.$$

Substituting

$$\sec y = u, \qquad \tan y = \pm\sqrt{\sec^2 y - 1} = \pm\sqrt{u^2 - 1},$$

we have

$$\frac{dy}{dx} = \frac{1}{u(\pm\sqrt{u^2 - 1})}\frac{du}{dx}.$$

The ambiguous sign is determined by the sign of $\tan y$, and hence is

$$+ \text{ if } 0 < y < \frac{\pi}{2}; \qquad \text{that is, if } u \text{ is } +,$$

$$- \text{ if } \frac{\pi}{2} < y < \pi; \qquad \text{that is, if } u \text{ is } -.$$

That is,

$$\frac{dy}{dx} = \frac{1}{u\sqrt{u^2 - 1}}\frac{du}{dx} \qquad \text{if } u > 1$$

$$= \frac{1}{-u\sqrt{u^2 - 1}}\frac{du}{dx} \qquad \text{if } u < -1,$$

and both of these are summarized in the single formula

$$\frac{dy}{dx} = \frac{1}{|u|\sqrt{u^2 - 1}} \frac{du}{dx}.$$

The formulas XIII to XVIII are used directly as given, but even more important are the integration formulas obtained immediately from the differential formulas XIII' to XVIII', namely,

$$
\int \frac{du}{\sqrt{1 - u^2}} = \sin^{-1} u + C, \qquad \int \frac{du}{1 + u^2} = \tan^{-1} u + C,
$$

$$
\int \frac{du}{u\sqrt{u^2 - 1}} = \int \frac{d(-u)}{(-u)\sqrt{u^2 - 1}} = \sec^{-1} |u| + C.
$$

$$(1)$$

Note that $\sec^{-1} u$ and $\sec^{-1} |u|$ are meaningless unless $|u| \geq 1$ (see Fig. 8–7).

EXAMPLE.

$$\int_0^1 \frac{dx}{1 + x^2} = \tan^{-1} x \Big]_0^1 = \tan^{-1} 1 - \tan^{-1} 0 = \frac{\pi}{4}.$$

PROBLEMS

1. Derive formula XIV.　　　　　2. Derive formula XV.

3. Derive formula XVI.　　　　　4. Derive formula XVIII.

Find dy/dx in each of the following:

5. $y = \sin^{-1} \dfrac{x}{2}$

6. $y = \dfrac{1}{3} \tan^{-1} \dfrac{x}{3}$

7. $y = \sec^{-1} 5x$

8. $y = \cos^{-1} 2x$

9. $y = \cot^{-1} \dfrac{2}{x} + \tan^{-1} \dfrac{x}{2}$

10. $y = \sin^{-1} \dfrac{x - 1}{x + 1}$

11. $y = \tan^{-1} \dfrac{x - 1}{x + 1}$

12. $y = x \sin^{-1} x + \sqrt{1 - x^2}$

13. $y = x (\sin^{-1} x)^2 - 2x + 2\sqrt{1 - x^2} \sin^{-1} x$

14. $y = x \cos^{-1} 2x - \frac{1}{2}\sqrt{1 - 4x^2}$

15. How far from the wall should the observer stand in order to maximize the angle of vision α in Problem 6, Article 8–2?

Evaluate the following integrals:

16. $\displaystyle\int_0^{1/2} \frac{dx}{\sqrt{1 - x^2}}$

17. $\displaystyle\int_{-1}^1 \frac{dx}{1 + x^2}$

18. $\displaystyle\int_{\sqrt{2}}^2 \frac{dx}{x\sqrt{x^2 - 1}}$

19. $\displaystyle\int_{-2}^{-\sqrt{2}} \frac{dx}{x\sqrt{x^2-1}}$ 20. $\displaystyle\int \frac{dx}{\sqrt{1-4x^2}}$ 21. $\displaystyle\int_{1/\sqrt{3}}^{1} \frac{dx}{x\sqrt{4x^2-1}}$

8–4   The natural logarithm. We have so far studied functions which are fairly familiar. Polynomials, rational functions, and other algebraic functions result from the familiar operations of arithmetic and algebra. The trigonometric functions can be identified with coordinates of points on a unit circle and with their ratios and reciprocals. The inverse trigonometric functions are probably less familiar, but nevertheless they can be understood without any knowledge of the calculus. But we are now going to study a function, the natural logarithm, which depends upon the calculus for its very definition.

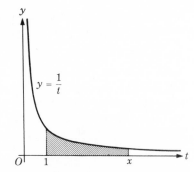

The natural logarithm* of x, which is indicated by the notation $\ln x$, is defined, for positive x, as the integral

$$\ln x = \int_1^x \frac{1}{t}\, dt. \qquad (1)$$

Fig. 8–8.   Shaded area is ln x.

For any x greater than 1, this integral represents the area bounded above by the curve $y = 1/t$, below by the t-axis, on the left by the line $t = 1$, and on the right by the line $t = x$. (See Fig. 8–8.)

If $x = 1$, the left and right boundaries of the area are identical and the area is zero,

$$\ln 1 = \int_1^1 \frac{1}{t}\, dt = 0. \qquad (2)$$

If x is less than 1, then the left boundary is the line $t = x$ and the right boundary is $t = 1$. In this case,

$$\ln x = \int_1^x \frac{1}{t}\, dt = -\int_x^1 \frac{1}{t}\, dt \qquad (3)$$

is the negative of the area under the curve between x and 1.

---

* The first discovery of logarithms is credited to a Scottish nobleman, John Napier (1550–1617). For a biographical sketch of Napier, see the *World of Mathematics*, Vol. 1, "The Great Mathematicians," by H. W. Turnbull, pp. 121–125.

In all cases, if x is any positive number, the value of the definite integral in Eq. (1) can be calculated to as many decimal places as may be desired by using inscribed rectangles, circumscribed rectangles, or trapezoids to approximate the appropriate area. (See Chapter 6. Another method for computing natural logarithms is illustrated below in Problems 8 and 9.) In any event, Eq. (1) defines a computable function of x over the domain $0 < x < +\infty$. We study its range in Article 8–7.

PROBLEMS

Use trapezoids of altitude $\Delta t = 0.1$ to approximate the appropriate areas to obtain approximations to the following natural logarithms, Problems 1–4.

1. $\ln 1.2$ 2. $\ln 1.4$ 3. $\ln 2$ 4. $\ln 0.5$

5. (a) Suppose h is small and positive. Does the approximation $\ln (1 + h) \approx h$ correspond to using an inscribed rectangle or a circumscribed rectangle to approximate the area from 1 to $1 + h$ under the curve $y = 1/t$? (b) Answer the same question in case h is negative.

6. Approximate $\ln (1 + h)$ by using the line L that is tangent to the curve $y = 1/t$ at $A(1, 1)$, as upper boundary of a trapezoid of altitude $|h|$. Sketch. Show that this leads to the approximation

$$\ln (1 + h) \approx h - \frac{h^2}{2}.$$

Use this result to approximate: (a) $\ln 1.04$, (b) $\ln 0.96$.

7. Let $aACBb$ be the polygon whose vertices are $a(1, 0)$, $A(1, 1)$, $C(\frac{4}{3}, \frac{2}{3})$, $B(2, \frac{1}{2})$, and $b(2, 0)$. Show that $\overleftrightarrow{AC}$ and $\overleftrightarrow{CB}$ are tangent to the hyperbola $y = 1/t$ at A and at B respectively. Use the area of the polygon to find an approximation to $\ln 2$. Sketch.

8. (a) Show, by long division or otherwise, that

$$\frac{1}{1 + u} = 1 - u + u^2 - \frac{u^3}{1 + u}.$$

(The division could be continued. We stop here only for sake of illustration.)

(b) In Eq. (1), make the substitution

$$t = 1 + u, \qquad dt = du$$

and make the corresponding change in the limits of integration, thus obtaining

$$\ln x = \int_0^{x-1} \frac{du}{1 + u}.$$

(c) Combine the results of (a) and (b) to obtain

$$\ln x = \int_0^{x-1} \left(1 - u + u^2 - \frac{u^3}{1+u} \right) du,$$

or

$$\ln x = (x - 1) - \tfrac{1}{2}(x - 1)^2 + \tfrac{1}{3}(x - 1)^3 - R,$$

where

$$R = \int_0^{x-1} \frac{u^3}{1+u} \, du.$$

(d) Show that, if $x > 1$ and $0 \le u \le x - 1$, then

$$\frac{u^3}{1+u} \le u^3.$$

Hence, deduce that

$$R \le \int_0^{x-1} u^3 \, du = \frac{(x-1)^4}{4}.$$

(e) Combining the results of (c) and (d), show that the approximation

$$\ln x \approx (x - 1) - \tfrac{1}{2}(x - 1)^2 + \tfrac{1}{3}(x - 1)^3$$

tends to overestimate the value of $\ln x$, but with an error not greater than $(x - 1)^4/4$.

(f) Use the result of (e) to estimate $\ln 1.2$.

9. (a) Show, by long division or otherwise, that if n is a positive integer,

$$\frac{1}{1+u} = 1 - u + u^2 - u^3 + \cdots + (-1)^{n-1} u^{n-1} + \frac{(-1)^n u^n}{1+u}.$$

(b) Using the result of part (a), show that, if $x > 1$ and

$$R_n(x) = \int_0^{x-1} \frac{u^n}{1+u} \, du,$$

then

$$0 < R_n(x) \le \frac{(x-1)^{n+1}}{n+1}.$$

(c) Combine parts (a) and (b) to deduce that the approximation

$$\ln x \approx (x - 1) - \tfrac{1}{2}(x - 1)^2 + \tfrac{1}{3}(x - 1)^3 + \cdots + \frac{(-1)^{n-1}}{n}(x - 1)^n$$

is in error by an amount not greater in absolute value than

$$\frac{(x-1)^{n+1}}{n+1},$$

for $x > 1$.

(d) If the approximation of part (c) is used to compute ln $(5/4)$, how large should n be to guarantee accuracy to three decimal places?

8–5   The derivative of ln x. Since the function $F(x) = \ln x$ is defined by the integral

$$F(x) = \int_1^x \frac{1}{t}\, dt \qquad (x > 0) \tag{1}$$

(see Fig. 8–9), it follows at once, from Theorem 4 of Article 6–12 that

$$F'(x) = \frac{1}{x}.$$

That is,

$$\frac{d\,(\ln x)}{dx} = \frac{1}{x}. \tag{2}$$

We can obtain a slightly more general formula by considering ln u, where u is a positive, differentiable, function of x. By the chain rule for derivatives,

$$\boxed{\frac{d \ln u}{dx} = \frac{d \ln u}{du}\frac{du}{dx} = \frac{1}{u}\frac{du}{dx}} \qquad \text{XIX}$$

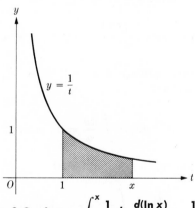

Fig. 8–9. $\ln x = \displaystyle\int_1^x \frac{1}{t}\, dt, \quad \dfrac{d(\ln x)}{dx} = \dfrac{1}{x}.$

or, in terms of differentials,

$$\boxed{d \ln u = \frac{du}{u}.} \qquad \text{XIX}'$$

EXAMPLE 1. Find dy/dx if $y = \ln (3x^2 + 4)$.

Solution. $\dfrac{dy}{dx} = \dfrac{1}{3x^2 + 4} \dfrac{d(3x^2 + 4)}{dx} = \dfrac{6x}{3x^2 + 4}.$

Equation (XIX′) leads at once to the integration formula

$$\int \frac{du}{u} = \ln u + C, \tag{3a}$$

provided u is positive. On the other hand, if u is negative then $-u$ is positive and

$$\int \frac{du}{u} = \int \frac{d(-u)}{-u} = \ln(-u) + C. \tag{3b}$$

The two results (3a, b) can be combined into a single result, namely,

$$\int \frac{du}{u} = \begin{cases} \ln u + C & \text{if} \quad u > 0, \\ \ln(-u) + C & \text{if} \quad u < 0, \end{cases}$$

or

$$\boxed{\int \frac{du}{u} = \ln|u| + C.} \tag{4}$$

We recall that the formula

$$\int u^n \, du = \frac{u^{n+1}}{n+1} + C, \qquad n \neq -1$$

failed to cover one case, namely, $n = -1$. Now Eq. (4) covers this case for us, since it tells us that

$$\int u^{-1} \, du = \int \frac{du}{u} = \ln|u| + C.$$

It is important, of course, to remember that

$$\int \frac{dx}{x^2} = \int x^{-2} \, dx = \frac{x^{-1}}{-1} + C$$

is *not* a logarithm.

EXAMPLE 2. Integrate

$$\int \frac{\cos \theta \, d\theta}{1 + \sin \theta}.$$

Solution. In Eq. (4), let

$$u = 1 + \sin \theta.$$

Then

$$du = \frac{du}{d\theta}\, d\theta = \cos\theta\, d\theta$$

so that

$$\int \frac{\cos\theta\, d\theta}{1 + \sin\theta} = \int \frac{du}{u} = \ln|u| + C$$

$$= \ln|1 + \sin\theta| + C.$$

PROBLEMS

Find dy/dx in each of the following problems (1 through 18).

1. $y = \ln(x^2 + 2x)$ 2. $y = (\ln x)^3$

3. $y = \ln(\cos x)$ 4. $y = \ln(\tan x + \sec x)$

5. $y = \ln(x\sqrt{x^2 + 1})$ 6. $y = \ln(3x\sqrt{x + 2})$

7. $y = x \ln x - x$ 8. $y = x^3 \ln(2x)$

9. $y = \frac{1}{2} \ln \frac{1 + x}{1 - x}$ 10. $y = \frac{1}{3} \ln \frac{x^3}{1 + x^3}$

11. $y = \ln \frac{x}{2 + 3x}$ 12. $y = \ln(x^2 + 4) - x \tan^{-1} \frac{x}{2}$

13. $y = \ln x - \frac{1}{2} \ln(1 + x^2) - \frac{\tan^{-1} x}{x}$

14. $y = x(\ln x)^3$ 15. $y = x[\sin(\ln x) + \cos(\ln x)]$

16. $y = x \sec^{-1} x - \ln(x + \sqrt{x^2 - 1}), \quad (x > 1)$

17. $y = x \ln(a^2 + x^2) - 2x + 2a \tan^{-1} \frac{x}{a}$

18. $y = \ln(\ln x)$

Evaluate the following integrals:

19. $\displaystyle\int \frac{dx}{2x + 3}$ 20. $\displaystyle\int \frac{dx}{2 - 3x}$

21. $\displaystyle\int \frac{x\, dx}{4x^2 + 1}$ 22. $\displaystyle\int \frac{\sin x\, dx}{2 - \cos x}$

23. $\displaystyle\int \frac{\cos x\, dx}{\sin x}$ 24. $\displaystyle\int \frac{2x - 5}{x}\, dx$

25. $\displaystyle\int \frac{x\, dx}{x + 1}$ 26. $\displaystyle\int \frac{x^2\, dx}{4 - x^3}$

27. $\displaystyle\int \frac{x\, dx}{1 - x^2}$ 28. $\displaystyle\int \frac{dx}{\sqrt{x}\,(1 + \sqrt{x})}$

29. $\displaystyle \int (\ln x)^2 \frac{dx}{x}$

30. $\displaystyle \int \frac{dx}{(2x + 3)^2}$

8–6   Properties of natural logarithms. In this article we shall establish the following properties of the natural logarithm:

$$\ln ax = \ln a + \ln x, \tag{1}$$

$$\ln \frac{x}{a} = \ln x - \ln a, \tag{2}$$

$$\ln x^n = n \ln x, \tag{3}$$

provided x and a are positive and n is a rational number.

The proofs of these results are all based on the fact that

$$y = \ln x$$

satisfies the differential equation

$$\frac{dy}{dx} = \frac{1}{x} \qquad \text{for all } x > 0,$$

plus the fact that if two functions have the same derivative for all $x > 0$, then the two functions can differ only by a constant. That is, if

$$\frac{dy_1}{dx} = \frac{dy_2}{dx} \qquad \text{for all } x > 0,$$

then

$$y_1 = y_2 + \text{constant} \qquad \text{for all } x > 0.$$

Now to prove Eq. (1), let

$$y_1 = \ln ax, \qquad y_2 = \ln x.$$

Then

$$\frac{dy_1}{dx} = \frac{1}{ax} \frac{d(ax)}{dx} = \frac{a}{ax} = \frac{1}{x} = \frac{dy_2}{dx}. \tag{4}$$

Therefore we have

$$\ln ax = \ln x + C. \tag{5}$$

To evaluate C it suffices to substitute $x = 1$:

$$\ln a = \ln 1 + C = 0 + C,$$

which gives

$$C = \ln a.$$

Hence, by (5),

$$\ln ax = \ln x + \ln a. \qquad \text{Q.E.D.}$$

To prove Eq. (2), we first put $x = 1/a$ in Eq. (1) and recall that $\ln 1 = 0$:

$$0 = \ln 1 = \ln a + \ln (1/a)$$

so that

$$\ln \frac{1}{a} = -\ln a. \tag{6}$$

Now apply Eq. (1) with a replaced by $1/a$ and $\ln a$ replaced by $\ln (1/a) = -\ln a$. The result is Eq. (2).

To prove Eq. (3), let

$$y_1 = \ln x^n.$$

Then

$$\frac{dy_1}{dx} = \frac{1}{x^n} \cdot nx^{n-1} = \frac{n}{x} = \frac{d}{dx}(n \ln x).$$

Hence $y_1 = \ln x^n$ and $y_2 = n \ln x$ have equal derivatives, so they differ at most by a constant:

$$\ln x^n = n \ln x + C. \tag{7}$$

But by taking $x = 1$, and remembering that $\ln 1 = 0$, we find $C = 0$, which gives Eq. (3). In particular, if $n = 1/m$, where m is a positive integer, we have

$$\ln \sqrt[m]{x} = \ln x^{1/m} = \frac{1}{m} \ln x. \tag{8}$$

PROBLEMS

Express the following logarithms in terms of the two given logarithms $a = \ln 2$, $b = \ln 3$. [For example: $\ln 1.5 = \ln \frac{3}{2} = \ln 3 - \ln 2 = b - a$.]

1. $\ln 16$ 2. $\ln \sqrt[3]{9}$ 3. $\ln 2\sqrt{2}$

4. $\ln 0.25$ 5. $\ln \frac{4}{9}$ 6. $\ln 12$

7. $\ln \frac{9}{8}$ 8. $\ln 36$ 9. $\ln 4.5$

10. $\ln \sqrt{13.5}$

8–7   **Graph of y = ln x.** The slope of the curve

$$y = \ln x \tag{1}$$

is given by

$$\frac{dy}{dx} = \frac{1}{x}, \tag{2}$$

which is positive for all $x > 0$. Hence the graph of $y = \ln x$ steadily rises from left to right. Since the derivative is continuous, the function $\ln x$ is itself continuous, and the curve has a continuously turning tangent.

The second derivative,

$$\frac{d^2y}{dx^2} = -\frac{1}{x^2},\tag{3}$$

is always negative, so the curve (1) is everywhere concave downward.

The curve passes through the point $(1, 0)$, since $\ln 1 = 0$. At this point its slope is $+1$, so the tangent line at this point makes an angle of $45°$ with the x-axis (if we use equal units on the x- and y-axes).

If we refer to the definition of $\ln 2$ as an integral,

$$\ln 2 = \int_1^2 \frac{1}{t}\, dt,$$

we see that it may be interpreted as the area in Fig. 8–8 with $x = 2$. By considering the areas of rectangles of base 1 and altitudes 1 or $\frac{1}{2}$, respectively circumscribed over or inscribed under the given area, we see that

$$0.5 < \ln 2 < 1.0.$$

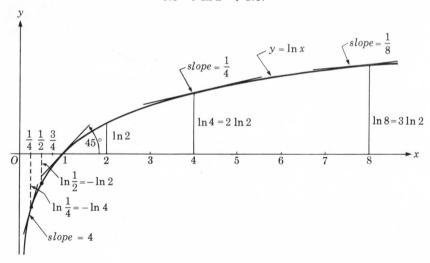

Fig 8–10. Graph of $y = \ln x$.

In fact, by more extensive calculations, the value of $\ln 2$ to 5 decimal places has been found to be

$$\ln 2 \approx 0.69315.$$

By Eq. (3) of Article 8–6 we have

$$\ln 4 = \ln 2^2 = 2 \ln 2 \approx 1.38630,$$
$$\ln 8 = \ln 2^3 = 3 \ln 2 \approx 2.07945,$$
$$\ln \tfrac{1}{2} = \ln 2^{-1} = -\ln 2 \approx -0.69315,$$
$$\ln \tfrac{1}{4} = \ln 2^{-2} = -2 \ln 2 \approx -1.38630,$$

and so on.

We now plot the points that correspond to $x = \tfrac{1}{4}, \tfrac{1}{2}, 1, 2, 4, 8$ on the curve $y = \ln x$ and connect them with a smooth curve. The curve we draw should have slope $1/x$ at the point of abscissa x and should everywhere be concave downward. The curve is shown in Fig. 8–10.

Since $\ln 2$ is greater than 0.5 and $\ln 2^n = n \ln 2$, it is clear that

$$\ln 2^n > 0.5n,$$

and hence $\ln x$ increases without limit as x does. That is,

$$\ln x \to +\infty \qquad \text{as} \qquad x \to +\infty. \tag{4}$$

On the other hand, as x approaches zero through positive values, $1/x$ tends to plus infinity. Hence, taking Eq. (6) of Article 8–6 into account, we have

$$\ln x = -\ln \frac{1}{x} \to -\infty \qquad \text{as} \qquad x \to 0+. \tag{5}$$

Summary. The natural logarithm, $y = \ln x$, is a function with the following properties:

1. Its *domain* is the set of positive real numbers, $x > 0$.

2. Its *range* is the set of all real numbers, $-\infty < y < +\infty$.

3. It is a *continuous, increasing* function of x everywhere on its domain. If $x_1 > x_2 > 0$, then $\ln x_1 > \ln x_2$. It provides a one-to-one mapping from its domain to its range.

4. *Multiplication* of numbers in the domain corresponds to *addition* of numbers in the range. That is, if

$$x_1 > 0, \qquad y_1 = \ln x_1,$$
$$x_2 > 0, \qquad y_2 = \ln x_2,$$

then

$$x_1 x_2 > 0 \qquad \text{and} \qquad y_1 + y_2 = \ln (x_1 x_2).$$

5. The *derivative* of $y = \ln x$ is $dy/dx = 1/x$.

PROBLEMS

1. Take $\ln 3 = 1.09861$ as known. Plot the points corresponding to $x = \frac{1}{9}$, $\frac{1}{3}$, 1, 3, and 9 on the curve $y = \ln x$. Also construct, through each of these points, a line segment tangent to the curve. Then sketch the curve itself. From the curve, read off $\ln 2$.

2. Let x_0 be the abscissa of the point $(x_0, 1)$ in which the line $y = 1$ intersects the curve $y = \ln x$. Show that the curve $y = x \ln x$ has a minimum at $[1/x_0, -(1/x_0)]$ and sketch the curve for $x > 0$. Does this curve possess a point of inflection? If so, find it (or them), and if not, state why not. (See Problem 5.)

3. Sketch the curve $x = \ln y$ for $y > 0$. What is its slope at the point (x, y)? Is it always concave upward, or downward, or does it have inflection points? Give reasons for your answers.

4. The curve $y = \ln x$ in Fig. 8–10 has the property that y becomes infinite when x does. But the ratio $(\ln x)/x$ approaches zero as x becomes infinite. Prove this latter statement by showing, first, that for $x > 1$

$$\ln x = \int_1^x \frac{1}{t} \, dt \leq \int_1^x \frac{1}{\sqrt{t}} \, dt = 2(\sqrt{x} - 1).$$

[*Hint:* Compare the areas under the curves $y_1 = 1/t$ and $y_2 = 1/\sqrt{t}$ for $1 \leq t \leq x$.]

5. From the result of Problem 4 that

$$\lim_{x \to +\infty} \frac{\ln x}{x} = 0,$$

deduce that $\lim\limits_{x \to 0+} x \ln x = 0$. [*Hint:* Let $x = 1/u$, $u \to +\infty$.]

6. Show that the curve $y = \ln x - (x - 1) + \frac{1}{2}(x - 1)^2$ has a point of inflection and a horizontal tangent at $(1, 0)$. Sketch the curve for $0 < x < 2$. (Compare Problem 8, Article 8–4.)

7. Suppose you had a table of natural logarithms giving $\ln x$ for each $x > 0$. How could you use this to find $\log_{10} N$, where $\log_{10} N = b$ means $N = 10^b$?

8–8   The exponential function. In Article 8–7 we discussed and sketched the graph of the curve $y = \ln x$ (Fig. 8–10). We now make the observation that the curve $y = \ln x$ must cross the horizontal line $y = 1$ for some value of x between 2 and 4, since $\ln x$ is continuous and $\ln 2$ is less than 1 while $\ln 4$ is greater than 1. The value of x for which $\ln x = 1$ is denoted by the letter e. It is one of the most important numbers in mathematics. It satisfies the basic equation

$$\ln e = 1. \tag{1}$$

From our discussion above, it follows that e lies between 2 and 4. Its value to 15 decimal places is

$$e = 2.7 \quad 1828 \quad 1828 \quad 45 \quad 90 \quad 45 \ldots \qquad (2)$$

By Eq. (3), Article 8–6, and Eq. (1) above, we have

$$\ln e^n = n \ln e = n \qquad (3)$$

for any rational number n. Thus, for example, we have

$$\ln e^2 = 2, \qquad \ln e^3 = 3, \qquad \ln e^{-1} = -1, \qquad \ln \sqrt{e} = \tfrac{1}{2},$$

and so on. Since only one number can have its natural logarithm equal to n, for any given n, we may restate Eq. (3) by saying that the number whose natural logarithm is n is e^n; i.e., the anti-natural-logarithm of n is e^n.

We now propose to study the antilogarithm, i.e., the *inverse* of the *logarithm*, as a function. To obtain this inverse function, we let

$$y = \text{inverse natural logarithm of } x$$

or

$$x = \ln y. \qquad (4)$$

The equation $x = \ln y$ defines a unique x for each positive real number y. Values of y greater than 1 correspond to x greater than zero; $y = 1$ to $x = 0$; $y < 1$ to $x < 0$. To each positive real number y there corresponds just one real number x such that $x = \ln y$. And conversely, to each real number x there corresponds just one positive real number y such that $x = \ln y$. The correspondence is one-to-one between the sets $y > 0$ and $-\infty < x < +\infty$, and hence it may be used to *define* y as a *function* of x, on the domain of all real numbers $-\infty < x < +\infty$. The *range* of this function is the set of all positive real numbers $y > 0$.

We have just seen, Eq. (3), that $x = \ln y = n$ if and only if $y = e^n$, provided n is a rational number. That is, Eq. (4) is equivalent to the equation

$$y = e^x \qquad (5)$$

for all rational values of x. We are therefore led to define e^x for all real values of x, irrational as well as rational, to be that number y whose natural logarithm is x:

$$\boxed{y = e^x \qquad \text{if and only if} \qquad x = \ln y.} \qquad (6)$$

The resulting function is a continuous, single-valued function of x, defined for all real x, $-\infty < x < +\infty$. It is called the *exponential function*, with e as base and exponent x. **The exponential function is the inverse of the natural logarithm.** Its graph, Fig. 8–11, may be obtained by reflecting the curve in Fig. 8–10 across the 45° line $y = x$. Notice, in particular, that $e^0 = 1$ since $\ln 1 = 0$.

To find the derivative of

$$y = e^x, \qquad (7)$$

we differentiate both sides of the equivalent equation

$$x = \ln y$$

implicitly with respect to x. Then

$$1 = \frac{1}{y}\cdot\frac{dy}{dx} \quad \text{or} \quad \frac{dy}{dx} = y. \quad (8)$$

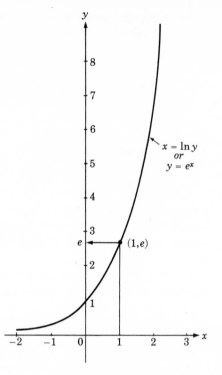

Figure 8–11

Taking account of Eq. (7), we therefore have

$$\frac{de^x}{dx} = e^x.$$

Here is a function which is not changed by differentiation! It is indestructible. It can be differentiated again and again without changing.

In Fig. 8–12 the line $\overleftrightarrow{QP}$ through the points $Q(x-1, 0)$ and $P(x, e^x)$ is

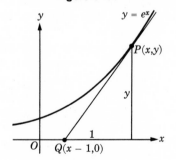

Figure 8–12

tangent to the curve $y = e^x$ at P, for the slope of $\overleftrightarrow{QP}$ is $y/1$ and the slope of the curve, at P, is also equal to y, by Eq. (8).

We obtain a slightly more general formula for the derivative of e^u, where u is a differentiable function of x, by applying the chain rule

$$\boxed{\frac{de^u}{dx} = \frac{de^u}{du}\frac{du}{dx} = e^u\frac{du}{dx}.} \qquad \text{XX}$$

In terms of differentials, we have from XX,

$$de^u = e^u \, du.$$

This in turn leads to the integration formula

$$\int e^u \, du = e^u + C.$$

(9)

EXAMPLE 1. Find dy/dx if $y = e^{\tan^{-1} x}$.

Solution.

$$\frac{dy}{dx} = e^{\tan^{-1} x} \frac{d \tan^{-1} x}{dx}$$

$$= e^{\tan^{-1} x} \cdot \frac{1}{1 + x^2} \cdot \frac{dx}{dx}$$

$$= \frac{e^{\tan^{-1} x}}{1 + x^2}.$$

EXAMPLE 2. Find the area under the curve $y = e^{-x}$ from $x = 0$ to $x = b(> 0)$ and show that this area *remains finite* as $b \to +\infty$.

Solution. The area from $x = 0$ to $x = b$ is given by

$$A_0^b = \int_0^b y \, dx = \int_0^b e^{-x} \, dx.$$

To evaluate this integral, we compare it with our standard forms and see that it is almost, but not exactly, like

$$\int e^u \, du = e^u + C.$$

To bring it into precisely this form, we let

$$u = -x, \qquad du = -dx$$

or

$$dx = -du,$$

so that

$$\int e^{-x} \, dx = \int e^u \, (-du) = -\int e^u \, du = -e^u + C = -e^{-x} + C.$$

Therefore

$$A_0^b = -e^{-x} \Big]_0^b = -e^{-b} + e^0 = 1 - e^{-b}.$$

From this we see that the number of square units of area in the shaded region of Fig. 8–13 is somewhat less than unity, for b large and positive, and moreover

$$\lim_{b \to +\infty} A_0^b = \lim_{b \to +\infty} (1 - e^{-b}) = 1,$$

since [see Eq. (11) below]

$$\lim_{b \to +\infty} e^{-b} = \lim_{b \to +\infty} \frac{1}{e^b} = 0.$$

Some properties of the function

$$y = e^x$$

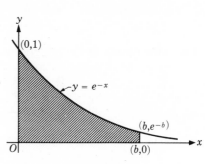

Figure 8–13

are worthy of additional comment.

In the first place, the exponential function satisfies the law

$$e^{x_1} \cdot e^{x_2} = e^{x_1 + x_2}. \tag{10}$$

For, if

$$y_1 = e^{x_1} \quad \text{and} \quad y_2 = e^{x_2}$$

then, by definition,

$$x_1 = \ln y_1 \quad \text{and} \quad x_2 = \ln y_2,$$

so that

$$x_1 + x_2 = \ln y_1 + \ln y_2 = \ln y_1 y_2$$

by Eq. (1), Article 8–6. Therefore, by definition,

$$y_1 y_2 = e^{x_1 + x_2},$$

which establishes Eq. (10).

Again, we have

$$e^{-x} = 1/e^x \tag{11}$$

for any real number x. For, if

$$y = e^{-x}$$

then, by definition,

$$-x = \ln y$$

or, from Eq. (6), Article 8–6,

$$x = -\ln y = \ln (1/y).$$

Therefore, by definition,

$$1/y = e^x \quad \text{or} \quad y = 1/e^x,$$

which establishes Eq. (11).

Powers of e are tabulated in many mathematical tables, such as Burington's. They may also be read directly from the LL-scales of a log-log slide rule. For example, if the number x on the D-scale in Fig. 8–14 is $x = 2$, then the corresponding readings on the LL-scales are:

$$e^2 = 7.4 \quad \text{on LL 3},$$
$$e^{0.2} = 1.2215 \text{ on LL 2},$$
$$e^{0.02} = 1.0202 \text{ on LL 1}.$$

The value of e^{-2} can be read from the LL00-scale on the reverse side of the slide rule opposite the 2 on the right half of the A-scale (the reading gives $e^{-2} = 0.135$). It is also possible to use

$$e^{-2} = \frac{1}{e^2} = \frac{1}{7.4} = 0.135$$

to arrive at the same result. The use of the LL-scales is described in the manual of instructions that comes with the log-log slide rule.

A table of e^x and e^{-x} is included at the end of the book for convenience and to give an appreciation of the rapid rate of increase of the exponential function for positive values of x.

PROBLEMS

1. Simplify each of the following expressions:

(a) $e^{\ln x}$

(b) $\ln (e^x)$

(c) $e^{-\ln (x^2)}$

(d) $\ln (e^{-x^2})$

(e) $\ln (e^{1/x})$

(f) $\ln (1/e^x)$

(g) $e^{\ln (1/x)}$

(h) $e^{-\ln (1/x)}$

(i) $e^{\ln 2 + \ln x}$

(j) $e^{2 \ln x}$

(k) $\ln (e^{x - x^2})$

(l) $\ln (x^2 e^{-2x})$

(m) $e^{x + \ln x}$

(n) $e^{\ln x - 2 \ln y}$

Figure 8–14

Find dy/dx in each of the following problems (2 through 19).

2. $y = x^2 e^x$

3. $y = e^{2x}(2 \cos 3x + 3 \sin 3x)$

4. $y = \ln \dfrac{e^x}{1 + e^x}$

5. $y = \frac{1}{2}(e^x - e^{-x})$

6. $y = \frac{1}{2}(e^x + e^{-x})$

7. $y = \dfrac{e^x - e^{-x}}{e^x + e^{-x}}$

8. $y = e^{\sin^{-1} x}$

9. $y = (1 + 2x)e^{-2x}$

10. $y = (9x^2 - 6x + 2)e^{3x}$

11. $y = \dfrac{ax - 1}{a^2} e^{ax}$

12. $y = e^{-x^2}$

13. $y = x^2 e^{-x^2}$

14. $y = e^x \ln x$

15. $y = \tan^{-1}(e^x)$

16. $y = \sec^{-1}(e^{2x})$

17. $e^{2x} = \sin(x + 3y)$

18. $y = e^{1/x}$

19. $\tan y = e^x + \ln x$

20. (a) Show that $y = Ce^{ax}$ is a solution of the differential equation $dy/dx = ay$ for any choice of the constant C. (b) Using the result of (a), find a solution of the differential equation $dy/dt = -2y$ satisfying the initial condition $y = 3$ when $t = 0$.

21. Show that $y = e^{-ax} u$ is a solution of the differential equation

$$\frac{d^2 y}{dx^2} + 2a \frac{dy}{dx} + (a^2 + b^2) y = 0$$

if and only if u satisfies the equation

$$\frac{d^2 u}{dx^2} + b^2 u = 0,$$

provided a and b are constants.

Evaluate the following integrals:

22. $\displaystyle\int e^{2x} \, dx$

23. $\displaystyle\int x e^{x^2} \, dx$

24. $\displaystyle\int e^{\sin x} \cos x \, dx$

25. $\displaystyle\int e^{x/3} \, dx$

26. $\displaystyle\int \dfrac{4 dx}{e^{3x}}$

27. $\displaystyle\int \dfrac{e^x \, dx}{1 + 2e^x}$

28. $\displaystyle\int_{e}^{e^2} \dfrac{dx}{x \ln x}$

29. $\displaystyle\int \dfrac{(e^x - e^{-x}) \, dx}{(e^x + e^{-x})}$

30. If a particle moves along the x-axis so that its position at time t is given by $x = ae^{\omega t} + be^{-\omega t}$, where a, b, ω, are constants, show that it is repelled from the origin with a force proportional to the displacement. [Assume that force = mass $\times$ acceleration.]

8–9   The function a^u. If a is any positive real number and

$$b = \ln a, \tag{1a}$$

then

$$a = e^b. \tag{1b}$$

The two equations (1a, b) may be combined to give the result

$$a = e^{\ln a}. \tag{2}$$

In words, **ln a is the power to which the base e may be raised to give a.**
     Suppose we now raise both sides of Eq. (2) to the power u, where u is any real number. We would like to have the law of exponents

$$(e^{\ln a})^u = e^{u \ln a}$$

be true. Hence we now make the following *definition:*

$$\boxed{a^u = e^{u \ln a}.} \tag{3}$$

This definition is equivalent to saying that

$$\boxed{\ln a^u = u \ln a,} \tag{3'}$$

since both Eqs. (3) and (3′) say that $u \ln a$ is the power to which e may be raised to produce a^u. But (3′) is the same as Eq. (3), Article 8–6, in case $u = n$ is a rational number. What we are now considering is the case where u may be any real number, rational or irrational, $-\infty < u < +\infty$. Our new definition of a^u includes the old case but goes beyond and extends it.

     Properties of a^u. By making use of the law of exponents, Eq. (10), Article 8–8,

$$e^{x_1} \cdot e^{x_2} = e^{x_1 + x_2}, \tag{4}$$

and the law of logarithms, Eq. (1), Article 8–6,

$$\ln ab = \ln a + \ln b, \tag{5}$$

together with the definition (3) and Eq. (2) above, the following laws may be established.

$$\left.
\begin{aligned}
&\text{(a) } a^0 = 1 \\
&\text{(b) } a^1 = a \\
&\text{(c) } a^u \cdot a^v = a^{u+v} \\
&\text{(d) } a^{-u} = \frac{1}{a^u} \\
&\text{(e) } (a^u)^v = a^{uv} \\
&\text{(f) } (ab)^u = a^u b^u
\end{aligned}
\right\} \tag{6}$$

The first two properties, $a^0 = 1$ and $a^1 = a$, are trivial consequences of Eqs. (2) and (3). To prove (6c), we use the definition

$$a^u \cdot a^v = e^{u \ln a} \cdot e^{v \ln a},$$

then Eq. (4),

$$e^{u \ln a} \cdot e^{v \ln a} = e^{(u+v) \ln a},$$

and then the definition

$$a^{u+v} = e^{(u+v) \ln a},$$

and combine the results into the following:

$$a^u \cdot a^v = e^{u \ln a} \cdot e^{v \ln a} = e^{(u+v) \ln a} = a^{u+v},$$

which establishes the result

$$a^u \cdot a^v = a^{u+v}.$$

Equation (6d) is a consequence of (6a) and (6b):

$$a^{-u} \cdot a^u = a^{-u+u} = a^0 = 1.$$

Equation (6e) is established as follows. Let

$$b = a^u = e^{u \ln a}, \tag{7a}$$

so that

$$(a^u)^v = b^v = e^{v \ln b}. \tag{7b}$$

But

$$\ln b = u \ln a, \tag{7c}$$

since $u \ln a$ is the power to which e may be raised to produce b, Eq. (7a). Now substitute from (7c) into (7b),

$$(a^u)^v = e^{v \ln b} = e^{vu \ln a}, \tag{7d}$$

and make use of the definition, Eq. (3),

$$a^{uv} = e^{uv \ln a}. \tag{7e}$$

When we compare Eqs. (7d, e), we see that we have

$$(a^u)^v = a^{uv},$$

since both expressions are equal to

$$e^{uv \ln a}.$$

The proof of (6f) is left as a problem.

With the definition of a^u now clarified, we are ready to calculate its derivative in case u is a differentiable function of x. We apply formula XX, Article 8–8, and remembering that $\ln a$ is constant when a is, we obtain

$$\frac{da^u}{dx} = \frac{de^{u \ln a}}{dx}$$

$$= e^{u \ln a} \cdot \frac{du}{dx} \cdot \ln a,$$

$$\boxed{\frac{da^u}{dx} = a^u \cdot \frac{du}{dx} \cdot \ln a.} \tag{8}$$

This gives us a formula for the derivative of any positive constant a raised to a variable power. There is very little reason to memorize the result, since it may always be derived very quickly by the method of logarithmic differentiation, which will presently be discussed. It illustrates the fact that the base e is the most desirable one to encounter, since $\ln e = 1$ and Eq. (8) is the same as formula XX in case $a = e$. It also enables us to write down a formula for the integral of $a^u \, du$. For, if we multiply both sides of Eq. (8) by dx to change it to differential form,

$$\boxed{da^u = \ln a \cdot a^u \, du,}$$

and then divide by $\ln a$, provided $a \neq 1$, we see that

$$\boxed{\int a^u \, du = \int \frac{1}{\ln a} \, da^u = \frac{a^u}{\ln a} + C, \qquad (a > 0, a \neq 1).} \tag{9}$$

Logarithmic differentiation. The properties

$$\left.\begin{array}{ll} \text{(a)} & \ln uv = \ln u + \ln v \\[4pt] \text{(b)} & \ln \dfrac{u}{v} = \ln u - \ln v \\[4pt] \text{(c)} & \ln u^n = n \ln u \\[4pt] \text{(d)} & \ln a^u = u \ln a \end{array}\right\} \tag{10}$$

can be used to advantage in calculating derivatives of products, quotients, roots, and powers, as illustrated in the examples that follow. The method, known as logarithmic differentiation, is to take the natural logarithm of both sides of an equation

$$y = f(x),$$

$$\ln y = \ln f(x),$$

simplify $\ln f(x)$ as much as possible by making use of the properties in Eq. (10), and then differentiate implicitly with respect to x:

$$\frac{d}{dx} \ln y = \frac{1}{y} \frac{dy}{dx}.$$

EXAMPLE 1. Derive Eq. (8).

Solution. Let $y = a^u$. Then

$$\ln y = \ln a^u = u \ln a,$$

$$\frac{1}{y} \frac{dy}{dx} = \frac{du}{dx} \ln a,$$

$$\frac{dy}{dx} = y \frac{du}{dx} \ln a,$$

or, since $y = a^u$,

$$\frac{da^u}{dx} = a^u \frac{du}{dx} \ln a.$$

EXAMPLE 2. If n is a real constant and u is a positive differentiable function of x, show that

$$\frac{du^n}{dx} = nu^{n-1} \frac{du}{dx}.$$

Solution. Let $y = u^n$. Then

$$\ln y = \ln u^n = n \ln u,$$

$$\frac{1}{y} \frac{dy}{dx} = n \frac{1}{u} \frac{du}{dx},$$

$$\frac{dy}{dx} = n \frac{y}{u} \frac{du}{dx} = n \frac{u^n}{u} \frac{du}{dx}$$

$$= nu^{n-1} \frac{du}{dx}. \qquad \text{Q.E.D.}$$

EXAMPLE 3. Find dy/dx if $y = x^x$, $x > 0$.

Solution. $\ln y = \ln x^x = x \ln x$,

$$\frac{1}{y}\frac{dy}{dx} = x \cdot \frac{1}{x} + \ln x = 1 + \ln x,$$

$$\frac{dy}{dx} = y(1 + \ln x) = x^x(1 + \ln x).$$

EXAMPLE 4. Find dy/dx if

$$y^{2/3} = \frac{(x^2 + 1)(3x + 4)^{1/2}}{\sqrt[5]{(2x - 3)(x^2 - 4)}}, \qquad (x > 2).$$

Solution.

$\ln y^{2/3} = \frac{2}{3} \ln y$

$\qquad = \ln (x^2 + 1) + \frac{1}{2} \ln (3x + 4) - \frac{1}{5} \ln (2x - 3) - \frac{1}{5} \ln (x^2 - 4)$ (a)

and

$$\frac{2}{3} \cdot \frac{1}{y}\frac{dy}{dx} = \frac{2x}{x^2 + 1} + \frac{1}{2} \cdot \frac{3}{3x + 4} - \frac{1}{5} \cdot \frac{2}{2x - 3} - \frac{1}{5} \cdot \frac{2x}{x^2 - 4},$$

so that

$$\frac{dy}{dx} = \frac{3y}{2}\left[\frac{2x}{x^2 + 1} + \frac{\frac{3}{2}}{3x + 4} - \frac{\frac{2}{5}}{2x - 3} - \frac{2x/5}{x^2 - 4}\right].$$

Remark. The restriction $x > 2$ ensures that all the quantities whose logarithms are indicated in (a) above are positive. If we want dy/dx at a point where y is negative, we may multiply our equation by -1 before taking logarithms; for if y is negative, then $-y$ is positive and $\ln (-y)$ is well defined.

Economists define the ratio of "marginal cost" to "average cost" as the "elasticity of total cost." That is, if the total cost of producing x units of a given product is $y = f(x)$ dollars, then the "average cost" is y/x dollars per unit. The "marginal cost," which is, roughly speaking, the additional cost of producing one more unit, is dy/dx. Then, by definition,

$$\text{elasticity of total cost} = \frac{dy/dx}{y/x} = \frac{dy/y}{dx/x} = \frac{d (\ln y)}{d (\ln x)}.$$

When the elasticity of total cost equals one, then marginal cost equals average cost (that is, $dy/dx = y/x$) and average cost has a stationary value [that is, $d(y/x)/dx = 0$]. [For further discussion, see R. G. D. Allen, *Mathematical Analysis for Economists* (Macmillan, 1939), p. 260 ff.]

PROBLEMS

Use the method of logarithmic differentiation to find dy/dx in each of the following problems (1 through 8).

1. $y^2 = x(x+1)$ $(x > 0)$ 2. $y = \sqrt[3]{\dfrac{x+1}{x-1}}$ $(x > 1)$

3. $y = \dfrac{x\sqrt{x^2+1}}{(x+1)^{2/3}}$ $(x > 0)$ 4. $y = \sqrt[3]{\dfrac{x(x+1)(x-2)}{(x^2+1)(2x+3)}}$ $(x > 2)$

5. $y = x^{\sin x}$ $(x > 0)$ 6. $y = (\sin x)^{\tan x}$ $(\sin x > 0)$

7. $y = 2^{\sec x}$ 8. $y = x^{\ln x}$ $(x > 0)$

9. Show that $(ab)^u = a^u b^u$ if a and b are any positive numbers and u is any real number.

10. Show that the derivative of average cost is zero when marginal cost and average cost are equal.

Evaluate the following integrals (11–15):

11. $\displaystyle\int_0^{\ln 2} e^{-2x}\, dx$ 12. $\displaystyle\int_0^{1.2} 3^x\, dx$

13. $\displaystyle\int_1^{\sqrt{2}} x\, 2^{-x^2}\, dx$ 14. $\displaystyle\int_0^1 5^{2t-2}\, dt$

15. $\displaystyle\int_0^{\pi/6} (\cos\theta) 4^{-\sin\theta}\, d\theta$

16. Let a be a number greater than one. Prove that the graph of $y = a^x$ has the following characteristics:

(a) If $x_1 > x_2$, then $a^{x_1} > a^{x_2}$.
(b) The graph is everywhere concave upward.
(c) The graph lies entirely above the x-axis.
(d) The slope at any point is proportional to the ordinate there, and the proportionality factor is the slope at the y-intercept of the graph.
(e) The curve approaches the negative x-axis as $x \to -\infty$.

8–10   **The function $\log_a u$.** We know that $\ln u$ is the power to which e may be raised to give u. For that reason, we say that e is the base of the system of natural logarithms in keeping with the following definition.

DEFINITION. *If u is positive and a is a positive number different from 1, we say that y is the logarithm of u to the base a, and write*

$$y = \log_a u, \tag{1a}$$

provided y is the power to which a may be raised to give u:

$$a^y = u. \tag{1b}$$

For example,

$$\log_5 25 = 2 \quad \text{since} \quad 5^2 = 25,$$

$$\log_2 \tfrac{1}{4} = -2 \quad \text{since} \quad 2^{-2} = \tfrac{1}{4}.$$

To find $x = \log_4 8$, we rewrite the equation as

$$4^x = 2^{2x} = 8 = 2^3,$$

from which we read $2x = 3$, $x = \tfrac{3}{2}$. In other words,

$$\log_4 8 = \tfrac{3}{2} \quad \text{since} \quad 4^{3/2} = (\sqrt{4})^3 = 8.$$

We may solve Eq. (1b) for y, and thereby obtain an expression for $\log_a u$, by taking natural logarithms and applying Eq. (3′) of Article 8–9:

$$\ln u = \ln a^y = y \ln a.$$

If $\ln a \neq 0$ (which is the case when a is different from 1), we may solve for y. The result is that

$$y = \frac{\ln u}{\ln a}$$

is the power to which a may be raised to produce u. In other words,

$$\boxed{\log_a u = \frac{\ln u}{\ln a}.} \tag{2}$$

Properties of $\log_a u$. The following properties follow readily from Eq. (2) above and the analogous properties of $\ln u$.

$$\boxed{\begin{array}{l} \text{(a)} \ \log_a uv = \log_a u + \log_a v \\[4pt] \text{(b)} \ \log_a \dfrac{u}{v} = \log_a u - \log_a v \\[4pt] \text{(c)} \ \log_a u^v = v \log_a u \end{array}} \tag{3}$$

Equation (3c), for example, is derived as follows:

$$\log_a u^v = \frac{\ln u^v}{\ln a} = \frac{v \ln u}{\ln a} = v \log_a u,$$

where we make use of Eq. (2), then Eq. (3′) of Article 8–9, and then Eq. (2) again.

If u is a differentiable positive function of x, we may differentiate both sides of Eq. (2) and thus obtain

$$\boxed{\frac{d \log_a u}{dx} = \frac{1}{u \ln a} \frac{du}{dx} \cdot} \tag{4}$$

It is clear that this formula is simpler for logarithms to the base e than for any other base. The only bases of practical importance are $a = e$ (natural logarithms) and $a = 10$ (common logarithms). Since $\ln 10 = 2.30259\ldots$, Eq. (4) is certainly less attractive for the case $a = 10$ than it is for the case $a = e$. This is the primary reason why natural logarithms are to be preferred over common logarithms in applications of the calculus.

Logarithms to the base 10 are used primarily as aids in performing arithmetical calculations such as multiplication, division, and raising numbers to powers. The use of slide rules, desk calculators, and new high-speed computing machinery is rapidly making this use of logarithms less and less important. Natural logarithms, on the other hand, are not in any immediate danger of becoming obsolete, since they occur naturally when some common kinds of differential equations are solved. [See Examples 1 and 2, Article 8–11.]

PROBLEMS

Determine the following logarithms:

1. (a) $\log_4 16$,   (b) $\log_8 32$,   (c) $\log_5 0.04$,   (d) $\log_{0.5} 4$.

2. (a) $\log_2 4$,   (b) $\log_4 2$,   (c) $\log_8 16$,   (d) $\log_{32} 4$.

3. Find x if $3^x = 2^{x+1}$.

4. Find x if $3^{\log_3 7} + 2^{\log_2 5} = 5^{\log_5 x}$.

5. Show that $\log_b u = \log_a u \cdot \log_b a$ if a, b, and u are positive numbers, $a \neq 1$, $b \neq 1$.

6. Given $\ln 2 = 0.69315$, $\ln 10 = 2.30259$, $\log_{10} 2 = 0.30103$. Find

(a) $\log_{10} 20$, $\log_{10} 200$, $\log_{10} 0.2$, $\log_{10} 0.02$,

(b) $\ln 20$, $\ln 200$, $\ln 0.2$, $\ln 0.02$.

7. Use the table of natural logarithms at the end of the book to evaluate the following logarithms to two significant figures:

(a) $\log_3 5$,   (b) $\log_5 3$,   (c) $\log_{1.4} 2.3$.

8. Use the tables at the end of the book to evaluate the following to two significant figures:

(a) $(1.6)^{1.5}$,   (b) $\dfrac{\ln 0.7}{\ln 1.3}$.

9. Find the derivatives of the following:

(a) $y = 3^{\tan x}$,   (b) $y = (x^2 + 1)^{\ln x}$,

(c) $s = 2^{-t^2}$,   (d) $r = \theta e^{-2\theta}$.

8-11 Differential equations. Suppose a quantity x changes at a rate that at any instant of time t is proportional to the amount of x present at that instant. This is expressed by the differential equation

$$\frac{dx}{dt} = kx, \tag{1}$$

where k is the proportionality constant. If the amount of x present at time $t = 0$ is x_0, the initial condition

$$x = x_0 \qquad \text{when} \qquad t = 0 \tag{2}$$

enables us to evaluate the constant of integration that enters when we integrate Eq. (1). The method of solution will be illustrated by an example.

EXAMPLE 1. As a result of leakage, an electrical condenser discharges at a rate proportional to the charge. If the charge Q has the value Q_0 at the time $t = 0$, find Q as a function of t.

Solution. The mathematical statement of the problem consists of the differential equation $dQ/dt = -kQ$ and the initial condition $t = 0$, $Q = Q_0$. Then

$$\frac{dQ}{Q} = -k \, dt,$$

$$\int \frac{dQ}{Q} = -k \int dt,$$

$$\ln Q = -kt + C. \tag{3}$$

The constant of integration C is evaluated by using the initial conditions:

$$t = 0, \quad Q = Q_0; \qquad \ln Q_0 = C.$$

Substituting this value of C back into (3) and transposing it to the left of the equation, we get

$$\ln Q - \ln Q_0 = -kt$$

or

$$\ln \frac{Q}{Q_0} = -kt.$$

Hence, $-kt$ is the power to which e must be raised to give Q/Q_0, that is,

$$\frac{Q}{Q_0} = e^{-kt} \qquad \text{or} \qquad Q = Q_0 e^{-kt}.$$

According to this equation, Q is never zero; that is, some charge would always remain. But when $kt = 10$, say, then $Q = Q_0 e^{-10}$ so that the charge Q has by then diminished to less than 5/1000 of 1 percent of its original value Q_0.

Remark. In this example, the function integrated was positive, so that we were able to omit the absolute value symbols and write simply $\ln Q$ in place of $\ln |Q|$. Occasionally we encounter a problem where the quantity whose logarithm we require is an unknown function which presumably could be either positive or negative. To change sign from one to the other, however, would mean that the quantity would become zero at the transition point, provided it is a *continuous* function (Fig. 8–15). An integral of the form

$$\int \frac{du}{u} \tag{4}$$

between points where u changes continuously from positive to negative or from negative to positive is a so-called *improper integral*, because the integrand $1/u$ becomes infinite at $u = 0$. We shall discuss improper integrals in more detail in a later chapter. At present we shall assume that any physical problems we encounter that lead to integrals of the form of (4) arise from physical situations in which infinities are excluded. Then if we know the sign of u at one point of the interval of integration, we shall assume that it always has the same sign throughout the whole interval.

EXAMPLE 2. Ohm's law, $E = Ri$, requires modification in a circuit containing self-inductance, as in a coil. The modified form is

$$L\frac{di}{dt} + Ri = E \tag{5}$$

for the series circuit shown in Fig. 8–16, where R denotes the resistance of the circuit in ohms, L is the self-inductance in henries, E is the impressed electromotive force (emf) in volts, i is the current in amperes, and t is the time in seconds. (See Sears, *Electricity and Magnetism,* Chapter 13.) We shall solve the differential equation (5) under the assumption that E is constant and

$$i = 0 \qquad \text{when} \qquad t = 0. \tag{6}$$

Figure 8–15

Figure 8–16

To integrate (5), we first separate the variables in order to have the terms involving the variable current i combined with di for purposes of integration. Thus

$$L\,di = (E - Ri)\,dt$$

and

$$\int \frac{L\,di}{E - Ri} = \int dt. \tag{7}$$

We let

$$u = E - Ri, \tag{8}$$

then

$$du = -R\,di, \qquad di = -\frac{1}{R}\,du,$$

so that (7) becomes

$$-\frac{L}{R}\int \frac{du}{u} = \int dt. \tag{9}$$

From (8) and the initial conditions (6) we see that $u = E - Ri$ has the positive value $u_0 = E$ at $t = 0$. We therefore assume that it remains positive, so that $|u| = u$ and the integral in (9) then gives

$$-\frac{L}{R}\ln u = t + C$$

or

$$-\frac{L}{R}\ln (E - Ri) = t + C. \tag{10}$$

The initial conditions $t = 0$, $i = 0$ enable us to evaluate the constant of integration:

$$C = -\frac{L}{R}\ln E.$$

When we substitute this back into (10) and transpose it to the left side of the equation, we obtain

$$\frac{L}{R}\left[\ln E - \ln (E - Ri)\right] = t,$$

$$\ln \frac{E}{E - Ri} = \frac{Rt}{L},$$

$$\frac{E}{E - Ri} = e^{(Rt)/L},$$

$$\frac{E - Ri}{E} = e^{-(Rt)/L},$$

$$1 - \frac{R}{E}i = e^{-(Rt)/L},$$

$$i = \frac{E}{R}\left(1 - e^{-(Rt)/L}\right). \tag{11}$$

We see from this that the current (for $t > 0$) is always less than, but increases toward, the steady state value

$$i_{s.s.} = \frac{E}{R}, \tag{12}$$

which is the current that would flow in the circuit if either $L = 0$ (no inductance) or $di/dt = 0$ (steady current, i = constant) in Eq. (5). Indeed, if $L \rightarrow 0$, then for all $t > 0$ the exponent [in (11)]

$$-\frac{Rt}{L} \rightarrow -\infty \quad \text{and} \quad i \rightarrow \frac{E}{R}.$$

A graph of the current versus time relation (11) is shown in Fig. 8–17.

Incidentally, in problems involving electrical circuits, the letter e is usually used to denote an emf and the letter ϵ is then used to denote the constant which we have called (and shall continue to call) e. Mathematicians have become accustomed to the use of ϵ to denote an arbitrarily small positive number, so they are not likely to change their notation; nor are the electrical engineers likely to change theirs. However, this lack of uniformity should not cause confusion, since the meaning of the symbols will usually be clear from the context.

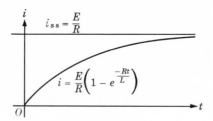

Figure 8–17

PROBLEMS

1. Suppose a body of mass m moving in a straight line with velocity v encounters a resistance proportional to the velocity and this is the only force acting on the body. If the body starts with velocity v_0, how far does it travel in time t? Assume $F = d(mv)/dt$.

2. A radioactive substance disintegrates at a rate proportional to the amount present. How much of the substance remains at time t if the initial amount is Q_0?

3. If the bacteria in a culture increase continuously at a rate proportional to the number present, and the initial number is N_0, find the number at time t.

In Problems 4–7, substitute $y = e^{rx}$ and find values of the constant r for which $y = e^{rx}$ is a solution of the given differential equation.

4. $\dfrac{d^2y}{dx^2} - 4\dfrac{dy}{dx} + 3y = 0$ 5. $\dfrac{d^2y}{dx^2} - \dfrac{dy}{dx} - 2y = 0$

6. $\dfrac{d^3y}{dx^3} + 6\dfrac{d^2y}{dx^2} + 5\dfrac{dy}{dx} = 0$ $\qquad$ 7. $\dfrac{d^4y}{dx^4} - 13\dfrac{d^2y}{dx^2} + 36y = 0$

8. By substitution, verify that

$$y = (c_1 + c_2\,x)e^{r_1 x}$$

satisfies the differential equation

$$\frac{d^2y}{dx^2} - 2r_1\frac{dy}{dx} + r_1^2\,y = 0$$

for all values of the constants c_1, c_2, and r_1.

9. By substitution, verify that $y = e^{ax}(c_1 \cos bx + c_2 \sin bx)$ satisfies the differential equation

$$\frac{d^2y}{dx^2} - 2a\frac{dy}{dx} + (a^2 + b^2)y = 0$$

for all values of the constants c_1, c_2, a, and b.

10. Sketch the curve $y = e^{-x} \cos 2x$ for $x \ge 0$. Show that it is tangent to the curves $y = \pm e^{-x}$ when $\cos 2x = \pm 1$.

REVIEW QUESTIONS AND EXERCISES FOR CHAPTER 8

1. Review the formulas for derivatives of sums, products, quotients, powers, sines, and cosines. Using these, develop formulas for derivatives of the other trigonometric functions.

2. Define the inverse sine, inverse cosine, inverse tangent, and inverse secant functions. What is the *domain* of each? What is its *range*? What is the derivative of each? Sketch the graph of each.

3. Define the natural logarithm function. What is its domain? What is its range? What is its derivative? Sketch its graph.

4. What is the inverse function of the natural logarithm called? What is the domain of this function? What is its range? What is its derivative? Sketch its graph.

5. Define the term "algebraic function." Define "transcendental function." To which class (algebraic or transcendental) do you think the "greatest integer" step-function (Fig. 2–6) belongs?

[It is often difficult to prove that a particular function belongs to one class or the other. Numbers are also classified as algebraic and transcendental. *References:* (1) W. J. Le Veque, *Topics in Number Theory*, Addison-Wesley, Vol. II, Chap. 5, pp. 161–200; (2) I. M. Niven, *Irrational Numbers*, Carus monograph number 11 of the Mathematical Association of America, (1956). Both π and e are transcendental numbers, and proofs may be found in the references cited. That π is transcendental was first proved by Ferdinand Lindemann in 1882. One result that follows from the transcendence of π is that it is impossible to construct, with unmarked straightedge and compass alone, a square whose area is equal to the area of a given circle. The first proof that e is transcendental was published by Charles Hermite in 1873. You may also enjoy reading about an interesting related feature of the graph of $y = \ln x$ in the article on logarithms on p. 301 of Vol. 14 of the *Encyclopedia Britannica* (1956 edition).]

6. Let n be an integer greater than 1. Divide the interval $1 \leq x \leq n$ into n equal subintervals and write an expression for the trapezoidal approximation to the area under the graph of $y = 1/x$, $1 \leq x \leq n$, based on this subdivision. Is this approximation less than, equal to, or greater than $\ln n$? Give a reason for your answer.

7. Prove that $\lim_{x \to \infty} (\ln x)/x = 0$, starting with the definition of $\ln x$ as an integral.

8. The *Encyclopedia Britannica* article on logarithms begins with the statement: "By shortening processes of computation, logarithms have doubled the working speed of astronomers and engineers." What property or properties of logarithms do you think the author of the article had in mind when he made that statement?

9. What is the meaning of the differential equation $dy/dt = ky$? What is the solution of this equation that satisfies the initial condition $y = y_0$ when $t = 0$?

MISCELLANEOUS PROBLEMS FOR CHAPTER 8

In each of the following problems (1 through 25), (a) find dy/dx, and (b) sketch the curve.

1. $y = \sin 2x$

2. $y = 4 \cos (2x + \pi/4)$

3. $y = 2 \sin x + \sin 2x$

4. $y = \dfrac{\sin x}{1 + \cos x}$

5. $x = \cos y$

6. $x = \tan y$

7. $y = 4 \sin \left(\dfrac{x}{2} + \pi\right)$

8. $y = 1 - \sin x$

9. $y = x - \sin x$

10. $y = \dfrac{\sin x}{x}$ (What happens as $x \to 0$? As $x \to \infty$?)

11. $y = \dfrac{\sin x}{x^2}$ (What happens as $x \to 0$? As $x \to \infty$?)

12. $y = x \sin \dfrac{1}{x}$ (What happens as $x \to \infty$? As $x \to 0$?)

13. $y = x^2 \sin \dfrac{1}{x}$ (What happens as $x \to \infty$? As $x \to 0$?)

14. $x = \tan \dfrac{\pi y}{2}$

15. (a) $y = \frac{1}{2}(e^x + e^{-x})$, (b) $y = \frac{1}{2}(e^x - e^{-x})$, (c) $y = \dfrac{e^x - e^{-x}}{e^x + e^{-x}}$

16. $y = xe^{-x}$

17. (a) $y = x \ln x$, (b) $y = \sqrt{x} \ln x$

18. (a) $y = \dfrac{\ln x}{x}$, (b) $y = \dfrac{\ln x}{\sqrt{x}}$, (c) $y = \dfrac{\ln x}{x^2}$

19. $y = e^{-x} \sin 2x$

20. (a) $y = 2x - \frac{1}{2}e^{2x}$, (b) $y = e^{(2x - \frac{1}{2}e^{2x})}$

21. (a) $y = x - e^x$, (b) $y = e^{(x - e^x)}$

22. $y = \ln (x + \sqrt{x^2 + 1})$

23. $y = \dfrac{1}{2} \ln \dfrac{1 + x}{1 - x}$

24. $y = \ln (x^2 + 4)$

25. $y = x \tan^{-1} \dfrac{x}{2}$

Find dy/dx in Problems 26–42.

26. $y = \dfrac{e^{2x} - e^{-2x}}{e^{2x} + e^{-2x}}$

27. $y = \ln \dfrac{\sec x + \tan x}{\sec x - \tan x}$

28. $y = x^2 e^{2x} \sin 3x$

29. $y = \sin^{-1}(x^2) - xe^{x^2}$

30. $y = \ln \left(\dfrac{x^4}{1 + x^3}\right) + 7^{x^{2/3}}$

31. $y = (x^2 + 2)^{2-x}$

32. $y = \dfrac{\ln x}{e^x}$

33. $y = \ln \dfrac{x}{\sqrt{x^2 + 1}}$

34. $y = \ln (4 - 3x)$

35. $y = \ln (3x^2 + 4x)$

375

36. $y = x \, (\ln x)^3$

37. $y = x \ln (x^3)$

38. $y = x^3 \ln x$

39. $y = \ln e^x$

40. $y = x^2 e^x$

41. $x = \ln y$

42. $y = \ln (\ln x)$

43. Find dy/dx by logarithmic differentiation for

(a) $y = \dfrac{x}{x^2 + 1}$, $x > 0$;

(b) $y = \sqrt[3]{\dfrac{x(x - 2)}{x^2 + 1}}$, $x > 2$.

44. If $f(x) = x + e^{4x}$, find $f(0)$ and $f'(0)$, and find an approximation for $f(0.01)$.

45. Find dy/dx for each of the following:

(a) $y = a^{x^2 - x}$,

(b) $y = \ln \dfrac{e^x}{1 + e^x}$,

(c) $y = x^x$,

(d) $y = x^{1/x}$.

46. Sketch the graphs of $y = \ln (1 - x)$ and $y = \ln (1/x)$.

47. Sketch (in a common figure) the graphs of $y = e^{-x}$ and $y = -e^{-x}$.

48. Solve for x: $\tan^{-1} x - \cot^{-1} x = \pi/4$.

49. If $\dfrac{dy}{dx} = \dfrac{e^x - e^{-x}}{e^x + e^{-x}}$, find $\dfrac{d^2y}{dx^2}$ and y.

50. If $dy/dx = 2/e^y$ and $y = 0$ when $x = 5$, find y as a function of x.

51. $P(x_1, y_1)$ and $Q(x_2, y_2)$ are any two points (in the first quadrant) lying on the hyperbola $xy = R$ (R positive). Show that the area bounded by the arc PQ, the lines $x = x_1$, $x = x_2$, and the x-axis is equal to the area bounded by the arc PQ, the lines $y = y_1$, $y = y_2$, and the y-axis.

52. By the trapezoidal rule, find $\int_0^2 e^{-x^2} \, dx$, using $n = 4$.

53. In a condenser discharging electricity the rate of change of the voltage in volts per second is proportional to the voltage, being numerically equal to minus one-fortieth of the voltage. Express the voltage as a function of the time. In how many seconds will the voltage decrease to 10 percent of its original value?

54. (a) Sketch the graph $2y = (e^x + e^{-x})$. Observe that whenever $P_1(x_1, y_1)$ is on the graph, so is the point $P_1'(-x_1, y_1)$. This implies a certain symmetry property of the graph. What is it? (b) Find the length of the curve from its lowest point to an arbitrary point $P_1(x_1, y_1)$ on it.

55. The area bounded by the x-axis and one arch of the curve $y = \sin x$ is revolved around the x-axis. Find the volume of the solid of revolution thus generated. Compare its volume with that of two inscribed cones.

56. A curve $y = f(x)$ goes through the points $(0, 0)$ and (x_1, y_1). It divides the rectangle $0 \le x \le x_1$, $0 \le y \le y_1$ into two regions: A above the curve and B below. Find the curve if the area of A is twice the area of B for all choices of $x_1 > 0$ and $y_1 > 0$.

57. Find a curve passing through the origin and such that the length s of the curve between the origin and any point (x, y) of the curve is given by

$$s = e^x + y - 1.$$

58. A particle starts at the origin and moves along the x-axis in such a way that its velocity at the point $(x, 0)$ is given by the formula $dx/dt = \cos^2 \pi x$. How long will it take to cover the distance from the origin to the point $x = \frac{1}{4}$? Will it ever reach the point $x = \frac{1}{2}$? Why?

59. A particle moves in a straight line with acceleration $a = 4/(4 - t)^2$. If when $t = 0$ the velocity is equal to 2, find how far the particle moves between $t = 1$ and $t = 2$.

60. The velocity of a certain particle moving along the x-axis is proportional to x. At time $t = 0$ the particle is located at $x = 2$ and at time $t = 10$ it is at $x = 4$. Find its position at $t = 5$.

61. Solve the differential equation $dy/dx = y^2 e^{-x}$ if $y = 2$ when $x = 0$.

62. It is estimated that the population of a certain country is now increasing at a rate of 2% per year. Assuming that this (instantaneous) rate will continue indefinitely, estimate what the population N will be t years from now, if the population now is N_0. How many years will it take for the population to double?

63. If $y = (e^{2x} - 1)/(e^{2x} + 1)$, show that $dy/dx = 1 - y^2$.

64. Determine the inflection points of the curve $y = e^{-(x/a)^2}$, where a is a positive constant. Sketch the curve. (This is closely related to the normal curve used in statistics.)

65. Find the volume generated when the area bounded by $y = e^{-x}$, $x = 0$, $x = \ln 2$, $y = 0$ is rotated about the x-axis.

66. Find the volume generated when the area bounded by $x = \sec y$, $x = 0$, $y = 0$, $y = \pi/3$ is rotated about the y-axis.

67. (a) Find dy/dx if $y = \ln (\sec x + \tan x)$. (b) Find the length of arc of the curve $y = \ln \sec x$ from $x = 0$ to $\pi/4$, using, at some stage, the result of part (a).

68. Find the length of the curve $x/a = (y/b)^2 - \frac{1}{8}(b^2/a^2) \ln (y/b)$ from $y = b$ to $y = 3b$, assuming a and b to be positive constants.

69. Find the volume generated by rotating about the x-axis the area bounded by $y = e^x$, $y = 0$, $x = 0$, $x = 2$.

70. Find the area bounded by the curve $y = (a/2)(e^{x/a} + e^{-x/a})$, the x-axis, and the lines $x = -a$ and $x = +a$.

71. The portion of a tangent to a curve included between the x-axis and the point of tangency is bisected by the y-axis. If the curve passes through $(1, 2)$, find its equation.

72. Use the trapezoidal rule with $n = 5$ to approximate the value of (a) $\ln 0.5$, (b) $\ln 3$.

73. (a) If $y = x \ln x - x$, find y'. (b) Use the results of 73(a) and 72(b) to evaluate $\int_1^3 \ln x \, dx$ approximately.

Evaluate the integrals in Problems 74 and 75.

74. (a) $\displaystyle\int \frac{dx}{4 - 3x}$ (b) $\displaystyle \frac{5 \, dx}{x - 3}$ (c) $\displaystyle\int_0^2 \frac{x \, dx}{x^2 + 2}$

75. (a) $\displaystyle\int_0^2 \frac{x \, dx}{(x^2 + 2)^2}$ (b) $\displaystyle\int \frac{x + 1}{x} \, dx$ (c) $\displaystyle\int \frac{x}{2x + 1} \, dx$

76. Given $\ln 2 = 0.6932$ and $\ln 5 = 1.6094$. Use the properties of logarithms to find numerical values for $\ln 0.1$, $\ln 0.25$, $\ln 10$, and $\ln 20$.

77. Find the volume generated by rotating about the x-axis the area in the first quadrant bounded by the curve $xy^2 = 1$, the x-axis, the line $x = 1$, and the line $x = 4$.

78. Find the volume generated if the area in Problem 78 is rotated about the y-axis.

Evaluate the integrals in Problems 79–80.

79. (a) $\displaystyle\int_0^1 \frac{x^2\,dx}{2 - x^3}$ (b) $\displaystyle\int_0^3 x(e^{x^2-1})\,dx$ (c) $\displaystyle\int_1^3 \frac{dx}{x}$

80. (a) $\displaystyle\int_0^5 \frac{x\,dx}{x^2 + 1}$ (b) $\displaystyle\int_0^1 (e^x + 1)\,dx$

81. In the inversion of raw sugar the time rate of change of the amount of raw sugar present varies as the amount of raw sugar remaining. If after 10 hr 1000 lb of raw sugar has been reduced to 800 lb, how much raw sugar will remain after 24 hr?

82. A cylindrical tank of radius 10 ft and height 20 ft, with its axis vertical, is full of water but has a leak at the bottom. Assuming that water escapes at a rate proportional to the depth of water in the tank and that 10% escapes during the first hour, find a formula for the volume of water left in the tank after t hr.

83. Let p be a positive integer ≥ 2. Show that

$$\lim_{n\to\infty} \left(\frac{1}{n+1} + \frac{1}{n+2} + \cdots + \frac{1}{p \cdot n}\right) = \ln p.$$

84. (a) If $(\ln x)/x = (\ln 2)/2$, does it necessarily follow that $x = 2$? (b) If $(\ln x)/x = -2 \ln 2$, does it necessarily follow that $x = \frac{1}{2}$? Give reasons for your answers.

85. Given that $\lim_{x\to\infty} (\ln x)/x = 0$ (see Article 8–7, Problem 4). Prove that (a) $\lim_{x\to\infty} (\ln x)/x^h = 0$ if h is any positive constant, (b) $\lim_{x\to+\infty} x^n/e^x = 0$ if n is any constant.

86. Show that $\lim_{h\to 0} (e^h - 1)/h = 1$, by considering the definition of the derivative of e^x at $x = 0$.

87. Prove that if x is any positive number, $\lim_{n\to\infty} n(\sqrt[n]{x} - 1) = \ln x$. [*Hint:* Take $x = e^{nh}$ and apply Problem 86.] *Remark:* This result provides a method for finding $\ln x$ (to any desired finite number of decimal places) using nothing fancier than repeated use of the operation of extracting square roots. For we may take $n = 2^k$, and then $\sqrt[n]{x}$ is obtained from x by taking k successive square roots.

88. Show that $(x^2/4) < x - \ln(1 + x) < (x^2/2)$ if $0 < x < 1$. [*Hint:* Let $f(x) = x - \ln(1 + x)$ and show that $(x/2) < f'(x) < x$.]

89. Prove that the area under the graph of $y = 1/x$ over the interval $a \leq x \leq b$ $(a > 0)$ is the same as the area over the interval $ka \leq x \leq kb$, for any $k > 0$.

90. Find the limit, as $n \to \infty$, of

$$\frac{e^{1/n} + e^{2/n} + \cdots + e^{(n-1)/n} + e^{n/n}}{n}.$$

In considering the ratio of two functions $f(x)$ and $g(x)$, we sometimes wish to know the value of $\lim_{x \to a} f(x)/g(x)$ at a point where both $f(x)$ and $g(x)$ approach zero or both approach ∞. In such cases we are led to meaningless expressions $0/0$ or ∞/∞ if we substitute $x = a$ in the numerator and denominator of the fraction. Thus: $\lim_{t \to \infty} (t^2 + t)/(2t^2 + 1)$ assumes the form ∞/∞ as $t \to \infty$, and $\lim_{t \to 0} \sin x/x$ assumes the form $0/0$ as $t \to 0$.

The following theorem, which we shall state without proof,* is very useful in finding limits of this kind.

THEOREM (*l'Hôpital's rule*). *If $f(a) = g(a) = 0$ or if $f(a) = g(a) = \infty$ and if the limit of the ratio $f'(t)/g'(t)$ as t approaches a exists, then*

$$\boxed{\lim_{t \to a} \frac{f(t)}{g(t)} = \lim_{t \to a} \frac{f'(t)}{g'(t)}.}$$

For our first example we have

$$\lim_{t \to \infty} \frac{t^2 + t}{2t^2 + 1} = \lim_{t \to \infty} \frac{2t + 1}{4t} \quad \left[\text{still} = \frac{\infty}{\infty} \right] \quad = \lim_{t \to \infty} \frac{2}{4} = \frac{1}{2}.$$

(Note that the method discussed in the problems for Article 3–4 could also be used.) For our second example

$$\lim_{x \to 0} \frac{\sin x}{x} = \lim_{x \to 0} \frac{\cos x}{1} = \frac{1}{1} = 1.$$

Use l'Hôpital's rule to evaluate the following limits.

91. $\lim_{t \to \infty} \dfrac{t^2 + 2t}{3t^2}$

92. $\lim_{x \to 1} \dfrac{x^3 - 3x + 2}{x^3 - x^2 - x + 1}$

93. $\lim_{x \to 0} \dfrac{\sin 7x}{x}$

94. $\lim_{t \to 0} \dfrac{1 - \cos t - \frac{1}{2}t^2}{t^4}$

95. $\lim_{x \to 0} \dfrac{e^x - 1}{x^2}$

96. $\lim_{x \to +\infty} \dfrac{\ln x}{x}$

97. $\lim_{x \to \infty} \dfrac{x^3}{e^x}$

98. $\lim_{x \to 0} \dfrac{\sin^2 x}{1 - \cos x}$

99. $\lim_{y \to 0} \dfrac{\sin^{-1} y - y}{y^3}$

100. $\lim_{t \to 0} \dfrac{5^t - e^t}{t}$

---

* For a proof see "L'Hôpital's Rule," by A. E. Taylor, *American Mathematical Monthly*, 59, pp. 20–24 (1952).

Methods of Integration

9–1 Basic formulas. Since indefinite integration is defined as the inverse of differentiation, the problem of evaluating an integral

$$\int f(x)\, dx \tag{1}$$

is equivalent to finding a function F such that

$$dF(x) = f(x)\, dx. \tag{2}$$

At first sight, this may seem like a hopeless task when we think of adopting a "trial-and-error" approach, and realize that it is simply impossible to try *all functions* as F in Eq. (2) hoping that we find one that does the job.* In fact, it is even possible to write down fairly simple integrals, such as

$$\int e^{-x^2}\, dx, \tag{3}$$

which cannot be expressed in terms of finite combinations of the so-called "elementary functions" which we have studied thus far. We shall leave a discussion of such integrals as (3) to a later time, and say simply that the words "finite combinations" must give way and an integral like (3) may then be expressed in terms of an infinite series.

In order to cut down on the amount of trial-and-error involved in integration, it is useful to build up a table of standard types of integral formulas by inverting formulas for differentials as we have done in the previous chapters. Then we try to match any integral that confronts us against one of the standard types. This usually involves a certain amount of algebraic manipulation.

A table of integrals, more extensive than the list of basic formulas given here, probably is, or will be, a part of the reader's library. In order to use such a table intelligently, it is necessary to become familiar with

---

* If f is continuous, then an integral function F satisfying Eq. (2) always exists. For example, for $F(x)$ we could take the area A_a^x discussed in Article 6–8. Theoretically, this, together with the fact that such an area can be calculated as a limit of sums of areas of rectangles, gives us a rule for computing $F(x)$. However, we are interested in avoiding these arithmetical calculations, if possible. Hence we prefer to find simple closed-form expressions for the integral whenever possible.

certain basic techniques which one can apply to reduce a given integral to a form that matches an entry in the tables. The examples and problems in this book should serve to develop our skill with these techniques. In order to concentrate on the techniques without becoming entangled in a mass of algebra, these problems and examples have been kept fairly simple. This in turn means that *these particular* problems can frequently be solved immediately by consulting an integral table. But the reader should realize that if he adopts such a course he will defeat the intended purpose of developing his own power. And it is this power which is important, rather than the specific answer to any given problem.

Perhaps a good way to develop the skill we are aiming for is for each student to build his own table of integrals. He may, for example, make a notebook in which the various sections are headed by the standard forms such as $\int u^n\, du$, $\int du/u$, $\int e^u\, du$, etc., and then under each heading he may include several examples to illustrate the range of application of the particular formula.

Making such a notebook probably has educational value. But once it is made, it should rarely be necessary to refer to it!

Success in integration hinges on the ability to spot what part of the integrand should be called u in order that one will also have du so that a known formula can be applied. This means that the *first requirement* for skill in integration is a thorough mastery of the formulas for differentiation. We therefore list certain formulas for differentials that have been derived in previous chapters, together with their integral counterparts.

1. $du = \dfrac{du}{dx}\, dx$ 1. $\displaystyle\int du = u + C$

2. $d(au) = a\, du$ 2. $\displaystyle\int a\, du = a\int du$

3. $d(u + v) = du + dv$ 3. $\displaystyle\int (du + dv) = \int du + \int dv$

4. $d(u^n) = nu^{n-1}\, du$ 4. $\displaystyle\int u^n\, du = \frac{u^{n+1}}{n+1} + C,\quad n \neq -1$

5. $d(\ln u) = \dfrac{du}{u}$ 5. $\displaystyle\int \frac{du}{u} = \ln |u| + C$

6. (a) $d(e^u) = e^u\, du$ 6. (a) $\displaystyle\int e^u\, du = e^u + C$

   (b) $d(a^u) = a^u \ln a\, du$ (b) $\displaystyle\int a^u\, du = \frac{a^u}{\ln a} + C$

7. $d (\sin u) = \cos u\, du$

7. $\int \cos u\, du = \sin u + C$

8. $d (\cos u) = -\sin u\, du$

8. $\int \sin u\, du = -\cos u + C$

9. $d (\tan u) = \sec^2 u\, du$

9. $\int \sec^2 u\, du = \tan u + C$

10. $d (\cot u) = -\csc^2 u\, du$

10. $\int \csc^2 u\, du = -\cot u + C$

11. $d (\sec u) = \sec u \tan u\, du$

11. $\int \sec u \tan u\, du = \sec u + C$

12. $d (\csc u) = -\csc u \cot u\, du$

12. $\int \csc u \cot u\, du = -\csc u + C$

13. $d (\sin^{-1} u) = \dfrac{du}{\sqrt{1 - u^2}}$

14. $d (\cos^{-1} u) = \dfrac{-du}{\sqrt{1 - u^2}}$

13. and 14. $\int \dfrac{du}{\sqrt{1 - u^2}} = \begin{cases} \sin^{-1} u + C \\ -\cos^{-1} u + C' \end{cases}$

15. $d (\tan^{-1} u) = \dfrac{du}{1 + u^2}$

16. $d (\cot^{-1} u) = \dfrac{-du}{1 + u^2}$

15. and 16. $\int \dfrac{du}{1 + u^2} = \begin{cases} \tan^{-1} u + C \\ -\cot^{-1} u + C' \end{cases}$

17. $d (\sec^{-1} u) = \dfrac{du}{|u|\sqrt{u^2 - 1}}$

18. $d (\csc^{-1} u) = \dfrac{-du}{|u|\sqrt{u^2 - 1}}$

17. and 18. $\int \dfrac{du}{u\sqrt{u^2 - 1}} = \begin{cases} \sec^{-1} |u| + C \\ -\csc^{-1} |u| + C \end{cases}$

At present, let us just consider this list a handy reference and *not* a challenge to our memories! A bit of examination will probably convince us that we are already rather familiar with the first twelve formulas for *differentials* and, so far as *integration* is concerned, part of our training in technique will show how we can get the *integrals* in the last six cases without memorizing the formulas for the differentials of the inverse trigonometric functions.

Just what types of functions can we integrate directly by use of this short table of integrals?

Powers. $\int u^n\, du, \quad \int \dfrac{du}{u}.$

Exponentials. $\int e^u\, du, \quad \int a^u\, du.$

Trigonometric functions. $\displaystyle\int \sin u \, du, \quad \int \cos u \, du.$

Algebraic functions.

$$\int \frac{du}{\sqrt{1 - u^2}}, \quad \int \frac{du}{1 + u^2}, \quad \int \frac{du}{u\sqrt{u^2 - 1}}.$$

Of course, there are additional combinations of trigonometric functions such as $\int \sec^2 u \, du$, etc., which are integrable accidentally, so to speak.

What common types of functions are *not* included in the table?

Logarithms. $\displaystyle\int \ln u \, du, \quad \int \log_a u \, du.$

Trigonometric functions. $\displaystyle\int \tan u \, du, \quad \int \cot u \, du, \quad \int \sec u \, du, \quad \int \csc u \, du.$

Algebraic functions. $\displaystyle\int \frac{du}{a^2 + u^2}, \quad$ etc. with $\quad a^2 \neq 1.$

$$\int \sqrt{a^2 \pm u^2} \, du, \quad \int \sqrt{u^2 - a^2} \, du, \quad \text{etc.}$$

Inverse functions. $\displaystyle\int \sin^{-1} u \, du, \quad \int \tan^{-1} u \, du, \quad \text{etc.}$

We shall eventually see how to handle all of these and some others, but there are no methods which will solve *all* integration problems in terms of elementary functions.

PROBLEMS

Evaluate each of the following integrals by reducing the integrand to one of the standard forms (1 through 18). In each case, indicate what you have called u and refer by number to the standard formula used.

1. $\displaystyle\int \sqrt{2x + 3} \, dx$

2. $\displaystyle\int \frac{dx}{3x + 5}$

3. $\displaystyle\int \frac{dx}{(2x - 7)^2}$

4. $\displaystyle\int \frac{(x + 1) \, dx}{x^2 + 2x + 3}$

5. $\displaystyle\int \frac{\sin x \, dx}{2 + \cos x}$

6. $\displaystyle\int \tan^3 2x \sec^2 2x \, dx$

7. $\displaystyle\int \frac{x \, dx}{\sqrt{1 - 4x^2}}$

8. $\displaystyle\int x^{1/3}\sqrt{x^{4/3} - 1} \, dx$

9. $\displaystyle\int \frac{x\,dx}{(3x^2+4)^3}$

10. $\displaystyle\int x^2\sqrt{x^3+5}\,dx$

11. $\displaystyle\int \frac{x^2\,dx}{\sqrt{x^3+5}}$

12. $\displaystyle\int \frac{x\,dx}{4x^2+1}$

13. $\displaystyle\int e^{2x}\,dx$

14. $\displaystyle\int \sin x\,e^{\cos x}\,dx$

15. $\displaystyle\int \frac{dx}{e^{3x}}$

16. $\displaystyle\int \frac{e^{\sqrt{x+1}}}{\sqrt{x+1}}\,dx$

17. $\displaystyle\int \cos^2 x\,\sin x\,dx$

18. $\displaystyle\int \frac{\cos x\,dx}{\sin^3 x}$

19. $\displaystyle\int \cot^3 x\,\csc^2 x\,dx$

20. $\displaystyle\int \tan 3x\,\sec^2 3x\,dx$

21. $\displaystyle\int \frac{e^{2x}+e^{-2x}}{e^{2x}-e^{-2x}}\,dx$

22. $\displaystyle\int \sin 2x\,\cos^2 2x\,dx$

23. $\displaystyle\int (1+\cos\theta)^3\sin\theta\,d\theta$

24. $\displaystyle\int te^{-t^2}\,dt$

25. $\displaystyle\int \frac{\cos x\,dx}{\sin x}$

26. $\displaystyle\int \frac{\cos x\,dx}{1+\sin x}$

27. $\displaystyle\int \sec^3 x\,\tan x\,dx$

28. $\displaystyle\int \frac{\sin\theta\,d\theta}{\sqrt{1+\cos\theta}}$

29. $\displaystyle\int \sec^2 3x\,e^{\tan 3x}\,dx$

30. $\displaystyle\int \cos 2t\sqrt{4-\sin 2t}\,dt$

31. $\displaystyle\int \frac{1+\cos 2x}{\sin^2 2x}\,dx$

32. $\displaystyle\int \frac{\sin^2 2x}{1+\cos 2x}\,dx$

33. $\displaystyle\int \frac{\csc^2 2t}{\sqrt{1+\cot 2t}}\,dt$

34. $\displaystyle\int e^{3x}\,dx$

35. $\displaystyle\int \frac{e^{\tan^{-1}2t}}{1+4t^2}\,dt$

36. $\displaystyle\int xe^{-x^2}\,dx$

37. $\displaystyle\int 3^x\,dx$

38. $\displaystyle\int 10^{2x}\,dx$

39. Each of the following integrals may be easily evaluated for a particular numerical value of n. Choose this value and integrate. For example,

$$\int x^n\cos(x^2)\,dx$$

is easily evaluated for $n=1$:

$$\int x\cos(x^2)\,dx = \tfrac{1}{2}\sin(x^2)+C.$$

(a) $\int x^n \ln x \, dx,$ (b) $\int x^n \, e^{x^3} \, dx,$ (c) $\int x^n \sin \sqrt{x} \, dx.$

40. The integral $\int_a^\infty e^{-x^2} \, dx$ arises in statistics and elsewhere. It is defined to mean the same thing as

$$\lim_{b \to +\infty} \int_a^b e^{-x^2} \, dx.$$

Show that if $x > a \geq 1$, then $e^{-x^2} < e^{-ax}$. Hence, by comparing the integral from a to ∞ of e^{-x^2} with the integral of e^{-ax} and evaluating the latter integral, show that

$$\int_a^\infty e^{-x^2} \, dx < \frac{1}{a} e^{-a^2}, \quad \text{if} \quad a \geq 1.$$

9–2   Powers of trigonometric functions.   The formula

$$\int u^n \, du = \begin{cases} \dfrac{u^{n+1}}{n+1} + C, & n \neq -1 \\[2mm] \ln |u| + C, & n = -1 \end{cases}$$

may be used to evaluate certain integrals involving powers of the trigonometric functions, as illustrated by the examples that follow. The same methods work for powers of other functions. The reader should pay attention to the *methods* rather than trying to remember specific results.

EXAMPLE 1. $\int \sin^n ax \cos ax \, dx.$

Solution. If we let $u = \sin ax$, then

$$du = \cos ax \, d(ax) = a \cos ax \, dx,$$

so that we need only multiply the integral by unity in the form of a times $1/a$. Since a and $1/a$ are constants, we may write a inside the integral sign and $1/a$ in front of the integral sign to have

$$\int \sin^n ax \cos ax \, dx = \frac{1}{a} \int (\sin ax)^n (a \cos ax \, dx)$$

$$= \frac{1}{a} \int u^n \, du$$

$$= \begin{cases} \dfrac{1}{a} \dfrac{u^{n+1}}{n+1} + C, & n \neq -1 \\[2mm] \dfrac{1}{a} \ln |u| + C, & n = -1; \end{cases}$$

that is,

$$\int \sin^n ax \cos ax \, dx = \frac{\sin^{n+1} ax}{(n+1)a} + C, \quad n \neq -1 \tag{1a}$$

and if $n = -1$, we get

$$\int \cot ax \, dx = \frac{1}{a} \ln |\sin ax| + C. \tag{1b}$$

Note that the success of the method depended upon having $\cos ax$ to go with the dx as part of du.

EXAMPLE 2. $\displaystyle\int \sin^3 x \, dx.$

Solution. The method of the previous example does not work because there is no $\cos x$ to go with dx to give du if we try letting $u = \sin x$. But if we write

$$\sin^3 x = \sin^2 x \cdot \sin x = (1 - \cos^2 x) \cdot \sin x$$

and let

$$u = \cos x, \quad du = -\sin x \, dx,$$

we have

$$\int \sin^3 x \, dx = \int (1 - \cos^2 x) \cdot \sin x \, dx = \int (1 - u^2) \cdot (-du)$$

$$= \int (u^2 - 1) \, du = \tfrac{1}{3} u^3 - u + C = \tfrac{1}{3} \cos^3 x - \cos x + C.$$

This *method* may be applied whenever an *odd* power of $\sin x$ or $\cos x$ is to be integrated. For example, any positive odd power of $\cos x$ has the form

$$\cos^{2n+1} x = \cos^{2n} x \cdot \cos x = (\cos^2 x)^n \cdot \cos x = (1 - \sin^2 x)^n \cdot \cos x,$$

with n an integer ≥ 0. Then if we let $u = \sin x$, $du = \cos x \, dx$, we have

$$\int \cos^{2n+1} x \, dx = \int (1 - \sin^2 x)^n \cdot \cos x \, dx = \int (1 - u^2)^n \cdot du.$$

The expression $(1 - u^2)^n$ may now be expanded by the binomial theorem and the result evaluated as a sum of individual integrals of the type $\int u^m \, du$.

EXAMPLE 3. $\displaystyle\int \sec x \tan x \, dx.$

Solution. Of course this is a standard form already, so there is no real problem in finding an answer. But in trigonometry we often express all trigonometric

functions in terms of sines and cosines, and we now investigate what this does
to the integral in question.

$$\int \sec x \tan x \, dx = \int \frac{1}{\cos x} \frac{\sin x}{\cos x} \, dx = \int \frac{\sin x \, dx}{\cos^2 x}.$$

Taking a clue from the previous examples (keeping in mind du as well as u),
we let

$$u = \cos x, \qquad du = -\sin x \, dx,$$

and then

$$\int \frac{\sin x \, dx}{\cos^2 x} = \int \frac{-du}{u^2} = -\int u^{-2} \, du = \frac{-u^{-1}}{-1} + C = \frac{1}{u} + C$$

$$= \frac{1}{\cos x} + C = \sec x + C.$$

EXAMPLE 4. $\int \tan^4 x \, dx.$

Solution. This does not lend itself readily to the use of sines and cosines,
since both of them occur to even powers. We say: $u = \tan x$ would require
$du = \sec^2 x \, dx$. Is there some way to include $\sec^2 x$? Yes; there is an identity
involving tangents and secants. How does it go? Since

$$\sin^2 x + \cos^2 x = 1,$$

if we divide through by $\cos^2 x$ we get

$$\tan^2 x + 1 = \sec^2 x \qquad \text{or} \qquad \tan^2 x = \sec^2 x - 1.$$

Then

$$\int \tan^4 x \, dx = \int \tan^2 x \cdot \tan^2 x \, dx = \int \tan^2 x \cdot (\sec^2 x - 1) \, dx$$

$$= \int \tan^2 x \sec^2 x \, dx - \int \tan^2 x \, dx.$$

The first of these is all set. But how about the $\tan^2 x$? Oh, yes,

$$\tan^2 x = \sec^2 x - 1,$$

so

$$\int \tan^4 x \, dx = \int \tan^2 x \sec^2 x \, dx - \int \tan^2 x \, dx$$

$$= \int \tan^2 x \sec^2 x \, dx - \int (\sec^2 x - 1) \, dx$$

$$= \int \tan^2 x \sec^2 x \, dx - \int \sec^2 x \, dx + \int dx.$$

In the first two of these, let

$$u = \tan x, \qquad du = \sec^2 x \, dx$$

and have

$$\int u^2 \, du - \int du = \tfrac{1}{3}u^3 - u + C'.$$

The other is a standard form, so

$$\int \tan^4 x \, dx = \tfrac{1}{3}\tan^3 x - \tan x + x + C.$$

The *method* works for any *even* power of tan x, but what is still better is a *reduction formula* derived as follows:

$$\int \tan^n x \, dx = \int \tan^{n-2}x \, (\sec^2 x - 1) \, dx$$

$$= \int \tan^{n-2} x \sec^2 x \, dx - \int \tan^{n-2} x \, dx$$

$$= \frac{\tan^{n-1} x}{n - 1} - \int \tan^{n-2} x \, dx.$$

This reduces the problem of integrating $\tan^n x \, dx$ to the problem of integrating $\tan^{n-2} x \, dx$. Since this decreases the exponent on tan x by 2, a repetition with the same formula will reduce the exponent by 2 again, and so on. Applying this to the problem above, we have

$$n = 4: \quad \int \tan^4 x \, dx = \frac{\tan^3 x}{3} - \int \tan^2 x \, dx,$$

$$n = 2: \quad \int \tan^2 x \, dx = \frac{\tan x}{1} - \int \tan^0 x \, dx,$$

$$\int \tan^0 x \, dx = \int 1 \, dx = x + C.$$

Therefore,

$$\int \tan^4 x \, dx = \tfrac{1}{3}\tan^3 x - [\tan x - x + C]$$

$$= \tfrac{1}{3}\tan^3 x - \tan x + x + C'.$$

This reduction formula works whether the original exponent n is even or odd, but if the exponent is odd, say $2m + 1$, after m steps it will be reduced by $2m$, leaving

$$\int \tan x \, dx = \int \frac{\sin x}{\cos x} \, dx = -\int \frac{d\,(\cos x)}{\cos x} = -\ln |\cos x| + C \qquad (2)$$

as the final integral to be evaluated.

These examples illustrate how it is possible, by using the trigonometric identities

$$\sin^2 x + \cos^2 x = 1, \qquad \tan^2 x + 1 = \sec^2 x,$$

and others readily derived from these, to evaluate the integrals of

(a) *odd* powers of sin x or cos x,
(b) *any* integral powers of tan x (or cot x), and
(c) *even* powers of sec x (or csc x).

The even powers of sec x, say $\sec^{2n} x$, can all be reduced to powers of tan x by employing the substitution $\sec^2 x = 1 + \tan^2 x$, and then using the reduction formula for integrating powers of tan x after expanding $\sec^{2n} x = (1 + \tan^2 x)^n$ by the binomial theorem. But it is even simpler to use the method below:

$$\int \sec^{2n} x \, dx = \int \sec^{2n-2} x \sec^2 x \, dx = \int (\sec^2 x)^{n-1} \sec^2 x \, dx$$

$$= \int (1 + \tan^2 x)^{n-1} \sec^2 x \, dx$$

$$= \int (1 + u^2)^{n-1} \, du, \qquad (u = \tan x).$$

When $(1 + u^2)^{n-1}$ is expanded by the binomial theorem, the resulting polynomial in u may be integrated term by term.

For example,

$$\int \sec^6 x \, dx = \int \sec^4 x \cdot \sec^2 x \, dx = \int (1 + \tan^2 x)^2 \cdot \sec^2 x \, dx$$

$$= \int (1 + 2u^2 + u^4) \, du \qquad (u = \tan x)$$

$$= u + \frac{2u^3}{3} + \frac{u^5}{5} + C$$

$$= \tan x + 2 \frac{\tan^3 x}{3} + \frac{\tan^5 x}{5} + C.$$

EXAMPLE 5. $\displaystyle\int \sec x \, dx.$

Solution. This is hard to evaluate unless one has seen the following trick!

$$\sec x = \frac{\sec x \, (\tan x + \sec x)}{\sec x + \tan x} = \frac{\sec x \tan x + \sec^2 x}{\sec x + \tan x}.$$

In this form the numerator is the derivative of the denominator. Therefore

$$\int \sec x \, dx = \int \frac{\sec x \tan x + \sec^2 x}{\sec x + \tan x} \, dx$$

$$= \int \frac{du}{u} \qquad (u = \sec x + \tan x)$$

$$= \ln |u| + C.$$

That is,

$$\boxed{\int \sec x \, dx = \ln |\sec x + \tan x| + C.} \qquad (3)$$

PROBLEMS

1. $\int \sin t \sqrt{1 + \cos t} \, dt$

2. $\int \frac{\sin \theta \, d\theta}{2 - \cos \theta}$

3. $\int \frac{\sec^2 2x \, dx}{1 + \tan 2x}$

4. $\int \tan 3x \, dx$

5. $\int \cos^3 x \, dx$

6. $\int \tan^2 4\theta \, d\theta$

7. (a) $\int \sin^3 x \cos^2 x \, dx$

8. $\int \sec^n x \tan x \, dx$

(b) $\int \frac{\sin^3 x \, dx}{\cos^2 x}$

9. $\int \tan^n x \sec^2 x \, dx$

10. $\int \sin^n x \cos x \, dx$

11. $\int \cos^n x \sin x \, dx$

12. $\int \sin^2 3x \cos 3x \, dx$

13. $\int \cos^3 2x \sin 2x \, dx$

14. $\int \sec^4 3x \tan 3x \, dx$

15. $\int \sec^4 3x \, dx$

16. $\int \cos^3 2x \, dx$

17. $\int \tan^3 2x \, dx$

18. $\int \tan^3 x \sec x \, dx$

19. $\int \sin^3 x \, dx$

20. $\int \frac{\cos x \, dx}{(1 + \sin x)^2}$

21. $\int \frac{\sec^2 x \, dx}{2 + \tan x}$

22. $\int \frac{\cos^3 t \, dt}{\sin^2 t}$

23. $\displaystyle\int \frac{e^x \, dx}{1 + e^x}$

24. $\displaystyle\int (\ln ax)^n \, \frac{dx}{x}$

25. $\displaystyle\int \frac{dx}{x \ln 3x}$

26. $\displaystyle\int \cot^3 x \, dx$

27. $\displaystyle\int \csc^3 2t \cot 2t \, dt$

28. $\displaystyle\int \csc^4 x \, dx$

29. Derive a reduction formula for $\int \cot^n ax \, dx$ and use the result to evaluate $\int \cot^4 3x \, dx$.

9–3   Even powers of sines and cosines.   In Article 9–2 we saw how we could evaluate integrals of odd powers of sines and cosines. Indeed, any integral of the form

$$\int \sin^m x \cos^n x \, dx \tag{1}$$

in which at least one of the exponents m and n is a positive odd integer may be evaluated by these methods.

EXAMPLE 1. $\displaystyle\int \cos^{2/3} x \sin^5 x \, dx.$

Solution.   Here we have $\sin x$ to an *odd* power. So we put one factor of $\sin x$ with dx and the remaining sine factors, namely $\sin^4 x$, can be expressed in terms of $\cos x$ without introducing any square roots, as follows:

$$\sin^4 x = (\sin^2 x)^2 = (1 - \cos^2 x)^2.$$

The $\sin x$ goes well with dx when we take

$$u = \cos x, \qquad du = -\sin x \, dx$$

and evaluate the integral as follows:

$$\int \cos^{2/3} x \sin^5 x \, dx = \int \cos^{2/3} x \, (1 - \cos^2 x)^2 \sin x \, dx$$

$$= \int u^{2/3} (1 - u^2)^2 (-du)$$

$$= -\int (u^{2/3} - 2u^{8/3} + u^{14/3}) \, du$$

$$= -[\tfrac{3}{5} u^{5/3} - \tfrac{6}{11} u^{11/3} + \tfrac{3}{17} u^{17/3}] + C$$

$$= -\cos^{5/3} x [\tfrac{3}{5} - \tfrac{6}{11} \cos^2 x + \tfrac{3}{17} \cos^4 x] + C.$$

If both the exponents m and n in the integral (1) are even integers, the method illustrated above won't work. So we use one or both of the following trigonometric identities:

$$\sin^2 A = \tfrac{1}{2}(1 - \cos 2A), \qquad (2a)$$

$$\cos^2 A = \tfrac{1}{2}(1 + \cos 2A). \qquad (2b)$$

These identities may be derived very quickly by adding or subtracting the equations

$$\cos^2 A + \sin^2 A = 1, \qquad \cos^2 A - \sin^2 A = \cos 2A,$$

and dividing by two.

EXAMPLE 2.

$$\int \cos^4 x \, dx = \int (\cos^2 x)^2 \, dx = \int \tfrac{1}{4}(1 + \cos 2x)^2 \, dx \qquad (a)$$

$$= \tfrac{1}{4}\int (1 + 2\cos 2x + \cos^2 2x) \, dx \qquad (b)$$

$$= \tfrac{1}{4}\int [1 + 2\cos 2x + \tfrac{1}{2}(1 + \cos 4x)] \, dx$$

$$= \tfrac{3}{8}x + \tfrac{1}{4}\sin 2x + \tfrac{1}{32}\sin 4x + C.$$

In (a), we used Eq. (2b) with $A = x$, and in (b), we used Eq. (2b) with $A = 2x$. The final integrations involve

$$\int \cos ax \, dx = \frac{1}{a}\int \cos ax \, d(ax) = \frac{1}{a}\sin ax + C'.$$

Remark. An integral such as

$$\int \sin^2 x \cos^4 x \, dx,$$

which involves even powers of both $\sin x$ and $\cos x$, can be changed to a sum of integrals each of which involves only powers of one of them. Then these may be handled by the method illustrated above.

EXAMPLE 3.

$$\int \sin^2 x \cos^4 x \, dx = \int (1 - \cos^2 x) \cos^4 x \, dx$$

$$= \int \cos^4 x \, dx - \int \cos^6 x \, dx.$$

We evaluated $\int \cos^4 x \, dx$ above, and

$$\int \cos^6 x \, dx = \int (\cos^2 x)^3 \, dx = \tfrac{1}{8} \int (1 + \cos 2x)^3 \, dx$$

$$= \tfrac{1}{8} \int (1 + 3 \cos 2x + 3 \cos^2 2x + \cos^3 2x) \, dx.$$

We now know how to handle each term of this integral. The reader may supply the details and show that the result is

$$\int \cos^6 x \, dx = \tfrac{5}{16}x + \tfrac{1}{4} \sin 2x + \tfrac{3}{64} \sin 4x - \tfrac{1}{48} \sin^3 2x + C.$$

PROBLEMS

Evaluate the following integrals:

1. $\displaystyle\int \sin^2 x \cos^3 x \, dx$

2. $\displaystyle\int \frac{\sin^3 x \, dx}{\cos^2 x}$

3. $\displaystyle\int \sin^2 2t \, dt$

4. $\displaystyle\int \cos^2 3\theta \, d\theta$

5. $\displaystyle\int \sin^4 ax \, dx$

6. $\displaystyle\int \sin^2 y \cos^2 y \, dy$

7. $\displaystyle\int \frac{dx}{\cos^2 x}$

8. $\displaystyle\int \frac{dx}{\sin^4 x}$

9. $\displaystyle\int \frac{\cos 2t \, dt}{\sin^4 2t}$

10. $\displaystyle\int \sin^6 x \, dx$

9–4   Integrals involving $\sqrt{a^2 - u^2}$, $\sqrt{a^2 + u^2}$, $\sqrt{u^2 - a^2}$, $a^2 + u^2$, **and** $a^2 - u^2$. Some of these follow directly from the corresponding integral formulas with $a = 1$ listed in Article 9–1. For example, we have

$$\int \frac{du}{1 + u^2} = \tan^{-1} u + C, \tag{1}$$

and to evaluate

$$\int \frac{du}{a^2 + u^2} \tag{2}$$

we factor a^2 out of the denominator and proceed as follows:

$$\int \frac{du}{a^2 + u^2} = \int \frac{du}{a^2 \left[1 + \left(\frac{u}{a}\right)^2\right]} = \frac{1}{a^2} \int \frac{a \, d\left(\frac{u}{a}\right)}{1 + \left(\frac{u}{a}\right)^2} = \frac{1}{a} \int \frac{dz}{1 + z^2}$$

$$= \frac{1}{a} \tan^{-1} z + C = \frac{1}{a} \tan^{-1} \frac{u}{a} + C. \qquad \left[z = \frac{u}{a}\right].$$

That is,

$$\int \frac{du}{a^2 + u^2} = \frac{1}{a} \tan^{-1} \frac{u}{a} + C. \tag{3}$$

The essential feature here was the introduction of a new variable by means of the substitution

$$z = \frac{u}{a} \qquad \text{or} \qquad u = az.$$

Such a substitution allows the a terms to be brought outside the integral sign, and the resulting integral may then match one of the inverse trigonometric formulas.

An alternative approach will show, however, that one may bypass the job of learning these formulas. In addition, this method, which we shall soon illustrate, permits the evaluation of many additional integrals.

The method leans primarily upon the following identities.

$$\begin{aligned}
1 - \sin^2 \theta &= \cos^2 \theta, \\
1 + \tan^2 \theta &= \sec^2 \theta, \\
\sec^2 \theta - 1 &= \tan^2 \theta.
\end{aligned} \tag{4}$$

These identities may be multiplied by a^2, with the result that the substitutions listed below have the following effects:

$$\left.\begin{aligned}
\text{(a)} \quad u &= a \sin \theta \quad \text{replaces} \quad a^2 - u^2 \text{ by } a^2 \cos^2 \theta. \\
\text{(b)} \quad u &= a \tan \theta \quad \text{replaces} \quad a^2 + u^2 \text{ by } a^2 \sec^2 \theta. \\
\text{(c)} \quad u &= a \sec \theta \quad \text{replaces} \quad u^2 - a^2 \text{ by } a^2 \tan^2 \theta.
\end{aligned}\right\} \tag{5}$$

It is thus seen that corresponding to each of the *binomial* expressions $a^2 - u^2$, $a^2 + u^2$, and $u^2 - a^2$, we have a substitution which replaces the binomial by a single squared term. The particular substitution to use will depend upon the form of the integrand. In the examples that follow, a is a positive constant.

EXAMPLE 1. $$\int \frac{du}{\sqrt{a^2 - u^2}}, \qquad a > 0.$$

Solution. We try the substitution (5a):

$$u = a \sin \theta, \qquad du = a \cos \theta \, d\theta,$$

$$a^2 - u^2 = a^2(1 - \sin^2 \theta) = a^2 \cos^2 \theta.$$

Then

$$\int \frac{du}{\sqrt{a^2 - u^2}} = \int \frac{a \cos \theta \, d\theta}{\sqrt{a^2 \cos^2 \theta}} = \int \frac{a \cos \theta \, d\theta}{\pm a \cos \theta} \quad (\pm \text{ depends on sign of } \cos \theta)$$

$$= \pm \int d\theta = \pm(\theta + C).$$

Since $\sin \theta = u/a$,

$$\theta = \sin^{-1} \frac{u}{a}$$

and

$$\int \frac{du}{\sqrt{a^2 - u^2}} = \pm \left(\sin^{-1} \frac{u}{a} + C \right).$$

Using only the *principal value* of $\sin^{-1} u/a$ means that θ will lie between $-\pi/2$ and $\pi/2$, hence $\cos \theta \geq 0$ and the ambiguous sign is $+$; that is,

$$\boxed{\int \frac{du}{\sqrt{a^2 - u^2}} = \sin^{-1} \frac{u}{a} + C.}$$ (6)

EXAMPLE 2. $$\int \frac{du}{\sqrt{a^2 + u^2}}, \quad a > 0.$$

Solution. This time we try

$$u = a \tan \theta,$$

$$du = a \sec^2 \theta \, d\theta,$$

$$a^2 + u^2 = a^2(1 + \tan^2 \theta) = a^2 \sec^2 \theta.$$

Then

$$\int \frac{du}{\sqrt{a^2 + u^2}} = \int \frac{a \sec^2 \theta \, d\theta}{\sqrt{a^2 \sec^2 \theta}}$$

$$= \pm \int \sec \theta \, d\theta \quad (\pm \text{ depends on sign of } \sec \theta).$$

By Eq. (3), Article 9–2, we know that

$$\int \sec \theta \, d\theta = \ln |\sec \theta + \tan \theta| + C.$$

If we take

$$\theta = \tan^{-1} \frac{u}{a}, \quad -\frac{\pi}{2} < \theta < \frac{\pi}{2},$$

then $\sec\theta$ is positive, and

$$
\begin{aligned}
\int \frac{du}{\sqrt{a^2 + u^2}} &= \int \sec\theta \, d\theta \\
&= \ln|\sec\theta + \tan\theta| + C \\
&= \ln\left|\frac{\sqrt{a^2 + u^2}}{a} + \frac{u}{a}\right| + C \\
&= \ln|\sqrt{a^2 + u^2} + u| + C',
\end{aligned}
\tag{7}
$$

where

$$
C' = C - \ln a.
$$

EXAMPLE 3. $\qquad \displaystyle\int \frac{du}{\sqrt{u^2 - a^2}}, \qquad |u| > a > 0.$

Solution. We try the substitution

$$
u = a\sec\theta,
$$

$$
du = a\sec\theta\tan\theta \, d\theta,
$$

$$
u^2 - a^2 = a^2(\sec^2\theta - 1) = a^2\tan^2\theta.
$$

Then

$$
\int \frac{du}{\sqrt{u^2 - a^2}} = \int \frac{a\sec\theta\tan\theta \, d\theta}{\sqrt{a^2\tan^2\theta}} = \pm\int\sec\theta \, d\theta \quad (\pm \text{ depends on sign of } \tan\theta).
$$

If we take

$$
\theta = \sec^{-1}\frac{u}{a}, \qquad 0 \le \theta \le \pi,
$$

then

$$
\tan\theta \text{ is positive if } 0 < \theta < \pi/2,
$$

$$
\tan\theta \text{ is negative if } \pi/2 < \theta < \pi,
$$

and, from Eq. (3) of Article 9–2,

$$
\pm\int\sec\theta \, d\theta = \pm\ln|\sec\theta + \tan\theta| + C.
$$

When $\tan\theta$ is positive, we must use the plus sign; when $\tan\theta$ is negative, the minus sign. Moreover,

$$
\sec\theta = \frac{u}{a}, \qquad \tan\theta = \pm\frac{\sqrt{u^2 - a^2}}{a}.
$$

So we have

$$\int \frac{du}{\sqrt{u^2 - a^2}} = \pm \ln \left| \frac{u}{a} \pm \frac{\sqrt{u^2 - a^2}}{a} \right| + C$$

$$= \begin{cases} \ln \left| \frac{u}{a} + \frac{\sqrt{u^2 - a^2}}{a} \right| + C \\ \text{or} \\ -\ln \left| \frac{u}{a} - \frac{\sqrt{u^2 - a^2}}{a} \right| + C. \end{cases}$$

But the two forms are actually equal, because

$$-\ln \left| \frac{u}{a} - \frac{\sqrt{u^2 - a^2}}{a} \right| = \ln \left| \frac{a}{u - \sqrt{u^2 - a^2}} \right|$$

$$= \ln \left| \frac{a(u + \sqrt{u^2 - a^2})}{(u - \sqrt{u^2 - a^2})(u + \sqrt{u^2 - a^2})} \right|$$

$$= \ln \left| \frac{a(u + \sqrt{u^2 - a^2})}{a^2} \right|$$

$$= \ln \left| \frac{u + \sqrt{u^2 - a^2}}{a} \right|.$$

Therefore

$$\boxed{\int \frac{du}{\sqrt{u^2 - a^2}} = \ln |u + \sqrt{u^2 - a^2}| + C',} \qquad (8)$$

where we have replaced $C - \ln a$ by C' in this final form.

EXAMPLE 4. $\int \dfrac{du}{a^2 + u^2}, \qquad a > 0.$

Solution. We try

$$u = a \tan \theta, \qquad du = a \sec^2 \theta \, d\theta,$$

$$a^2 + u^2 = a^2(1 + \tan^2 \theta) = a^2 \sec^2 \theta.$$

Then

$$\int \frac{du}{a^2 + u^2} = \int \frac{a \sec^2 \theta \, d\theta}{a^2 \sec^2 \theta}$$

$$= \frac{1}{a} \int d\theta = \frac{1}{a} \theta + C.$$

Since $u = a \tan \theta$,

$$\tan \theta = \frac{u}{a}, \qquad \theta = \tan^{-1} \frac{u}{a},$$

and

$$\int \frac{du}{a^2 + u^2} = \frac{1}{a} \tan^{-1} \frac{u}{a} + C. \tag{9}$$

EXAMPLE 5. $\qquad \displaystyle\int \frac{x^2 \, dx}{\sqrt{9 - x^2}}.$

Solution. If we substitute

$$x = 3 \sin \theta, \qquad \frac{-\pi}{2} < \theta < \frac{\pi}{2},$$

$$dx = 3 \cos \theta \, d\theta,$$

$$9 - x^2 = 9(1 - \sin^2 \theta) = 9 \cos^2 \theta,$$

then we find

$$\int \frac{x^2 \, dx}{\sqrt{9 - x^2}} = \int \frac{9 \sin^2 \theta \cdot 3 \cos \theta \, d\theta}{3 \cos \theta} = 9 \int \sin^2 \theta \, d\theta.$$

This is considerably simpler than the integral we started with. To evaluate it, we make use of the identity

$$\sin^2 \theta = \tfrac{1}{2}(1 - \cos 2\theta).$$

Then

$$\int \sin^2 \theta \, d\theta = \tfrac{1}{2} \int (1 - \cos 2\theta) \, d\theta = \tfrac{1}{2}[\theta - \tfrac{1}{2} \sin 2\theta] + C$$

$$= \tfrac{1}{2}[\theta - \sin \theta \cos \theta] + C.$$

Substituting this above, we get

$$\int \frac{x^2 \, dx}{\sqrt{9 - x^2}} = \frac{9}{2} [\theta - \sin \theta \cos \theta] + C$$

$$= \frac{9}{2} \left[\sin^{-1} \frac{x}{3} - \frac{x\sqrt{9 - x^2}}{9} \right] + C.$$

The trigonometric substitutions (a), (b), and (c) of Eq. (5) can be easily remembered by thinking of the theorem of Pythagoras and taking a and u as two of the sides and θ as an angle in a right triangle. Thus $\sqrt{a^2 - u^2}$ suggests a as hypotenuse and u as a leg, $\sqrt{a^2 + u^2}$ suggests a and u as the legs, and $\sqrt{u^2 - a^2}$ suggests u as hypotenuse and a as a leg. These situations are shown in Fig. 9–1.

The trigonometric identities, Eqs. (4), are simply equivalent expres-

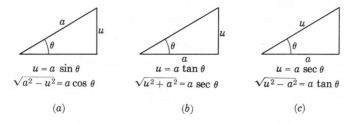

$$u = a \sin \theta$$
$$\sqrt{a^2 - u^2} = a \cos \theta$$

$$u = a \tan \theta$$
$$\sqrt{u^2 + a^2} = a \sec \theta$$

$$u = a \sec \theta$$
$$\sqrt{u^2 - a^2} = a \tan \theta$$

(a)   (b)   (c)

Figure 9–1

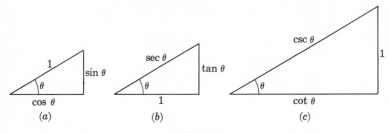

(a)   (b)   (c)

Figure 9–2

sions of the theorem of Pythagoras applied to the right triangles in Fig. 9–2. The triangles in Figs. 9–2(b) and (c) are obtained from the basic triangle in Fig. 9–2(a) by dividing its sides all by $\cos \theta$ or $\sin \theta$ respectively to obtain similar triangles.

PROBLEMS

Evaluate the following integrals:

1. $\displaystyle\int_0^{0.6a} \frac{x\, dx}{\sqrt{a^2 - x^2}}$

2. $\displaystyle\int \frac{dx}{\sqrt{1 - 4x^2}}$

3. $\displaystyle\int_0^a \sqrt{a^2 - x^2}\, dx$

4. $\displaystyle\int \frac{dx}{\sqrt{4 - (x-1)^2}}$

5. $\displaystyle\int \sec 2t\, dt$

6. $\displaystyle\int_0^2 \frac{dx}{\sqrt{4 + x^2}}$

7. $\displaystyle\int_0^1 \frac{dx}{\sqrt{4 - x^2}}$

8. $\displaystyle\int \frac{x\, dx}{\sqrt{4 + x^2}}$

9. $\displaystyle\int_0^2 \frac{x\, dx}{4 + x^2}$

10. $\displaystyle\int_0^2 \frac{dx}{4 + x^2}$

11. $\displaystyle\int_0^1 \frac{dx}{4 - x^2}$

12. $\displaystyle\int \csc u \, du$

13. $\displaystyle\int \frac{dx}{x\sqrt{a^2 + x^2}}$

14. $\displaystyle\int \frac{x + 1}{\sqrt{4 - x^2}} \, dx$

15. $\displaystyle\int \frac{dx}{\sqrt{2 - 5x^2}}$

16. $\displaystyle\int \frac{\sin \theta \, d\theta}{\sqrt{2 - \cos^2 \theta}}$

17. $\displaystyle\int \frac{dx}{x\sqrt{x^2 - a^2}}$

18. $\displaystyle\int \frac{dx}{x\sqrt{a^2 - x^2}}$

19. $\displaystyle\int \frac{dx}{(a^2 - x^2)^{3/2}}$

20. $\displaystyle\int \frac{dx}{(a^2 + x^2)^2}$

9–5   Integrals involving $ax^2 + bx + c$.   The general quadratic

$$f(x) = ax^2 + bx + c, \qquad a \neq 0 \tag{1}$$

can be reduced to the form $a(u^2 + B)$ by completing the square as follows:

$$ax^2 + bx + c = a\left(x^2 + \frac{b}{a}x\right) + c$$

$$= a\left(x^2 + \frac{b}{a}x + \frac{b^2}{4a^2}\right) + c - \frac{b^2}{4a}$$

$$= a\left(x + \frac{b}{2a}\right)^2 + \frac{4ac - b^2}{4a},$$

and then substituting

$$u = x + \frac{b}{2a}, \qquad B = \frac{4ac - b^2}{4a^2}. \tag{2}$$

When the integrand involves the square root of $f(x) = ax^2 + bx + c$, we restrict attention to the case where $f(x)$ is not negative. If a is negative and B is positive, the square root is imaginary. We disregard this case and consider

$$\sqrt{a(u^2 + B)}$$

1. when a is positive, and
2. when a and B are both negative.

In the first case the relation

$$\sqrt{a(u^2 + B)} = \sqrt{a}\sqrt{u^2 + B}$$

allows us to reduce the problem to a consideration of $\sqrt{u^2 + B}$, which we handle by the methods of Article 9–4. In the second case, when a and B are both negative, then $-a$ and $-B$ are positive and

$$\sqrt{a(u^2 + B)} = \sqrt{-a(-B - u^2)}$$

$$= \sqrt{-a}\sqrt{-B - u^2} \qquad (-a > 0, -B > 0),$$

and taking $-B = A^2$, say, we consider $\sqrt{A^2 - u^2}$ as in Article 9–4.

When the integrand does not involve an even root of $f(x)$, there need be no restriction on the signs of a and B. In these cases also, we try to make use of the trigonometric substitutions of the previous section, or we simply apply the integration formulas derived there.

EXAMPLE 1.
$$\int \frac{dx}{\sqrt{2x - x^2}}.$$

Solution. The algebraic transformations proceed as follows:

$$\sqrt{2x - x^2} = \sqrt{-(x^2 - 2x)} = \sqrt{-(x^2 - 2x + 1) + 1}$$

$$= \sqrt{1 - u^2}, \qquad (u = x - 1).$$

Then, with $u = x - 1$,

$$du = dx$$

and

$$\int \frac{dx}{\sqrt{2x - x^2}} = \int \frac{du}{\sqrt{1 - u^2}} = \sin^{-1} u + C;$$

that is,

$$\int \frac{dx}{\sqrt{2x - x^2}} = \sin^{-1} (x - 1) + C.$$

EXAMPLE 2.
$$\int \frac{dx}{4x^2 + 4x + 2}.$$

Solution. Again we start with the algebraic transformations:

$$4x^2 + 4x + 2 = 4(x^2 + x) + 2$$

$$= 4(x^2 + x + \tfrac{1}{4}) + (2 - \tfrac{4}{4}) = 4u^2 + 1, \qquad (u = x + \tfrac{1}{2}).$$

Then we let

$$u = x + \tfrac{1}{2}, \qquad du = dx,$$

and

$$\int \frac{dx}{4x^2 + 4x + 2} = \int \frac{du}{4u^2 + 1}$$

$$= \frac{1}{4} \int \frac{du}{u^2 + \frac{1}{4}}$$

$$= \frac{1}{4} \int \frac{du}{u^2 + a^2} \quad (a = \tfrac{1}{2})$$

$$= \frac{1}{4} \frac{1}{a} \tan^{-1} \frac{u}{a} + C$$

$$= \frac{1}{2} \tan^{-1} (2x + 1) + C.$$

EXAMPLE 3. $\displaystyle \int \frac{(x + 1)\, dx}{\sqrt{2x^2 - 6x + 4}}.$

Solution. The quadratic part may be reduced as follows:

$$2x^2 - 6x + 4 = 2(x^2 - 3x) + 4 = 2(x^2 - 3x + \tfrac{9}{4}) + 4 - \tfrac{9}{2} = 2(u^2 - a^2)$$

with

$$u = x - \tfrac{3}{2}, \qquad a = \tfrac{1}{2}.$$

Then

$$x = u + \tfrac{3}{2}, \qquad dx = du, \qquad x + 1 = u + \tfrac{5}{2},$$

and

$$\int \frac{(x + 1)\, dx}{\sqrt{2x^2 - 6x + 4}} = \int \frac{(u + \tfrac{5}{2})\, du}{\sqrt{2(u^2 - a^2)}}$$

$$= \frac{1}{\sqrt{2}} \int \frac{u\, du}{\sqrt{u^2 - a^2}} + \frac{5}{2\sqrt{2}} \int \frac{du}{\sqrt{u^2 - a^2}}.$$

In the former of these, we let

$$z = u^2 - a^2, \qquad dz = 2u\, du, \qquad u\, du = \tfrac{1}{2}\, dz,$$

and to the latter we apply Eq. (8), Article 9–4. That is,

$$\frac{1}{\sqrt{2}} \int \frac{u\, du}{\sqrt{u^2 - a^2}} = \frac{1}{2\sqrt{2}} \int \frac{dz}{\sqrt{z}} = \frac{1}{2\sqrt{2}} \int z^{-(1/2)}\, dz = \frac{1}{2\sqrt{2}} \frac{z^{1/2}}{\frac{1}{2}} + C_1$$

$$= \sqrt{\frac{u^2 - a^2}{2}} + C_1$$

and

$$\frac{5}{2\sqrt{2}} \int \frac{du}{\sqrt{u^2 - a^2}} = \frac{5}{2\sqrt{2}} \ln |u + \sqrt{u^2 - a^2}| + C_2,$$

so that

$$\int \frac{(x+1)\,dx}{\sqrt{2x^2 - 6x + 4}} = \sqrt{\frac{u^2 - a^2}{2}} + \frac{5}{2\sqrt{2}} \ln |u + \sqrt{u^2 - a^2}| + C$$

$$= \sqrt{\frac{x^2 - 3x + 2}{2}} + \frac{5}{2\sqrt{2}} \ln |x - \frac{3}{2} + \sqrt{x^2 - 3x + 2}| + C.$$

PROBLEMS

1. $\displaystyle\int_1^3 \frac{dx}{x^2 - 2x + 5}$

2. $\displaystyle\int \frac{x\,dx}{\sqrt{x^2 - 2x + 5}}$

3. $\displaystyle\int \frac{(x+1)\,dx}{\sqrt{2x - x^2}}$

4. $\displaystyle\int \frac{(x-1)\,dx}{\sqrt{x^2 - 4x + 3}}$

5. $\displaystyle\int \frac{x\,dx}{\sqrt{5 + 4x - x^2}}$

6. $\displaystyle\int \frac{dx}{\sqrt{x^2 - 2x - 8}}$

7. $\displaystyle\int \frac{(1-x)\,dx}{\sqrt{8 + 2x - x^2}}$

8. $\displaystyle\int \frac{x\,dx}{\sqrt{x^2 + 4x + 5}}$

9. $\displaystyle\int \frac{x\,dx}{x^2 + 4x + 5}$

10. $\displaystyle\int \frac{(2x+3)\,dx}{4x^2 + 4x + 5}$

9–6   Integration by the method of partial fractions.   In algebra we learned how to combine fractions over a common denominator. In integration, it is desirable to reverse the process and split a fraction into a sum of fractions having simpler denominators. The technique of doing this is known as the *method of partial fractions.*

EXAMPLE 1.

$$\frac{2}{x+1} + \frac{3}{x-3} = \frac{2(x-3) + 3(x+1)}{(x+1)(x-3)} = \frac{5x-3}{(x+1)(x-3)}.$$

The reverse process consists in finding constants A and B such that

$$\frac{5x-3}{(x+1)(x-3)} = \frac{A}{x+1} + \frac{B}{x-3}.$$

(Pretend, for a moment, that we don't know that $A = 2$, $B = 3$ will work.

We call A and B *undetermined coefficients*.) Clearing of fractions, we have

$$5x - 3 = A(x - 3) + B(x + 1)$$
$$= (A + B)x - 3A + B.$$

This will be an identity in x if and only if coefficients of like powers of x on the two sides of the equation are equal:

$$A + B = 5, \quad -3A + B = -3.$$

These two equations in two unknowns determine

$$A = 2, \quad B = 3.$$

More generally, suppose we wish to separate a rational function

$$\frac{f(x)}{g(x)} \tag{1}$$

into a sum of partial fractions. Success in doing so hinges upon two things:

1. The degree of $f(x)$ should be less than the degree of $g(x)$. If this is not the case, we first perform a long division, then work with the remainder term. This remainder can always be put into the required form.

2. The factors of $g(x)$ should be known. Theoretically, any polynomial $g(x)$ with real coefficients can be expressed as a product of real linear and quadratic factors. In practice, it may be difficult to perform the factorization.

Let us assume that these two conditions prevail. Let $x - r$ be a linear factor of $g(x)$. Suppose $(x - r)^m$ is the highest power of $x - r$ that divides $g(x)$. Then, to this factor, assign the sum of m partial fractions, as follows:

$$\frac{A_1}{x - r} + \frac{A_2}{(x - r)^2} + \cdots + \frac{A_m}{(x - r)^m}.$$

Next, let $x^2 + px + q$ be a quadratic factor of $g(x)$. Suppose

$$(x^2 + px + q)^n$$

is the highest power of this factor that divides $g(x)$. Then, to this factor, assign the sum of n partial fractions:

$$\frac{B_1 x + C_1}{x^2 + px + q} + \frac{B_2 x + C_2}{(x^2 + px + q)^2} + \cdots + \frac{B_n x + C_n}{(x^2 + px + q)^n}.$$

Do this for each of the distinct linear and quadratic factors of $g(x)$. Then set the original fraction $f(x)/g(x)$ equal to the sum of all these partial fractions. Clear the resulting equation of fractions and arrange the terms in decreasing powers of x. Equate the coefficients of corresponding powers of x, and solve the resulting equations for the undetermined coefficients.

EXAMPLE 2. Express $\dfrac{4 - 2x}{(x^2 + 1)(x - 1)^2}$ as a sum of partial fractions.

Solution. Let

$$\frac{-2x + 4}{(x^2 + 1)(x - 1)^2} = \frac{Ax + B}{x^2 + 1} + \frac{C}{x - 1} + \frac{D}{(x - 1)^2}.$$

Then

$$-2x + 4 = (Ax + B)(x - 1)^2 + C(x - 1)(x^2 + 1) + D(x^2 + 1)$$
$$= (A + C)x^3 + (-2A + B - C + D)x^2 + (A - 2B + C)x$$
$$+ (B - C + D).$$

In order that this shall be an identity in x, it is both necessary and sufficient that the coefficient of each power of x which occurs should be the same on the left side of the equation as it is on the right side. Imposing this condition successively upon the coefficients of x^3, x^2, x, and x^0 respectively, we have

$$0 = A + C,$$
$$0 = -2A + B - C + D,$$
$$-2 = A - 2B + C,$$
$$4 = B - C + D.$$

If we subtract the second equation from the fourth, we can solve for A:

$$2A = 4, \qquad A = 2.$$

Then from the first equation, we have

$$C = -A = -2.$$

Knowing A and C, we find B from the third equation,

$$B = 1.$$

Finally, from the fourth equation, we have

$$D = 4 - B + C = 1.$$

Hence

$$\frac{-2x + 4}{(x^2 + 1)(x - 1)^2} = \frac{2x + 1}{x^2 + 1} - \frac{2}{x - 1} + \frac{1}{(x - 1)^2}.$$

EXAMPLE 3. Evaluate

$$\int \frac{x^5 - x^4 - 3x + 5}{x^4 - 2x^3 + 2x^2 - 2x + 1}\, dx.$$

Solution. The integrand is a fraction, but not a proper fraction. Hence we divide first, thus obtaining

$$\frac{x^5 - x^4 - 3x + 5}{x^4 - 2x^3 + 2x^2 - 2x + 1} = x + 1 + \frac{-2x + 4}{x^4 - 2x^3 + 2x^2 - 2x + 1}. \quad (2)$$

The denominator factors as follows:

$$x^4 - 2x^3 + 2x^2 - 2x + 1 = (x^2 + 1)(x - 1)^2.$$

By the result of Example 2, we have for the remainder term

$$\frac{-2x + 4}{(x^2 + 1)(x - 1)^2} = \frac{2x + 1}{x^2 + 1} - \frac{2}{x - 1} + \frac{1}{(x - 1)^2}. \quad (3)$$

Hence, substituting from (3) into (2), multiplying by dx, and integrating, we have

$$\int \frac{x^5 - x^4 - 3x + 5}{x^4 - 2x^3 + 2x^2 - 2x + 1}\, dx$$

$$= \int \left[x + 1 + \frac{2x + 1}{x^2 + 1} - \frac{2}{x - 1} + \frac{1}{(x - 1)^2} \right] dx$$

$$= \frac{x^2}{2} + x + \ln(x^2 + 1) + \tan^{-1} x - 2 \ln |x - 1|$$

$$- \frac{1}{x - 1} + K.$$

In theory, any rational function of x can be integrated by the method of partial fractions. Once the necessary algebra has been done, the problem reduces to that of evaluating integrals of the following two types:

$$\int \frac{dx}{(x - r)^h}, \quad (4a)$$

$$\int \frac{(ax + b)\, dx}{(x^2 + px + q)^k}. \quad (4b)$$

The first of these becomes simply $\int u^{-h}\, du$ when we let $u = x - r$. In the second type it is preferable to complete the square in the denominator:

$$x^2 + px + q = \left(x + \frac{p}{2}\right)^2 + q - \frac{p^2}{4},$$

and then let

$$u = x + \frac{p}{2}, \qquad c^2 = q - \frac{p^2}{4}.$$

Then

$$ax + b = a\left(u - \frac{p}{2}\right) + b = au + b', \qquad b' = b - a\frac{p}{2},$$

and we consider

$$\int \frac{au + b'}{(u^2 + c^2)^k}\, du = \frac{a}{2} \int (u^2 + c^2)^{-k}(2u\, du) + b' \int \frac{du}{(u^2 + c^2)^k}. \quad (5)$$

The first integral on the right in (5) readily yields to the substitution $z = u^2 + c^2$. In the second integral, we let

$$u = c \tan \theta, \qquad du = c \sec^2 \theta\, d\theta, \qquad u^2 + c^2 = c^2 \sec^2 \theta,$$

and obtain

$$\int \frac{du}{(u^2 + c^2)^k} = c^{1-2k} \int \cos^{2k-2} \theta\, d\theta \qquad \left(\theta = \tan^{-1}\frac{u}{c}\right). \quad (6)$$

In the next article we shall obtain a reduction formula for $\int \cos^n \theta\, d\theta$, which may be used to evaluate the integral in (6). The trigonometric identity

$$\cos^2 \theta = \frac{1 + \cos 2\theta}{2} \quad (7)$$

may also be used to advantage.

EXAMPLE 4. Evaluate

$$\int \frac{dx}{1 - x^2}.$$

Solution. By partial fractions,

$$\frac{1}{1 - x^2} = \frac{A}{1 - x} + \frac{B}{1 + x},$$

$$1 = A(1 + x) + B(1 - x)$$

$$= A + B + (A - B)x,$$

$$A + B = 1, \qquad A - B = 0,$$

$$A = B = \tfrac{1}{2}.$$

Therefore,

$$\int \frac{1}{1-x^2}\, dx = \int \left(\frac{\frac{1}{2}}{1-x} + \frac{\frac{1}{2}}{1+x} \right) dx$$

$$= -\tfrac{1}{2}\ln|1-x| + \tfrac{1}{2}\ln|1+x| + C$$

$$= \frac{1}{2}\ln \left| \frac{1+x}{1-x} \right| + C. \tag{8}$$

EXAMPLE 5. Evaluate $\int \sec\theta\, d\theta$.

Solution. We did this in Example 5, Article 9–2, by a trick. We can now do it in a more straight-forward manner by writing $\sec\theta$ as $1/\cos\theta$ and proceeding as follows:

$$\int \sec\theta\, d\theta = \int \frac{d\theta}{\cos\theta}$$

$$= \int \frac{\cos\theta\, d\theta}{\cos^2\theta}$$

$$= \int \frac{dx}{1-x^2} \qquad [x = \sin\theta]$$

$$= \tfrac{1}{2}\ln \left| \frac{1+x}{1-x} \right| + C \qquad [\text{Eq. (8)}]$$

$$= \ln \sqrt{\frac{1+\sin\theta}{1-\sin\theta}} + C. \tag{9}$$

This answer is equivalent to Eq. (3), Article 9–2, as may be seen by multiplying numerator and denominator by $1 + \sin\theta$:

$$\sqrt{\frac{1+\sin\theta}{1-\sin\theta}} = \sqrt{\frac{(1+\sin\theta)^2}{1-\sin^2\theta}} = \left| \frac{1+\sin\theta}{\cos\theta} \right|$$

$$= |\sec\theta + \tan\theta|.$$

PROBLEMS

1. $\displaystyle\int \frac{x\, dx}{x^2 + 4x - 5}$

2. $\displaystyle\int \frac{x\, dx}{x^2 - 2x - 3}$

3. $\displaystyle\int \frac{(x+1)\, dx}{x^2 + 4x - 5}$

4. $\displaystyle\int \frac{x^2\, dx}{x^2 + 2x + 1}$

5. $\displaystyle\int \frac{dx}{x(x+1)^2}$

6. $\displaystyle\int \frac{dx}{(x+1)(x^2+1)}$

7. $\displaystyle\int \frac{dx}{x(x^2 + x + 1)}$

8. $\displaystyle\int \frac{\sin\theta\, d\theta}{\cos^2\theta + \cos\theta - 2}$

9. $\displaystyle\int \frac{e^t\,dt}{e^{2t}+3e^t+2}$ 10. $\displaystyle\int \frac{dx}{(x^2+1)^2}$

11. $\displaystyle\int \frac{x^4\,dx}{(x^2+1)^2}$

9–7 Integration by parts. There are really just two general methods of integration. One of these is the method of substitution, which we have illustrated in Articles 9–2 through 9–5. The method of partial fractions is really not a method of *integration* so much as it is a method of *algebraic transformation* of a rational function into an integrable form. The second general method of integration, called *integration by parts*, depends upon the formula for the differential of a product:

$$d(uv) = u\,dv + v\,du$$

or

$$u\,dv = d(uv) - v\,du.$$

When this is integrated, we have

$$\boxed{\int u\,dv = uv - \int v\,du + C.} \quad (1)$$

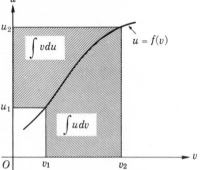

Figure 9–3

By way of comment on the formula (1) for integration by parts, we observe that it expresses one integral, $\int u\,dv$, in terms of a second integral, $\int v\,du$. If by proper choice of u and dv the second integral is simpler than the first, we may be able to evaluate it quite simply and thus arrive at an answer.

In a definite integral, appropriate limits must be supplied. We may then interpret the formula for integration by parts,

$$\int_{(1)}^{(2)} u\,dv = uv\Big]_{(1)}^{(2)} - \int_{(1)}^{(2)} v\,du,$$

geometrically in terms of areas (see Fig. 9–3).

EXAMPLE 1. $\displaystyle\int \ln x\,dx.$

Solution. If we try to match $\ln x\,dx$ with $u\,dv$, we may take $u = \ln x$ and $dv = dx$. Then, to use (1), we see that we also require

$$du = d\,(\ln x) = \frac{dx}{x}$$

and

$$v = \int dv = \int dx = x + C_1,$$

so that

$$\int \ln x \, dx = (\ln x)(x + C_1) - \int (x + C_1) \frac{dx}{x} + C_2$$

$$= x \ln x + C_1 \ln x - \int dx - \int C_1 \frac{dx}{x} + C_2$$

$$= x \ln x + C_1 \ln x - x - C_1 \ln x + C_2 = x \ln x - x + C_2.$$

Note that the first constant of integration C_1 does not appear in the final answer. This is generally true, for if we write $v + C_1$ in place of v in the right side of (1), we obtain

$$u(v + C_1) - \int (v + C_1) \, du = uv + C_1 u - \int v \, du - \int C_1 \, du = uv - \int v \, du,$$

where it is understood that a constant of integration must still be added in the final result. It is therefore customary to drop the first constant of integration when determining v as $\int dv$. On the other hand, there is occasionally an advantage in taking C_1 equal to some specific constant. For instance, if we consider

$$\int \ln (x + 1) \, dx$$

and let

$$u = \ln (x + 1) \qquad \text{and} \qquad dv = dx,$$

then

$$du = \frac{dx}{x + 1} \qquad \text{and} \qquad v = x + C_1.$$

Equation (1) then gives

$$\int \ln (x + 1) \, dx = (x + C_1) \ln (x + 1) - \int \frac{x + C_1}{x + 1} \, dx.$$

Now taking $C_1 = 1$ greatly simplifies the second integral and leads to the result

$$\int \ln (x + 1) \, dx = (x + 1) \ln (x + 1) - x + C_2.$$

EXAMPLE 2.
$$\int \tan^{-1} x \, dx.$$

Solution. This is typical of the inverse trigonometric functions. Let

$$u = \tan^{-1} x \qquad \text{and} \qquad dv = dx;$$

then

$$du = \frac{dx}{1+x^2} \quad \text{and} \quad v = x,$$

so that

$$\int \tan^{-1} x \, dx = x \tan^{-1} x - \int \frac{x \, dx}{1+x^2} = x \tan^{-1} x - \tfrac{1}{2} \ln(1+x^2) + C.$$

Sometimes an integration by parts must be repeated to obtain an answer, as in the following example.

EXAMPLE 3. $\int x^2 e^x \, dx.$

Solution. Let

$$u = x^2 \quad \text{and} \quad dv = e^x \, dx.$$

Then

$$du = 2x \, dx \quad \text{and} \quad v = e^x,$$

so that

$$\int x^2 e^x \, dx = x^2 e^x - 2 \int x e^x \, dx.$$

The integral on the right is similar to the original integral, except that we have reduced the power of x from 2 to 1. If we could now reduce it from 1 to 0, we could see success ahead. In $\int x e^x \, dx$, we therefore let

$$U = x \quad \text{and} \quad dV = e^x \, dx,$$

so that

$$dU = dx \quad \text{and} \quad V = e^x.$$

Then

$$\int x e^x \, dx = x e^x - \int e^x \, dx = x e^x - e^x + c,$$

and

$$\int x^2 e^x \, dx = x^2 e^x - 2x e^x + 2 e^x + C.$$

EXAMPLE 4. Obtain a reduction formula for $J_n \equiv \int \cos^n x \, dx.$

Solution. We may think of $\cos^n x$ as $\cos^{n-1} x \cdot \cos x$. Then we let

$$u = \cos^{n-1} x \quad \text{and} \quad dv = \cos x \, dx,$$

so that

$$du = (n-1) \cos^{n-2} x \, (-\sin x \, dx) \quad \text{and} \quad v = \sin x.$$

Hence

$$J_n = \cos^{n-1} x \sin x + (n-1) \int \sin^2 x \cos^{n-2} x \, dx$$

$$= \cos^{n-1} x \sin x + (n-1) \int (1 - \cos^2 x) \cos^{n-2} x \, dx,$$

or

$$\int \cos^n x \, dx = \cos^{n-1} x \sin x + (n - 1) \int \cos^{n-2} x \, dx - (n - 1) \int \cos^n x \, dx.$$

The last integral on the right may now be transposed to the left to give

$$[1 + (n - 1)]J_n = nJ_n.$$

We then divide by n, and the final result is

$$\int \cos^n x \, dx = \frac{\cos^{n-1} x \sin x}{n} + \frac{n - 1}{n} \int \cos^{n-2} x \, dx. \qquad (2)$$

This allows us to reduce the exponent on $\cos x$ by 2 and is a very useful formula. When n is a positive integer, we may apply the formula repeatedly until the remaining integral is either

$$\int \cos x \, dx = \sin x + C \quad \text{or} \quad \int \cos^0 x \, dx = \int dx = x + C.$$

For example, with $n = 4$, we get

$$\int \cos^4 x \, dx = \frac{\cos^3 x \sin x}{4} + \frac{3}{4} \int \cos^2 x \, dx,$$

and with $n = 2$,

$$\int \cos^2 x \, dx = \frac{\cos x \sin x}{2} + \frac{1}{2} \int dx.$$

Therefore,

$$\int \cos^4 x \, dx = \frac{\cos^3 x \sin x}{4} + \frac{3}{4} \left(\frac{\cos x \sin x}{2} + \frac{1}{2} x \right) + C.$$

The reader may find it instructive to derive the companion formula:

$$\int \sin^n x \, dx = -\frac{\sin^{n-1} x \cos x}{n} + \frac{n - 1}{n} \int \sin^{n-2} x \, dx. \qquad (3)$$

The integral in the following example occurs in electrical engineering problems. Its evaluation requires two integrations by parts, followed by solving for the unknown integral in a method analogous to that used above in finding reduction formulas.

EXAMPLE 5. $\qquad \int e^{ax} \cos bx \, dx.$

Solution. Let

$$u = e^{ax} \quad \text{and} \quad dv = \cos bx\, dx.$$

Then

$$du = ae^{ax}\, dx \quad \text{and} \quad v = \frac{1}{b}\sin bx,$$

so that

$$\int e^{ax}\cos bx\, dx = \frac{e^{ax}\sin bx}{b} - \frac{a}{b}\int e^{ax}\sin bx\, dx.$$

The second integral is like the first except that it has $\sin bx$ in place of $\cos bx$. If we apply integration by parts to it, letting

$$U = e^{ax} \quad \text{and} \quad dV = \sin bx\, dx,$$

then

$$dU = ae^{ax}\, dx \quad \text{and} \quad V = -\frac{1}{b}\cos bx,$$

so that

$$\int e^{ax}\cos bx\, dx = \frac{e^{ax}\sin bx}{b} - \frac{a}{b}\left[-\frac{e^{ax}\cos bx}{b} + \frac{a}{b}\int e^{ax}\cos bx\, dx \right].$$

Now the unknown integral appears on the left with a coefficient of unity and on the right with a coefficient of $-a^2/b^2$. Transposing this term to the left and dividing by the new coefficient

$$1 + \frac{a^2}{b^2} = \frac{a^2 + b^2}{b^2},$$

we have

$$\boxed{\int e^{ax}\cos bx\, dx = e^{ax}\left(\frac{b\sin bx + a\cos bx}{a^2 + b^2} \right) + C.} \qquad (4)$$

PROBLEMS

1. $\displaystyle\int x\ln x\, dx$

2. $\displaystyle\int x^n \ln ax\, dx \quad (n \neq -1)$

3. $\displaystyle\int x\tan^{-1} x\, dx$

4. $\displaystyle\int \sin^{-1} ax\, dx$

5. $\displaystyle\int x\sin ax\, dx$

6. $\displaystyle\int x^2 \cos ax\, dx$

7. $\displaystyle\int x\sec^2 ax\, dx$

8. $\displaystyle\int e^{ax}\sin bx\, dx$

9. $\displaystyle\int \sin(\ln x)\, dx$

10. $\displaystyle\int \cos(\ln x)\, dx$

11. $\displaystyle\int \ln(a^2 + x^2)\, dx$

12. $\displaystyle\int x\cos(2x + 1)\, dx$

13. $\displaystyle\int x \sin^{-1} x \, dx$

14. $\displaystyle\int_1^2 x \sec^{-1} x \, dx$

15. $\displaystyle\int_1^4 \sec^{-1} \sqrt{x} \, dx$

16. $\displaystyle\int x^2 \tan^{-1} x \, dx$

Derive the following reduction formulas and apply each one to the specific problem given:

17. (a) $\displaystyle\int x^m (\ln x)^n \, dx = \frac{x^{m+1} (\ln x)^n}{m + 1} - \frac{n}{m + 1} \int x^m (\ln x)^{n-1} \, dx$

(b) $\displaystyle\int x^3 (\ln x)^2 \, dx$

18. (a) $\displaystyle\int \sin^n x \, dx = -\frac{\sin^{n-1} x \cos x}{n} + \frac{n-1}{n} \int \sin^{n-2} x \, dx$

(b) $\displaystyle\int_0^{\pi/6} \sin^4 3x \, dx$

19. (a) $\displaystyle\int x^n e^x \, dx = x^n e^x - n \int x^{n-1} e^x \, dx$, (b) $\displaystyle\int x^3 e^x \, dx$

20. (a) $\displaystyle\int \sec^n x \, dx = \frac{\sec^{n-2} x \tan x}{(n - 1)} + \frac{n - 2}{n - 1} \int \sec^{n-2} x \, dx$

(b) $\displaystyle\int \sec^3 x \, dx$ [See Eq. (3), Article 9–2.]

(c) $\displaystyle\int \sqrt{a^2 + x^2} \, dx$ [*Hint:* Let $x = a \tan \theta$.]

21. Find the second degree polynomial $P(x)$ that has the following properties: (a) $P(0) = 1$, (b) $P'(0) = 0$, and (c) the indefinite integral

$$\int \frac{P(x) \, dx}{x^3 (x - 1)^2}$$

is a rational function. (That is, no logarithmic terms occur in the answer.)

9–8 Integration of rational functions of sin x and cos x and other trigonometric integrals. It has been discovered that the substitution

$$\boxed{z = \tan \frac{x}{2}} \tag{1}$$

enables one to reduce the problem of integrating any rational function of $\sin x$ and $\cos x$ to a problem involving a rational function of z. This in turn can be integrated by the method of partial fractions discussed in Article 9–6. Thus the substitution (1) is a very powerful tool. This method is cumbersome, however, and is used only when the simpler methods outlined previously have failed.

To see the effect of the substitution, we calculate

$$\cos x = 2 \cos^2 \frac{x}{2} - 1 = \frac{2}{\sec^2 \frac{x}{2}} - 1$$

$$= \frac{2}{1 + \tan^2 \frac{x}{2}} - 1 = \frac{2}{1 + z^2} - 1$$

or

$$\cos x = \frac{1 - z^2}{1 + z^2},$$ (2a)

and

$$\sin x = 2 \sin \frac{x}{2} \cos \frac{x}{2} = 2 \frac{\sin \frac{x}{2}}{\cos \frac{x}{2}} \cdot \cos^2 \frac{x}{2} = 2 \tan \frac{x}{2} \cdot \frac{1}{\sec^2 \frac{x}{2}} = \frac{2 \tan \frac{x}{2}}{1 + \tan^2 \frac{x}{2}}$$

or

$$\sin x = \frac{2z}{1 + z^2}.$$ (2b)

Finally,

$$x = 2 \tan^{-1} z,$$

so that

$$dx = \frac{2 \, dz}{1 + z^2}.$$ (2c)

EXAMPLE 1.

$$\int \sec x \, dx = \int \frac{dx}{\cos x} \quad \text{becomes} \quad \int \frac{2 \, dz}{1 + z^2} \cdot \frac{1 + z^2}{1 - z^2} = \int \frac{2 \, dz}{1 - z^2}.$$

To this we apply the method of partial fractions:

$$\frac{2}{1 - z^2} = \frac{A}{1 - z} + \frac{B}{1 + z},$$

$$2 = A(1 + z) + B(1 - z)$$

$$= (A + B) + (A - B)z,$$

which requires

$$A + B = 2, \qquad A - B = 0.$$

Hence

$$A = B = 1$$

and

$$\int \frac{2\,dz}{1 - z^2} = \int \frac{dz}{1 - z} + \int \frac{dz}{1 + z} = -\ln|1 - z| + \ln|1 + z| + C$$

$$= \ln\left|\frac{1 + z}{1 - z}\right| + C$$

$$= \ln\left|\frac{1 + \tan\frac{x}{2}}{1 - \tan\frac{x}{2}}\right| + C = \ln\left|\frac{\tan\frac{\pi}{4} + \tan\frac{x}{2}}{1 - \tan\frac{\pi}{4}\tan\frac{x}{2}}\right| + C = \ln\left|\tan\left(\frac{\pi}{4} + \frac{x}{2}\right)\right| + C.$$

That is,

$$\int \sec x\,dx = \ln\left|\tan\left(\frac{\pi}{4} + \frac{x}{2}\right)\right| + C \tag{3}$$

is an alternative form, which may be used in place of Eq. (3), Article 9–2, or Eq. (9), Article 9–6.

EXAMPLE 2.

$$\int \frac{dx}{1 + \cos x} = \int \frac{2\,dz}{1 + z^2}\frac{1 + z^2}{2} = \int dz = z + C = \tan\frac{x}{2} + C.$$

EXAMPLE 3.

$$\int \frac{dx}{2 + \sin x} = \int \frac{2\,dz}{1 + z^2}\left[\frac{1 + z^2}{2 + 2z + 2z^2}\right] = \int \frac{dz}{z^2 + z + 1} = \int \frac{dz}{(z + \frac{1}{2})^2 + \frac{3}{4}}$$

$$= \int \frac{du}{u^2 + a^2} \qquad [u = z + \tfrac{1}{2}, \quad a = \sqrt{3}/2]$$

$$= \frac{1}{a}\tan^{-1}\frac{u}{a} + C = \frac{2}{\sqrt{3}}\tan^{-1}\frac{2z + 1}{\sqrt{3}} + C$$

$$= \frac{2}{\sqrt{3}}\tan^{-1}\frac{1 + 2\tan\frac{x}{2}}{\sqrt{3}} + C.$$

We have already made repeated use of trigonometric identities to aid us in evaluating integrals. The following types of integrals:

$$\int \sin mx \sin nx\,dx, \qquad \int \sin mx \cos nx\,dx, \qquad \int \cos mx \cos nx\,dx, \tag{4}$$

arise in connection with alternating-current theory, heat transfer problems, bending of beams, cable stress analysis in suspension bridges, and many other places where trigonometric series (or Fourier series) are applied to problems in mathematics, science, and engineering. The integrals in (4) can be evaluated by the method of integration by parts, but two such integrations are required in each case. A simpler way to evaluate them is to exploit the trigonometric identities

(a) $\sin mx \sin nx = \frac{1}{2}[\cos (m - n)x - \cos (m + n)x]$,

(b) $\sin mx \cos nx = \frac{1}{2}[\sin (m - n)x + \sin (m + n)x]$,   (5)

(c) $\cos mx \cos nx = \frac{1}{2}[\cos (m - n)x + \cos (m + n)x]$.

These identities follow at once from

$$\cos (A + B) = \cos A \cos B - \sin A \sin B,$$
$$\cos (A - B) = \cos A \cos B + \sin A \sin B,$$ (6a)

and

$$\sin (A + B) = \sin A \cos B + \cos A \sin B,$$
$$\sin (A - B) = \sin A \cos B - \cos A \sin B.$$ (6b)

For example, if we add the two equations in (6a) and then divide by 2, we obtain (5c) by taking $A = mx$ and $B = nx$. The identity in (5a) is obtained in a similar fashion by subtracting the first equation in (6a) from the second equation. Finally, if we add the two equations in (6b) we are led to the identity in (5b).

EXAMPLE 4. $\displaystyle\int \sin 3x \cos 5x \, dx = \frac{1}{2}\int [\sin (-2x) + \sin 8x] \, dx$

$$= \frac{1}{2}\int (\sin 8x - \sin 2x) \, dx$$

$$= -\frac{\cos 8x}{16} + \frac{\cos 2x}{4} + C.$$

PROBLEMS

1. $\displaystyle\int_0^{\pi} \frac{dx}{1 + \sin x}$

2. $\displaystyle\int_{\pi/2}^{\pi} \frac{dx}{1 - \cos x}$

3. $\displaystyle\int \frac{dx}{1 - \sin x}$

4. $\displaystyle\int_0^{\pi/2} \frac{dx}{2 + \cos x}$

5. $\displaystyle\int \frac{\cos x \, dx}{2 - \cos x}$

6. $\displaystyle\int_0^{\pi/2} \cos 3x \sin 2x \, dx$

7. $\displaystyle\int_{-\pi}^{\pi} \sin 3x \sin 2x \, dx$

8. $\displaystyle\int_{-\pi}^{\pi} \sin^2 3x \, dx$

9. Two functions f and g are said to be *orthogonal* on an interval $a \leq x \leq b$ if $\int_a^b f(x) \, g(x) \, dx = 0$. (a) Prove that $\sin mx$ and $\sin nx$ are orthogonal on any interval of length 2π provided m and n are integers such that $m^2 \neq n^2$. (b) Prove the same for $\sin mx$ and $\cos nx$. (c) Prove the same for $\cos mx$ and $\cos nx$.

9-9 Further substitutions. Some integrals involving fractional powers of the variable x may be simplified by substituting $x = z^n$, where n is the least common multiple of the denominators of the exponents.

For example

$$\int \frac{\sqrt{x}\, dx}{1 + \sqrt[4]{x}}$$

may be simplified by taking

$$x = z^4, \qquad dx = 4z^3\, dz.$$

This leads to

$$\int \frac{\sqrt{x}\, dx}{1 + \sqrt[4]{x}} = \int \frac{z^2 \cdot 4z^3\, dz}{1 + z}$$

$$= 4\int \left(z^4 - z^3 + z^2 - z + 1 - \frac{1}{z+1} \right) dz$$

$$= 4\left[\frac{z^5}{5} - \frac{z^4}{4} + \frac{z^3}{3} - \frac{z^2}{2} + z - \ln|z + 1| \right] + C$$

$$= \tfrac{4}{5}x^{5/4} - x + \tfrac{4}{3}x^{3/4} - 2x^{1/2} + 4x^{1/4} - 4\ln|1 + \sqrt[4]{x}| + C.$$

In $\int x^3 \sqrt{x^2 + a^2}\, dx$, on the other hand, the substitution

$$z^2 = x^2 + a^2$$

or

$$x^2 = z^2 - a^2$$

and

$$2x\, dx = 2z\, dz$$

leads to

$$\int x^3 \sqrt{x^2 + a^2}\, dx = \int x^2 \sqrt{x^2 + a^2} \cdot x\, dx = \int (z^2 - a^2) \cdot z^2 \cdot dz$$

$$= \int (z^4 - a^2 z^2)\, dz$$

$$= \tfrac{1}{5}(x^2 + a^2)^{5/2} - \tfrac{1}{3}a^2(x^2 + a^2)^{3/2} + C$$

$$= \frac{3x^2 - 2a^2}{15}(x^2 + a^2)^{3/2} + C.$$

Even when it is not clear at the start that a substitution will work, it is advisable to try one that seems reasonable and pursue it until it either gives results or appears to make matters worse. In the latter case, try something else! Sometimes a chain of substitutions $u = f(x)$, $v = g(u)$,

$z = h(v)$, etc., will produce results when it is by no means obvious that this will work. The criterion of success is whether the new integrals so obtained appear to be simpler than the original integral. In this regard, it is handy to remember that any rational function of x can be integrated by the method of partial fractions and that any rational function of $\sin x$ and $\cos x$ can be integrated by using the substitution $z = \tan x/2$. If we can reduce a given integral to one of these types, we then know how to finish the job.

Even in these cases, however, it is frequently simpler to use special methods suggested by the particular integrand rather than to use the general methods. For instance, one would hardly let $z = \tan x/2$ in order to evaluate $\int \sin x \, dx = -\cos x + C$. And reference to Eqs. (5) and (6), Article 9-6, and the accompanying discussion shows that a trigonometric substitution is used to evaluate certain of the integrals that arise in the method of partial fractions. It may be more convenient to use the same substitution *before* going through the algebraic reductions instead of *after* doing so.

For example, consider the integral

$$\int_{-1}^{+1} \sqrt{\frac{1+x}{1-x}} \, dx, \tag{1}$$

which appears in the so-called "lifting line theory" in aerodynamics. If we let

$$\frac{1+x}{1-x} = z^2, \tag{2}$$

we shall, of course, get rid of the radical. Whether this is really a good substitution or not depends upon how complicated the expression is for dx in terms of z and dz. To settle this question, we solve for x as follows:

$$1 + x = z^2 - xz^2,$$

$$x(z^2 + 1) = z^2 - 1,$$

$$x = \frac{z^2 - 1}{z^2 + 1}. \tag{3}$$

Hence

$$dx = \frac{4z \, dz}{(z^2 + 1)^2}$$

and the integral becomes

$$\int \sqrt{\frac{1+x}{1-x}} \, dx = \int \frac{4z^2 \, dz}{(z^2 + 1)^2}.$$

Now the integrand on the right is a rational function of z and we could proceed by the method of partial fractions. But the $z^2 + 1$ in the denominator also lends itself to the substitution

$$z = \tan \theta. \tag{4}$$

We try this, and have

$$dz = \sec^2 \theta \, d\theta, \qquad z^2 + 1 = \tan^2 \theta + 1 = \sec^2 \theta,$$

so that

$$\int \frac{4z^2 \, dz}{(z^2 + 1)^2} = \int \frac{4 \tan^2 \theta \cdot \sec^2 \theta \, d\theta}{\sec^4 \theta} = 4 \int \frac{\sin^2 \theta}{\cos^2 \theta} \cdot \frac{1}{\sec^2 \theta} \, d\theta = 4 \int \sin^2 \theta \, d\theta,$$

and the last integral can now be evaluated at once to give

$$4 \int \sin^2 \theta \, d\theta = 2 \left[\theta - \frac{\sin 2\theta}{2} \right] + C. \tag{5}$$

We now have two alternative courses of action for evaluating the *definite integral*, (1): namely,

(a) we may reverse the substitutions (3) and (4) and replace (5) by its equivalent in terms of x. Then the definite integral (1) could be evaluated by substituting the limits of integration. Or,

(b) we may determine new limits of integration corresponding to the new variable of integration.

We illustrate the second line of attack. In the original integral, (1), x varies from -1 to $+1$. As this happens, the left side of (2) varies from 0 to $+\infty$, and since we have tacitly taken

$$z = \sqrt{\frac{1 + x}{1 - x}}$$

as the *positive* square root, we see that then z varies from 0 to $+\infty$. Finally, from (4) we have $\theta = \tan^{-1} z$, so that θ varies from 0 to $\pi/2$ as z varies from 0 to $+\infty$. Combining these results, we have

$$\int_{-1}^{+1} \sqrt{\frac{1 + x}{1 - x}} \, dx = \int_0^\infty \frac{4z^2 \, dz}{(z^2 + 1)^2} \qquad \left[z = \sqrt{\frac{1 + x}{1 - x}} \right]$$

$$= 4 \int_0^{\pi/2} \sin^2 \theta \, d\theta \qquad [\theta = \tan^{-1} z]$$

$$= 2 \left[\theta - \frac{\sin 2\theta}{2} \right]_0^{\pi/2} = \pi.$$

The reader will find it instructive to evaluate the integral in (1) by making the alternative substitution

$$x = \cos 2t, \qquad dx = -2 \sin 2t \, dt = -4 \sin t \cos t \, dt,$$

which is particularly well adapted to the integrand in question, since

$$1 + \cos 2t = 2 \cos^2 t$$

and

$$1 - \cos 2t = 2 \sin^2 t.$$

But the shortest way of all is to notice that for $-1 < x < 1$ we have

$$\sqrt{\frac{1+x}{1-x}} = \frac{1+x}{\sqrt{1-x^2}},$$

and hence

$$\int \sqrt{\frac{1+x}{1-x}} \, dx = \int \frac{1+x}{\sqrt{1-x^2}} \, dx$$

$$= \sin^{-1} x - \sqrt{1-x^2} + C. \tag{6}$$

PROBLEMS

1. $\displaystyle \int \frac{1-\sqrt{x}}{1+\sqrt{x}} \, dx$

2. $\displaystyle \int \frac{dx}{a+b\sqrt{x}}$ (a and b constants)

3. $\displaystyle \int x^2 \sqrt{x+a} \, dx$

4. $\displaystyle \int \frac{\sqrt{x+a} \, dx}{x+b}$ ($b > a$)

5. $\displaystyle \int \sqrt{\frac{a+x}{b+x}} \, dx$ ($b \neq a$)

6. $\displaystyle \int \frac{dx}{x+\sqrt{x^2+a^2}}$ ($a > 0$)

7. $\displaystyle \int_0^1 \frac{x^3 \, dx}{(x^2+1)^{3/2}}$

8. $\displaystyle \int \frac{dx}{x(ax^n+c)}$ ($anc \neq 0$)

9. $\displaystyle \int_3^8 \frac{(t+2) \, dt}{t\sqrt{t+1}}$

10. $\displaystyle \int \frac{dx}{x-x^{2/3}}$

11. $\displaystyle \int_0^3 \frac{\sqrt{x+1}-1}{\sqrt{x+1}+1} \, dx$

12. $\displaystyle \int \frac{dx}{x(1-\sqrt[4]{x})}$

13. $\displaystyle \int \frac{y^{2/3} \, dy}{y+1}$

14. $\displaystyle \int \frac{z^5 \, dz}{\sqrt{1+z^3}}$

15. $\displaystyle \int \frac{\sqrt{t^3-1}}{t} \, dt$

16. $\displaystyle \int_0^{\ln 2} \frac{dw}{(1+e^w)}$

17. $\displaystyle\int_0^{\pi/2} \frac{\sin 2\theta \; d\theta}{2 + \cos \theta}$

18. $\displaystyle\int \frac{\sin x \; dx}{\tan x + \cos x}$

19. $\displaystyle\int \frac{dx}{x^3 + 1}$

20. $\displaystyle\int \frac{dy}{y^{1/3} - y^{1/2}}$

9–10 Improper integrals. An integral of the type discussed in the previous article,

$$\int_{-1}^{+1} \sqrt{\frac{1+x}{1-x}} \; dx,$$

is called an *improper* integral because the function

$$f(x) = \sqrt{\frac{1+x}{1-x}}$$

which appears after the integral sign becomes infinite at one of the limits of integration, in this case at $x = +1$. More generally, integrals of the following two types are called improper integrals:

(a) $\int_a^b f(x) \, dx$, where $f(x)$ becomes infinite at a value of x between a and b inclusive,

(b) $\int_a^\infty f(x) \, dx$ or $\int_{-\infty}^b f(x) \, dx$, where one or both of the limits of integration are infinite.

In the example above, we had

$$\int_{-1}^1 \sqrt{\frac{1+x}{1-x}} \; dx = \int_0^\infty \frac{4z^2 \; dz}{(z^2 + 1)^2}, \qquad \left[z = \sqrt{\frac{1+x}{1-x}} \right]$$

where the integral on the left is an improper integral of the first type and the integral on the right is an improper integral of the second type.

Figure 9–4 illustrates the case where the function becomes infinite at one of the limits of integration. If we interpret the integral in terms of area under the curve $y = f(x)$, say from -1 to $+1$ as in the figure, we see that the curve extends to infinity as x approaches 1 and the area from -1 to $+1$ is not well defined. Nevertheless, we can certainly define the area from $x = -1$ to $x = b$, where b is any positive number *less* than one; for example, we can take $b = 0.999$. This defines a function of b:

$$g(b) = \int_{-1}^b f(x) \; dx.$$

If this function has a finite limit as b approaches $+1$ from the left, we

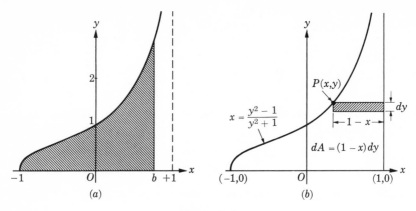

Figure 9–4

define this limit to be the value of the improper integral

$$\int_{-1}^{+1} f(x)\, dx = \lim_{b \to 1-} \int_{-1}^{b} f(x)\, dx.$$

In this case we also say that the improper integral *converges*. On the other hand, we say that the integral *diverges* if the function g has no definite finite limit as $b \to 1-$.

In the particular example above, we find, from Eq. (6) of Article 9–9, that

$$\int_{-1}^{b} \sqrt{\frac{1+x}{1-x}}\, dx = \sin^{-1} x - \sqrt{1-x^2}\,\Big]_{-1}^{b}$$

$$= \sin^{-1} b - \sqrt{1-b^2} + \frac{\pi}{2}\,.$$

This is the number denoted above by $g(b)$. When b is slightly less than $+1$, $\sin^{-1} b$ is slightly less than $\pi/2$ and $\sqrt{1-b^2}$ is nearly zero. Hence

$$\lim_{b \to 1-} \int_{-1}^{b} \sqrt{\frac{1+x}{1-x}}\, dx = \lim_{b \to 1-}\left[\sin^{-1} b - \sqrt{1-b^2} + \frac{\pi}{2}\right]$$

$$= \frac{\pi}{2} - 0 + \frac{\pi}{2} = \pi.$$

The given integral therefore converges and its value is π.

The same result is obtained if, instead of finding the area by summing vertical elements (Fig. 9–4a), we sum horizontal elements (Fig. 9–4b). Then we find

$$A = \int_{y=0}^{\infty} (1-x)\, dy = \int_{0}^{\infty} \frac{2}{y^2+1}\, dy.$$

This time, the integral to be evaluated is an improper integral of the second type because the range of integration extends to infinity. In this case we investigate the integral from $y = 0$ to $y = c$ for large values of c:

$$\int_0^c \frac{2\,dy}{y^2 + 1} = 2 \tan^{-1} c,$$

and we *define* the integral from 0 to ∞ as the limit of this as $c \to \infty$ (if the limit exists). That is,

$$\int_0^\infty \frac{2\,dy}{y^2 + 1} = \lim_{c \to \infty} \int_0^c \frac{2\,dy}{y^2 + 1} = \lim_{c \to \infty} (2 \tan^{-1} c) = \pi.$$

The limit does exist, since $\tan^{-1} c$ approaches $\pi/2$ as c increases indefinitely. As a second example, we consider

$$\int_0^1 \frac{dx}{x}.$$

The function f in this case is defined by

$$f(x) = \frac{1}{x},$$

which becomes infinite at $x = 0$. We cut off the point $x = 0$ and start our integration at some positive number $b < 1$. (See Fig. 9–5.) That is, we consider the integral

$$\int_b^1 \frac{dx}{x} = \ln x \Big]_b^1 = \ln 1 - \ln b = \ln \frac{1}{b},$$

and investigate its behavior as b approaches zero from the right. Since

$$\lim_{b \to 0+} \int_b^1 \frac{dx}{x} = \lim_{b \to 0+} \left(\ln \frac{1}{b} \right) = +\infty,$$

we say that the integral from $x = 0$ to $x = 1$ *diverges*.

The method to be used when the function f becomes infinite at an interior point of the range of integration is illustrated in the following example.

Consider

$$\int_0^3 \frac{dx}{(x-1)^{2/3}}.$$

Figure 9–5

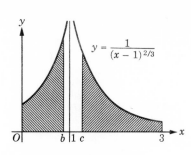

Figure 9–6

The function

$$f(x) = \frac{1}{(x-1)^{2/3}}$$

becomes infinite at $x = 1$, which lies between the limits of integration 0 and 3. In such a case, we again cut out the point where $f(x)$ becomes infinite. This time we integrate from 0 to b, where b is slightly less than 1, and start again on the other side of 1 at c and integrate from c to 3 (Fig. 9–6). Then we get the two integrals

$$\int_0^b \frac{dx}{(x-1)^{2/3}} \quad \text{and} \quad \int_c^3 \frac{dx}{(x-1)^{2/3}}$$

to investigate. If the first of these has a definite limit as $b \to 1-$ and if the second also has a definite limit as $c \to 1+$, then we say that the improper integral converges and that its value is given by

$$\int_0^3 \frac{dx}{(x-1)^{2/3}} = \lim_{b\to 1-} \int_0^b \frac{dx}{(x-1)^{2/3}} + \lim_{c\to 1+} \int_c^3 \frac{dx}{(x-1)^{2/3}}.$$

If either limit fails to exist, we say that the given improper integral *diverges*. For this example,

$$\lim_{b\to 1-} \int_0^b (x-1)^{-2/3}\, dx = \lim_{b\to 1-} [3(b-1)^{1/3} - 3(0-1)^{1/3}] = +3$$

and

$$\lim_{c\to 1+} \int_c^3 (x-1)^{-2/3}\, dx = \lim_{c\to 1+} [3(3-1)^{1/3} - 3(c-1)^{1/3}] = 3\sqrt[3]{2}.$$

Since both limits exist and are finite, the original integral is said to converge and its value is $3 + 3\sqrt[3]{2}$.

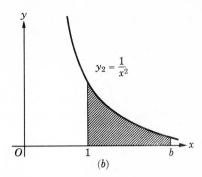

$$(a) \qquad\qquad\qquad (b)$$

Figure 9–7

As further examples of the second type of improper integral, we consider

$$\int_1^\infty \frac{dx}{x} \quad \text{and} \quad \int_1^\infty \frac{dx}{x^2} .$$

The two curves

$$y_1 = \frac{1}{x} \quad \text{and} \quad y_2 = \frac{1}{x^2}$$

both approach the x-axis as $x \to \infty$ (Fig. 9–7). In the first case,

$$\int_1^b \frac{dx}{x} = \ln x \Big]_1^b = \ln b.$$

If we now let b take on larger and larger positive values, the logarithm of b increases indefinitely and

$$\lim_{b \to \infty} \int_1^b \frac{dx}{x} = \infty .$$

We therefore say that

$$\int_1^\infty \frac{dx}{x} = \infty$$

and that the integral *diverges*.

In the second case,

$$\int_1^b \frac{dx}{x^2} = -\frac{1}{x} \Big]_1^b = 1 - \frac{1}{b} .$$

This does have a definite limit, namely 1, as b increases indefinitely, and we say that the integral from 1 to ∞ converges and that its value is 1. That is,

$$\int_1^\infty \frac{dx}{x^2} = \lim_{b \to \infty} \int_1^b \frac{dx}{x^2} = \lim_{b \to \infty} \left(1 - \frac{1}{b} \right) = 1.$$

Sometimes we can determine whether a given integral converges or diverges by comparing it with a simpler integral.

For example, even though we cannot find any simpler expression for

$$I(b) \equiv \int_1^b e^{-x^2} \, dx,$$

we can show that

$$\lim_{b \to \infty} I(b)$$

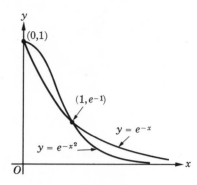

exists and is finite. For the function $I(b)$ represents the area between the x-axis and the curve

$$y = e^{-x^2}$$

Figure 9-8

between $x = 1$ and $x = b$. Clearly, this is an increasing function of b, so that there are two alternatives: either

(a) $I(b)$ becomes infinite as $b \to \infty$,

or

(b) $I(b)$ has a finite limit as $b \to \infty$.

We show that the first alternative cannot be the true one. We do this by comparing the area under the given curve $y = e^{-x^2}$ with the area under the curve $y = e^{-x}$ (Fig. 9-8). The latter area, from $x = 1$ to $x = b$, is given by the integral

$$\int_1^b e^{-x} \, dx = -e^{-x} \Big]_1^b = e^{-1} - e^{-b},$$

which approaches the finite limit e^{-1} as $b \to \infty$. Since e^{-x^2} is less than e^{-x} for all x greater than one, the area under the given curve is certainly no greater than e^{-1} no matter how large b is.

The discussion above is summarized in the following inequalities:

$$I(b) = \int_1^b e^{-x^2} \, dx \leq \int_1^b e^{-x} \, dx = e^{-1} - e^{-b} \leq e^{-1},$$

that is,

$$I(b) \leq e^{-1} < 0.37.$$

Therefore $I(b)$ does not become infinite as $b \to \infty$, so alternative (a) is ruled out and alternative (b) must hold; that is,

$$\int_1^\infty e^{-x^2} \, dx = \lim_{b \to \infty} \int_1^b e^{-x^2} \, dx$$

converges to a definite finite value. We have not calculated what this limit is, but we know that it exists and is less than 0.37.

It should be pointed out that an improper integral may diverge without becoming infinite.

For example, the integral

$$\int_0^b \cos x \, dx = \sin b$$

takes all values between -1 and $+1$ as b varies between $2n\pi - \pi/2$ and $2n\pi + \pi/2$, where n is any integer. Hence,

$$\lim_{b \to \infty} \int_0^b \cos x \, dx$$

does not exist. We might say that this integral "diverges by oscillation."

PROBLEMS

Show that the following improper integrals converge and evaluate them.

1. $\displaystyle\int_0^\infty \frac{dx}{x^2 + 1}$

2. $\displaystyle\int_0^1 \frac{dx}{\sqrt{x}}$

3. $\displaystyle\int_{-1}^1 \frac{dx}{x^{2/3}}$

4. $\displaystyle\int_1^\infty \frac{dx}{x^{1.001}}$

5. $\displaystyle\int_0^4 \frac{dx}{\sqrt{4 - x}}$

6. $\displaystyle\int_0^1 \frac{dx}{\sqrt{1 - x^2}}$

7. $\displaystyle\int_0^\infty e^{-x} \cos x \, dx$

8. $\displaystyle\int_0^1 \frac{dx}{x^{0.999}}$

Determine whether each of the following improper integrals converges or diverges.

9. $\displaystyle\int_1^\infty \frac{dx}{\sqrt{x}}$

10. $\displaystyle\int_1^\infty \frac{dx}{x^3}$

11. $\displaystyle\int_1^\infty \frac{dx}{x^3 + 1}$

12. $\displaystyle\int_0^\infty \frac{dx}{x^3}$

13. $\displaystyle\int_0^\infty \frac{dx}{x^3 + 1}$

14. $\displaystyle\int_0^\infty \frac{dx}{1 + e^x}$

15. $\displaystyle\int_0^{\pi/2} \tan x \, dx$

16. $\displaystyle\int_{-1}^1 \frac{dx}{x^2}$

17. $\displaystyle\int_{-1}^{1} \frac{dx}{x^{2/5}}$

18. $\displaystyle\int_{0}^{\infty} \frac{dx}{\sqrt{x}}$

19. $\displaystyle\int_{0}^{\infty} \frac{dx}{\sqrt{x+x^4}}$ [*Hint:* Compare the integral with $\int dx/\sqrt{x}$ for x near zero and with $\int dx/x^2$ for large x.]

9–11 Numerical methods for approximating definite integrals. Certain important integrals which arise in physical and mathematical problems cannot be expressed in terms of the so-called elementary functions. For example, the length of one arch of the curve $y = \sin x$, Fig. 9–9, is given by

$$L = \int_{0}^{\pi} \sqrt{1 + \cos^2 x}\, dx.$$

The integral cannot be evaluated by any of the methods we have studied thus far. Nevertheless it can be evaluated numerically to any required number of decimal places by several methods. The trapezoidal rule is one. We indicate another below.

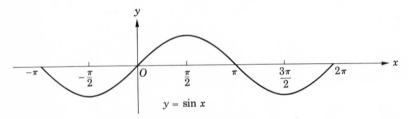

Figure 9–9

Any definite integral $\int_{a}^{b} f(x)\, dx$ can be interpreted as an area or as a combination of areas, some added and some subtracted. Such an integral can therefore be approximated by any method of approximating these areas. Instruments called *planimeters* are useful in this connection, but they have two drawbacks: (a) the curve $y = f(x)$ must be drawn with some care, and (b) the accuracy of the planimeter is limited to approximately the order of 1%. Simpson's method, which we shall now study, avoids both of these drawbacks.

This method is based on the simple formula

$$A_p = \frac{h}{3}\,[y_0 + 4y_1 + y_2]$$

for the area under the arc of the parabola

$$y = Ax^2 + Bx + C$$

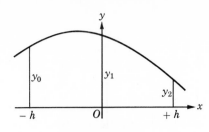

Figure 9–10

between $x = -h$ and $x = +h$, as in Fig. 9–10.*

This result is readily established as follows: in the first place, we have

$$A_p = \int_{-h}^{h} (Ax^2 + Bx + C)\, dx$$

$$= \frac{2Ah^3}{3} + 2Ch.$$

Since the curve passes through the three points $(-h, y_0)$, $(0, y_1)$, and (h, y_2), we also have

$$y_0 = Ah^2 - Bh + C, \qquad y_1 = C, \qquad y_2 = Ah^2 + Bh + C,$$

from which there follows

$$C = y_1,$$
$$Ah^2 - Bh = y_0 - y_1,$$
$$Ah^2 + Bh = y_2 - y_1,$$
$$2Ah^2 = y_0 + y_2 - 2y_1.$$

Hence, expressing the area A_p in terms of the ordinates y_0, y_1, and y_2, we have

$$A_p = \frac{h}{3}[2Ah^2 + 6C] = \frac{h}{3}[(y_0 + y_2 - 2y_1) + 6y_1]$$

or

$$A_p = \frac{h}{3}[y_0 + 4y_1 + y_2]. \tag{1}$$

Simpson's rule follows from applying this result to successive pieces of the curve $y = f(x)$ between $x = a$ and $x = b$. Each separate piece of the curve, covering an x-subinterval of width $2h$, is approximated by an arc of a parabola through its ends and its mid-point. The area under each parabolic arc is then given by an expression like Eq. (1) and the results are added to give

$$A_S = \frac{h}{3}[y_0 + 4y_1 + 2y_2 + 4y_3 + 2y_4 + \cdots + 2y_{n-2} + 4y_{n-1} + y_n],$$

$$\tag{2}$$

which is taken as the approximate value of $\int_a^b f(x)\, dx$. In Eq. (2), $y_0, y_1, y_2, \ldots, y_n$ are the ordinates of the curve $y = f(x)$ at the points of

---

* We choose the interval $-h \leq x \leq h$ to simplify the algebra. There is no loss in generality in so doing, because the area does not depend on the location of the y-axis.

abscissas $x_0 = a$, $x_1 = a + h$, $x_2 = a + 2h$, ..., $x_n = a + nh = b$ corresponding to a subdivision of the interval $a \leq x \leq b$ into n equal subintervals each of width $h = (b - a)/n$. (See Fig. 9–11.) The number n of subdivisions must be an *even* integer in order to apply the method. The application of the rule, Eq. (2), does not require a graph of the curve $y = f(x)$ nor a

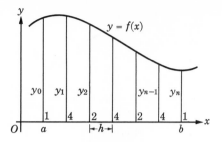

Figure 9–11

determination of the approximating parabolic arcs. All of the work is strictly arithmetical. Furthermore, it is clear on geometrical grounds that the smaller the value of h that is taken, the greater will be the accuracy of the approximation, since a parabola that passes through three points of the given curve that are close to one another will usually remain close to the curve throughout the entire strip of width $2h$. By an extension of the Mean Value Theorem, it is possible to prove* that if f is continuous on $a \leq x \leq b$ and four times differentiable on $a < x < b$, then there is a number c between a and b such that

$$\int_a^b f(x)\, dx = A_S - \frac{b - a}{180} f^{(4)}(c) \cdot h^4.$$

EXAMPLE 1. Use Simpson's rule with four subdivisions to find the approximate value of $\ln 2 = \int_1^2 (1/x)\, dx$.

Solution. We arrange the work in tabular form as follows:

x	$y = 1/x$	Weighting factor	Product
1.00	1.00000	1	1.00000
1.25	0.80000	4	3.20000
1.50	0.66667	2	1.33333
1.75	0.57143	4	2.28572
2.00	0.50000	1	0.50000
			Sum = 8.31905

Since $h = \frac{1}{4}$, we must multiply the last sum by $h/3 = \frac{1}{12}$. Hence

$$A_S = \tfrac{1}{12}(8.31905) = 0.69325.$$

---

* See, for example, J. M. H. Olmsted, *Intermediate Analysis* (Appleton-Century-Crofts), page 146.

The approximation
$$\ln 2 \approx 0.69325$$
is in error by 1 part in 6900 or about one-seventieth of one percent. Greater accuracy may be obtained by taking twice as many subdivisions.

PROBLEMS

Find approximate numerical values for the following definite integrals by using Simpson's rule (a) with $n = 2$, and (b) with $n = 4$. Where possible, compare your answer with (c), the exact value.

1. $\displaystyle\int_0^2 x^2\, dx$

2. $\displaystyle\int_0^\pi \sin x\, dx$

3. $\displaystyle\int_0^\pi \sqrt{\sin x}\, dx$

4. $\displaystyle\int_0^\pi \frac{dx}{2 + \cos x}$

5. $\displaystyle\int_0^\pi \frac{\sin x}{x}\, dx$

6. $\displaystyle\int_0^1 \frac{dx}{x^2 + 1}$

7. Show that $\int_3^\infty e^{-3x}\, dx = \frac{1}{3} e^{-9} = 0.000041$, and hence that $\int_3^\infty e^{-x^2}\, dx < 0.000041$. Therefore, $\int_0^\infty e^{-x^2}\, dx$ can be replaced by $\int_0^3 e^{-x^2}\, dx$ without introducing any errors in the first three decimal places of the answer. Evaluate this last integral by Simpson's rule with $n = 6$. (This illustrates one method by which a convergent improper integral may be approximated numerically.)

REVIEW QUESTIONS AND EXERCISES FOR CHAPTER 9

1. What are some of the general methods presented in this chapter for finding an indefinite integral?

2. What substitution(s) would you consider trying if the integrand contained the following:

(a) $\sqrt{x^2 + 9}$,

(b) $\sqrt{x^2 - 9}$,

(c) $\sqrt{9 - x^2}$,

(d) $\sin^3 x \cos^2 x$,

(e) $\sin^2 x \cos^2 x$,

(f) $\dfrac{1 + \sin \theta}{2 + \cos \theta}$?

3. What method(s) would you try if the integrand contained:

(a) $\sin^{-1} x$,

(b) $\ln x$,

(c) $\sqrt{1 + 2x - x^2}$,

(d) $x \sin x$,

(e) $\dfrac{2x + 3}{x^2 - 5x + 6}$,

(f) $\sin 5x \cos 3x$,

(g) $\dfrac{1 - \sqrt{x}}{1 + \sqrt[4]{x}}$,

(h) $x\sqrt{2x + 3}$?

4. What numerical methods do you know for approximating a definite integral? How can an approximation usually be improved upon to give greater accuracy?

5. Discuss two types of improper integral. Define convergence and divergence of each type. Give examples of convergent and divergent integrals of each type.

MISCELLANEOUS PROBLEMS FOR CHAPTER 9

Evaluate the following integrals:

1. $\int \dfrac{\cos x \, dx}{\sqrt{1 + \sin x}}$

2. $\int \dfrac{\sin^{-1} x \, dx}{\sqrt{1 - x^2}}$

3. $\int \dfrac{\tan x \, dx}{\cos^2 x}$

4. $\int \dfrac{dx}{1 - \sin x}$

5. $\int e^{\ln \sqrt{x}} \, dx$

6. $\int \dfrac{\cos \sqrt{x}}{\sqrt{x}} \, dx$

7. $\int \dfrac{dx}{\sqrt{x^2 + 2x + 2}}$

8. $\int \dfrac{(3x - 7) \, dx}{(x - 1)(x - 2)(x - 3)}$

9. $\int x^2 e^x \, dx$

10. $\int \sqrt{x^2 + 1} \, dx$

11. $\int \dfrac{e^t \, dt}{1 + e^{2t}}$

12. $\int \dfrac{dx}{e^x + e^{-x}}$

13. $\int \dfrac{dx}{1 + \sqrt{x}}$

14. $\int \dfrac{dx}{\sqrt{1 + \sqrt{x}}}$

15. $\int t^{2/3} (t^{5/3} + 1)^{2/3} \, dt$

16. $\int \dfrac{\cot x \, dx}{\ln (\sin x)}$

17. $\int \dfrac{dt}{\sqrt{e^t + 1}}$

18. $\int \dfrac{dt}{\sqrt{1 - e^{-t}}}$

19. $\int \dfrac{\sin x \, e^{\sec x}}{\cos^2 x} \, dx$

20. $\int \dfrac{\cos x \, dx}{1 + \sin^2 x}$

21. $\int \dfrac{dx}{\sqrt{2x - x^2}}$

22. $\int \dfrac{\sin x \, dx}{1 + \cos^2 x}$

23. $\int \dfrac{\cos 2t}{1 + \sin 2t} \, dt$

24. $\int \dfrac{dx}{\sin x \cos x}$

25. $\int \sqrt{1 + \sin x} \, dx$

26. $\int \sqrt{1 - \sin x} \, dx$

27. $\int \dfrac{dx}{\sqrt{(a^2 - x^2)^3}}$

28. $\int \dfrac{dx}{\sqrt{(a^2 + x^2)^3}}$

29. $\int \dfrac{\sin x \, dx}{\cos^2 x - 5 \cos x + 4}$

30. $\int \dfrac{e^{2x} \, dx}{\sqrt[3]{1 + e^x}}$

31. $\displaystyle\int \frac{dx}{x(x+1)(x+2)\cdots(x+m)}$

32. $\displaystyle\int \frac{dx}{x^6 - 1}$

33. $\displaystyle\int \frac{dy}{y(2y^3 + 1)^2}$

34. $\displaystyle\int \frac{x\,dx}{1 + \sqrt{x}}$

35. $\displaystyle\int \frac{dx}{x(x^2 + 1)^2}$

36. $\displaystyle\int \ln\sqrt{x - 1}\,dx$

37. $\displaystyle\int \frac{dx}{e^x - 1}$

38. $\displaystyle\int \frac{d\theta}{1 - \tan^2 \theta}$

39. $\displaystyle\int \frac{(x + 1)\,dx}{x^2(x - 1)}$

40. $\displaystyle\int \frac{x\,dx}{x^2 + 4x + 3}$

41. $\displaystyle\int \frac{du}{(e^u - e^{-u})^2}$

42. $\displaystyle\int \frac{4dx}{x^3 + 4x}$

43. $\displaystyle\int \frac{dx}{5x^2 + 8x + 5}$

44. $\displaystyle\int \frac{\sqrt{x^2 - a^2}}{x}\,dx$

45. $\displaystyle\int e^x \cos 2x\,dx$

46. $\displaystyle\int \frac{dx}{x(3\sqrt{x} + 1)}$

47. $\displaystyle\int \frac{dx}{x(1 + \sqrt[3]{x})}$

48. $\displaystyle\int \frac{\cot\theta\,d\theta}{1 + \sin^2 \theta}$

49. $\displaystyle\int \frac{z^5\,dz}{\sqrt{1 + z^2}}$

50. $\displaystyle\int \frac{e^{4t}\,dt}{(1 + e^{2t})^{2/3}}$

51. $\displaystyle\int \frac{dx}{x^{1/5}\sqrt{1 + x^{4/5}}}$

52. $\displaystyle\int x \sec^2 x\,dx$

53. $\displaystyle\int x \sin^{-1} x\,dx$

54. $\displaystyle\int \frac{(x^3 + x^2)\,dx}{x^2 + x - 2}$

55. $\displaystyle\int \frac{x^3 + 1}{x^3 - x}\,dx$

56. $\displaystyle\int \frac{x\,dx}{(x - 1)^2}$

57. $\displaystyle\int \frac{(2e^{2x} - e^x)\,dx}{\sqrt{3e^{2x} - 6e^x - 1}}$

58. $\displaystyle\int \frac{(x + 1)\,dx}{(x^2 + 2x - 3)^{2/3}}$

59. $\displaystyle\int \frac{dy}{(2y + 1)\sqrt{y^2 + y}}$

60. $\displaystyle\int \frac{dx}{x^2\sqrt{a^2 - x^2}}$

61. $\displaystyle\int (1 - x^2)^{3/2}\,dx$

62. $\displaystyle\int \ln\left(x + \sqrt{1 + x^2}\right)\,dx$

63. $\displaystyle\int x \tan^2 x\,dx$

64. $\displaystyle\int \frac{\tan^{-1} x}{x^2}\,dx$

65. $\int x \cos^2 x \, dx$

66. $\int x^2 \sin x \, dx$

67. $\int x \sin^2 x \, dx$

68. $\int \dfrac{dt}{t^4 + 4t^2 + 3}$

69. $\int \dfrac{du}{e^{4u} + 4e^{2u} + 3}$

70. $\int x \ln \sqrt{x + 2} \, dx$

71. $\int (x + 1)^2 e^x \, dx$

72. $\int \sec^{-1} x \, dx$

73. $\int \dfrac{8 \, dx}{x^4 + 2x^3}$

74. $\int \dfrac{x \, dx}{x^4 - 16}$

75. $\int_0^{\pi/2} \dfrac{\cos x \, dx}{\sqrt{1 + \cos x}}$

76. $\int \dfrac{\cos x \, dx}{\sin^3 x - \sin x}$

77. $\int \dfrac{du}{(e^u + e^{-u})^2}$

78. $\int \dfrac{x \, dx}{1 + \sqrt{x} + x}$

79. $\int \dfrac{\sec^2 t \, dt}{\sec^2 t - 3 \tan t + 1}$

80. $\int \dfrac{dt}{\sec^2 t + \tan^2 t}$

81. $\int \dfrac{dx}{1 + \cos^2 x}$

82. $\int e^{2t} \cos(e^t) \, dt$

83. $\int \ln \sqrt{x^2 + 1} \, dx$

84. $\int x \ln (x^3 + x) \, dx$

85. $\int x^3 e^{x^2} \, dx$

86. $\int \dfrac{\cos x \, dx}{\sqrt{4 - \cos^2 x}}$

87. $\int \dfrac{\sec^2 x \, dx}{\sqrt{4 - \sec^2 x}}$

88. $\int x^2 \sin (1 - x) \, dx$

89. $\int \dfrac{dx}{1 + \sin x}$

90. $\int \dfrac{dx}{1 + 2 \sin x}$

91. $\int \dfrac{dx}{\sin^3 x}$

92. $\int \dfrac{dx}{\cot^3 x}$

93. $\int (\sin^{-1} x)^2 \, dx$

94. $\int x \ln \sqrt[3]{3x + 1} \, dx$

95. $\int \dfrac{x^3 \, dx}{(x^2 + 1)^2}$

96. $\int \dfrac{x \, dx}{\sqrt{1 - x}}$

97. $\int x\sqrt{2x + 1} \, dx$

98. $\int \ln (x + \sqrt{x^2 - 1}) \, dx$

99. $\int \ln\left(x - \sqrt{x^2 - 1}\right) dx$

100. $\int \dfrac{dt}{t - \sqrt{1 - t^2}}$

101. $\int e^{-x} \tan^{-1}\left(e^x\right) dx$

102. $\int \sin^{-1} \sqrt{x}\, dx$

103. $\int \ln\left(x + \sqrt{x}\right) dx$

104. $\int \tan^{-1} \sqrt{x}\, dx$

105. $\int \ln\left(x^2 + x\right) dx$

106. $\int \ln\left(\sqrt{x} + \sqrt{1 + x}\right) dx$

107. $\int \cos \sqrt{x}\, dx$

108. $\int \sin \sqrt{x}\, dx$

109. $\int \tan^{-1} \sqrt{x + 1}\, dx$

110. $\int \sqrt{1 - x^2}\, \sin^{-1} x\, dx$

111. $\int x \sin^2 (2x)\, dx$

112. $\int \dfrac{\tan x\, dx}{\tan x + \sec x}$

113. $\int \dfrac{dt}{\sqrt{e^{2t} + 1}}$

114. $\int \dfrac{dx}{(\cos^2 x + 4 \sin x - 5) \cos x}$

115. $\int \dfrac{dt}{a + be^{ct}}, \quad abc \neq 0$

116. $\int \sqrt{\dfrac{1 - \cos x}{\cos \alpha - \cos x}}\; dx, \quad \alpha \text{ constant}, \quad 0 < \alpha < x < \pi$

117. $\int \dfrac{dx}{\sin x - \cos x}$

118. $\int \ln \sqrt{1 + x^2}\, dx$

119. $\int \ln\left(2x^2 + 4\right) dx$

120. $\int \dfrac{x^3}{\sqrt{1 - x^2}}\, dx$

121. $\int \dfrac{dx}{x(2 + \ln x)}$

122. $\int \dfrac{\cos 2x - 1}{\cos 2x + 1}\, dx$

123. $\int \dfrac{dx}{x^3 + 1}$

124. $\int \dfrac{e^{2x}\, dx}{\sqrt[4]{e^x + 1}}$

125. $\int \dfrac{e^x\, dx}{1 + e^{2x}}$

126. $\int e^{\sqrt{t}}\, dt$

127. $\int \sin \sqrt{x + 1}\, dx$

128. $\int \cos \sqrt{1 - x}\, dx$

Evaluate each of the following limits, Problems 129–135, by identifying it with an appropriate definite integral and evaluating the latter.

129. $\lim\limits_{n\to\infty}\left(\dfrac{1}{n+1}+\dfrac{1}{n+2}+\cdots+\dfrac{1}{2n}\right)$

130. $\lim\limits_{n\to\infty}\left(\dfrac{1}{\sqrt{n^2}}+\dfrac{1}{\sqrt{n^2+n}}+\dfrac{1}{\sqrt{n^2+2n}}+\cdots+\dfrac{1}{\sqrt{n^2+(n-1)n}}\right)$

131. $\lim\limits_{n\to\infty}\left(\dfrac{\sin 0+\sin\dfrac{\pi}{n}+\sin\dfrac{2\pi}{n}+\cdots+\sin\dfrac{(n-1)\pi}{n}}{n}\right)$

132. $\lim\limits_{n\to\infty}\left(\dfrac{1+\sqrt[n]{e}+\sqrt[n]{e^2}+\sqrt[n]{e^3}+\cdots+\sqrt[n]{e^{n-1}}}{n}\right)$

133. $\lim\limits_{n\to\infty}\left(\dfrac{n}{n^2+0^2}+\dfrac{n}{n^2+1^2}+\dfrac{n}{n^2+2^2}+\cdots+\dfrac{n}{n^2+(n-1)^2}\right)$

134. $\lim\limits_{n\to\infty}\sum\limits_{k=1}^{n}\ln\sqrt[n]{1+\dfrac{k}{n}}$

135. $\lim\limits_{n\to\infty}\sum\limits_{k=0}^{n-1}\dfrac{1}{\sqrt{n^2-k^2}}$

136. Show that $\int_0^\infty x^3 e^{-x^2}\,dx$ is a convergent integral, and evaluate it.

137. Show that $\int_0^1 \ln x\,dx$ is a convergent integral and find its value. Sketch the integrand $y=\ln x$ for $0<x\le 1$.

138. Assuming that $|\alpha|\neq|\beta|$, prove that

$$\lim_{T\to\infty}\frac{1}{T}\int_0^T \sin\alpha x\,\sin\beta x\,dx = 0.$$

139. Evaluate: $\lim\limits_{h\to 0}\dfrac{1}{h}\int_2^{2+h} e^{-x^2}\,dx.$

140. At points of the curve $y^2=4px$ lines of length $h=y$ are drawn perpendicular to its plane. Find the area of the surface formed by these lines at points of the curve between $(0,0)$ and $(p,2p)$.

141. A plane figure is bounded by a $90°$ arc of a circle of radius r and a straight line. Find its area and its centroid.

142. Find the coordinates of the center of gravity of the area bounded by the curves $y=e^x$, $x=1$, and $y=1$.

143. At points of a circle of radius r, perpendiculars to its plane are erected, the perpendicular at each point P being of length ks, where s is the arc of the circle from a fixed point A to P. Find the area of the surface formed by the perpendiculars along the arc beginning at A and extending once around the circle.

144. A plate in the first quadrant, bounded by the curves $y=e^x$, $y=1$, and $x=4$, is submerged vertically in water with its upper corner on the sur-

face. The surface of the water is given by the line $y = e^4$. Find the total force on one side of the plate if the weight of water is 62.5 lb/ft^3, and if the units of x and y are also measured in feet.

145. The area under the curve $xy = 1$, for $x \geq 1$, is rotated about the x-axis. If A is the area under the curve, V is the volume generated, and S is the surface area of this volume: (a) is A finite? (b) is V finite? (c) is S finite? Give reasons for your answers.

146. Answer the questions of Problem 145 if the curve given there is replaced by the curve $y = e^{-x}$. Give reasons for your answers.

147. Find the centroid of the area bounded by $y = e^x$, $y = 0$, $x = 0$, $x = 1$.

148. Find the centroid of the area bounded by $y = \ln x$, $x = 1$, $y = 1$.

149. Find the length of arc of $y = \ln x$ from $x = 1$ to $x = e$.

150. The arc of Problem 149 is rotated about the y-axis. Find the surface area generated. Check your answer by comparing it with the area of a frustum of a suitably related cone.

151. Find the length of arc of the curve $y = e^x$ from $x = 0$ to $x = 2$.

152. The arc of Problem 151 is rotated about the x-axis. Find the surface area generated. Compare this area with the area of a suitably related frustum of a cone to check your answer.

153. One arch of the curve $y = \cos x$ is rotated about the x-axis. Find the surface area generated.

154. Use Simpson's rule to compute, approximately, the length of arc of $y = \cos x$ from $x = -\pi/2$ to $x = \pi/2$. Check your answer by consulting a table of elliptic integrals if one is available.

155. A thin wire is bent into the shape of one arch of the curve $y = \cos x$.. Find its center of mass (see Problems 153, 154).

156. The area between the graph of $y = \ln (1/x)$, the x-axis, and the y-axis is revolved around the x-axis. Find the volume of the solid it generates.

157. Find the total perimeter of the curve $x^{2/3} + y^{2/3} = a^{2/3}$.

158. Find the length of arc of the curve $y = \ln (\cos x)$ from $x = 0$ to $x = \pi/3$.

159. Find the area of the surface generated by rotating the curve $x^{2/3} + y^{2/3} = a^{2/3}$ about the x-axis.

160. A thin homogeneous wire is bent into the shape of one arch of the curve $x^{2/3} + y^{2/3} = a^{2/3}$. Find its center of mass (see Problems 157, 159).

161. Determine whether the integral $\int_1^\infty \ln x (dx/x^2)$ converges or diverges.

162. Sketch the curves:

(a) $y = x - e^x$, show behavior for large $|x|$;

(b) $y = e^{(x-e^x)}$, show behavior for large $|x|$.

Show that the following integrals converge and compute their values:

(c) $\displaystyle\int_{-\infty}^{b} e^{(x-e^x)}\, dx,$ (d) $\displaystyle\int_{-\infty}^{\infty} e^{(x-e^x)}\, dx.$

163. The gamma function $\Gamma(x)$ is defined, for $x > 0$, by the definite integral

$$\Gamma(x) = \int_0^\infty t^{x-1} e^{-t}\, dt.$$

(a) Sketch graphs of the integrand $y = t^{x-1} e^{-t}$ vs. t, $t > 0$, for the three typical cases $x = \frac{1}{2}$, 1, 3. Find maxima, minima, and points of inflection (if they exist).

(b) Show that the integral converges if $x > 0$.

(c) Show that the integral diverges if $x \leq 0$.

(d) Using integration by parts, show that $\Gamma(x + 1) = x\Gamma(x)$, for $x > 0$.

(e) Using the result of part (b), show that, if n is a positive integer, $\Gamma(n) = (n - 1)!$ where $0! = 1$ (by definition) and if m is a positive integer, $m!$ is the product of the positive integers from 1 through m inclusive.

(f) Discuss how one might compute a table of values of $\Gamma(x)$ for the domain $1 \leq x \leq 2$, say. Consult such a table, if available, and sketch the graph of $y = \Gamma(x)$ for $0 < x \leq 3$.

164. Determine whether the integral $\int_0^\infty t^{x-1} (\ln t) e^{-t} dt$ converges or diverges for fixed $x > 0$. Sketch the integrand $y = t^{x-1} \ln t\, e^{-t}$ vs. t, $t > 0$, for the two cases $x = \frac{1}{2}$ and $x = 3$.

165. Solve the differential equation $d^2x/dt^2 = -k^2x$, subject to the initial conditions $x = a$, $dx/dt = 0$ when $t = 0$. [Hint: Let $dx/dt = v$, $d^2x/dt^2 = dv/dt = v\, dv/dx$.]

166. Find $\displaystyle \lim_{n \to \infty} \int_0^1 \frac{ny^{n-1}}{1 + y}\, dy.$

167. Prove that if n is a positive integer, or zero, then

$$\int_{-1}^1 (1 - x^2)^n\, dx = \frac{2^{2n+1} (n!)^2}{(2n + 1)!},$$

with $0! = 1$; $n! = 1 \cdot 2 \cdots n$ for $n \geq 1$.

Determinants and Linear Equations

10–1 Introduction. Matrices and determinants have their origin in connection with the problem of solving simultaneous linear equations. For example, if we wish to find the point of intersection of two straight lines

$$a_1 x + b_1 y = c_1, \qquad a_2 x + b_2 y = c_2, \tag{1}$$

we seek a pair of numbers x and y which satisfy both equations simultaneously. There are several methods of doing this, but one fairly common method is to find equations equivalent to the given equations but having the property that the unknowns (x and y) are separated. This may be achieved, for example, by multiplying the first equation by b_2, the second equation by $-b_1$, and adding, to obtain the equation

$$(a_1 b_2 - a_2 b_1) x = c_1 b_2 - c_2 b_1; \tag{2a}$$

and by multiplying the first equation by $-a_2$, the second by a_1, and adding, to obtain the equation

$$(a_1 b_2 - a_2 b_1) y = a_1 c_2 - a_2 c_1. \tag{2b}$$

Equations (2a) and (2b) must be satisfied by any pair of numbers x and y which satisfy the original equations, (1). They have the added merit of being easy to solve, since each equation contains only one of the unknowns. Thus, we find that the only pair of numbers which can satisfy Eqs. (1) is

$$x = \frac{c_1 b_2 - c_2 b_1}{a_1 b_2 - a_2 b_1}, \qquad y = \frac{a_1 c_2 - a_2 c_1}{a_1 b_2 - a_2 b_1}, \tag{3}$$

provided

$$a_1 b_2 - a_2 b_1 \neq 0. \tag{4}$$

By direct substitution from (3) back into (1) we find, conversely, that these values of x and y do indeed satisfy both of the original equations.

We shall verify that this is so for the first equation and leave to the reader the computation for the second. Substituting for x and y from (3) into (1_1), we find

$$a_1 x + b_1 y = a_1 \left(\frac{c_1 b_2 - c_2 b_1}{a_1 b_2 - a_2 b_1} \right) + b_1 \left(\frac{a_1 c_2 - a_2 c_1}{a_1 b_2 - a_2 b_1} \right)$$

$$= \frac{a_1 c_1 b_2 - a_1 c_2 b_1 + b_1 a_1 c_2 - b_1 a_2 c_1}{a_1 b_2 - a_2 b_1}$$

$$= \frac{c_1 (a_1 b_2 - a_2 b_1)}{a_1 b_2 - a_2 b_1} = c_1.$$

443

In the exceptional case where $a_1b_2 - a_2b_1$ is zero, the left sides of Eqs. (2a) and (2b) are both zero and the Eqs. (1) are inconsistent unless

$$c_1b_2 - c_2b_1 = a_1c_2 - a_2c_1 = 0$$

as well. In this case, we have a pair of equations of straight lines having equal slopes and one of two things happens:

(a) The straight lines coincide and there are infinitely many number-pairs (x, y) which satisfy the equations, or else
(b) the lines are parallel and there are no number-pairs (x, y) which satisfy the equations simultaneously.

For example, if the equations are

$$2x + 3y = 5, \qquad 4x + 6y = 10,$$

these represent just one line. Then x may have any value, and provided $y = (5 - 2)x/3$, the point (x, y) will lie on the line. But if the equations are

$$2x + 3y = 5, \qquad 4x + 6y = 11,$$

then the lines are parallel and we say that the equations are inconsistent, because no pair of numbers x and y can satisfy both equations simultaneously.

Let us, then, rule out the case of parallel or coincident lines and discuss the results obtained in (3) when condition (4) is satisfied. The expression $a_1b_2 - a_2b_1$ is defined to be the *determinant* of the *coefficient matrix*

$$M_2 = \begin{bmatrix} a_1 & b_1 \\ a_2 & b_2 \end{bmatrix}$$

The entries in this 2-by-2 matrix are the coefficients of x and y from Eqs. (1), in the same order. We shall denote the determinant of this matrix M_2 by D_2. The determinant is written

$$D_2 = \begin{vmatrix} a_1 & b_1 \\ a_2 & b_2 \end{vmatrix}$$

replacing the large square brackets used for the matrix by straight vertical bars. By definition,

$$\begin{bmatrix} a_1 & b_1 \\ a_2 & b_2 \end{bmatrix} = a_1b_2 - a_2b_1. \tag{5}$$

Such an expression is called a determinant of order two, since it contains two rows and two columns. To evaluate such a determinant, multiply the diagonal elements in the upper-left and lower-right corners to get a_1b_2, then multiply the elements on the other diagonal and subtract this product, a_2b_1, from the former.

For example,

$$\begin{vmatrix} 3 & 2 \\ 7 & 5 \end{vmatrix} = 3 \cdot 5 - 7 \cdot 2 = 15 - 14 = 1$$

and

$$\begin{vmatrix} 4 & -3 \\ 2 & -6 \end{vmatrix} = 4 \cdot (-6) - 2 \cdot (-3) = -24 + 6 = -18.$$

Remark. While the symbol $|M|$ is frequently used to denote the determinant of the matrix M, other notations are also used. For example, det (M) is one such notation. It is a good one because it emphasizes the fact that the *determinant function*, det, has square matrices for its domain. If the entries of a square matrix are integers, rational numbers, or real numbers, then the determinant of the matrix is likewise an integer, a rational number, or a real number.

Caution: If M is a square matrix, its determinant $|M|$ may be positive, negative, or zero. So the determinant does not behave like an absolute value in spite of the superficial resemblance in the notation. Specifically, for a 1-by-1 matrix $[a]$ we define det $([a])$ to be the number a itself, not its absolute value. That is,

$$|[a]| = \det ([a]) = a.$$

Now the equations

$$a_1 x + b_1 y = c_1, \qquad a_2 x + b_2 y = c_2$$

have the solutions (3), which may be expressed by determinants as

$$x = \frac{\begin{vmatrix} c_1 & b_1 \\ c_2 & b_2 \end{vmatrix}}{\begin{vmatrix} a_1 & b_1 \\ a_2 & b_2 \end{vmatrix}}, \qquad y = \frac{\begin{vmatrix} a_1 & c_1 \\ a_2 & c_2 \end{vmatrix}}{\begin{vmatrix} a_1 & b_1 \\ a_2 & b_2 \end{vmatrix}}. \qquad (6)$$

In the equations for both x and y, the denominator is the determinant of the matrix of coefficients, arranged in order, from the given equations. The numerator for x is a determinant which may be obtained from the denominator determinant by suppressing from the latter the coefficients of x and writing the constants c_1 and c_2 in their places. The numerator for y may similarly be obtained from the denominator determinant by suppressing from the latter the coefficients of y and writing the constants c_1 and c_2 in their places. In applying this rule, it is assumed that the denominator determinant is not zero. If it is zero, one has the case where there is no solution if the equations are inconsistent, or there are infinitely many solutions if the straight lines coincide. If the denominator determinant is zero, Eqs. (6) are not to be used.

EXAMPLE. $2x - 3y = 8, \qquad 3x + y = 1.$

Then

$$x = \frac{\begin{vmatrix} 8 & -3 \\ 1 & 1 \end{vmatrix}}{\begin{vmatrix} 2 & -3 \\ 3 & 1 \end{vmatrix}} = \frac{8 \cdot 1 - 1 \cdot (-3)}{2 \cdot 1 - 3 \cdot (-3)} = \frac{8 + 3}{2 + 9} = 1,$$

$$y = \frac{\begin{vmatrix} 2 & 8 \\ 3 & 1 \end{vmatrix}}{\begin{vmatrix} 2 & -3 \\ 3 & 1 \end{vmatrix}} = \frac{2 \cdot 1 - 3 \cdot 8}{2 \cdot 1 - 3 \cdot (-3)} = \frac{-22}{11} = -2.$$

PROBLEMS

Expand the following second order determinants:

1. $\begin{vmatrix} 3 & 4 \\ 2 & 5 \end{vmatrix}$ 2. $\begin{vmatrix} 0 & 3 \\ -1 & 7 \end{vmatrix}$ 3. $\begin{vmatrix} 5 & 7 \\ 6 & 2 \end{vmatrix}$ 4. $\begin{vmatrix} a & b \\ 2a & 2b \end{vmatrix}$

Solve the following sets of simultaneous equations by means of determinants. In every case, check your answers by substituting them back into the original equations.

5. $2x + 3y = 5, \quad 3x - y = 2$
6. $4x - 3y = 6, \quad 3x - 2y = 5$

7. Show that the two lines

$$a_1 x + b_1 y = c_1 \qquad \text{and} \qquad a_2 x + b_2 y = c_2$$

are parallel if and only if the determinant D_2, Eq. (5), is zero.

8. Show that all the determinants appearing in Eq. (6) are zero if the equation $a_2 x + b_2 y = c_2$ is a multiple of the equation $a_1 x + b_1 y = c_1$, that is, if there is a constant k such that $a_2 = k a_1$, $b_2 = k b_1$, and $c_2 = k c_1$.

9. Suppose the elements of the determinant

$$F = \begin{vmatrix} u_1 & v_1 \\ u_2 & v_2 \end{vmatrix}$$

are differentiable functions of x. Show that

$$\frac{dF}{dx} = \begin{vmatrix} \dfrac{du_1}{dx} & \dfrac{dv_1}{dx} \\ u_2 & v_2 \end{vmatrix} + \begin{vmatrix} u_1 & v_1 \\ \dfrac{du_2}{dx} & \dfrac{dv_2}{dx} \end{vmatrix}.$$

In particular, verify the result for the case

$$F = \begin{vmatrix} \cos x & -\sin x \\ \sin x & \cos x \end{vmatrix}.$$

10. Solve the equations

$$x' \cos \alpha - y' \sin \alpha = x, \qquad x' \sin \alpha + y' \cos \alpha = y$$

for x' and y' in terms of x and y by means of determinants.

10–2   Determinants of order 3. A third order determinant,

$$D_3 = \begin{vmatrix} a_1 & b_1 & c_1 \\ a_2 & b_2 & c_2 \\ a_3 & b_3 & c_3 \end{vmatrix}, \tag{1}$$

contains nine elements arranged in three horizontal rows and three vertical columns. Each element has an "address" in the determinant given by its row number r and its column number s. Thus in (1) the element b_3 is in the third row and second column; that is, $r = 3$, $s = 2$ for b_3. Similarly, for the element c_1, $r = 1$ and $s = 3$. We have used different letters a, b, and c to denote the different columns in (1) and subscripts 1, 2, and 3 on these letters to denote the rows.

To obtain the expanded value of the determinant of the third order as in (1), one forms *all possible products* $a_i b_j c_k$, where the subscripts i, j, and k form some permutation of the numbers 1, 2, and 3. There are precisely six possible products of this kind, namely, $a_1 b_2 c_3$, $a_1 b_3 c_2$, $a_2 b_1 c_3$, $a_2 b_3 c_1$, $a_3 b_1 c_2$, and $a_3 b_2 c_1$. One must next attach an algebraic sign to each of these six products according to the rule that the sign is to be plus if the subscripts i, j, and k in $a_i b_j c_k$ form an *even permutation* of the integers 1, 2, 3; and the sign is to be minus if i, j, k is an *odd permutation* of 1, 2, 3. This terminology will now be explained.

When the numbers 1, 2, 3 are arranged in their normal order, we say there are no inversions among them. If, on the other hand, they are arranged in some other order, such as 3, 1, 2, we say that we now have a *permutation* of them and the permutation is called "even" or "odd" according as the number of *inversions* (defined below) is an even integer $(0, 2, 4, \ldots)$ or an odd integer $(1, 3, 5, 7, \ldots)$ respectively.

The number of inversions in any permutation is determined as follows. If in a given permutation i is any integer which is followed by a smaller integer, we say that there is an *inversion* relative to i and the smaller integer. The number of integers following i and smaller than i gives the total number of inversions relative to i. The total number of inversions relative to all the integers of a permutation may be called the *index* of that permutation. In the permutation

$$5 \quad 2 \quad 1 \quad 4 \quad 3,$$

for example, we may count the following:

relative to	*the number of inversions is*
5	4
2	1
1	0
4	1
3	0

Thus the index of the given permutation is

$$4 + 1 + 1 = 6,$$

and the permutation is said to be *even* because 6 is an even integer.

Let us now examine in turn each of the six products in the expansion of D_3, count the inversions in its subscripts, and then affix a plus sign if this number is even and a minus sign if the number is odd.

Product	Subscripts	Index	Signed product
$a_1b_2c_3$	1 2 3	0	$+a_1b_2c_3$
$a_1b_3c_2$	1 3 2	1	$-a_1b_3c_2$
$a_2b_1c_3$	2 1 3	1	$-a_2b_1c_3$
$a_2b_3c_1$	2 3 1	2	$+a_2b_3c_1$
$a_3b_1c_2$	3 1 2	2	$+a_3b_1c_2$
$a_3b_2c_1$	3 2 1	3	$-a_3b_2c_1$

We are now in a position to complete the definition of a third order determinant. Form all possible signed products ($\pm$) $a_ib_jc_k$, where i, j, k is a permutation of 1, 2, 3 in some order and the sign is plus or minus according as the number of inversions in i, j, k is even or odd. The expanded value of the determinant is the algebraic sum of these signed products:

$$D_3 = \begin{vmatrix} a_1 & b_1 & c_1 \\ a_2 & b_2 & c_2 \\ a_3 & b_3 & c_3 \end{vmatrix} = a_1b_2c_3 + a_2b_3c_1 + a_3b_1c_2 - a_3b_2c_1 - a_2b_1c_3 - a_1b_3c_2. \tag{2}$$

The expansion (2) can also be expressed in several ways as the sum of three second order minor determinants each multiplied by an element of a row or column of D_3. For example, it is a simple matter to verify by direct computation that the expanded value in (2) is precisely the same as

$$D_3 = \begin{vmatrix} a_1 & b_1 & c_1 \\ a_2 & b_2 & c_2 \\ a_3 & b_3 & c_3 \end{vmatrix} = a_1 \begin{vmatrix} b_2 & c_2 \\ b_3 & c_3 \end{vmatrix} - b_1 \begin{vmatrix} a_2 & c_2 \\ a_3 & c_3 \end{vmatrix} + c_1 \begin{vmatrix} a_2 & b_2 \\ a_3 & b_3 \end{vmatrix}. \qquad (3)$$

Here, we say that we have expanded D_3 by minors according to elements of its first row. The *minor* of the element in the rth row and sth column of a determinant of any order n is the determinant of the matrix of order $n - 1$ obtained by suppressing all the elements in the rth row and sth column in the original array. The minor of a_1 is found by covering up the first row and first column in D_3, and then taking the determinant of this submatrix. The result, which we shall call A_1, is

$$A_1 = \begin{vmatrix} b_2 & c_2 \\ b_3 & c_3 \end{vmatrix} = b_2 c_3 - b_3 c_2.$$

Similarly, the minor of b_1 is found by covering up the first row and second column of D_3, and the result, denoted by $-B_1$, is

$$-B_1 = \begin{vmatrix} a_2 & c_2 \\ a_3 & c_3 \end{vmatrix} = a_2 c_3 - a_3 c_2.$$

The *negative* of this minor is called the cofactor of b_1 in D_3 and that is why we call the minor $-B_1$ so that the cofactor is $+B_1$. In general, the *cofactor* of the element in the rth row and sth column of a determinant is related to its minor according to the law

$$\text{cofactor} = (-1)^{r+s} \text{ minor}. \qquad (4)$$

Using cofactors instead of minors in the expansion (3), with A_1, B_1, and C_1 denoting the cofactors of a_1, b_1, and c_1 respectively, we have

$$D_3 = a_1 A_1 + b_1 B_1 + c_1 C_1; \qquad (5)$$

that is, *the determinant is the sum of the products of the elements of the first row by their corresponding cofactors.*

It may also be verified by comparison with the expansion in (2) that the determinant is the sum of the products of the elements of *any* row (or column) by their corresponding cofactors. The cofactor of an element is simply its *signed minor*, the sign being + or − according to the law in Eq. (4). The sign may also be obtained from a checkerboard arrangement of + and − signs. One starts with + in the upper left corner and changes sign in going from any square to an adjacent square as follows:

$$\begin{vmatrix} + & - & + \\ - & + & - \\ + & - & + \end{vmatrix}.$$

EXAMPLE 1. Evaluate:

$$D = \begin{vmatrix} 2 & 2 & 1 \\ -1 & 0 & -1 \\ 3 & -1 & 3 \end{vmatrix}.$$

Solution. We exploit the presence of small numbers and the zero in the second row and expand the determinant by cofactors of the elements of this row.

$$D = -(-1) \begin{vmatrix} 2 & 1 \\ -1 & 3 \end{vmatrix} + 0 \begin{vmatrix} 2 & 1 \\ 3 & 3 \end{vmatrix} - (-1) \begin{vmatrix} 2 & 2 \\ 3 & -1 \end{vmatrix}$$
$$= +(6+1) + 0 + (-2-6) = -1.$$

Actually, we need not have written the cofactor of 0, since it contributes nothing to the answer.

EXAMPLE 2. Show that the equation

$$\begin{vmatrix} x & y & 1 \\ -1 & 2 & 1 \\ 1 & 0 & 1 \end{vmatrix} = 0$$

represents a straight line which passes through the points $(-1, 2)$ and $(1, 0)$.

Solution. Expanding the determinant by cofactors of the elements of its first row and equating the result to zero, we get

$$x \begin{vmatrix} 2 & 1 \\ 0 & 1 \end{vmatrix} - y \begin{vmatrix} -1 & 1 \\ 1 & 1 \end{vmatrix} + 1 \begin{vmatrix} -1 & 2 \\ 1 & 0 \end{vmatrix} = 0,$$

or

$$2x + 2y - 2 = 0,$$

or

$$x + y = 1.$$

This is the equation of a straight line. Clearly, by substitution, the given points satisfy the equation.

Another fairly convenient device for evaluating a third order determinant consists in repeating the first two columns of the determinant to the right of it, and then taking the sum of the products along diagonals parallel to the main diagonal minus the products along the diagonals which run up from left to right. This is illustrated schematically in the accompanying diagram. A word of caution: The method does not work for determinants of order 4 or higher!

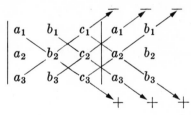

EXAMPLE.

$$\begin{vmatrix} 3 & 2 & 1 \\ 2 & 3 & 1 \\ 1 & 2 & 3 \end{vmatrix} \begin{matrix} 3 & 2 \\ 2 & 3 \\ 1 & 2 \end{matrix} = (27 + 2 + 4) - (3 + 6 + 12) = 12.$$

PROBLEMS

1. Find the index of the permutation 4 1 3 2.

2. Verify Eq. (3) by expanding the second order determinants on the right and comparing the result with Eq. (2).

3. Find the *cofactor* of the element in the second row and first column of the determinant

$$\begin{vmatrix} 2 & 3 & 4 \\ 3 & 2 & -1 \\ 4 & 3 & 7 \end{vmatrix}.$$

4. Show that the third order determinant, Eq. (2), is equal to the sum of the products of the elements of the second column by their corresponding cofactors.

5. Evaluate the determinant

$$\begin{vmatrix} 2 & 2 & 1 \\ 1 & 3 & 2 \\ 3 & 1 & -1 \end{vmatrix}$$

by two different methods.

Evaluate each of the following third order determinants:

6. $\begin{vmatrix} 1 & 3 & -2 \\ 2 & -1 & 1 \\ -2 & 2 & 3 \end{vmatrix}$ 7. $\begin{vmatrix} 2 & 0 & 2 \\ 0 & 3 & -3 \\ -3 & -2 & 0 \end{vmatrix}$

10–3 Determinants of order _n_. To denote a determinant of order n, it is advantageous to use a slightly different notation from that introduced above. Namely, we shall not use different letters of the alphabet to represent the elements in the different columns, but shall instead use double subscripts and write a_{ij} to denote the element in the ith row, jth column of the determinant:

$$D_n = \begin{vmatrix} a_{11} & a_{12} & a_{13} & \dots & a_{1n} \\ a_{21} & a_{22} & a_{23} & \dots & a_{2n} \\ \dots & \dots & \dots & \dots & \dots \\ a_{n1} & a_{n2} & a_{n3} & \dots & a_{nn} \end{vmatrix}. \tag{1}$$

The expanded value of D_n is the sum of all signed products:

$$(\pm)a_{1i_1}a_{2i_2}a_{3i_3} \dots a_{ni_n}, \tag{2}$$

where $i_1, i_2, \dots, i_n$ is a permutation of the integers $1, 2, 3, \dots, n$ in some order and the sign is $+$ or $-$ according as the permutation is even or odd.

For a determinant of order 4, for example, we shall have

$$D_4 = \sum(\pm)a_{1i_1}a_{2i_2}a_{3i_3}a_{4i_4},$$

where i_1, i_2, i_3, i_4 is to range over all permutations of 1, 2, 3, 4. There are $4! = 24$ such permutations and accordingly the determinant D_4 will be the sum of 24 signed products.

In general, a determinant of order n is the sum of $n!$ signed products. Since this number increases rapidly with n, it is desirable to develop equivalent ways of expanding determinants, but ways which will be less laborious than the direct application of the definition. This is the purpose behind the discussion which follows.

PROBLEMS

Write out the 24 permutations of the numbers 1, 2, 3, 4. What is the index of the permutation 4 3 2 1? In the expansion of the determinant D_4, what sign is to be attached to the product $a_{14}a_{23}a_{32}a_{41}$?

10–4   Properties of determinants of order n.

THEOREM 1. *If all elements of any row of D_n are zero, the expanded value of the determinant is zero.*

Proof. Each of the signed products contains one factor from each row (because the first subscripts include all the integers $1, 2, \dots, n$), so that each product is zero under the given hypothesis. Hence their sum is also zero; that is, $D_n = 0$.

THEOREM 2. *If D_n and D'_n are two determinants of the nth order which differ only in that the elements in some one row of D'_n are k times the corre-*

sponding elements in D_n, then the expanded value of D'_n is k times the value of D_n.

The proof is similar to the proof of Theorem 1 and is omitted. The result permits us to factor out any common factor from a row of a determinant and write the factor in front of the new determinant. For example:

$$\begin{vmatrix} a_{11} & a_{12} & a_{13} \\ ka_{21} & ka_{22} & ka_{23} \\ a_{31} & a_{32} & a_{33} \end{vmatrix} = k \begin{vmatrix} a_{11} & a_{12} & a_{13} \\ a_{21} & a_{22} & a_{23} \\ a_{31} & a_{32} & a_{33} \end{vmatrix}.$$

THEOREM 3. *If D'_n is obtained from D_n by interchanging two adjacent rows of D_n, then $D'_n = -D_n$.*

Proof. Suppose D'_n is obtained from D_n by interchanging its kth and $(k+1)$th rows. Then, denoting the elements by a'_{ij} and a_{ij} respectively, we have

$$a'_{ij} = a_{ij} \quad \text{if} \quad i \neq k, \quad i \neq k+1,$$

while

$$a'_{kj} = a_{k+1,j}, \quad a'_{k+1,j} = a_{kj}, \quad j \overset{\cdot}{=} 1, 2, \ldots, n.$$

By definition, D_n is the sum of signed products:

$$\pm a_{1i_1} a_{2i_2} a_{3i_3} \cdots a_{ni_n}, \tag{1}$$

while D'_n is the sum of similar products with primes throughout. Let P be a typical product in the expansion of D_n:

$$P = \pm a_{1i_1} a_{2i_2} \cdots a_{ki_k} a_{k+1,i_{k+1}} \cdots a_{ni_n}, \tag{2}$$

where the sign is determined by the number of inversions in the permutation $i_1, i_2, \ldots, i_n$. If we interchange a_{ki_k} and $a_{k+1,i_{k+1}}$ in (2), we obtain a typical product in the expansion of D'_n except that the sign is now to be determined by the number of inversions in the permutation

$$\underbrace{i_1, i_2, \ldots, i_{k-1},}_{Q'} \ \underbrace{i_{k+1}, i_k,}_{R'} \ \underbrace{i_{k+2}, \ldots, i_n.}_{S'} \tag{3}$$

Next, we shall show that the number of inversions in (3) differs by unity from the number of inversions in

$$\underbrace{i_1, i_2, \ldots, i_{k-1},}_{Q} \ \underbrace{i_k, i_{k+1},}_{R} \ \underbrace{i_{k+2}, \ldots, i_n,}_{S} \tag{4}$$

which determines the sign in (2).

We have indicated the permutations in (3) and (4) as composed of three segments. Suppose we examine the number of inversions in (3), term by term, and record the total number q' relative to elements in Q' which are followed by smaller elements in Q', R', and S'. Similarly, we record the numbers of inversions r' and s' from the segments R' and S', so that the total number of inversions in (3) is

$$I' = q' + r' + s'.$$

We repeat the process for the permutation (4) and obtain the total number of inversions:

$$I = q + r + s,$$

where the letters have meanings which are clear by analogy. But $q = q'$ and $s = s'$, and we need only look more closely at the relation between r and r'. The number r' consists of two parts:

$$r' = r'_1 + r'_2,$$

where r'_1 is the number of inversions caused by the occurrence in R' of numbers which are greater than numbers in S', and r'_2 is 0 or 1, depending upon whether $i_{k+1} < i_k$ or $i_{k+1} > i_k$. Defining r_1 analogously, we write

$$r = r_1 + r_2$$

and observe that $r_1 = r'_1$, since the segments R and S contain the same integers as do the segments R' and S'. But r_2 is not equal to r'_2, but rather $r_2 = 1$ if $i_k > i_{k+1}$ and $r_2 = 0$ if $i_k < i_{k+1}$. That is,

$$r_2 = r'_2 \pm 1.$$

This leads to the end result that

$$I = I' \pm 1,$$

so that one of the permutations (3) or (4) is even and the other is odd. Therefore every product P in D_n undergoes a change in sign in becoming a product P' in D'_n. The sum of all the products P is therefore the negative of the sum of the products P'; that is, $D_n = -D'_n$ or $D'_n = -D_n$.

To illustrate the relationship $I' = I \pm 1$, let us consider an example. For instance, suppose we interchange the 3 and the 7 in the permutation

$$\underbrace{8, 1, 4,}_{Q} \quad \underbrace{3, 7,}_{R} \quad \underbrace{6, 2, 5}_{S}$$

and thus obtain

$$\underbrace{8, 1, 4,}_{Q'} \quad \underbrace{7, 3,}_{R'} \quad \underbrace{6, 2, 5.}_{S'}$$

We may record the number of inversions relative to a given number directly beneath it as follows:

Q	R	S	Q'	R'	S'
$\overbrace{8, 1, 4,}$	$\overbrace{3, 7,}$	$\overbrace{6, 2, 5}$	$\overbrace{8, 1, 4,}$	$\overbrace{7, 3,}$	$\overbrace{6, 2, 5}$

$$7 + 0 + 2 + 1 + 3 + 2 + 0 + 0 \qquad 7 + 0 + 2 + 4 + 1 + 2 + 0 + 0$$

$$I = \quad q \quad + \quad r \quad + \quad s \qquad I' = \quad q' \quad + \quad r' \quad + \quad s'$$

Thus

$$q = q' = 7 + 0 + 2 = 9,$$
$$s = s' = 2 + 0 + 0 = 2,$$

but

$$r = 1 + 3 = 4 \quad \text{while} \quad r' = 4 + 1 = 5; \quad \text{hence} \quad I' = I + 1.$$

When we interchanged the 3 and the 7 we added one inversion to the total, namely, the inversion caused by having 7 ahead of 3. All other inversions were unaltered; hence we increased the index of the permutation by one, from $I = 15$ to $I' = 16$.

THEOREM 4. *If D_n' is obtained from D_n by interchanging any pair of rows, then $D_n' = -D_n$.*

Proof. By Theorem 3, the theorem is true if the two rows in question are adjacent. Suppose, then, in the general case, that the two rows are not adjacent but that there are m intervening rows. Call the two rows to be interchanged α and β. By successively interchanging α and an *adjacent* row, m times, we may bring α adjacent to β. This changes the sign of the determinant m times. Next, interchange α and β and then continue to move β one row at a time, interchanging it with the m rows mentioned above, until it comes into the position originally occupied by α. This changes the sign $(m + 1)$ times and results in the determinant D_n' in which the rows α and β of D_n have been interchanged. Altogether, the sign has been changed $m + (m + 1) = 2m + 1$ times; that is

$$D_n' = (-1)^{2m+1} D_n.$$

But $2m + 1$ is odd for any integer m; hence

$$D_n' = -D_n.$$

THEOREM 5. *If two rows of D_n are identical, then $D_n = 0$.*

Proof. Interchange the two identical rows and call the result D_n'. Then $D_n' = -D_n$ by Theorem 4. But the interchange of two *identical* rows leaves D_n unaltered; that is, $D_n' = D_n$. Therefore $D_n = -D_n$, $2D_n = 0$; hence $D_n = 0$.

456   DETERMINANTS AND LINEAR EQUATIONS

COROLLARY. *If two rows of D_n are proportional, then $D_n = 0$.*

Proof. Suppose the elements of row α are all k times the corresponding elements of row β. Then, by Theorem 2, the determinant is k times a determinant whose α and β rows are identical, and this is zero by Theorem 5.

EXAMPLE.

$$\begin{vmatrix} 1 & 3 & -2 \\ 2 & 4 & 5 \\ -4 & -12 & 8 \end{vmatrix} = -4 \begin{vmatrix} 1 & 3 & -2 \\ 2 & 4 & 5 \\ 1 & 3 & -2 \end{vmatrix} = 0.$$

The -4 may be factored out of the third row. Then the first and third rows are identical and the result is zero by Theorem 5.

THEOREM 6. *Suppose each element a_{kj} in the kth row of D_n is a sum*

$$a_{kj} = b_{kj} + c_{kj}, \qquad j = 1, 2, \ldots, n.$$

Let D_n' be obtained from D_n by replacing the elements a_{kj} of the kth row by b_{kj}, and let D_n'' be obtained from D_n by replacing the elements of the kth row by c_{kj}. Then

$$D_n = D_n' + D_n''.$$

Proof. Each product in the expansion of D_n contains a term

$$a_{ki_k} = b_{ki_k} + c_{ki_k}$$

as a factor and leads to a product in the expansion of D_n' plus a product in the expansion of D_n''. Adding these (signed) products leads to the result stated.

EXAMPLE.

$$\begin{vmatrix} a_{11} & a_{12} & a_{13} \\ b_{21} + c_{21} & b_{22} + c_{22} & b_{23} + c_{23} \\ a_{31} & a_{32} & a_{33} \end{vmatrix} = \begin{vmatrix} a_{11} & a_{12} & a_{13} \\ b_{21} & b_{22} & b_{23} \\ a_{31} & a_{32} & a_{33} \end{vmatrix} + \begin{vmatrix} a_{11} & a_{12} & a_{13} \\ c_{21} & c_{22} & c_{23} \\ a_{31} & a_{32} & a_{33} \end{vmatrix}$$

THEOREM 7. *The value of a determinant of order n is unaltered if to each element of any row is added k times the corresponding element of some other row, where k is any constant.*

Proof. Let D_n be the given determinant and let D_n' be the result of adding k times the rth row of D_n to its tth row ($r \neq t$). Then, by Theorem 6, D_n' is the sum of two determinants, one of which is D_n and the other is zero by the corollary to Theorem 5.

EXAMPLE.

$$
\begin{vmatrix}
a_1 & b_1 & c_1 \\
a_2 & b_2 & c_2 \\
a_3 + ka_1 & b_3 + kb_1 & c_3 + kc_1
\end{vmatrix}
=
\begin{vmatrix}
a_1 & b_1 & c_1 \\
a_2 & b_2 & c_2 \\
a_3 & b_3 & c_3
\end{vmatrix}
+
\begin{vmatrix}
a_1 & b_1 & c_1 \\
a_2 & b_2 & c_2 \\
ka_1 & kb_1 & kc_1
\end{vmatrix}
$$

The second determinant on the right is zero, since its third row is proportional to its first row.

THEOREM 8. *Let D_n be a determinant of order n and let D'_n be obtained by taking the 1st, 2nd, ..., nth rows respectively of D_n as the 1st, 2nd, ..., nth columns respectively of D'_n. Then*

$$D'_n = D_n.$$

Proof. If we denote the elements in the ith row and jth column of D_n and D'_n respectively by a_{ij} and a'_{ij}, the relation between D'_n and D_n is expressed by the equations

$$a'_{ij} = a_{ji}, \qquad i, j = 1, 2, \ldots, n.$$

By definition,

$$D'_n = \Sigma \pm a'_{1j_1} a'_{2j_2} \ldots a'_{nj_n},$$

where $j_1, j_2, \ldots, j_n$ is a permutation of $1, 2, \ldots, n$. In terms of the elements a_{ij} of D_n, this is the same as

$$D'_n = \Sigma \pm a_{j_1 1} a_{j_2 2} \ldots a_{j_n n},$$

and each signed product

$$\pm a_{j_1 1} a_{j_2 2} \ldots a_{j_n n} \tag{5}$$

corresponds to one and only one signed product

$$\pm a_{1i_1} a_{2i_2} \ldots a_{ni_n} \tag{6}$$

in the expansion of D_n in the following manner. Since $j_1, j_2, \ldots, j_n$ is a permutation of $1, 2, \ldots, n$, we may rearrange the factors in the product (5) so as to have the first subscripts appearing in the natural order $1, 2, 3,$ $\ldots, n$. This induces a permutation $i_1, i_2, \ldots, i_n$ in the second subscripts and gives the product (6), except that there is at least a possibility that the signs in (5) and in (6) may not agree. The fact is, however, that the signs do agree, since the permutation $j_1, j_2, \ldots, j_n$ in (5) and the related permutation $i_1, i_2, \ldots, i_n$ in (6) are both even or both odd, as we shall prove below. Let us accept this as true for the present; then D'_n is the sum of all signed products (5) and D_n is the sum of the equal signed products (6), that is,

$$D'_n = D_n.$$

Let us now prove the statement that the permutations $j_1, \ldots, j_n$ and $i_1, \ldots, i_n$ above are both even or both odd. To this end, we consider the two sequences of double subscripts

$$P': \quad (j_1 1), (j_2 2), \ldots, (j_n n) \tag{7}$$

and

$$P: \quad (1 i_1), (2 i_2), \ldots, (n i_n). \tag{8}$$

In P' the second subscripts are in their natural order $1, 2, \ldots, n$, so that there are no inversions in their order. Hence the total number T' of inversions in P', counting inversions in the first subscripts $j_1, j_2, \ldots, j_n$ plus inversions in the second subscripts, is the same as the index I' of the permutation $j_1, j_2, \ldots, j_n$. Similarly, the total number T of inversions in P, counting inversions in the first subscripts $1, 2, \ldots, n$ plus inversions in the second subscripts $i_1, i_2, \ldots, i_n$, is equal to the index I of the permutation $i_1, i_2, \ldots, i_n$. Now (8) may be obtained from (7) by a sequence of transpositions of adjacent terms. Each such transposition changes the number of inversions in the first subscripts by ± 1 and also changes the number of inversions in the second subscripts by ± 1, hence changes the sum total of inversions by 2, 0, or -2, but always by an *even* number. Thus T and T' differ by an even integer, so that I and I' also differ by an even integer. Thus the permutations are both even or both odd as was asserted.

EXAMPLE. The term $a_{21} a_{32} a_{13}$ has its second subscripts arranged in natural order. The index of the permutation 2, 3, 1 of its first subscripts is 2. If we rearrange the factors so as to put the first subscripts in natural order, we have $a_{13} a_{21} a_{32}$. Then the second subscripts form the permutation 3, 1, 2, which also has index 2.

Remark. The import of Theorem 8 is that each theorem about determinants which contains the word "row" in its statement is true when the word "column" is substituted everywhere for the word row. For example, Theorem 5 is true if stated for columns instead of rows: "If two columns of a determinant are identical, the determinant is zero." For we may, by Theorem 8, interchange rows and columns in the original determinant. (In some theorems a second interchange of rows and columns may be required to establish the end result.)

THEOREM 9. *If D has the special form*

$$D = \begin{vmatrix} a_{11} & 0 & 0 & \ldots & 0 \\ a_{21} & a_{22} & a_{23} & \ldots & a_{2n} \\ \ldots & \ldots & \ldots & \ldots & \ldots \\ a_{n1} & a_{n2} & a_{n3} & \ldots & a_{nn} \end{vmatrix}, \tag{9}$$

in which all elements after the first in its first row are zero, then D is a_{11} times its minor; that is,

$$D = a_{11} \begin{vmatrix} a_{22} & a_{23} & \cdots & a_{2n} \\ \cdots & \cdots & \cdots & \cdots \\ a_{n2} & a_{n3} & \cdots & a_{nn} \end{vmatrix}. \tag{10}$$

Proof. In the expansion for D,

$$D = \sum \pm a_{1i_1} a_{2i_2} \cdots a_{ni_n},$$

each product is zero except possibly those in which $i_1 = 1$. Hence

$$D = a_{11}(\sum \pm a_{2i_2} \cdots a_{ni_n})$$

and the signed products in the sum are precisely the same as the signed products in the expansion of the minor of a_{11}.

COROLLARY. *The value of a triangular determinant*

$$D = \begin{vmatrix} a_{11} & 0 & 0 & \cdots & 0 \\ a_{21} & a_{22} & 0 & \cdots & 0 \\ \cdots & \cdots & \cdots & \cdots & \cdots \\ a_{n1} & a_{n2} & a_{n3} & \cdots & a_{nn} \end{vmatrix}, \tag{11}$$

in which all elements above the main diagonal are zero, is simply the product of the elements on this diagonal; that is,

$$D = a_{11}a_{22} \cdots a_{nn}.$$

It should, of course, be noted that Theorem 9 has a companion theorem for the case where the elements below a_{11} in the first column are zero. Also, the value of a triangular determinant which is zero everywhere *below* the main diagonal is just the product of the diagonal elements.

THEOREM 10. *If D has the special form*

$$D = \begin{vmatrix} a_{11} & a_{12} & \cdots & a_{1n} \\ \cdots & \cdots & \cdots & \cdots \\ 0 & 0 & a_{ij} & 0 \\ \cdots & \cdots & \cdots & \cdots \\ a_{n1} & a_{n2} & \cdots & a_{nn} \end{vmatrix}, \tag{12}$$

in which all elements of the ith row are zero except for the element a_{ij} in the jth column, then

$$D = (-1)^{i+j}a_{ij}D_{ij}, \tag{13}$$

where D_{ij} is the minor of a_{ij} obtained by covering up the ith row and jth column in D.

Proof. By $(i-1)$ successive row transpositions followed by $(j-1)$ column transpositions, the element a_{ij} of D may be brought into the upper left corner of a determinant D' having the special form described in Theorem 9. The minor of this element in D' is the same as the minor D_{ij} of the element a_{ij} in D. Hence

$$D' = a_{ij}D_{ij}.$$

But, by Theorem 4 and its analog for columns,

$$D' = (-1)^{(i-1)+(j-1)}D$$

or

$$D = (-1)^{i+j}D',$$

so that

$$D = (-1)^{i+j}a_{ij}D_{ij}.$$

Of course, a companion theorem for columns is also true. The results may be summarized by saying that whenever all but one of the elements of a row or column of a determinant are zero, the order of the determinant may be reduced by unity by simply multiplying the element times its signed minor, the sign being given by $(-1)^{i+j}$, where i and j are the row and column numbers of the element in question.

EXAMPLE 1. Exploiting the first row of the fourth order determinant below, we have

$$\begin{vmatrix} 0 & 2 & 0 & 0 \\ 3 & 4 & 0 & 0 \\ -2 & -7 & 4 & 0 \\ 6 & 8 & -1 & 5 \end{vmatrix} = -2 \begin{vmatrix} 3 & 0 & 0 \\ -2 & 4 & 0 \\ 6 & -1 & 5 \end{vmatrix} = -120.$$

The 2 in the first row and second column must be multiplied by $(-1)^{1+2}$ times its minor. The minor is a triangular determinant whose value is simply $(3)\,(4)\,(5) = 60$.

In the next example, we illustrate how Theorem 7 and the corresponding theorem for columns are used to transform a given determinant into the special form where all but one of the elements of a row or column are zero. The order of the determinant is then reduced by one and the process repeated if desired. Note that several applications of Theorem 7 may be combined in one step provided the same base row (or column) is used to modify several other rows (or columns). In every case, the base row itself is *not* changed. That is, if we multiply the first row by 3 and add it to the second row, we thereby get a new second row, but we do not change the first row when we do this. Of course we may now, if we wish, use a new base row to alter the first row.

EXAMPLE 2. In the following fourth order determinant we use the first row to obtain zeros in all but one place in the fourth column. We denote the second row by R_2, and so forth, and replace

$$R_2 \quad \text{by} \quad R_2 + R_1,$$

$$R_3 \quad \text{by} \quad R_3 + R_1,$$

$$R_4 \quad \text{by} \quad R_4 + 3R_1,$$

and do not change R_1.

$$D = \begin{vmatrix} 1 & 3 & 2 & -1 \\ 2 & -1 & 3 & 1 \\ -1 & 2 & 1 & 1 \\ -2 & -5 & 2 & 3 \end{vmatrix} = \begin{vmatrix} 1 & 3 & 2 & -1 \\ 3 & 2 & 5 & 0 \\ 0 & 5 & 3 & 0 \\ 1 & 4 & 8 & 0 \end{vmatrix}.$$

This determinant is equal to the element -1 in its first row and fourth column times $(-1)^{4+1}$ times the minor obtained by deleting the first row and fourth column; that is,

$$D = (-1)(-1)^{4+1} \begin{vmatrix} 3 & 2 & 5 \\ 0 & 5 & 3 \\ 1 & 4 & 8 \end{vmatrix}.$$

This third order determinant can be evaluated at once, or we may further transform it to get another zero in its first column by adding -3 times its third row to its first row. Thus

$$D = \begin{vmatrix} 0 & -10 & -19 \\ 0 & 5 & 3 \\ 1 & 4 & 8 \end{vmatrix} = (1)(-1)^{3+1} \begin{vmatrix} -10 & -19 \\ 5 & 3 \end{vmatrix} = +(-30 + 95) = 65.$$

PROBLEMS

1. Following the notation used in the proof of Theorem 3, calculate the numbers q, r, s and q', r', s' relative to the permutations

$$\underbrace{5, 1,}_{Q} \quad \underbrace{3, 6,}_{R} \quad \underbrace{2, 4}_{S} \quad \text{and} \quad \underbrace{5, 1,}_{Q'} \quad \underbrace{6, 3,}_{R'} \quad \underbrace{2, 4.}_{S'}$$

Apply Theorem 5 to the following problems (2 and 3):

2. Show that the determinantal equation

$$\begin{vmatrix} x^2 & x & 1 \\ 4 & 2 & 1 \\ 9 & -3 & 1 \end{vmatrix} = 0$$

has roots $x = 2$, $x = -3$.

3. Let $P_1(x_1, y_1)$, $P_2(x_2, y_2)$, and $P_3(x_3, y_3)$ be the vertices of a triangle. Show that the area of the triangle is the absolute value of

$$\tfrac{1}{2} \begin{vmatrix} x_1 & y_1 & 1 \\ x_2 & y_2 & 1 \\ x_3 & y_3 & 1 \end{vmatrix}.$$

[*Hint:* Write the coordinates of P_2 and P_3 as

$$x_2 = x_1 + a \cos \alpha, \qquad y_2 = y_1 + a \sin \alpha,$$
$$x_3 = x_1 + b \cos \beta, \qquad y_3 = y_1 + b \sin \beta,$$

where $a = |P_1 P_2|$, $b = |P_1 P_3|$, while α and β are angles from the horizontal to $\overrightarrow{P_1 P_2}$ and $\overrightarrow{P_1 P_3}$ respectively. Sketch.]

4. Evaluate:

$$\begin{vmatrix} 1 & 3 & -1 & 2 \\ 2 & 1 & 3 & 1 \\ -1 & 2 & -1 & 3 \\ -2 & 1 & 2 & -3 \end{vmatrix}.$$

5. Evaluate:

$$\begin{vmatrix} 4 & 3 & -2 & 7 \\ 8 & 1 & -4 & 6 \\ 6 & 2 & -3 & 11 \\ 10 & 4 & -5 & -8 \end{vmatrix}.$$

6. Show that the determinant

$$\begin{vmatrix} 1 & x_1 & x_1^2 \\ 1 & x_2 & x_2^2 \\ 1 & x_3 & x_3^2 \end{vmatrix}$$

is equal to the product

$$(x_3 - x_1)(x_3 - x_2)(x_2 - x_1). \qquad [\textit{Hint:} \text{ Use Theorem 5.}]$$

7. Generalize the result of Problem 6, and show that

$$
\begin{vmatrix}
1 & x_1 & x_1^2 & \cdots & x_1^{n-1} \\
1 & x_2 & x_2^2 & \cdots & x_2^{n-1} \\
1 & x_3 & x_3^2 & \cdots & x_3^{n-1} \\
\cdots & \cdots & \cdots & & \cdots \\
1 & x_n & x_n^2 & \cdots & x_n^{n-1}
\end{vmatrix}
= \underset{i>j}{\Pi} \, (x_i - x_j),
$$

where the Π symbol denotes the product of all factors of the form $(x_i - x_j)$ that can be formed with $i > j$, i and j ranging between 1 and n inclusive; i.e., $n \geq i > j \geq 1$. There are $[n(n - 1)]/2$ such factors.

10–5 Expansion by cofactors. In the expansion of a determinant

$$
D =
\begin{vmatrix}
a_{11} & a_{12} & \cdots & a_{1n} \\
a_{21} & a_{22} & \cdots & a_{2n} \\
\cdots & \cdots & \cdots & \cdots \\
a_{n1} & a_{n2} & \cdots & a_{nn}
\end{vmatrix}
\tag{1}
$$

as the sum of all signed products

$$
D = \Sigma \pm a_{1i_1} a_{2i_2} \cdots a_{ni_n},
\tag{2}
$$

we may arrange the products in blocks from which common factors may be removed. Thus, for example, we may collect all those products for which $i_1 = 1$ in (2), then all terms in which $i_1 = 2$, and so forth. The result may be written in the form

$$
D = a_{11}A_{11} + a_{12}A_{12} + \cdots + a_{1n}A_{1n},
\tag{3}
$$

where A_{1j} is called the cofactor of $a_{1j}; j = 1, \ldots, n$. More generally, we could single out the kth row of D instead of its first row, and write the expression in the form

$$
D = a_{k1}A_{k1} + a_{k2}A_{k2} + \cdots + a_{kn}A_{kn},
\tag{4}
$$

which is called the expansion of D by cofactors of the elements of the kth row.

We may interpret Eq. (4) as follows. If we were to take all elements $a_{k2}, a_{k3}, \ldots, a_{kn}$ after the first, in the kth row of D, to be zero, then by (4) the resulting determinant D' would have the value

$$
D' = a_{k1}A_{k1};
$$

that is,

$$D' = \begin{vmatrix} a_{11} & a_{12} & \ldots & a_{1n} \\ \ldots & \ldots & \ldots & \ldots \\ a_{k1} & 0 & \ldots & 0 \\ \ldots & \ldots & \ldots & \ldots \\ a_{n1} & a_{n2} & \ldots & a_{nn} \end{vmatrix} = a_{k1}A_{k1}. \tag{5}$$

In general, the right side of (4) may be interpreted as the sum of n determinants of the type exhibited in (5), in which all elements of the kth row are replaced by zeros except for one element a_{kj}; that is,

$$D = \begin{vmatrix} a_{11} & a_{12} & a_{13} & \ldots & a_{1n} \\ \ldots & \ldots & \ldots & \ldots & \ldots \\ a_{k1} & a_{k2} & a_{k3} & \ldots & a_{kn} \\ \ldots & \ldots & \ldots & \ldots & \ldots \\ a_{n1} & a_{n2} & a_{n3} & \ldots & a_{nn} \end{vmatrix} = \begin{vmatrix} a_{11} & a_{12} & \ldots & a_{1n} \\ \ldots & \ldots & \ldots & \ldots \\ a_{k1} & 0 & \ldots & 0 \\ \ldots & \ldots & \ldots & \ldots \\ a_{n1} & a_{n2} & \ldots & a_{nn} \end{vmatrix}$$

$$+ \begin{vmatrix} a_{11} & a_{12} & \ldots & a_{1n} \\ \ldots & \ldots & \ldots & \ldots \\ 0 & a_{k2} & \ldots & 0 \\ \ldots & \ldots & \ldots & \ldots \\ a_{n1} & a_{n2} & \ldots & a_{nn} \end{vmatrix} + \cdots + \begin{vmatrix} a_{11} & a_{12} & \ldots & a_{1n} \\ \ldots & \ldots & \ldots & \ldots \\ 0 & 0 & \ldots & a_{kn} \\ \ldots & \ldots & \ldots & \ldots \\ a_{n1} & a_{n2} & \ldots & a_{nn} \end{vmatrix}. \tag{6}$$

This may also be interpreted as a generalization of Theorem 6 of the preceding article and may in fact be obtained by repeated application of that theorem.

Now each of the determinants in (6) which has all but one element zero in its kth row may be evaluated by means of Theorem 10 of the preceding article. The results are summarized in the following theorem.

THEOREM 1. *The sum of the products of the elements of any row (or column) by their respective cofactors is equal to the determinant. The cofactor of the element in the kth row and jth column is $(-1)^{k+j}$ times its minor.*

In expanding a determinant by cofactors, it may be convenient first to transform the determinant into a form in which all elements, except one, of some row (or column) are zero. This method was illustrated in the preceding article in connection with Theorem 10.

On the other hand, if we wish to avoid these preliminary transformations, we may do so at the expense of using all the elements of a row times their respective cofactors. Thus a fourth order determinant reduces to four third order determinants, in general.

EXAMPLE 1. Show that

$$\begin{vmatrix} x & y & 1 \\ x_1 & y_1 & 1 \\ x_2 & y_2 & 1 \end{vmatrix} = 0$$

is the equation of the straight line through the points (x_1, y_1) and (x_2, y_2) provided the two points are distinct.

Solution. If the determinant is expanded by elements of its first row, the result is a linear equation of the form $Ax + By + C = 0$, which represents a straight line since one, at least, of A and B is not zero. Furthermore, if one substitutes (x_1, y_1) for (x, y) in the determinant, the first two rows are identical and the equation is satisfied. Hence (x_1, y_1) does lie on the line. The same is true of (x_2, y_2).

THEOREM 2. *If the elements of any row (or column) are multiplied by the cofactors of the corresponding elements of some other row (or column) and the products added, the result is zero.*

Proof. The result may be interpreted as the expansion of a determinant having two identical rows (or columns) and hence is zero by a previous theorem. We shall illustrate this interpretation for a third order determinant. Start with any determinant

$$D = \begin{vmatrix} a_{11} & a_{12} & a_{13} \\ a_{21} & a_{22} & a_{23} \\ a_{31} & a_{32} & a_{33} \end{vmatrix}$$

and expand it by cofactors of any row, say the second to be specific. Then

$$D = a_{21}A_{21} + a_{22}A_{22} + a_{23}A_{23}. \tag{7}$$

Suppose one now replaces a_{21}, a_{22}, and a_{23} by other numbers, say c_1, c_2, and c_3 respectively in (7), with a result

$$D' = c_1A_{21} + c_2A_{22} + c_3A_{23}. \tag{8}$$

This may be interpreted as the expansion by cofactors relative to the second row in

$$D' = \begin{vmatrix} a_{11} & a_{12} & a_{13} \\ c_1 & c_2 & c_3 \\ a_{31} & a_{32} & a_{33} \end{vmatrix}, \tag{9}$$

since the cofactors of c_1, c_2, and c_3 in D' are precisely the original cofactors A_{21}, A_{22}, A_{23} respectively. In particular, if c_1, c_2, and c_3 are taken to be the elements of either the first or the third row of D, then (8) is the sum of products of elements of that row by the cofactors of corresponding elements of a different row, while simultaneously the determinant D' in (9) then has two identical rows, and hence $D' = 0$ as stated in the theorem.

These two theorems form the basis for the solution, by determinants, of n simultaneous linear equations in n unknowns, which we shall discuss in the next article.

PROBLEMS

1. Suppose the elements of the determinant

$$F = \begin{vmatrix} u_1 & v_1 & w_1 \\ u_2 & v_2 & w_2 \\ u_3 & v_3 & w_3 \end{vmatrix}$$

are differentiable functions of x. Prove that

$$\frac{dF}{dx} = \begin{vmatrix} \dfrac{du_1}{dx} & \dfrac{dv_1}{dx} & \dfrac{dw_1}{dx} \\ u_2 & v_2 & w_2 \\ u_3 & v_3 & w_3 \end{vmatrix} + \begin{vmatrix} u_1 & v_1 & w_1 \\ \dfrac{du_2}{dx} & \dfrac{dv_2}{dx} & \dfrac{dw_2}{dx} \\ u_3 & v_3 & w_3 \end{vmatrix} + \begin{vmatrix} u_1 & v_1 & w_1 \\ u_2 & v_2 & w_2 \\ \dfrac{du_3}{dx} & \dfrac{dv_3}{dx} & \dfrac{dw_3}{dx} \end{vmatrix}.$$

State the result in words as a rule for differentiating a determinant of order 3. Can you generalize the result to a determinant of any order n?

2. Write out the sum of the products of the elements of the second row times the cofactors of the corresponding elements of the third row in the determinant

$$\begin{vmatrix} 2 & 3 & -1 \\ -2 & -3 & 2 \\ 3 & 2 & 1 \end{vmatrix}.$$

10–6 Solution of simultaneous linear equations. In the discussion to follow we shall work with three equations in three unknowns in order to simplify the writing, but the argument used may be applied to n equations in n unknowns. We shall accordingly denote the unknowns by x_1, x_2, and x_3, since such a notation lends itself to generalization. The equations may then be represented by

$$a_{11}x_1 + a_{12}x_2 + a_{13}x_3 = c_1,$$

$$a_{21}x_1 + a_{22}x_2 + a_{23}x_3 = c_2, \tag{1}$$

$$a_{31}x_1 + a_{32}x_2 + a_{33}x_3 = c_3.$$

The coefficients of the unknowns may be used to form the determinant

$$D = \begin{vmatrix} a_{11} & a_{12} & a_{13} \\ a_{21} & a_{22} & a_{23} \\ a_{31} & a_{32} & a_{33} \end{vmatrix}, \tag{2}$$

which is called the determinant of the system. In forming this determinant, the first row contains the coefficients, in order, of the unknowns x_1, x_2, x_3 in the first equation. Similarly, each row in D corresponds to one equation of the system, and each column of D corresponds to one of the unknowns.

The solution of the equations (1) by determinants is given by the following theorem, which is known as "Cramer's rule":

THEOREM. *If the determinant D of the coefficients in a system of n linear equations in n unknowns is not zero, then the equations have a unique solution. In the solution, each unknown may be expressed as a fraction of two determinants with denominator D and with numerator obtained from D by replacing the column of coefficients of the unknown in question by the constants $c_1, c_2, \ldots, c_n$.*

Proof. Suppose x_1, x_2, x_3 are three numbers which satisfy the system (1). Then if we multiply these equations by constants and add to get new equations, the same three numbers must satisfy these equations also. Now we choose multipliers in the following way.

Suppose, first, that we wish to find x_1. We calculate the cofactors A_{11}, A_{21}, and A_{31} of the elements in the first column of D. Then we multiply the first equation by A_{11}, the second by A_{21}, and the third by A_{31}, and add. The resulting new equation is

$$(a_{11}A_{11} + a_{21}A_{21} + a_{31}A_{31})x_1 + (a_{12}A_{11} + a_{22}A_{21} + a_{32}A_{31})x_2$$

$$+ (a_{13}A_{11} + a_{23}A_{21} + a_{33}A_{31})x_3 = c_1A_{11} + c_2A_{21} + c_3A_{31}. \tag{3}$$

In this equation, the coefficient which multiplies x_1 is the sum of products of the elements of the first column of D by their cofactors, which by Theorem 1 of the previous article is just D. But the coefficient which multiplies x_2 is the sum of products of the elements of the second column of D by the cofactors of the corresponding elements of the first column of D, and this is zero by Theorem 2 above. Similarly, the coefficient of x_3 is zero. Hence (3) contains only x_1 and has the form

$$x_1 \begin{vmatrix} a_{11} & a_{12} & a_{13} \\ a_{21} & a_{22} & a_{23} \\ a_{31} & a_{32} & a_{33} \end{vmatrix} = \begin{vmatrix} c_1 & a_{12} & a_{13} \\ c_2 & a_{22} & a_{23} \\ c_3 & a_{32} & a_{33} \end{vmatrix}, \tag{4}$$

where we have simply written out the determinant D on the left, while the right sides of (4) and (3) are equal, as can be seen at once if the determinant in (4) is expanded by cofactors according to the elements of its first column. Hence, if the determinant D is not zero, the value that x_1 must have, if x_1, x_2, x_3 are to satisfy the system (1), may be found by division:

$$x_1 = \frac{\begin{vmatrix} c_1 & a_{12} & a_{13} \\ c_2 & a_{22} & a_{23} \\ c_3 & a_{32} & a_{33} \end{vmatrix}}{\begin{vmatrix} a_{11} & a_{12} & a_{13} \\ a_{21} & a_{22} & a_{23} \\ a_{31} & a_{32} & a_{33} \end{vmatrix}}.$$

The same argument may be repeated for each of the other unknowns; we simply multiply the equations of the system (1) by the cofactors in D of the elements in the column of D which corresponds to the unknown in question, and then add the results to obtain a new equation. In the equation thus obtained all terms drop out except for the one unknown, and the value of the unknown is then found to be precisely the kind of a fraction described in the theorem.

EXAMPLE 1.
$$x + y + z = 1,$$
$$2x - y + z = 0,$$
$$x + 2y - z = 4.$$

Solution. The determinant of the system is

$$D = \begin{vmatrix} 1 & 1 & 1 \\ 2 & -1 & 1 \\ 1 & 2 & -1 \end{vmatrix}.$$

Suppose we are interested in finding z. We then calculate the cofactors of the elements of the third column of D, namely,

$$\begin{vmatrix} 2 & -1 \\ 1 & 2 \end{vmatrix} = 5, \qquad - \begin{vmatrix} 1 & 1 \\ 1 & 2 \end{vmatrix} = -1, \qquad \begin{vmatrix} 1 & 1 \\ 2 & -1 \end{vmatrix} = -3.$$

Multiplying the first equation by 5, the second by -1, and the third by -3, and adding, we obtain

$$(5 - 2 - 3)x + (5 + 1 - 6)y + (5 - 1 + 3)z = 5 - 12,$$

or

$$7z = -7, \qquad z = -1.$$

The method described shows that if the original equations have a solution, then it must be given by Cramer's rule. It does not, however, show that these values of the unknowns actually do satisfy the original equations. This may be done by substituting the answers back into the original equations.

For the first equation in (1), written in the form

$$a_{11}x_1 + a_{12}x_2 + a_{13}x_3 - c_1 = 0,$$

when we substitute the expressions for x_1, x_2, and x_3 in terms of determinants, and clear of fractions, the left side becomes

$$a_{11} \begin{vmatrix} c_1 & a_{12} & a_{13} \\ c_2 & a_{22} & a_{23} \\ c_3 & a_{32} & a_{33} \end{vmatrix} + a_{12} \begin{vmatrix} a_{11} & c_1 & a_{13} \\ a_{21} & c_2 & a_{23} \\ a_{31} & c_3 & a_{33} \end{vmatrix}$$

$$+ a_{13} \begin{vmatrix} a_{11} & a_{12} & c_1 \\ a_{21} & a_{22} & c_2 \\ a_{31} & a_{32} & c_3 \end{vmatrix} - c_1 \begin{vmatrix} a_{11} & a_{12} & a_{13} \\ a_{21} & a_{22} & a_{23} \\ a_{31} & a_{32} & a_{33} \end{vmatrix}. \qquad (5)$$

In each of the first two determinants, move the column of constants c_1, c_2, c_3 to the right, changing signs twice in the first determinant and once in the second. The result may then be identified as the expansion, by cofactors relative to the first row, of the fourth order determinant

$$\begin{vmatrix} a_{11} & a_{12} & a_{13} & c_1 \\ a_{11} & a_{12} & a_{13} & c_1 \\ a_{21} & a_{22} & a_{23} & c_2 \\ a_{31} & a_{32} & a_{33} & c_3 \end{vmatrix}. \qquad (6)$$

This is zero, since its first two rows are identical. A determinant similar to the one in (6) also results when the expressions for the unknowns are substituted into the remaining equations in (1), except that the first row becomes the same as the third or fourth row respectively. Thus the expressions given by Cramer's rule give the unique solution of the system of equations, when D is not zero.

EXAMPLE 2. To illustrate Cramer's rule, we solve the following system by determinants.

$$2x + y - z = 0,$$
$$x - y + z = 6,$$
$$x + 2y + z = 3.$$

The determinant of the coefficients is

$$D = \begin{vmatrix} 2 & 1 & -1 \\ 1 & -1 & 1 \\ 1 & 2 & 1 \end{vmatrix} = \begin{vmatrix} 2 & 1 & -1 \\ 3 & 0 & 0 \\ 3 & 3 & 0 \end{vmatrix} = -9.$$

Since $D \neq 0$, we may solve by determinants. Thus

$$x = \frac{\begin{vmatrix} 0 & 1 & -1 \\ 6 & -1 & 1 \\ 3 & 2 & 1 \end{vmatrix}}{D} = \frac{-18}{-9} = 2,$$

$$y = \frac{\begin{vmatrix} 2 & 0 & -1 \\ 1 & 6 & 1 \\ 1 & 3 & 1 \end{vmatrix}}{D} = \frac{9}{-9} = -1,$$

$$z = \frac{\begin{vmatrix} 2 & 1 & 0 \\ 1 & -1 & 6 \\ 1 & 2 & 3 \end{vmatrix}}{D} = \frac{-27}{-9} = 3.$$

As a check, we quickly verify that $x = 2$, $y = -1$, $z = 3$ actually do satisfy the original three equations.

The question naturally arises as to what the situation is regarding the solvability of the original equations when the determinant of coefficients is zero. A complete answer will not be given here, but is given in more advanced algebra courses where the subject of matrices is studied. Some idea of the complications which may arise may be gained from considering the case of three equations in three unknowns. Each such equation represents a plane in space, and the determinant of coefficients vanishes if

(a) any two of the planes are parallel or coincident, or

(b) the line of intersection of two of the planes is parallel to, or lies in, the third plane.

A solution of the system of simultaneous equations corresponds to a point on all three planes. If the cases (a) or (b) occur, there may be no point at all which lies on all three planes, or there may [for example, if the two planes in (a) are identical] be infinitely many points on all three planes. (See Fig. 10–1.) In particular, there are infinitely many solutions if the three planes all intersect along one straight line.

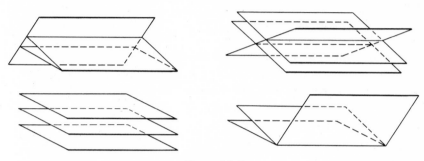

Figure 10–1

In any case where $D = 0$, one should attempt to solve the system of equations by the method of "successive elimination" illustrated below. In fact, this method is usually more economical than the solution by determinants, even in those cases where D does not vanish.

EXAMPLE 3.
$$2x - y + z = 4,$$
$$x + 3y + 2z = 12,$$
$$3x + 2y + 3z = 16.$$

Solution. The determinant of coefficients is

$$D = \begin{vmatrix} 2 & -1 & 1 \\ 1 & 3 & 2 \\ 3 & 2 & 3 \end{vmatrix} = \begin{vmatrix} 2 & -1 & 1 \\ 3 & 2 & 3 \\ 3 & 2 & 3 \end{vmatrix} = 0.$$

Multiply the second equation by 2 and by 3 respectively and subtract from the first and third equations to eliminate x from them. The three new equations are

$$x + 3y + 2z = 12,$$
$$-7y - 3z = -20,$$
$$-7y - 3z = -20.$$

Here the third equation is superfluous, since it contains no information not already given by the second equation. Thus we need only solve

$$x + 3y = 12 - 2z,$$
$$7y = 20 - 3z.$$

In these, let z have any value whatever. Then we have a solution, provided we take

$$y = \frac{20 - 3z}{7}$$

and

$$x = 12 - 2z - 3y \quad \text{or} \quad x = \frac{24 - 5z}{7}.$$

It is easily verified, by substitution into the original equations, that

$$x = \frac{24 - 5z}{7}, \quad y = \frac{20 - 3z}{7}, \quad z \text{ arbitrary}$$

do satisfy the equations. For example,

$$z = -5, \quad x = 7, \quad y = 5 \quad \text{and} \quad z = 2, \quad x = 2, \quad y = 2$$

are particular solutions.

PROBLEMS

Solve the following systems of simultaneous equations by Cramer's rule:

1. $x + y + z = 2,$
   $2x - y + z = 0,$
   $x + 2y - z = 4$

2. $2x + y - z = 2,$
   $x - y + z = 7,$
   $x + 2y + z = 4$

3. By multiplying the following equations by appropriate factors and adding, eliminate x, y, and t:

$$x + y + z + t = 6,$$
$$x - 2y + 3z + t = 2,$$
$$3x + y - z + 2t = 6,$$
$$2x + 3y + 2z - t = 2.$$

4. For what value of k may the following set of equations fail to have a unique solution?

$$x + y - z = 3,$$
$$kx - y + 2z = 5,$$
$$x + 2y - z = 4.$$

10–7   Homogeneous linear equations. There is one case in particular where one rather hopes that the determinant of the coefficients will be zero. That is in the case of homogeneous equations:

$$a_{11}x_1 + a_{12}x_2 + a_{13}x_3 = 0,$$

$$a_{21}x_1 + a_{22}x_2 + a_{23}x_3 = 0, \tag{1}$$

$$a_{31}x_1 + a_{32}x_2 + a_{33}x_3 = 0,$$

where $x_1 = x_2 = x_3 = 0$ always gives a solution regardless of the coefficients a_{ij}. Since this solution contains no distinguishing information which is characteristic of the particular system of equations, it is referred to as the *trivial solution*. The question of interest in such a case is whether or not a *nontrivial* solution can be found. By Cramer's rule, it follows that the answer is in the negative if $D \neq 0$. On the other hand, if $D = 0$, it is true that nontrivial solutions do exist, as we shall prove in the next theorem.

THEOREM. *A necessary and sufficient condition for existence of nontrivial solutions of a system of n homogeneous linear equations in n unknowns is that the determinant of coefficients be zero.*

Proof (by induction on n). If $n = 1$, the system of equations is just $a_{11}x_1 = 0$ and this implies that $a_{11} = 0$ or $x_1 = 0$. Therefore, if the "determinant" a_{11} is not zero, only the trivial solution $x_1 = 0$ exists. But if the determinant a_{11} is zero, then x_1 may have any value; in particular, $x_1 = 1$ gives a nontrivial solution.

Suppose now that n is a positive integer and the theorem is known to be true for the smaller integer $n - 1$. We then proceed as follows to reduce the problem to the case of $n - 1$ equations in $n - 1$ unknowns. Let the given system of n equations in n unknowns be

$$a_{11}x_1 + a_{12}x_2 + \cdots + a_{1n}x_n = 0,$$

$$a_{21}x_1 + a_{22}x_2 + \cdots + a_{2n}x_n = 0, \tag{E}$$

$$\vdots$$

$$a_{n1}x_1 + a_{n2}x_2 + \cdots + a_{nn}x_n = 0.$$

Case 1. If it happens that $a_{11} = a_{21} = \cdots = a_{n1} = 0$, so that x_1 doesn't actually appear in any of equations (E), we may take $x_1 = 1$, $x_2 = x_3 = \cdots = x_n = 0$ and have a nontrivial solution of (E).

Case 2. Suppose that x_1 does appear in (E) with a nonzero coefficient. If necessary, we could rearrange the equations to have a nonzero coefficient of x_1 in the first equation. So, with no loss in generality, suppose

$$a_{11} \neq 0.$$

Then we replace (E) by the equivalent set of equations (E′):

$$x_1 + b_{12}x_2 + b_{13}x_3 + \cdots + b_{1n}x_n = 0,$$
$$b_{22}x_2 + b_{23}x_3 + \cdots + b_{2n}x_n = 0, \qquad \text{(E′)}$$
$$\vdots$$
$$b_{n2}x_2 + b_{n3}x_3 + \cdots + b_{nn}x_n = 0.$$

We divide the first equation of (E) by a_{11}, thus getting the first equation of (E′) with leading coefficient one. This equation is multiplied by a_{k1} and the result subtracted from the kth equation of (E), thus giving the kth equation of (E′); $k = 2, 3, \ldots, n$. These operations are reversible. Hence any solution of the system (E) is a solution of (E′), and conversely. The determinant $D′$ of the coefficients of the system (E′) may be obtained from the determinant D of the system (E) by dividing the first row by a_{11}, then subtracting a_{k1} times the new first row from the kth row; $k = 2, 3, \ldots, n$. Hence

$$D′ = \frac{D}{a_{11}}.$$

Therefore $D′ = 0$ if and only if $D = 0$.

But if

$$D′ = \begin{vmatrix} 1 & b_{12} & b_{13} & \cdots & b_{1n} \\ 0 & b_{22} & b_{23} & \cdots & b_{2n} \\ 0 & b_{32} & b_{33} & \cdots & b_{3n} \\ \vdots & & & & \\ 0 & b_{n2} & b_{n3} & \cdots & b_{nn} \end{vmatrix}$$

is expanded by cofactors of its first column, we see it is equal to B_{11}, the cofactor of the element in its upper left corner:

$$B_{11} = \begin{vmatrix} b_{22} & b_{23} & \cdots & b_{2n} \\ b_{32} & b_{33} & \cdots & b_{3n} \\ \cdots & \cdots & \cdots & \cdots \\ b_{n2} & b_{n3} & \cdots & b_{nn} \end{vmatrix}.$$

This is also the determinant of the $n - 1$ equations in $n - 1$ unknowns that we get by temporarily ignoring the first equation of the system (E′).

We now apply our inductive hypothesis to this system of $n - 1$ equations. By our assumption, the theorem is true for $n - 1$ equations in $n - 1$ unknowns. Therefore if $D = 0$, then $B_{11} = 0$, and the last $n - 1$

equations have a solution in which $x_2, x_3, \ldots, x_n$ are not all zero. From this we get a nontrivial solution of the full system (E′), and hence of (E), by solving the first equation for x_1 in terms of the numbers $x_2, x_3, \ldots x_n$:

$$x_1 = -b_{12}x_2 - b_{13}x_3 - \cdots - b_{1n}x_n.$$

So, if $D = 0$, the system has a nontrivial solution.

Conversely, if $D \neq 0$, then $B_{11} \neq 0$, and the only solution of the last $n - 1$ equations of (E′) is $x_2 = x_3 = \cdots = x_n = 0$. To satisfy the first equation of (E′), we must then also take $x_1 = 0$. That is, if $D \neq 0$, the system has only the trivial solution. Q.E.D.

COROLLARY. *m homogeneous linear equations in n unknowns always have nontrivial solutions if $m < n$.*

Proof. Augment the given set of equations by adjoining $n - m$ equations of the form

$$0 \cdot x_1 + 0 \cdot x_2 + \cdots + 0 \cdot x_n = 0.$$

The determinant of coefficients of the new set of n equations in n unknowns has one or more rows of zeros; hence its value is zero. Therefore it has nontrivial solutions. Q.E.D.

EXAMPLE 1.
$$x + 3y + 2z = .0,$$
$$2x - y + z = 0,$$
$$3x + 2y + 3z = 0.$$

Solution. The coefficient of x in the first equation is already 1. We subtract twice the first equation from the second, and three times the first from the third. The new system is

$$x + 3y + 2z = 0,$$
$$-7y - 3z = 0,$$
$$-7y - 3z = 0.$$

The last two equations are identical:

$$7y + 3z = 0.$$

Infinitely many numbers satisfy this equation. We may, for example, let

$$z = a \qquad (a \text{ arbitrary})$$

so long as we then take

$$y = \frac{-3a}{7}.$$

The original system requires that

$$x = -3y - 2z = \frac{9a}{7} - 2a = \frac{-5a}{7}.$$

In particular, if we take $a = 1$, we have a solution

$$x = -\tfrac{5}{7}, \qquad y = -\tfrac{3}{7}, \qquad z = 1.$$

Another solution, with $a = 7$, is

$$x = -5, \qquad y = -3, \qquad z = 7.$$

Every solution in this case is proportional to this solution; that is,

$$x = -5k, \qquad y = -3k, \qquad z = 7k$$

represents the general solution of the system. Assigning different values to k, $-\infty < k < +\infty$, corresponds to letting the point (x, y, z) trace out the line of intersection of the three given planes.

EXAMPLE 2.
$$x + 2y - 3z + 4t = 0,$$
$$2x - y + z - 2t = 0.$$

Solution. Subtract twice the first equation from the second:

$$x + 2y - 3z + 4t = 0,$$
$$-5y + 7z - 10t = 0.$$

In this system, or an augmented system with two more equations of the form

$$0 \cdot z + 0 \cdot t = 0, \qquad 0 \cdot t = 0,$$

we may take

$$t = a, \qquad (a \text{ arbitrary})$$

$$z = b, \qquad (b \text{ arbitrary})$$

$$y = \frac{7z - 10t}{5} = -2a + \tfrac{7}{5}b,$$

$$x = -2y + 3z - 4t = \frac{b}{5}.$$

Here we have four equations and only two unknowns, so it is not surprising that there are two "degrees of freedom" evidenced by the two arbitrary numbers a and b. If we take $a = 0$, $b = 5$, we get a solution $x_1 = 1$, $y_1 = 7$, $z_1 = 5$, $t_1 = 0$. If we take $a = 1$, $b = 0$, we get another solution $x_2 = 0$, $y_2 = -2$, $z_2 = 0$, $t_2 = 1$. The solution corresponding to $a = 1$, $b = 5$ is $x_3 = x_2 + x_1$, $y_3 = y_2 + y_1$, and so on.

EXAMPLE 3. For what values of r is $x = Ae^{rt}$, $y = Be^{rt}$ a nontrivial solution of the pair of differential equations

$$\frac{dx}{dt} = x - 2y, \qquad \frac{dy}{dt} = y - 2x?$$

Solution. Substituting the expressions given for x and y into the differential equations produces

$$Are^{rt} = Ae^{rt} - 2Be^{rt},$$

$$Bre^{rt} = Be^{rt} - 2Ae^{rt}.$$

Dividing by e^{rt} and collecting terms, we get

$$(r - 1)A + 2B = 0,$$

$$2A + (r - 1)B = 0.$$

These are two homogeneous linear equations for A and B. The determinant is

$$D = \begin{vmatrix} r - 1 & 2 \\ 2 & r - 1 \end{vmatrix} = (r - 1)^2 - 4.$$

The equations have only the trivial solution $A = B = 0$ if $D \neq 0$. To get a nontrivial solution, it is necessary that $D = 0$, or

$$r = 1 \pm 2 = 3 \quad \text{or} \quad -1.$$

Case 1. $r = 3$. Then the two equations for A and B are identical:

$$2A + 2B = 0, \quad \text{or} \quad B = -A.$$

So one solution is

$$x = Ae^{3t}, \quad y = -Ae^{3t}.$$

Case 2. $r = -1$. Then the equations for A and B become

$$-2A + 2B = 0, \quad 2A - 2B = 0,$$

or

$$B = A.$$

So another solution is

$$x = Ae^{-t}, \quad y = Ae^{-t}.$$

PROBLEMS

1. For what value of k do the following equations possess a nontrivial solution?

$$2x + 3y - 4z = 0,$$

$$x + ky + 3z = 0,$$

$$3x + ky - 2z = 0.$$

2. Find at least one nontrivial solution of the equations

$$x + y - z = 0,$$
$$3x - y - z = 0,$$
$$x - 3y + z = 0,$$

or else show that there is no nontrivial solution.

3. Suppose the determinant of the coefficients of the system of equations (1) is zero. Show that

$$x_1 = kA_{11}, \qquad x_2 = kA_{12}, \qquad x_3 = kA_{13}$$

is a solution of the system, for any k, where A_{11} is the cofactor of a_{11}, and so on. Could cofactors of elements of other rows than the first be used? Give a reason for your answer.

4. Verify that the system of equations

$$2x - y + z = 0,$$
$$x + 2y - z = 0,$$
$$4x + 3y - z = 0$$

has nontrivial solutions. Find some of them by using the results of Problem 3 above.

The following sets of simultaneous differential equations, Problems 5–12, possess nonzero solutions of the form $x = Ae^{rt}$, $y = Be^{rt}$ for certain values of the constants A, B, and r. Find them.

5. $\dfrac{dx}{dt} = 2x + 2y, \qquad \dfrac{dy}{dt} = x + y$

6. $\dfrac{dx}{dt} = 3x + y, \qquad \dfrac{dy}{dt} = -x + y$

7. $\dfrac{dx}{dt} = x + y, \qquad \dfrac{dy}{dt} = x + y$

8. $\dfrac{dx}{dt} = 2x + 3y, \qquad \dfrac{dy}{dt} = -x - 2y$

9. $\dfrac{dx}{dt} + x - 2y = 0, \qquad \dfrac{dy}{dt} - 2x + y = 0$

10. $\dfrac{dx}{dt} + 2x - y = 0, \qquad \dfrac{dy}{dt} - x + 2y = 0$

11. $\dfrac{dx}{dt} + 2x = 0, \qquad \dfrac{dy}{dt} - 4x - 2y = 0$

12. $\dfrac{dx}{dt} = 3x + 4y, \qquad \dfrac{dy}{dt} + x + 2y = 0$

13. If $x = A_1 e^{r_1 t}$, $y = B_1 e^{r_1 t}$ is one solution of any of the sets of differential

equations of Problems 3–10 above, and $x = A_2 e^{r_2 t}$, $y = B_2 e^{r_2 t}$ is another solution, prove that

$$x = A_1 e^{r_1 t} + A_2 e^{r_2 t},$$

$$y = B_1 e^{r_1 t} + B_2 e^{r_2 t}$$

is also a solution.

REVIEW QUESTIONS AND EXERCISES FOR CHAPTER 10

1. What methods are available for evaluating a determinant?

2. What is the effect on a determinant if:

(a) Two rows are interchanged?

(b) Three rows are permuted cyclically (the first one to be moved goes to the position of the second, the second to the position of the third, the third back to the position of the first)?

(c) Each element of a row is divided by 3?

(d) Each element of a column is subtracted from the corresponding element of a different column?

3. Under what conditions do n linear equations in n unknowns have a unique solution? When they fail to have a unique solution, they may have no solution or more than one solution. Discuss the possibilities for $n = 3$.

4. Define "homogeneous linear equations." When does a system of n homogeneous linear equations in n unknowns have nontrivial solutions? When do they have a unique solution, and what is that solution?

5. State Cramer's rule. Illustrate for three equations in three unknowns.

In each of the following problems (1–10), solve by Cramer's rule, or by the method of elimination, or show that the system of equations has no solution.

1. $2x + 3y = 5,$
   $4x - y = 3$

2. $3x + y - z = 2,$
   $x - 2y + z = 0,$
   $4x - y + z = 3$

3. $x - y + 2z = 2,$
   $x + 3y + z = 1,$
   $-7x + y + 4z = 0$

4. $x + y + z = 1,$
   $x - y = 4,$
   $x + y - 2z = 4$

5. $x + 2y + 3z = 0,$
   $x - 5y + 3z = 0,$
   $3x - z = 0$

6. $2x + y = 0,$
   $-x + 2y + z = 2,$
   $x - 2y + 5z = 5$

7. $x - y + 2z = 2,$
   $3x - 2y + 4z = 5,$
   $2y - 3z + 2 = 0$

8. $2x - y + 3z = 6,$
   $4x + y = 9,$
   $7x + 2y - z = 15$

9. $x + y + 3z = 6,$
   $x - 3y - 3z = -4,$
   $5x - 3y + 3z = 8$

10. $x - y - 3z - t = 1,$
    $2x + 4y - 2t = 2,$
    $3x + 4y - 2z = 0,$
    $x + 2z - 3t = 3$

11. Show that the three points $P_1(x_1, y_1)$, $P_2(x_2, y_2)$, $P_3(x_3, y_3)$ are collinear if and only if

$$\begin{vmatrix} x_1 & y_1 & 1 \\ x_2 & y_2 & 1 \\ x_3 & y_3 & 1 \end{vmatrix} = 0.$$

12. Let $P_1(x_1, y_1)$, $P_2(x_2, y_2)$, $P_3(x_3, y_3)$ be vertices of a triangle. Let

$$\begin{vmatrix} x & y & 1 \\ x_2 & y_2 & 1 \\ x_3 & y_3 & 1 \end{vmatrix} \equiv Ax + By + C.$$

Let $b = |P_2P_3|$ and let h be the length of the altitude from P_1 to the base $\overline{P_2P_3}$.
(a) Show that $b = \sqrt{A^2 + B^2}$. (b) Show that

$$h = \left| \frac{1}{b} D \right|,$$

where
$$D = \begin{vmatrix} x_1 & y_1 & 1 \\ x_2 & y_2 & 1 \\ x_3 & y_3 & 1 \end{vmatrix}.$$

(c) Hence deduce that the area of the triangle is $\frac{1}{2}|D|$. [Compare "Area of a Triangle and the Determinant" by G. M. Petersen, *Amer. Math. Monthly*, Vol. 62 (1955), p. 249.] (d) Find the area of the triangle with vertices $P_1(1, -1)$, $P_2(3, 1)$, $P_3(2, 4)$.

13. Show that

$$\begin{vmatrix} 1 & 1 & 1 \\ a & b & c \\ a^3 & b^3 & c^3 \end{vmatrix} = (b - a)(c - a)(c - b)(a + b + c).$$

14. Let u, v, and w be functions of x with $u' = du/dx$, $u'' = d^2u/dx^2$, $v' = dv/dx$, etc. If

$$A = \begin{vmatrix} u & v & w \\ u' & v' & w' \\ u'' & v'' & w'' \end{vmatrix},$$

show that

$$\frac{dA}{dx} = \begin{vmatrix} u & v & w \\ u' & v' & w' \\ u''' & v''' & w''' \end{vmatrix}.$$

15. Show, without expanding, that

$$\begin{vmatrix} b + c & a & 1 \\ c + a & b & 1 \\ b + a & c & 1 \end{vmatrix} = 0.$$

16. Reduce the following to an array with only four nonzero entries and thus evaluate the determinant

$$\begin{vmatrix} -1 & 1 & 1 & 1 \\ 1 & -1 & 1 & 1 \\ 1 & 1 & -1 & 1 \\ 1 & 1 & 1 & -1 \end{vmatrix}.$$

17. Solve the following system of equations:

$$x + y + z = a + b + c,$$

$$bx + cy + az = ab + bc + ca,$$

$$b^2x + c^2y + a^2z = ca^2 + ab^2 + bc^2,$$

where a, b, c are three given numbers, different from each other.

18. Show that

$$F(x) = \begin{vmatrix} A+x & a+x & a+x \\ b+x & B+x & a+x \\ b+x & b+x & C+x \end{vmatrix}$$

defines a linear function of x, and that

$$F(0) = \frac{af(b) - bf(a)}{a - b},$$

where

$$f(x) = (A - x)(B - x)(C - x).$$

19. If

$$\Delta_1 = \begin{vmatrix} a_{11} & a_{12} \\ a_{21} & a_{22} \end{vmatrix} \quad \text{and} \quad \Delta_2 = \begin{vmatrix} b_{11} & b_{12} \\ b_{21} & b_{22} \end{vmatrix},$$

show that

$$\begin{vmatrix} c_{11} & c_{12} \\ c_{21} & c_{22} \end{vmatrix} = \Delta_1\Delta_2,$$

where $c_{ij} = a_{i1}b_{1j} + a_{i2}b_{2j}$

20. (a) If three lines

$$a_1x + b_1y + c_1 = 0,$$

$$a_2x + b_2y + c_2 = 0,$$

$$a_3x + b_3y + c_3 = 0$$

pass through a point, show that $\Delta = 0$, where

$$\Delta = \begin{vmatrix} a_1 & b_1 & c_1 \\ a_2 & b_2 & c_2 \\ a_3 & b_3 & c_3 \end{vmatrix}.$$

(b) If $\Delta = 0$, do the lines necessarily pass through a point? [*Hint:* Consider the case of three parallel lines.]

21. If the equations

$$a_1x + b_1y + c_1 = 0,$$

$$a_2x + b_2y + c_2 = 0,$$

$$a_3x + b_3y + c_3 = 0$$

have a simultaneous solution, show that constants K_1, K_2, and K_3 not all zero exist such that

$$K_1(a_1x + b_1y + c_1) + K_2(a_2x + b_2y + c_2)$$

$$+ K_3(a_3x + b_3y + c_3) \equiv 0, \qquad \text{for all } x \text{ and } y.$$

Is the converse true? [*Hint:* For the converse, consider the equations

$$x + y - 1 = 0, \qquad x + y - 2 = 0, \qquad x + y - 3 = 0.]$$

Plane Analytic Geometry

11-1 Curves and equations. Analytic geometry combines algebra and calculus with geometry in the following typical problems:

(a) to study the geometric properties of a curve when its equation is given, or

(b) to find an equation of the curve when its geometric properties are known.

The cardinal principle of analytic geometry is that an equation

$$F(x, y) = 0 \tag{1}$$

determines a curve which is the locus of all and only those points $P(x, y)$ whose coordinates satisfy the given equation. Thus every point on the curve must satisfy the equation and every point which satisfies the equation is on the curve. We have already had some experience in analyzing a given equation to find the turning points and points of inflection of the curve it represents. We shall now consider certain other important characteristics which we may find by investigating a given equation.

In this chapter we shall assume that the scales on the x- and y-axes are the same, unless we specifically note otherwise.

Symmetry. If the equation of the curve is unaltered when x is replaced by $-x$, that is, if

$$F(x, y) = F(-x, y),$$

then the points (x_1, y_1) and $(-x_1, y_1)$ are both on the curve when either of them is. Then the curve is symmetric with respect to the y-axis. (See Fig. 11–1a.) In particular, an equation which contains only even powers of x represents such a curve.

Other symmetries which are easily detected are:

Symmetry about the x-axis if the equation is unaltered when y is replaced by $-y$; in particular if only even powers of y occur.

Symmetry about the origin if the equation is unaltered when x and y are replaced by $-x$ and $-y$ respectively (Fig. 11–1c).

Symmetry about the 45° line $y = x$ if the equation is unaltered when x and y are interchanged (Fig. 11–1d).

EXAMPLE 1. $x^2 + y^2 = 1$.
Symmetric about both axes, about the origin, and about the line $y = x$.

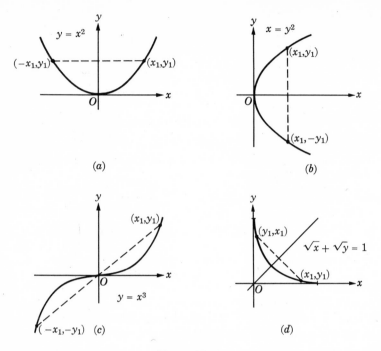

Figure 11–1

EXAMPLE 2. $x^2 - y^2 = 1$.
Symmetric about both axes and the origin. Not symmetric about the line $y = x$.

EXAMPLE 3. $xy = 1$.
Not symmetric about either axis. Symmetric about the origin and about the line $y = x$.

Extent. Only real values of x and y are considered in determining the points (x, y) whose coordinates satisfy a given equation. When even powers of a variable appear in the equation, the solution for that variable may involve square roots (or other even roots). The *extent* of the curve may then be limited by the condition that negative numbers do not have real square roots.

EXAMPLE 4. $x^2 + y^2 = 1$.
When this equation is solved for y, we get

$$y = \pm\sqrt{1 - x^2}.$$

The quantity under the radical is negative if $|x| > 1$. The extent of the curve in the x-direction is therefore limited to the interval $-1 \le x \le 1$. By symmetry about the line $y = x$, the curve is also limited in the y-direction to $-1 \le y \le 1$.

EXAMPLE 5. $x^2 - y^2 = 1$.
Solving for y, we get

$$y = \pm\sqrt{x^2 - 1}.$$

In this case, y is imaginary unless $|x| \geq 1$. There is no curve between the two lines $x = -1$ and $x = +1$. Solving for x, we get

$$x = \pm\sqrt{1 + y^2}.$$

The quantity under the radical is positive (actually it is greater than or equal to one) for all real values of y, $-\infty < y < +\infty$. The extent of this curve is not limited in the y-direction.

Intercepts. The point or points where a given curve crosses the x-axis can be found by setting $y = 0$ in the equation and solving for x. These points are called the *x-intercepts*. The y-intercepts are found in an analogous way by setting $x = 0$. If the labor involved in finding the intercepts is not excessive, they may be determined and will give specific points on the curve.

EXAMPLE 6. $x^2 + y^2 = 1$.
Setting $y = 0$, we have $x^2 = 1$. Therefore $(1, 0)$ and $(-1, 0)$ are the x-intercepts. By symmetry, $(0, 1)$ and $(0, -1)$ are the y-intercepts.

EXAMPLE 7. $x^2 - y^2 = 1$.
Setting $y = 0$, we find the x-intercepts are $(1, 0)$ and $(-1, 0)$. Setting $x = 0$, we obtain $y^2 = -1$, which has no real solutions. The curve does not have intercepts on the y-axis (see Example 5).

EXAMPLE 8. $xy = 1$.
Setting either $x = 0$ or $y = 0$ leads to the equation $0 = 1$, which has no solutions. There are no x- or y-intercepts.

Asymptotes. As the point $P(x, y)$ on a given curve moves farther and farther away from the vicinity of the origin, it may happen that the distance between P and some fixed line tends to zero. In such a case the line is called an *asymptote* of the curve. For example, if the equation of the curve has the form

$$y = \frac{N(x)}{D(x)}, \tag{2}$$

where $N(x)$ and $D(x)$ are polynomials without any factors in common, and if $x = c$ is a root of the equation

$$D(x) = 0, \tag{3}$$

then as the x-coordinate of the tracing point $P(x, y)$ approaches c, two things will occur:

1. $y \to \infty$, hence the distance $|OP| \to \infty$, and

2. $(x - c) \to 0$; that is, the horizontal distance $|P'P|$ between the curve and the vertical line $x = c$ tends to zero (see Fig. 11–2). In other words, *the line $x = c$ is an asymptote of the curve in Eq. (2) if $x = c$ makes the denominator, $D(x)$, vanish.* Such asymptotes are thus found by solving the equation explicitly for y in terms of x; then, if the result is a fraction, we set the denominator of the fraction equal to zero and solve for the numerical values of x. A similar procedure with the roles of x and y reversed shows that values of y which cause the denominator to vanish in the expression

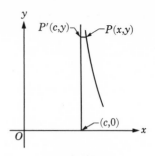

Figure 11–2

$$x = \frac{f(y)}{g(y)} \tag{4}$$

may give horizontal asymptotes of the curve. An alternate method for finding such asymptotes is to let $x \to \pm\infty$ (provided the extent of the curve does not prohibit this) in Eq. (2) and find the limiting values of y.

EXAMPLE 9. (Fig. 11–3) $y^2(x^2 - x) = x^2 + 1$. $\tag{5}$
Solving for y, we obtain

$$y = \pm\sqrt{\frac{x^2 + 1}{x(x - 1)}}. \tag{6}$$

The expression under the radical must not be negative, so no portion of the curve lies between the lines $x = 0$ and $x = 1$. But all values of $x > 1$ and all negative values of x, that is, $x < 0$, are permissible. As x approaches zero *from the left*, $y \to \pm\infty$ and as x approaches one *from the right*, $y \to \pm\infty$. The lines $x = 0$ and $x = 1$ are asymptotes of the curve. Since arbitrarily large values of $|x|$ are permitted, we also investigate the behavior of the curve as $x \to -\infty$ and again as $x \to +\infty$. The expression

$$\frac{\infty^2 + 1}{\infty(\infty - 1)},$$

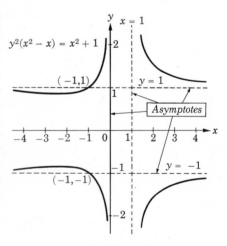

Figure 11–3

which appears if we substitute $x = \infty$ directly into (6), is meaningless, but if we write the equation of the curve in the equivalent form

$$y^2 = \frac{x^2 + 1}{x^2 - x} = \frac{1 + \dfrac{1}{x^2}}{1 - \dfrac{1}{x}}, \tag{7}$$

we readily see that $y^2 \to 1$ as $x \to \infty$ or as $x \to -\infty$. Thus the lines $y = 1$ and $y = -1$ are also asymptotes of the curve. We now scrutinize Eq. (7) more closely to see whether or not y^2 is necessarily always greater than one, or always less than one, or may be equal to one. Certainly when x tends to $+\infty$, the numerator in (7) is greater than one, while the denominator is less than one, hence the fraction is larger than one; that is,

$$y^2 > 1, \qquad y^2 \to 1 \quad \text{as} \quad x \to +\infty. \tag{8}$$

On the other hand, when x tends to $-\infty$, both $1/x^2$ and $-1/x$ are positive, so that both the numerator and denominator in (7) are greater than one. However, $1/x^2$ will be less than $-1/x$, so that the numerator is less than the denominator; that is,

$$y^2 < 1, \qquad y^2 \to 1 \quad \text{as} \quad x \to -\infty. \tag{9}$$

To determine whether or not we may ever have $y^2 = 1$, we try it, say in (5), and find

$$y^2 = 1 \qquad \text{when} \qquad x = -1. \tag{10}$$

We now have quite a bit of information about the curve represented by Eq. (5). It is immediately evident that the curve is symmetric about the x-axis, because y may be replaced by $-y$ without changing the equation. There is no curve between $x = 0$ and $x = 1$. The lines $x = 0$, $x = 1$, $y = 1$, $y = -1$ are asymptotes of the curve. It crosses $y = 1$ and $y = -1$ at $x = -1$. There is no x-intercept, because putting $y = 0$ in Eq. (5) requires $0 = x^2 + 1$, which has only imaginary roots. Using this information, we may sketch the curve with a fair degree of accuracy (see Fig. 11–3). In fact, it becomes apparent that the curve has a minimum (and a symmetrically located maximum) somewhat to the left of $x = -1$, and that there is also a point of inflection to the left of this turning point. To find these points accurately requires that we determine dy/dx and d^2y/dx^2. The turning points will be found to occur at $(-1 - \sqrt{2}, \pm\sqrt{2\sqrt{2} - 2})$. The algebra involved in finding the points of inflection is excessive.

Direction at a point. The three curves

(a) $y = x$, $dy/dx = 1$,

(b) $y = x^2$, $dy/dx = 2x$,

(c) $y = \sqrt{x}$, $dy/dx = 1/(2\sqrt{x})$

all pass through the origin and the point $(1, 1)$. But their behavior for small values of x is radically different. The individual nature of any one of them in the vicinity of $(0, 0)$ is better indicated if the *direction* of the curve at that point is also given. This, of course, means that it is desirable to find the slope of each of them at $(0, 0)$. We find the inclination angles are respectively $45°$, $0°$, and $90°$ (see Fig. 11–4).

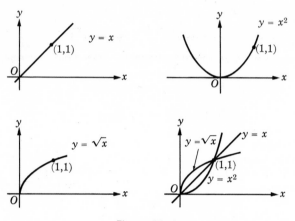

Figure 11–4

EXAMPLE 10. (Fig. 11–5) $y^2 = x^2(1 - x^2)$.

This curve has symmetry with respect to both axes and the origin. Its extent in the x-direction is limited to $|x| \le 1$. Differentiating implicitly, we find

$$y' = \frac{x - 2x^3}{y}.$$

At one x-intercept, $(1, 0)$, the slope is infinite. At the origin, which is another intercept, the expression we have for y' becomes $0/0$, which is meaningless. However, if we replace y in the denominator by its equivalent expression in terms of x, we obtain

$$y' = \frac{x(1 - 2x^2)}{\pm x\sqrt{1 - x^2}} = \pm \frac{1 - 2x^2}{\sqrt{1 - x^2}}.$$

At $x = 0$, this gives $y' = \pm1$. The same result can be obtained by considering the limit, as P approaches the origin O, of the slope of the secant line through O and a second point $P(x, y)$ on the curve. Denoting this slope by m_{sec}, we have

$$m_{\text{sec}} = \frac{\text{rise}}{\text{run}} = \frac{y - 0}{x - 0} = \pm\sqrt{1 - x^2}.$$

When $P \to O$, $x \to 0$, and $m_{\text{sec}} \to \pm1$. The double sign means, of course, that if P approaches O along the branch of the curve given by

$$y = x\sqrt{1 - x^2},$$

the limit of the slope of the secant is $+1$, while the branch given by

$$y = -x\sqrt{1 - x^2}$$

has slope -1 at the origin (Fig. 11–5). We also find turning points at $x = \pm\sqrt{\frac{1}{2}}$, $y = \pm\frac{1}{2}$. It is worth noting that we may determine the extent of the curve in the y-direction by comparing the equation of the curve in the form

$$x^4 - x^2 + y^2 = 0$$

with the quadratic equation

$$az^2 + bz + c = 0,$$

whose solutions are

$$z = \frac{-b \pm \sqrt{b^2 - 4ac}}{2a}.$$

Taking $z = x^2$, $a = 1$, $b = -1$, and $c = y^2$, this leads to

$$x^2 = \frac{1 \pm \sqrt{1 - 4y^2}}{2},$$

and it is seen that there is no portion of the curve above the line $y = \frac{1}{2}$ or below the line $y = -\frac{1}{2}$. The curve is sketched in Fig. 11–5.

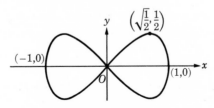

Figure 11–5

We observe in Example 10 that the equation is of the second degree in y and of the fourth degree in x. A line parallel to the y-axis has the equation $x =$ constant. Solving the equation of the curve and the equation of the line simultaneously will therefore produce at most two values of y, that is, such a line will cut the curve in at most two points. Similarly, because $y^2 = x^2(1 - x^2)$ is of the fourth degree in x, a line parallel to the x-axis will cut the curve in at most four points. The line $y = c$ and the curve will, in fact, have

(a) no intersections if $|c| > \frac{1}{2}$,

(b) two intersections if $|c| = \frac{1}{2}$,

(c) four intersections if $0 < |c| < \frac{1}{2}$,

(d) three intersections if $c = 0$.

In cases (b) and (d), the results may be interpreted as limiting cases of (c) with some of the intersections coinciding.

PROBLEMS

Analyze each of the equations below to investigate the following properties of the curve: (a) symmetry, (b) extent, (c) intercepts, (d) asymptotes, (e) slope at the intercepts. Locate a few points, and sketch the curve, taking into account the information discovered above.

1. $y^2 = x(x - 2)$

2. $y^2 = \dfrac{x}{x - 2}$

3. $x^4 + y^4 = 1$

4. $x^2 = \dfrac{1 + y^2}{1 - y^2}$

5. $x^2 = \dfrac{y^2 + 1}{y^2 - 1}$

6. $y = x + \dfrac{1}{x}$

7. $y = x^2 + 1$

8. $y = \dfrac{1}{x^2 + 1}$

9. $y = x^2 - 1$

10. $y = \dfrac{1}{x^2 - 1}$

11–2   Tangents and normals. In Chapter 1 we learned that a straight line of slope m which passes through the point (x_1, y_1) is represented by an equation

$$y - y_1 = m(x - x_1). \tag{1}$$

The equation of a line *tangent* to a given curve $y = f(x)$ at a given point (x_1, y_1) on the curve can be found at once by taking

$$m = \left(\frac{dy}{dx}\right)_{(x_1, y_1)} = f'(x_1)$$

in Eq. (1), which then becomes

$$\boxed{y - y_1 = f'(x_1)(x - x_1).} \tag{2}$$

In this equation x_1, y_1, and $f'(x_1)$ are all *constants*; the variables x and y appear only linearly.

The line through $P_1(x_1, y_1)$ and perpendicular to the tangent line is called

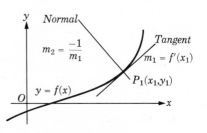

Figure 11–6

the *normal* to the curve at P_1. Its slope is the negative reciprocal of the slope of the tangent, that is,

$$m_2 = -\frac{1}{m_1} = \frac{-1}{f'(x_1)},$$

and the equation of the *normal* is

$$y - y_1 = \frac{-1}{f'(x_1)} (x - x_1). \tag{3}$$

EXAMPLE 1. The tangent to the curve

$$y^2 = 4px \tag{4}$$

at the point $P_1(x_1, y_1)$ intersects the x-axis at M and the y-axis at N. Show that N is the mid-point of the segment $\overline{MP_1}$.

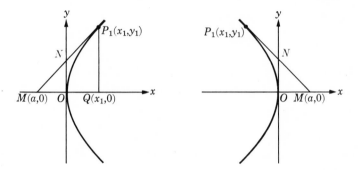

Figure 11–7

Solution. The curve is symmetric about the x-axis and lies entirely to the right of the y-axis if p is positive, or entirely to the left of the y-axis if p is negative (Fig. 11–7).

Its slope at any point is found from

$$\frac{dy}{dx} = \frac{2p}{y}.$$

The tangent to the curve at the origin is vertical and for this point the problem becomes meaningless. But if P_1 is any point on the curve (4) other than the origin, then the equation of the line tangent to the curve at P_1 is

$$y - y_1 = \frac{2p}{y_1} (x - x_1).$$

The point $M(a, 0)$ where this line cuts the x-axis *lies on the line*, and hence

$$-y_1 = \frac{2p}{y_1} (a - x_1),$$

which gives

$$a = x_1 - \frac{y_1^2}{2p}. \tag{5}$$

The point (x_1, y_1) is *on the curve*, and hence

$$y_1^2 = 4px_1,$$

so that

$$\frac{y_1^2}{2p} = 2x_1,$$

which reduces (5) to

$$a = -x_1. \tag{6}$$

Equation (6) tells us that the origin bisects the line segment $\overline{MQ}$ joining $M(-x_1, 0)$ and $Q(x_1, 0)$. Hence, by similar triangles, point N bisects the segment $\overline{MP_1}$.

EXAMPLE 2. Show that the normal to the curve

$$x^2 + y^2 = a^2 \tag{7}$$

at any point (x_1, y_1) on it passes through the origin.

Solution. Differentiating (7) implicitly and solving for dy/dx, we find

$$\frac{dy}{dx} = -\frac{x}{y}$$

as the slope of the *tangent* at (x, y). The slope of the *normal* at (x_1, y_1) is therefore

$$m = \frac{y_1}{x_1},$$

and the equation of the normal is

$$y - y_1 = \frac{y_1}{x_1} (x - x_1). \tag{8}$$

When we clear of fractions, (8) reduces to

$$x_1 y = y_1 x.$$

Clearly, the origin lies on this line, since the coordinates $x = 0$, $y = 0$ satisfy the equation.

EXAMPLE 3. Show that the number of tangent lines that can be drawn from the point $Q(h, k)$ to the curve

$$y = x^2 \tag{9}$$

is two, one, or zero according as k is less than h^2, equal to h^2, or greater than h^2, respectively.

Figure 11–8

Solution. Figure 11–8 represents the curve and the three cases $k < h^2, k = h^2,$ $k > h^2$. From the fact that $d^2y/dx^2 = 2$ is always positive, so that the curve is concave upward, we see that the results stated are equivalent to saying that two tangents can be drawn from a point on the convex side of the curve, no tangents from a point on the concave side of the curve, and only one tangent from a point on the curve. This is geometrically evident, but we shall adopt an analytical approach as follows.

Suppose that a tangent *can* be drawn to the curve from Q touching the curve at some point $P_1(x_1, y_1)$ which is at present not known. Then, using Eq. (2), we find the equation of this tangent line to be

$$y - y_1 = 2x_1(x - x_1).$$

Since $Q(h, k)$ is *on this line*, its coordinates must satisfy the equation

$$k - y_1 = 2x_1(h - x_1). \tag{10a}$$

Also, since (x_1, y_1) is *on the curve*, its coordinates must satisfy the equation

$$y_1 = x_1^2. \tag{10b}$$

Now in reality, h and k are known to us but x_1 and y_1 are not. We therefore have two equations, (10a) and (10b), for two unknowns, x_1 and y_1. We eliminate y_1 between them and obtain

$$k - x_1^2 = 2hx_1 - 2x_1^2$$

or

$$x_1^2 - 2hx_1 + k = 0.$$

If we solve this for x_1 by means of the quadratic formula, we obtain

$$x_1 = h \pm \sqrt{h^2 - k}. \tag{10c}$$

Only real values of x_1 correspond to points P_1 on the curve; hence no tangent may be drawn if $h^2 - k$ is negative, which is the same condition as saying k is greater than h^2. If $h^2 = k$, then the two roots in (10c) coincide and give only one point, namely $x_1 = h$, $y_1 = k = h^2$, to which the tangent can be

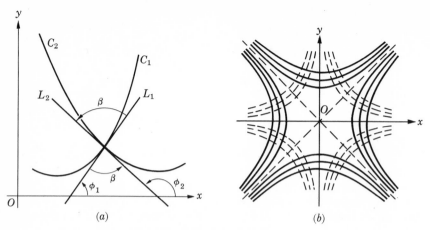

Figure 11-9

drawn. But if $k < h^2$, the two roots in (10c) are distinct and each root gives a value of x_1 which with $y_1 = x_1^2$ determines a point P_1 such that the line $\overleftrightarrow{QP_1}$ is tangent to the curve, so that two tangents may be drawn.

Angle between two curves. Let C_1 and C_2 be two curves which intersect at a point P. Then the angle between C_1 and C_2 at P is, by definition, the angle β between their tangents at P (Fig. 11–9a). If these tangents are, respectively, L_1 and L_2, they have slopes

$$m_1 = \tan \phi_1, \qquad m_2 = \tan \phi_2.$$

Then $\tan \beta$ can be found from m_1 and m_2 as follows. Since

$$\beta = \phi_2 - \phi_1,$$

we have

$$\boxed{\tan \beta = \tan (\phi_2 - \phi_1) = \frac{\tan \phi_2 - \tan \phi_1}{1 + \tan \phi_2 \tan \phi_1} = \frac{m_2 - m_1}{1 + m_2 m_1}.} \qquad (11)$$

Here β is measured in the counterclockwise direction from L_1 to L_2.

We recall that the lines L_1 and L_2 are perpendicular if $m_2 = -1/m_1$. In this case we say that the curves C_1 and C_2 are *orthogonal*.

EXAMPLE 4. Show that every curve of the family

$$xy = a, \qquad a \neq 0 \qquad (12a)$$

is orthogonal to every curve of the family

$$x^2 - y^2 = b, \qquad b \neq 0. \tag{12b}$$

Solution. The two families of curves are sketched in Fig. 11–9(b). At a point $P(x, y)$ on any curve of (12a), the slope is

$$\frac{dy}{dx} = -\frac{y}{x}, \tag{13a}$$

and on any curve of (12b) the slope is

$$\frac{dy}{dx} = \frac{x}{y}. \tag{13b}$$

At a point of intersection, the values of x and y in (13b) are the same as in (13a), and the two curves are orthogonal because these slopes are negative reciprocals of each other. The cases $x = 0$ or $y = 0$ cannot occur in Eqs. (13) if (x, y) is a point of intersection of any curve (12a) and a curve (12b), since a and b are restricted to be constants different from zero. That every curve in (12a) does in fact intersect every curve in (12b) follows from the fact that the equation

$$x^2 - \frac{a^2}{x^2} = b,$$

which results from eliminating y between (12a) and (12b), has real roots for every pair of nonzero real constants a and b.

The curves in (12b) are called *orthogonal trajectories* of the curves in (12a). Such mutually orthogonal systems of curves are of particular importance in physical problems related to electrical potential, where the curves in one family correspond to lines of flow and those in the other family correspond to lines of constant potential. They also occur in hydrodynamics and in heat flow problems.

PROBLEMS

1. Find the equation of the line that is tangent to the curve $y^2 - 2x - 4y - 1 = 0$ at the point $(-2, 1)$.

2. Find the equation of the line that is normal to the curve $xy + 2x - 5y - 2 = 0$ at the point $(3, 2)$.

3. Find the equations of the lines that are tangent to the curve $y = x^3 - 6x + 2$ and are parallel to the line $y = 6x - 2$.

4. Find the equations of the lines that are normal to the curve $xy + 2x - y = 0$ and parallel to the line $2x + y = 0$.

5. Show that the two lines that are drawn from $(\frac{3}{2}, 0)$ tangent to the curve $x^2 - 4y + 4 = 0$ are perpendicular.

6. Show that the two lines that are drawn from any point on the line $x = -p$ tangent to the curve $y^2 = 4px$ are perpendicular ($p = $ constant).

7. Does the line that is tangent to the curve $y = x^3$ at the point $(1, 1)$ intersect the curve at any other point? If so, find the point.

8. A line is drawn from the point $P_0(1, 5)$ tangent to the curve $y = x^3$ at a point $P_1(x_1, y_1)$ on it. Find the coordinates of P_1. Is there more than one possibility for the point P_1? Why?

9. Find all lines that can be drawn normal to the curve $x^2 - y^2 = 5$ and parallel to the line $2x + 3y = 10$. Sketch the curve and the lines.

10. Find all lines that can be drawn tangent to the curve $4xy = 1$ from the point $P(-1, 2)$. Sketch the curve and the lines.

11. The line that is normal to the curve $y = x^2 + 2x - 3$ at $(1, 0)$ intersects the curve at what other point?

12. If l represents the distance from a fixed point $P_1(x_1, y_1)$ to a variable point $P(x, y)$ on a curve $y = f(x)$ (Fig. 11–10), then

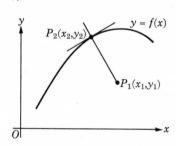

$$l^2 = (x - x_1)^2 + [f(x) - y_1]^2.$$

Show that the derivative $d(l^2)/dx$ is equal to zero when $x = x_2$ if and only if the line $\overleftrightarrow{P_1P_2}$ is normal to the curve at $P_2[x_2, f(x_2)]$.

13. Show that the curve $2x^2 + 3y^2 = 5$ and the curve $y^2 = x^3$ intersect at right angles.

Figure 11–10

14. Let $P_1(x_1, y_1)$ and $P_2(x_2, y_2)$ be any two points on the curve $y = ax^2 + bx + c$, $a \neq 0$. If a line is drawn tangent to the curve at (x_0, y_0) and is parallel to the chord $\overline{P_1P_2}$, show that $x_0 = (x_1 + x_2)/2$.

15. For what values of b is the line $y = 12x + b$ tangent to the curve $y = x^3$?

16. For what values of m is the line $y = mx$ tangent to the curve $y^2 + x^2 - 4x + 3 = 0$?

17. Find the interior angles of the triangle whose vertices are $A(1, 1)$, $B(3, -1)$, and $C(5, 2)$.

18. Find the slope of the line that bisects the angle ACB in the previous problem.

19. Let A, B, C be the interior angles of a triangle in which no angle is a right angle. By calculating $\tan(A + B + C)$ and observing that $A + B + C = 180°$, show that the equation

$$\tan A + \tan B + \tan C = \tan A \tan B \tan C$$

must be satisfied.

20. Calculate the interior angles of the triangle whose vertices are $A(1, 2)$, $B(2, -1)$, and $C(-1, 1)$, and check your results by showing that they satisfy the equation

$$\tan A + \tan B + \tan C = \tan A \tan B \tan C.$$

(See Problem 19, above.)

21. Find the angles between the following pairs of curves:

(a) $3x + y = 5$, $2x - y = 4$,   (b) $y = x^2$, $xy = 1$,

(c) $x^2 + y^2 = 16$, $y^2 = 6x$,   (d) $x^2 + xy + y^2 = 7$, $y = 2x$.

11-3   Newton's method for approximating roots of equations. Suppose we want to find a real root of the equation $f(x) = 0$. If the equation is linear or quadratic, we know simple rules to use. There are formulas for solving third and fourth degree equations, too, though they are less familiar. But there are no algebraic formulas for solving equations of the fifth degree or higher. Moreover, even the quadratic formula doesn't immediately give the answer in decimal form. Often we must look up the square root in a table or compute it. Newton's method, however, has these advantages:

(a) It applies to an equation of any degree. Indeed, it even applies to nonpolynomial equations such as $2 \sin x - x = 0$.

(b) It gives the answer in numerical form. We continue the computations until we have the degree of accuracy we want.

Its disadvantage is that the arithmetic becomes involved unless a calculating machine is used.

Newton's method proceeds as follows. If the equation we want to solve is $f(x) = 0$, we make a rough graph of $y = f(x)$. We estimate the root r, where the curve crosses the x-axis. This estimate is our first approximation; call it x_1. The next approximation, x_2, is the place where the *tangent*

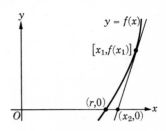

Figure 11-11

to the curve at $(x_1, f(x_1))$ crosses the x-axis, Fig. 11-11. The equation of this tangent line is

$$y - f(x_1) = f'(x_1)(x - x_1). \qquad (1)$$

We assume that this line is not parallel to the x-axis, that is, $f'(x_1) \neq 0$. (If we started at a place where the slope is zero, we must start over again at a nearby place where the slope isn't zero.) Then the line crosses the x-axis at a point with coordinates $x = x_2$, $y = 0$ which satisfy (1). Hence

$$0 - f(x_1) = f'(x_1)(x_2 - x_1)$$

and

$$x_2 = x_1 - \frac{f(x_1)}{f'(x_1)}. \qquad (2)$$

Equation (2) provides the basis for an iterative process, since we may now replace x_1 by x_2 on the right side and call the new result x_3 instead of x_2. More generally, having arrived at an approximation x_n, we replace

x_1 by x_n on the right side of (2) and x_2 by x_{n+1}, thus:

$$x_{n+1} = x_n - \frac{f(x_n)}{f'(x_n)} . \qquad (3)$$

A computing machine can be programmed with feedback to keep repeating the process of Eq. (3) automatically, as indicated in Fig. 11–12.

Previous guess → $\boxed{x_{n+1} = x_n - \dfrac{f(x_n)}{f'(x_n)}}$ → New guess
(x_n) (x_{n+1})

Fig. 11–12. Feedback for iterating Newton's method.

EXAMPLE 1. Use Newton's method to solve $x^2 = 5$ to two decimals.

Solution. We take $f(x) = x^2 - 5$, and sketch the curve

$$y = f(x) = x^2 - 5.$$

A root of the equation $x^2 = 5$ corresponds to a place where this curve crosses the x-axis. From the graph (Fig. 11–13) we see that one crossing is between 2 and 3, and is closer to 2 than to 3. We therefore take $x_1 = 2$ as our first approximation. Then we compute x_2 from Eq. (2). Here we have

$$f(x) = x^2 - 5, \qquad f(2) = -1,$$
$$f'(x) = 2x, \qquad f'(2) = 4.$$

Hence

$$x_2 = 2 - (-\tfrac{1}{4}) = \tfrac{9}{4} = 2.25.$$

To get the next approximation, we use Eq. (3) with $n = 2$:

$$x_3 = x_2 - \frac{f(x_2)}{f'(x_2)}$$

with

$$f(x_2) = f(\tfrac{9}{4}) = (\tfrac{9}{4})^2 - 5 = \tfrac{1}{16}$$
$$f'(x_2) = f'(\tfrac{9}{4}) = 2(\tfrac{9}{4}) = \tfrac{9}{2}.$$

Hence

$$x_3 = \frac{9}{4} - \frac{\tfrac{1}{16}}{\tfrac{9}{2}} = \frac{161}{72} = 2.236^+.$$

Since $(2.236)^2 = 4.999696$ and $(2.237)^2 = 5.004169$, it is clear that the positive root is between 2.236 and 2.237, hence is 2.24 to two decimal places.

EXAMPLE 2. Newton's method may be used to find cube roots, fourth roots, and so on. We illustrate the method for finding the cube root of 2. That is, we try to find a root of the equation $x = \sqrt[3]{2}$ or $x^3 = 2$. We put $f(x) = x^3 - 2$

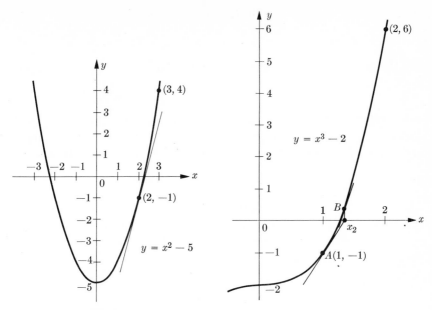

Figure 11–13   **Figure 11–14**

and sketch the graph of $y = f(x)$, Fig. 11–14. Since $f(1) = -1$ and $f(2) = 6$, we let our first approximation be $x_1 = 1$. Then Eq. (2) becomes

$$
\begin{aligned}
x_2 &= x_1 - \frac{f(x_1)}{f'(x_1)} \\
&= x_1 - \frac{(x_1^3 - 2)}{3x_1^2} \\
&= \tfrac{2}{3}x_1 + \tfrac{1}{3}(2/x_1^2).
\end{aligned}
\tag{4}
$$

We have written Eq. (4) in a form that shows x_2 is a "weighted average" of x_1 (with coefficient $\tfrac{2}{3}$) and of $2/x_1^2$ (with coefficient $\tfrac{1}{3}$). The sum of these coefficients is 1, but we "weight" x_1 in our average twice as heavily as we do $2/x_1^2$. This same procedure may of course be repeated with x_2 in place of x_1 on the right side of (4) and x_3 on the left. In general we have

$$
x_{n+1} = \tfrac{2}{3}x_n + \tfrac{1}{3}(2/x_n^2).
\tag{5}
$$

If at any stage the numbers x_n and $2/x_n^2$ are equal, then x_{n+1} is also equal to this common value, and it is $\sqrt[3]{2}$, since

$$
x_n = 2/x_n^2
$$

implies

$$
x_n^3 = 2.
$$

Starting with $x_1 = 1$, we find the first three approximations are

$$x_1 = 1, \qquad x_2 = \tfrac{4}{3} = 1.33^+, \qquad x_3 = \tfrac{91}{72} = 1.264^-.$$

A table of cube roots gives $\sqrt[3]{2} = 1.259921$ to six decimal places. Our third approximation is too large by about 0.004, but 1.26 is correct to two decimal places.

Remark 1. The accuracy of Newton's method for functions f which possess continuous first and second derivatives can be estimated by applying the Mean Value Theorem. One estimate, obtainable that way, is

$$|x_2 - r| \le (x_1 - r)^2 (M/m), \tag{6}$$

where M is the maximum absolute value of the second derivative and m the minimum absolute value of the first derivative in an interval that contains the root r and the estimates x_1 and x_2. The error decreases if the first guess is accurate enough to make

$$\left| (x_1 - r)\,\frac{M}{m} \right| < 1. \tag{7}$$

In Example 1, for instance, we had $f(x) = x^2 - 5, f'(x) = 2x, f''(x) = 2$, $r = \sqrt{5}$, $x_1 = 2$, and all other approximations x_n between 2 and $\tfrac{9}{4}$. Hence in (6) we could take $M = 2$, $m = 4$ and have

$$|x_2 - \sqrt{5}| \le \tfrac{1}{2}(x_1 - \sqrt{5})^2.$$

The same inequality applies to any two successive approximations x_{n+1} and x_n,

$$|x_{n+1} - \sqrt{5}| \le \tfrac{1}{2}(x_n - \sqrt{5})^2.$$

This inequality shows that the number of decimal places of accuracy doubles with each successive iteration.

In Example 2, $f(x) = x^3 - 2, f'(x) = 3x^2, f''(x) = 6x, r = \sqrt[3]{2} = 1.26^-$, $x_1 = 1$, $x_2 = \tfrac{4}{3}$, and all other approximations lie between x_1 and x_2. Hence in (6) we may take $M = 6(\tfrac{4}{3}) = 8$, $m = 3$, and get

$$|x_2 - \sqrt[3]{2}| \le (\tfrac{8}{3})(x_1 - \sqrt[3]{2})^2.$$

The condition (7) is satisfied since the left side of the inequality (7) is actually less than 0.7.

Remark 2. We can get a good picture of how the Newton process converges in a favorable situation like that shown in Fig. 11–15. Here x_1 is to the left of r. The tangent to the curve at $A(x_1, f(x_1))$ crosses the x-axis at x_2 to the right of r. The second tangent line, through $B(x_2, f(x_2))$ crosses at x_3, much nearer r. And the third tangent line, through $C(x_3, f(x_3))$,

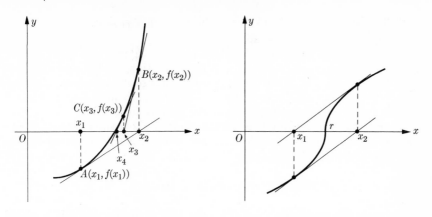

Figure 11-15   Figure 11-16

is practically indistinguishable from the curve itself in the vicinity of the root r.

Remark 3. In some cases, Newton's method may not converge. For instance, if the graph of $y = f(x)$ is like Fig. 11-16, we may have

$$x_1 = r - h, \qquad x_2 = r + h,$$

and successive approximations go back and forth between these two values alternately. A function such as

$$f(x) = \begin{cases} \sqrt{x - r} & \text{for} \quad x \ge r \\ -\sqrt{r - x} & \text{for} \quad x \le r \end{cases} \tag{8}$$

has this property. No amount of iteration of the process will bring us any closer to the root r than our initial guess.

PROBLEMS

Sketch the graph of $y = f(x)$ in each of the following problems (1 through 6). Show that $f(a)$ and $f(b)$ have opposite signs and use Newton's method to estimate the root of the equation $f(x) = 0$ between a and b. One might use $x_1 = (a + b)/2$ as first approximation.

1. $f(x) = x^2 + x - 1$, $a = 0$, $b = 1$
2. $f(x) = x^3 + x - 1$, $a = 0$, $b = 1$
3. $f(x) = x^4 + x - 3$, $a = 1$, $b = 2$
4. $f(x) = x^4 - 2$, $a = 1$, $b = 2$
5. $f(x) = 2 - x^4$, $a = -1$, $b = -2$
6. $f(x) = \sqrt{2x + 1} - \sqrt{x + 4}$, $a = 2$, $b = 4$

7. Suppose our first guess is lucky, in the sense that x_1 is a root of $f(x) = 0$. What happens to x_2 and later approximations?

8. In Example 2, take $x_3 = 1.26$ and compute x_4 to five decimal places. Compare with the six-place $\sqrt[3]{2}$ given in the text. How does your result check with the statement that "when one approximation is good to two decimal places, the next Newton's-method approximation will be good to about four decimals"?

9. To find $x = \sqrt[q]{a}$, we apply Newton's method to $f(x) = x^q - a$. Here we assume that a is a positive real number and q is a positive integer. Show that x_2 is a "weighted average" of x_1 and a/x_1^{q-1}, and find the coefficients m_1, m_2 such that

$$x_2 = m_1 x_1 + m_2(a/x_1^{q-1}), \qquad m_1 > 0, \quad m_2 > 0, \quad m_1 + m_2 = 1.$$

What conclusion would you reach if x_1 and a/x_1^{q-1} were equal? What would be the value of x_2 in that case? [You may also wish to read the article by J. P. Ballantine, "An Averaging Method of Extracting Roots," *American Mathematical Monthly*, Vol. 63, 1956, pp. 249–252, where more efficient ways of averaging are discussed. Also see J. S. Frame, "The Solution of Equations by Continued Fractions," ibid., Vol. 60, 1953, pp. 293–305.]

10. In Example 2, let $e_1 = x_1 - r$ and $e_2 = x_2 - r$ be the errors in our first two approximations of $r = \sqrt[3]{2}$. Show algebraically that $e_2 = e_1^2(2x_1 + r)/(3x_1^2)$. Similar equations relate the errors in any two successive approximations. All our approximations in Example 2 lie between $x_1 = 1$ and $x_2 = \frac{4}{3}$, inclusive. Deduce that the factor $(2x_n + r)/(3x_n^2)$ is not greater than $(\frac{8}{3} + r)/3$, which in turn is less than $(2.67 + 1.26)/3 = 1.31$. Therefore, $e_{n+1} \leq 1.31 e_n^2$.

11. Show that Newton's method applied to $f(x)$ in Eq. (8) leads to $x_2 = r + h$ if $x_1 = r - h$, and to $x_2 = r - h$ if $x_1 = r + h$, $h > 0$. Interpret the result geometrically.

12. (See Remark 3.) Is it possible that successive approximations actually get "worse," in that x_{n+1} is farther away from the root r than x_n is? Can you find such a "pathological" example? [*Hint:* Try cube roots in place of square roots in Eq. (8).]

13. Using the following hints, derive the inequality (6).

(1) By the Mean Value Theorem there is a number a between x_1 and r such that

$$f(x_1) - f(r) = f'(a)(x_1 - r).$$

If the minimum of the absolute value of $f'(x)$ in an interval containing x_1 and r is m, and $m \neq 0$, then $f'(a) \neq 0$. We assume that r is a root of $f(r) = 0$. Hence

$$x_1 - r = \frac{f(x_1)}{f'(a)}. \tag{a}$$

(2) By Eq. (2),

$$x_2 - x_1 = -\frac{f(x_1)}{f'(x_1)}. \tag{b}$$

(3) Add (a) and (b) to get

$$x_2 - r = \frac{f(x_1)}{f'(a)f'(x_1)} [f'(x_1) - f'(a)]$$

$$= \frac{x_1 - r}{f'(x_1)} [f'(x_1) - f'(a)]. \tag{c}$$

(4) By the Mean Value Theorem there is a number b between x_1 and a such that

$$f'(x_1) - f'(a) = f''(b)(x_1 - a). \tag{d}$$

(5) From (c) and (d), deduce that

$$x_2 - r = (x_1 - r)(x_1 - a)\frac{f''(b)}{f'(x_1)}, \tag{e}$$

where a and b are numbers between x_1 and r. In particular, therefore,

$$|x_1 - a| \le |x_1 - r|. \tag{f}$$

Now deduce (6) from (e) and (f).

11–4   Distance between two points. Equations of loci. It is at once apparent from Fig. 11–17 and the theorem of Pythagoras that the distance d between the two points $P_1(x_1, y_1)$ and $P_2(x_2, y_2)$ is given by

$$\boxed{d = \sqrt{(x_2 - x_1)^2 + (y_2 - y_1)^2}.} \tag{1}$$

This formula is particularly useful in finding the equation of a curve when its geometric character depends upon one or more distances, as in the example below.

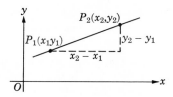

Figure 11–17

EXAMPLE 1. Find the locus of $P(x, y)$ if the distance from P to the origin is equal to the distance from P to the line $L: x = 4$.

Solution. The distance from P to L is the perpendicular distance $|PQ|$ from P to $Q(4, y)$, where Q has the same ordinate as P, Fig. 11–18. Thus

$$|PQ| = \sqrt{(4 - x)^2 + (y - y)^2} = |4 - x|.$$

The distance $|OP|$ is

$$|OP| = \sqrt{x^2 + y^2}.$$

The condition of the locus is $|OP| = |PQ|$, or

$$\sqrt{x^2 + y^2} = |4 - x|. \tag{1}$$

If (1) holds, so does the equation we get by squaring:

$$x^2 + y^2 = 16 - 8x + x^2$$

or

$$y^2 = 16 - 8x. \tag{2}$$

That is, if a point belongs to the locus, then its coordinates must satisfy Eq. (2). The converse is also true, for if Eq. (2) holds, then

$$\begin{aligned}
\sqrt{x^2 + y^2} &= \sqrt{x^2 + (16 - 8x)} \\
&= \sqrt{(x - 4)^2} \\
&= |x - 4| \\
&= |4 - x|,
\end{aligned}$$

and hence

$$|OP| = |PQ|.$$

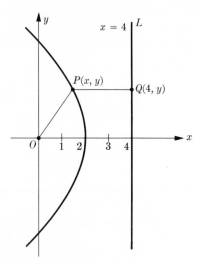

Figure 11–18

Therefore Eq. (2) expresses both the necessary and the sufficient condition on the coordinates of $P(x, y)$ for P to belong to the locus.

PROBLEMS

In Problems 1–8, use the distance formula to derive the equation of the locus of points $P(x, y)$ that satisfy the specified conditions. Analyze the equation and sketch its graph.

1. P is equidistant from the two points $A(-2, 1)$ and $B(2, -3)$.
2. The distance from P to $F_1(-1, 0)$ is twice its distance to $F_2(2, 0)$.
3. The product of its distances from $F_1(-2, 0)$ and $F_2(2, 0)$ is 4.
4. The sum of the distances from P to $F_1(1, 0)$ and $F_2(0, 1)$ is constant and the curve passes through the origin.
5. The distance of P from the line $x = -2$ is 2 times its distance from the point $(2, 0)$.
6. The distance of P from the point $(-3, 0)$ is 4 more than its distance from the point $(3, 0)$.
7. The distance of P from the line $y = 1$ is 3 less than its distance from the origin.

8. P is 3 units from the point $(2, 3)$.

9. Find a point that is equidistant from the three points $A(0, 1)$, $B(1, 0)$, $C(4, 3)$. What is the radius of the circle through A, B, and C?

10. Find the distance from the point $P_1(x_1, y_1)$ to the straight line $Ax + By + C = 0$.

11–5 The circle.

DEFINITION. *A circle is the locus of points in a plane at a given distance from a given point.*

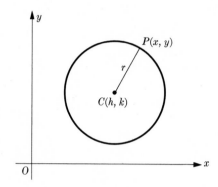

Figure 11–19

Equation of a circle. Let $C(h, k)$ be the given point, the center of the circle. Let r be the given distance, the radius of the circle. Let $P(x, y)$ be a point on the circle. Then

$$|CP| = r, \tag{1}$$

or

$$\sqrt{(x - h)^2 + (y - k)^2} = r,$$

or

$$(x - h)^2 + (y - k)^2 = r^2. \tag{2}$$

If (1) is satisfied so is (2), and conversely. Therefore (2) is the equation of the locus.

EXAMPLE 1. Find the equation of the circle with center at the origin and with radius r.

Solution. If $h = k = 0$, Eq. (2) becomes

$$x^2 + y^2 = r^2. \tag{3}$$

EXAMPLE 2. Find the circle through the origin with center at $C(2, -1)$.

Solution. Its equation, (2), is of the form

$$(x - 2)^2 + (y + 1)^2 = r^2.$$

Since it goes through the origin, $x = y = 0$ must satisfy the equation. Hence

$$(0 - 2)^2 + (0 + 1)^2 = r^2$$

or

$$r^2 = 5.$$

The equation is

$$(x - 2)^2 + (y + 1)^2 = 5.$$

EXAMPLE 3. What is the locus of points $P(x, y)$ whose coordinates satisfy the inequality

$$(x - h)^2 + (y - k)^2 < r^2? \quad (4)$$

Solution. The left side of (4) is the square of the distance $|CP|$ from $C(h, k)$ to $P(x, y)$. The inequality is satisfied if and only if

$$|CP| < r,$$

that is, P lies inside the circle of radius r with center at $C(h, k)$, Fig. 11–20.

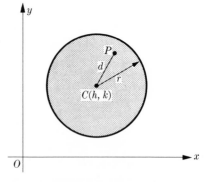

EXAMPLE 4. Analyze the equation

Figure 11–20

$$x^2 + y^2 + 4x - 6y = 12.$$

Solution. We complete the squares in the x terms and y terms and get

$$(x^2 + 4x + 4) + (y^2 - 6y + 9) = 12 + 4 + 9$$

or

$$(x + 2)^2 + (y - 3)^2 = 25.$$

This is of the same form as Eq. (2); therefore it represents a circle with center $C(-2, 3)$ and radius $r = 5$. Its graph is shown in Fig. 11–21.

Remark 1. An equation of the form

$$\boxed{Ax^2 + Ay^2 + Dx + Ey + F = 0, \quad A \neq 0,} \quad (5)$$

can often be reduced to the form of Eq. (2) by completing the squares as we did in Example 4. More specifically, we may divide (5) by A and

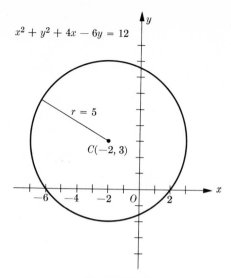

$x^2 + y^2 + 4x - 6y = 12$

$r = 5$

$C(-2, 3)$

Figure 11-21

write

$$\left(x^2 + \frac{D}{A}x\right) + \left(y^2 + \frac{E}{A}y\right) = -\frac{F}{A}. \tag{6}$$

To complete the squares for x, we must add $(D/2A)^2 = D^2/(4A^2)$; and for y we add $(E/2A)^2 = E^2/(4A^2)$. Of course we must add to both sides of Eq. (6), thus obtaining

$$\left(x + \frac{D}{2A}\right)^2 + \left(y + \frac{E}{2A}\right)^2 = -\frac{F}{A} + \frac{D^2 + E^2}{4A^2}$$

$$= \frac{D^2 + E^2 - 4AF}{4A^2}. \tag{7}$$

Equation (7) is like Eq. (2), with

$$r^2 = \frac{D^2 + E^2 - 4AF}{4A^2}, \tag{8}$$

provided this expression is positive. Then (5) represents a circle with center at $(-D/2A, -E/2A)$ and radius $r = \sqrt{(D^2 + E^2 - 4AF)/(4A^2)}$.

If (8) is equal to zero, the locus reduces to a single point, and if it is negative, there are no points (with real coordinates) that satisfy Eq. (7) or Eq. (5).

It is recommended that the reader apply the method of Example 4, rather than using formulas, to handle problems of this type. The thing to remember is that an equation like (5), which is *quadratic in x and in y, with equal coefficients of x^2 and y^2, and with no xy term, represents a circle* (or a single point, or no real locus).

Remark 2. Equation (5) can be divided by A and be replaced by an equation of the form

$$\boxed{x^2 + y^2 + C_1x + C_2y + C_3 = 0,} \tag{9}$$

where C_1, C_2, C_3 are three constants. The three coefficients in (9) can often be determined so as to satisfy three prescribed conditions: for example, that the circle go through three given (noncollinear) points; or be tangent to three given nonconcurrent lines; or be tangent to two lines and pass through a given point not on either line.

EXAMPLE 5. Find the circle through the three points $A(1, 0)$, $B(0, 1)$, and $C(2, 2)$.

Solution 1. Let Eq. (9) be the equation of the circle. Then substitute for x and y the coordinates of A, B, and C, since these points are to be on the circle.

$$
\begin{array}{llll}
\text{Point} & x^2 + y^2 + & C_1x + & C_2y + C_3 = 0 & \\
A(1, 0) & 1 & + C_1 & + C_3 = 0 & \\
B(0, 1) & 1 & & + C_2 + C_3 = 0 & \\
C(2, 2) & 4 + 4 & + 2C_1 & + 2C_2 + C_3 = 0 &
\end{array} \tag{10}
$$

Equations (10) are three equations for the three unknowns. Subtracting the second equation from the first, we get

$$C_2 = C_1.$$

Substitute C_1 for C_2 in the third equation:

$$8 + 4C_1 + C_3 = 0.$$

Subtract the first equation from this:

$$7 + 3C_1 = 0.$$

Hence

$$C_2 = C_1 = -\tfrac{7}{3}$$

and

$$C_3 = -1 - C_1 = \tfrac{4}{3}.$$

Therefore, the equation is

$$x^2 + y^2 - \tfrac{7}{3}x - \tfrac{7}{3}y + \tfrac{4}{3} = 0$$

or

$$3x^2 + 3y^2 - 7x - 7y + 4 = 0.$$

Of course this example could equally well have been solved starting with Eq. (2), which contains the three unknowns h, k, and r. Or we could have found the center Q of the circle by locating the point of intersection of the perpendicular bisectors of the segments $\overline{AB}$ and $\overline{BC}$. The radius is the distance from the center Q to any one of the three points A, B, or C.

Solution 2 (using determinants). The determinantal equation

$$\begin{vmatrix} x^2 + y^2 & x & y & 1 \\ x_1^2 + y_1^2 & x_1 & y_1 & 1 \\ x_2^2 + y_2^2 & x_2 & y_2 & 1 \\ x_3^2 + y_3^2 & x_3 & y_3 & 1 \end{vmatrix} = 0 \tag{11}$$

has the form of Eq. (5) when expanded by cofactors of elements of its first row. In addition, if x is replaced by x_1 and y by y_1, the first row becomes identical with the second and the equation is satisfied. The equation is also satisfied if x and y are replaced by x_2 and y_2 or by x_3 and y_3. Hence (11) represents a circle through the three points $P_1(x_1, y_1)$, $P_2(x_2, y_2)$, and $P_3(x_3, y_3)$, provided the cofactor of $x^2 + y^2$,

$$A_{11} = \begin{vmatrix} x_1 & y_1 & 1 \\ x_2 & y_2 & 1 \\ x_3 & y_3 & 1 \end{vmatrix},$$

is not zero. This 3×3 determinant vanishes if and only if the three points are collinear (see Problem 11, Miscellaneous Problems for Chapter 10), in which case there is no circle through the three points if they are distinct.

In the present example, Eq. (11) is

$$\begin{vmatrix} x^2 + y^2 & x & y & 1 \\ 1 & 1 & 0 & 1 \\ 1 & 0 & 1 & 1 \\ 8 & 2 & 2 & 1 \end{vmatrix} = 0.$$

The expanded value of the determinant is

$$-3(x^2 + y^2) + 7x + 7y - 4,$$

which gives the same result as found above.

PROBLEMS

In each of the following problems (1 through 6), find the equation of the circle having the given center $C(h, k)$ and radius r.

1. $C(0, 2)$, $r = 2$ 2. $C(-2, 0)$, $r = 3$

3. $C(3, -4)$, $r = 5$　　　　　　　4. $C(1, 1)$, $r = \sqrt{2}$

5. $C(-2, -1)$, $r = \sqrt{6}$　　　　6. $C(-4, 2)$, $r = 4$

In each of the following problems (7 through 12), find the center and radius of the given circle.

7. $x^2 + y^2 - 2y = 3$　　　　　　8. $x^2 + y^2 + 2x = 8$

9. $3x^2 + 3y^2 + 6x = 1$　　　　　10. $2x^2 + 2y^2 + x + y = 0$

11. $x^2 + y^2 + 2x - 4y + 5 = 0$　　12. $x^2 + y^2 + 4x + 4y + 9 = 0$

13. The center of a circle is $C(2, 2)$. The circle goes through the point $A(4, 5)$. Find its equation.

14. The center of a circle is $C(-1, 1)$. The circle is tangent to the line $x + 2y = 4$. Find its equation.

15. A circle passes through the points $A(2, -2)$ and $B(3, 4)$. Its center is on the line $x + y = 2$. Find its equation.

16. Show geometrically that the lines that are drawn from the exterior point $P_1(x_1, y_1)$ tangent to the circle $(x - h)^2 + (y - k)^2 = r^2$ have length l given by

$$l^2 = (x_1 - h)^2 + (y_1 - k)^2 - r^2.$$

17. Find the equation of the circle that passes through the three points, $A(2, 3)$, $B(3, 2)$, and $C(-4, 3)$.

18. Find the locus of the point $P(x, y)$ if the sum of the squares of its distances from the two points $(-5, 2)$ and $(1, 4)$ is always 52. Identify and sketch the curve.

19. Is the point $(0.1, 3.1)$ inside, outside, or on the circle $x^2 + y^2 - 2x - 4y + 3 = 0$? Why?

20. If the distance from $P(x, y)$ to the point $(6, 0)$ is twice its distance from the point $(0, 3)$, show that the locus is a circle and find the center and radius.

21. Find the circle inscribed in the triangle whose sides are the lines $4x + 3y = 24$, $3x - 4y = 18$, $4x - 3y + 32 = 0$. [*Hint:* The distance from the point (h, k) to the line $ax + by = c$ is

$$\frac{|ah + bk - c|}{\sqrt{a^2 + b^2}}$$

by the answer to Problem 10, Article 11–4.]

22. Let P be a point outside a given circle C. Let $\overleftrightarrow{PT}$ be tangent to C at T. Let the line $\overleftrightarrow{PN}$ from P through the center of C intersect C at M and N. Prove that $|PM| \cdot |PN| = (|PT|)^2$.

23. It is known that any angle inscribed in a semicircle is a right angle. Prove the converse: i.e., if for every choice of the point $P(x, y)$ on a curve C joining O and A, the angle OPA is a right angle, then the curve is a circle or a semicircle having $\overline{OA}$ as diameter.

24. Suppose that Eqs. (2) and (9) represent the same circle. (a) Express C_1, C_2, and C_3 in terms of h, k, and r. (b) Express h, k, and r in terms of C_1, C_2, and C_3.

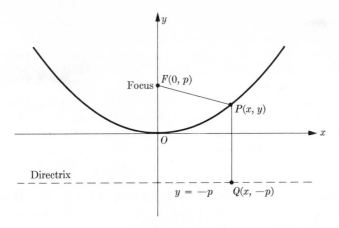

Figure 11–22

11–6   The parabola.

DEFINITION.   *A parabola is the locus of points in a plane equidistant from a given point and a given line. The given point is called the* focus *of the parabola and the given line the* directrix.

Equation. We choose the y-axis through the focus F and perpendicular to the directrix L, and take the origin halfway between F and L. If the distance between F and L is $2p$, we may assign F coordinates $(0, p)$ and the equation of L is $y = -p$, as in Fig. 11–22. Then $P(x, y)$ is on the parabola if and only if the distances $|PF|$ and $|PQ|$ are equal:

$$|PF| = |PQ|, \tag{1}$$

where $Q(x, -p)$ is the foot of the perpendicular from P to L. From the distance formula,

$$|PF| = \sqrt{x^2 + (y - p)^2} \quad \text{and} \quad |PQ| = \sqrt{(y + p)^2}.$$

When we equate these two expressions, square, and simplify, we get

$$\boxed{x^2 = 4py.} \tag{2}$$

This equation must be satisfied by any point on the locus. Conversely, if (2) is satisfied, then

$$
\begin{aligned}
|PF| &= \sqrt{x^2 + (y - p)^2} \\
&= \sqrt{4py + (y^2 - 2py + p^2)} \\
&= \sqrt{(y + p)^2} \\
&= |PQ|
\end{aligned}
$$

and $P(x, y)$ is on the locus. In other words, Eq. (2) is both a necessary and a sufficient condition on the coordinates x and y of points on the parabola.

Discussion. In Eq. (2) assume p is positive. Then y cannot be negative, for real x, and the curve lies above the x-axis. It is symmetric about the y-axis, since x appears only to an even power.

The axis of symmetry of the parabola is also called the "axis of the parabola." The point on this axis midway between the focus and the directrix is on the parabola, since it is equidistant from the focus and the directrix. It is called the *vertex* of the parabola. The origin is the vertex of the parabola in Fig. 11–22. The tangent to a parabola at its vertex is parallel to the directrix. From Eq. (2) we find the slope of the tangent at any point is $dy/dx = x/2p$, and this is zero at the origin. The second derivative is $d^2y/dx^2 = 1/2p$, which is positive, so the curve is concave upward. A geometric method for constructing points on a parabola (in contrast to using its equation to locate points) is described in Problem 24, p. 472.

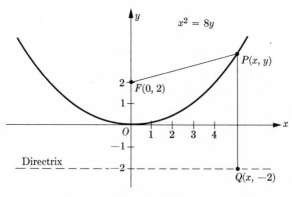

Figure 11–23

EXAMPLE 1. Find the focus and directrix of the parabola

$$x^2 = 8y. \tag{3}$$

Solution. Equation (3) matches (2) if we take $4p = 8$, $p = 2$. The focus is on the axis of symmetry (the y-axis), p units from the vertex, that is, at $F(0, 2)$. The directrix is the line $y = -2$. Every point on the graph of (3) is equidistant from $F(0, 2)$ and the line $y = -2$.

Remark 1. Suppose the parabola opens downward, as in Fig. 11–24, with its focus $F(0, -p)$ and directrix the line $y = p$. The effect is to change the sign of p in Eq. (2), which now becomes

$$\boxed{x^2 = -4py.} \tag{4}$$

Figure 11–24

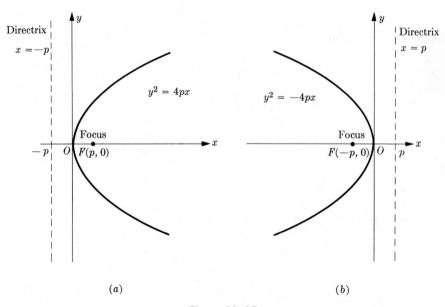

(a)   (b)

Figure 11–25

We may also interchange the roles of x and y in Eqs. (2) and (4). The resulting equations

$$y^2 = 4px \qquad (5a)$$

and

$$y^2 = -4px \qquad (5b)$$

also represent parabolas, but now they are symmetric about the x-axis because y appears only to an even power. The *vertex* is still at the origin. The directrix is perpendicular to the axis of symmetry, and p units from the vertex. The focus is on the axis of symmetry, also p units from the vertex, and "inside" the curve. If we assume p is positive in Eqs. (5), then (5a) opens toward the right, because x must be greater than or equal to zero, while (5b) opens toward the left. Figure 11–25 shows graphs of parabolas of these two types.

Translation of axes. If the vertex of the parabola is at the point $V(h, k)$, Eqs. (2), (4), and (5) no longer apply in those forms. However, it is easy to determine what the appropriate equation is, by considering a new coordinate system, with its origin O' at V, and axes parallel to the original axes. Every point P in the plane then has two sets of coordinates, say x and y in the original system, and x', y' in the new. To go from O to P, we have a horizontal displacement x and a vertical displacement y. The abscissa may be resolved into two horizontal displacements: h from O to O' and x' from O' to P. Similarly, the ordinate is the resultant of two vertical displacements: k from O to O' and y' from O' to P. Thus the two sets of coordinates are related as follows:

Fig. 11–26.   Diagram for translation of axes.

$$\left\{\begin{aligned} x &= x' + h \\ y &= y' + k \end{aligned}\right\} \qquad \text{(6a)}$$

or

$$\left\{\begin{aligned} x' &= x - h \\ y' &= y - k \end{aligned}\right\}. \qquad \text{(6b)}$$

Equations (6) are called the equations for *translation of axes*, because the new coordinate axes may be obtained by moving the old axes to the position of the new ones in a motion known as a pure translation without rotation.

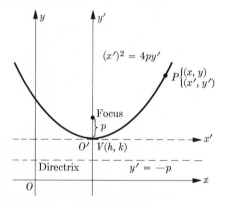

Figure 11–27

Suppose, now, we consider a parabola, with vertex $V(h, k)$ and opening upward as in Fig. 11–27. In terms of $x'y'$-coordinates, Eq. (2) provides us with the equation of the parabola in the form

$$(x')^2 = 4py'. \tag{7}$$

By using Eqs. (6), we may express this in xy-coordinates by the equation

$$(x - h)^2 = 4p(y - k). \tag{8a}$$

The axis of symmetry of the parabola in (8a) is the line $x = h$. Observe that this corresponds to setting the quadratic term $(x - h)^2$ in (8a) equal to zero. When p is positive, $y - k$ must be greater than or equal to zero in (8a), for real $x - h$, and therefore the graph opens upward. The focus is on the axis of symmetry, p units above the vertex at $x = h$, $y = k + p$. The directrix is p units below the vertex and perpendicular to the axis of symmetry.

Other forms of equations of parabolas are:

$$(x - h)^2 = -4p(y - k), \tag{8b}$$

$$(y - k)^2 = 4p(x - h), \tag{8c}$$

$$(y - k)^2 = -4p(x - h). \tag{8d}$$

Equation (8b) has a graph symmetric about $x = h$, opening downward; (8c) symmetric about $y = k$ and opening to the right ($x \geq h$); (8d) symmetric about $y = k$ and opening to the left ($x \leq h$).

EXAMPLE 2. Discuss the parabola

$$y = x^2 + 4x. \tag{9}$$

Solution. We complete the square in the x terms by adding 4 to both sides of Eq. (9):

$$y + 4 = x^2 + 4x + 4$$
$$= (x + 2)^2.$$

This is of the form

$$(x - h)^2 = 4p(y - k)$$

with

$$h = -2, \quad k = -4,$$
$$4p = 1, \quad p = \tfrac{1}{4}.$$

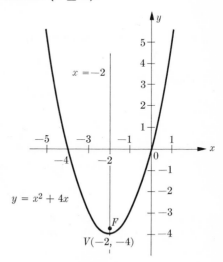

Figure 11–28

The vertex of the parabola is $V(-2, -4)$; its axis of symmetry $(x+2)^2 = 0$; and it opens upward because $y \geq -4$ for real x. The graph is shown in Fig. 11–28. The focus is on the axis of symmetry, $\frac{1}{4}$ unit above the vertex, at $F(-2, -3\frac{3}{4})$. The directrix is parallel to the x-axis, $\frac{1}{4}$ unit below the vertex. Its equation is $y = -4\frac{1}{4}$.

Remark 2. The clue to an equation of a parabola is that it is quadratic in one of the coordinates and linear in the other. Whenever we have such an equation we may reduce it to one of the standard forms (8a, b, c, d) by completing the square in the coordinate which appears quadratically. We then put the linear terms in the form $\pm 4p(x-h)$ or $\pm 4p(y-k)$. Then the information about vertex, distance from vertex to focus, axis of symmetry, and direction the curve opens can all be read from the equation in this standard form.

EXAMPLE 3. Discuss the equation

$$2x^2 + 5y - 3x + 4 = 0.$$

Solution. This equation is quadratic in x, linear in y. We divide by 2, the coefficient of x^2, and collect all the x terms on one side of the equation:

$$x^2 - \tfrac{3}{2}x = -\tfrac{5}{2}y - 2.$$

Now we complete the square by adding $(-\tfrac{3}{4})^2 = \tfrac{9}{16}$ to both sides:

$$(x - \tfrac{3}{4})^2 = -\tfrac{5}{2}y - 2 + \tfrac{9}{16}$$

$$= -\tfrac{5}{2}y - \tfrac{23}{16}.$$

To get the y terms in the form $-4p(y-k)$, we factor out $-\tfrac{5}{2}$, and write

$$(x - \tfrac{3}{4})^2 = -\tfrac{5}{2}(y + \tfrac{23}{40}).$$

This has the form

$$(x - h)^2 = -4p(y - k)$$

with

$$h = \tfrac{3}{4}, \qquad k = -\tfrac{23}{40}, \qquad 4p = \tfrac{5}{2}.$$

Hence the vertex is $V(\tfrac{3}{4}, -\tfrac{23}{40})$. The axis of symmetry is $(x - \tfrac{3}{4})^2 = 0$, or $x = \tfrac{3}{4}$; and the distance from the vertex to the focus is

$$p = \tfrac{5}{8}.$$

Since $y - k$ must here be ≤ 0 for real x, the curve opens downward, and the focus is p units below the vertex at $F(\tfrac{3}{4}, -\tfrac{6}{5})$. The graph is shown in Fig. 11–29.

Remark 3. In Fig. 11–30, $\overleftrightarrow{T'PT}$ is tangent to the parabola, F is the focus, and $\overrightarrow{PL}$ is parallel to the axis of the parabola. The angles $\alpha = \angle LPT$

Figure 11-29

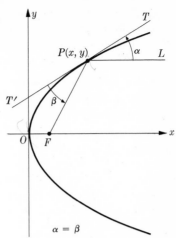

Figure 11-30

and $\beta = \angle T'PF$ are equal (see Problem 31). This accounts for the property of a parabolic reflector that rays originating from the focus are reflected parallel to the axis. Or, rays coming into the reflector parallel to the axis are reflected to the focus. These properties are used in parabolic mirrors of telescopes and in parabolic radar antennas.

PROBLEMS

In each of the following problems (1 through 6), the vertex V and focus F of a parabola are given. Find the equation of the parabola and of its directrix. Sketch the graph showing the focus, vertex, and directrix.

1. $V(0, 0)$, $F(0, 2)$
2. $V(0, 0)$, $F(-2, 0)$
3. $V(-2, 3)$, $F(-2, 4)$
4. $V(0, 3)$, $F(-1, 3)$
5. $V(-3, 1)$, $F(0, 1)$
6. $V(1, -3)$, $F(1, 0)$

In each of the following problems (7 through 12), the vertex V and directrix L of a parabola are given. Find the equation of the parabola and its focus. Sketch the graph showing the focus, vertex, and directrix.

7. $V(2, 0)$; L is the y-axis.
8. $V(1, -2)$; L is the x-axis.
9. $V(-3, 1)$; L is the line $x = 1$.
10. $V(-2, -2)$; L is the line $y = -3$.
11. $V(0, 1)$; L is the line $x = -1$.
12. $V(0, 1)$; L is the line $y = 2$.

In each of the following problems (13 through 22), find the vertex, axis of symmetry, focus, and directrix of the given parabola. Sketch the curve, showing these features.

13. $x^2 + 8y - 2x = 7$

14. $x^2 - 2y + 8x + 10 = 0$

15. $y^2 + 4x = 8$

16. $x^2 - 8y = 4$

17. $x^2 + 2x - 4y - 3 = 0$

18. $y^2 + x + y = 0$

19. $4y^2 - 8y + 3x - 2 = 0$

20. $y^2 + 6y + 2x + 5 = 0$

21. $3x^2 - 8y - 12x = 4$

22. $3x - 2y^2 - 4y + 7 = 0$

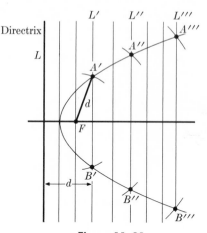

Figure 11–31

23. What is the locus of points whose coordinates satisfy the inequality $x^2 < 8y$? Sketch.

24. Explain why the following method of locating points on the graph of a parabola is valid.

(a) Construct a family of lines parallel to the directrix.

(b) Set a compass to measure the distance d from the directrix to one of these lines L'. With the focus as center, construct an arc of radius d intersecting L' in points A' and B', as in Fig. 11–31.

(c) Repeat the process with other lines L'', L''', and so on, constructing points A'', B'', A''', B''', and so on. The points so constructed lie on a parabola with focus F, directrix L.

25. Use the method of Problem 24 to construct the graph of the parabola with focus $F(2, 2)$ and directrix the line $x + y = 0$.

26. Find the equation of the parabola of Problem 25. [*Hint:* The distance from a point (x, y) to the line $Ax + By + C = 0$ is $|Ax + By + C|/\sqrt{A^2 + B^2}$ by the answer to Problem 10, Article 11–4.]

27. Find the equation of the parabolic arch of base b and altitude h in Fig. 11–32.

28. Given the three points $(-1, 2)$, $(1, -1)$, and $(2, 1)$. (a) Find a parabola passing through the given points and having its axis parallel to the x-axis. (b) Find a parabola passing through the given points and having its axis parallel to the y-axis.

29. Suppose a and b are positive numbers. Sketch the parabolas $y^2 = 4a^2 - 4ax$ and $y^2 = 4b^2 + 4bx$ in the same diagram. Show that they have a common focus, the same for any a and b. Show that they intersect at $(a - b, \pm 2\sqrt{ab})$, and that each "a-parabola" is orthogonal to every "b-parabola." (Using different values of a and b, we obtain families of confocal parabolas. Each family is a set of orthogonal trajectories of the other family. See Article 11–2.)

30. What is the locus of the equation

$$(2x + y - 3)(x^2 + y^2 - 4)(x^2 - 8y) = 0?$$

Give a reason for your answer.

31. Prove that the angles α and β in Fig. 11–30 are equal.

32. Prove that the tangent to the parabola $y^2 = 4px$ at $P_1(x_1, y_1)$ intersects the axis of symmetry x_1 units to the left of the vertex. (This provides a simple method for constructing the tangent to a parabola at any point on it.)

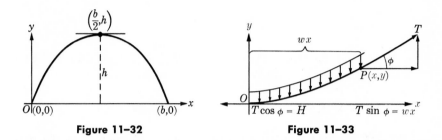

Figure 11–32   Figure 11–33

33. Show that the area of a parabolic segment of altitude h and base b is $\frac{2}{3}bh$ (see Problem 27).

34. Show that the volume generated by rotating the area bounded by the parabola $y = (4h/b^2)x^2$ and the line $y = h$ about the y-axis is equal to one and one-half times the volume of the corresponding inscribed cone.

35. The condition for equilibrium of the section OP of a cable that supports a weight of w pounds per foot measured along the horizontal (Fig. 11–33) is

$$\frac{dy}{dx} = \frac{wx}{H} \left(= \frac{T \sin \phi}{T \cos \phi} \right),$$

where the origin O is taken at the low point of the cable and H is the horizontal tension at O. Show that the curve in which the cable hangs is a parabola.

36. Assume, from optics, that when a ray of light is reflected by a mirror the angle of incidence is equal to the angle of reflection. If a mirror is formed by rotating a parabola about its axis and silvering the resulting surface, show that a ray of light emanating from the focus of the parabola is reflected parallel to the axis.

11–7   The ellipse.

DEFINITION. *An ellipse is the locus of points $P(x, y)$ the sum of whose distances from two fixed points is constant.*

If the two fixed points, called *foci*, are taken at $F_1(-c, 0)$ and $F_2(c, 0)$

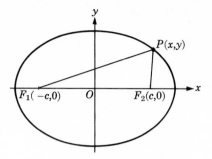

Figure 11–34

(Fig. 11–34), and the sum of the distances $|PF_1| + |PF_2|$ is denoted by $2a$, then the coordinates of P must satisfy the equation

$$\sqrt{(x+c)^2 + y^2} + \sqrt{(x-c)^2 + y^2} = 2a.$$

To simplify this expression, we transpose the second radical to the right side of the equation, square, and simplify, to obtain

$$a - \frac{c}{a}x = \sqrt{(x-c)^2 + y^2}.$$

Again we square and simplify, and obtain

$$\frac{x^2}{a^2} + \frac{y^2}{a^2 - c^2} = 1. \tag{1}$$

Since the sum $|PF_1| + |PF_2| = 2a$ of two sides of the triangle F_1F_2P is greater than the third side $|F_1F_2| = 2c$, the term $(a^2 - c^2)$ in (1) is positive and has a real positive square root which we denote by b:

$$b = \sqrt{a^2 - c^2}. \tag{2}$$

Then (1) takes the more compact form

$$\boxed{\frac{x^2}{a^2} + \frac{y^2}{b^2} = 1,} \tag{3}$$

from which it is readily seen that the curve is symmetric about both axes and lies inside the rectangle bounded by the lines $x = a$, $x = -a$, $y = b$, $y = -b$. The intercepts of the curve are at $(\pm a, 0)$ and $(0, \pm b)$. The curve intersects each axis at an angle of $90°$, since

$$\frac{dy}{dx} = \frac{-b^2x}{a^2y}$$

is zero at $x = 0$, $y = \pm b$ and is infinite at $y = 0$, $x = \pm a$.

We have shown that the coordinates of P must satisfy (1) if P satisfies the geometric condition $|PF_1| + |PF_2| = 2a$. Conversely, if x and y satisfy the algebraic equation (1) with $0 < c < a$, then

$$y^2 = (a^2 - c^2)\frac{a^2 - x^2}{a^2},$$

and substituting this in the radicals below, we find that

$$|PF_1| = \sqrt{(x + c)^2 + y^2} = \left| a + \frac{c}{a}x \right| \tag{4a}$$

and

$$|PF_2| = \sqrt{(x - c)^2 + y^2} = \left| a - \frac{c}{a}x \right|. \tag{4b}$$

Since x is restricted to the range $-a \le x \le a$, the value of $(c/a)x$ lies between $-c$ and c, so that both $a + (c/a)x$ and $a - (c/a)x$ are positive, both being between $a + c$ and $a - c$. Hence the absolute values in (4a) and (4b) yield

$$|PF_1| = a + \frac{c}{a}x, \qquad |PF_2| = a - \frac{c}{a}x, \tag{5}$$

and, adding these, we see that $|PF_1| + |PF_2|$ has a value $2a$ independent of the position of P on the curve. Thus the *geometric property* and *algebraic equation* are equivalent.

In Eq. (3), $b^2 = a^2 - c^2$ is less than a^2. The *major axis* of the ellipse is the segment of length $2a$ between the x-intercepts $(\pm a, 0)$. The *minor axis* is the segment of length $2b$ between the y-intercepts $(0, \pm b)$. The numbers a and b are also referred to respectively as semimajor axis and semiminor axis. If these semiaxes are $a = 4$, $b = 3$, then Eq. (3) is

$$\frac{x^2}{16} + \frac{y^2}{9} = 1. \tag{6a}$$

On the other hand, if we interchange the roles of x and y in (6a), we get the equation

$$\frac{x^2}{9} + \frac{y^2}{16} = 1, \tag{6b}$$

which must also represent an ellipse, but one with its major axis vertical rather than horizontal. Graphs of Eqs. (6a) and (6b) are given in Fig. 11–35 (a) and (b).

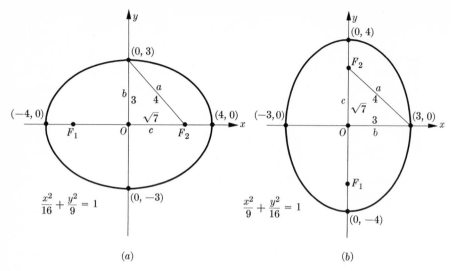

Figure 11–35

There is never any need for confusion in analyzing equations like (6a) and (6b). We simply find the intercepts on the axes of symmetry; then we know which way the major axis runs. The foci are always on the major axis. And if we use the letters a, b, and c to represent the lengths of semi-major axis, semiminor axis, and half-distance between foci, then Eq. (2) tells us that

$$b^2 = a^2 - c^2$$

or

$$\boxed{a^2 = b^2 + c^2.} \tag{7}$$

Hence a is the hypotenuse of a right triangle of sides b and c, as in Fig. 11–35. When we start with an equation like (6a) or (6b), we can read off a^2 and b^2 from it at once. Then Eq. (7) determines c^2 as their difference. So in either of Eqs. (6a) and (6b) we have

$$c^2 = 16 - 9 = 7.$$

Therefore the foci are $\sqrt{7}$ units from the center of the ellipse as shown.

Center not at the origin. The *center* of an ellipse is defined as the point of intersection of its axes of symmetry. If the center is at $C(h, k)$, and the axes of the ellipse are parallel to the x- and y-axes, then we may introduce new coordinates

$$x' = x - h, \qquad y' = y - k, \tag{8}$$

using C as origin O' of $x'y'$-coordinates. The equation of the ellipse in the new coordinates is either

$$\frac{x'^2}{a^2} + \frac{y'^2}{b^2} = 1 \qquad (9a)$$

or

$$\frac{x'^2}{b^2} + \frac{y'^2}{a^2} = 1, \qquad (9b)$$

depending upon which way the major axis runs.

EXAMPLE 1. Analyze the equation $9x^2 + 4y^2 + 36x - 8y + 4 = 0$.

Solution. In order to complete the squares, we collect the x terms and the y terms separately, thus

$$9(x^2 + 4x) + 4(y^2 - 2y) = -4,$$

and then complete the square in each set of parentheses to obtain

$$9(x^2 + 4x + 4) + 4(y^2 - 2y + 1) = -4 + 36 + 4.$$

We now divide both sides by 36 and write

$$\frac{(x+2)^2}{4} + \frac{(y-1)^2}{9} = 1.$$

Setting

$$x' = x + 2, \qquad y' = y - 1,$$

we see that the new origin $x' = 0$, $y' = 0$ is the same as the point $x = -2$, $y = 1$. In terms of the new coordinates, the equation is

$$\frac{x'^2}{4} + \frac{y'^2}{9} = 1,$$

which represents an ellipse with intercepts at $(0, \pm 3)$ on the y'-axis and $(\pm 2, 0)$ on the x'-axis. To locate the foci, we use the relation

$$b = \sqrt{a^2 - c^2}$$

to find

$$c = \sqrt{a^2 - b^2}.$$

Here

$$a^2 = 9, \qquad b^2 = 4,$$

so

$$c = \sqrt{5}.$$

The foci are at the points $(0, \pm\sqrt{5})$ on the y'-axis or at $(-2, 1 \pm \sqrt{5})$ in terms of the original coordinates.

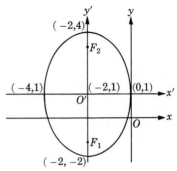

Figure 11–36

We recall (Fig. 11–34) that the essential *geometric* property of an ellipse is that the sum of the distances from any point on it to the two foci is a constant, namely,

$$|PF_1| + |PF_2| = 2a.$$

The essential *algebraic* property of its equation when written in the form of a quadratic without a cross-product term is that the x^2 and y^2 terms have the same sign.

In order to discuss the properties of the ellipse in more detail, we shall assume that its equation has been reduced to the form

$$\frac{x^2}{a^2} + \frac{y^2}{b^2} = 1, \qquad a > b > 0. \tag{10}$$

Although the distance c from the center of the ellipse to a focus does not appear in its equation, we may still determine c as in the examples above from the equation

$$c^2 = a^2 - b^2, \tag{11}$$

which is another way of writing Eq. (7).

A simple geometric method of finding c is shown by Fig. 11–37 and is based on the following considerations. Since the sum of the distances

$$|PF_1| + |PF_2| = 2a$$

for *every point* P on the ellipse, then certainly this must hold when P is taken to be at the y-intercept B. But the y-axis is the perpendicular

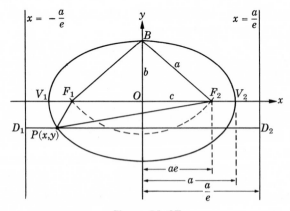

Figure 11–37

bisector of the line segment $\overline{F_1 F_2}$, so every point on it is equidistant from F_1 and F_2. We therefore have

$$|BF_1| + |BF_2| = 2a \qquad \text{and} \qquad |BF_1| = |BF_2|;$$

$$|BF_1| = |BF_2| = a.$$

We may therefore use B as the center of a circular arc of radius a. It will cut the x-axis in the two foci F_1 and F_2. Equation (11) then follows at once from applying the Theorem of Pythagoras to the right triangle OBF_2 in the figure.

Eccentricity. If we keep a fixed and vary c over the range $0 \le c \le a$, the resulting ellipses will vary in shape, being circular when $c = 0$ and becoming flatter as c increases, until in the extreme case $c = a$, the "ellipse" reduces to the line segment $\overline{F_1 F_2}$ joining the two foci (Fig. 11–38). The ratio

$$\boxed{e = c/a,} \qquad (12)$$

called the *eccentricity* of the ellipse, varies from 0 to 1 and indicates the degree of departure from circularity.

We recall that a parabola has one focus and one directrix. Each ellipse has two foci and two directrices. The directrices are lines perpendicular to the major axis of the ellipse at distances $\pm a/e$ from its center. The *parabola* has the property that

$$|PF| = 1 \cdot |PD| \qquad (13)$$

for any point P on it, where F is the focus and D is the point nearest P on the directrix.

Figure 11–38

For an *ellipse*, it is not difficult to show that the equations which take the place of (13) are

$$|PF_1| = e \cdot |PD_1|, \qquad |PF_2| = e \cdot |PD_2|. \qquad (14)$$

Here e is the eccentricity, P is any point on the ellipse, F_1 and F_2 are the foci, and D_1 and D_2 are the points nearest P on the two directrices. In Eq. (14), the corresponding directrix and focus must be used; that is, if one uses the distance from P to the focus F_1, one must also use the distance from P to the directrix at the same end of the ellipse (see Fig. 11–37). We thus associate the directrix $x = -a/e$ with the focus $F_1(-c, 0)$, and the directrix $x = a/e$ with the focus $F_2(c, 0)$. In terms of the semimajor axis a and eccentricity $e < 1$, as one goes away from the center along the major axis, one finds successively

> a *focus* at distance ae from the center,
> a *vertex* at distance a from the center,
> a *directrix* at distance a/e from the center.

An interesting feature of the "focus-and-directrix" property is that it furnishes a common bond uniting the parabola, ellipse, and hyperbola. Namely, if a point $P(x, y)$ is such that its distance $|PF|$ from a fixed point (the focus) is proportional to its distance $|PD|$ from a fixed line (the directrix), that is, so that

$$|PF| = e \cdot |PD|, \tag{15}$$

where e is a constant of proportionality, then the locus of P is

(a) a *parabola* if $e = 1$,

(b) an *ellipse* of eccentricity e if $e < 1$, and

(c) a *hyperbola* of eccentricity e if $e > 1$.

Constructions. There are several methods of constructing an ellipse. One of these simply uses the definition directly. The two ends of a string of length $2a$ are held fixed at the foci F_1 and F_2 and a pencil traces the curve as it is held taut against the string (see Fig. 11–39).

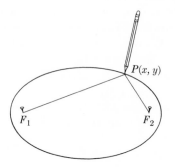

Figure 11-39

A second method makes use of a straight edge $\overline{AB}$ of length $a + b$. Place point A on the y-axis and B on the x-axis, and on the graph paper, make a dot at $P(x, y)$ at distance a from A (see Fig. 11–40). In terms of the angle θ that line $\overleftrightarrow{AB}$ makes with the (negative) x-axis, we have

$$x = a \cos \theta, \qquad y = b \sin \theta, \tag{16}$$

and hence

$$\frac{x^2}{a^2} + \frac{y^2}{b^2} = \cos^2\theta + \sin^2\theta = 1.$$

Therefore $P(x, y)$ is on the ellipse, Eq. (10).

A third method is to construct two concentric circles of radii a and b (Fig. 11–41). A line making an angle θ with the horizontal is drawn from

Figure 11-40

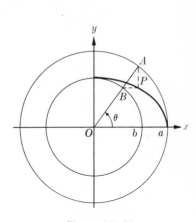

Figure 11-41

the center cutting the two circles in points A and B respectively. The vertical line through A and the horizontal line through B intersect in a point P whose coordinates also satisfy (16). By varying the angle θ from 0 to 360°, as many points as desired may be obtained on the ellipse.

PROBLEMS

In each of the following problems (1 through 5), find the equation of an ellipse having the given center C, focus F, and semimajor axis a. Sketch the graph and give the eccentricity of each ellipse.

1. $C(0, 0)$, $F(0, 2)$, $a = 4$ 2. $C(0, 0)$, $F(-3, 0)$, $a = 5$

3. $C(0, 2)$, $F(0, 0)$, $a = 3$ 4. $C(-3, 0)$, $F(-3, -2)$, $a = 4$

5. $C(2, 2)$, $F(-1, 2)$, $a = \sqrt{10}$

6. The end points of the major and minor axes of an ellipse are $(1, 1)$, $(3, 4)$, $(1, 7)$, and $(-1, 4)$. Sketch the ellipse, give its equation, and find its foci.

7. Find the center, vertices, and foci of the ellipse $25x^2 + 9y^2 - 100x + 54y - 44 = 0$. Sketch the curve.

8. Sketch each of the following ellipses:

(a) $9x^2 + 4y^2 = 36$,   (b) $4x^2 + 9y^2 = 144$,

(c) $\dfrac{(x-1)^2}{16} + \dfrac{(y+2)^2}{4} = 1$,   (d) $4x^2 + y^2 = 1$,

(e) $16(x-2)^2 + 9(y+3)^2 = 144$.

9. Find the equation of the ellipse that passes through the origin and has foci at $(-1, 1)$ and $(1, 1)$.

10. Find the eccentricity and the directrices of the ellipse $x^2/7 + y^2/16 = 1$.

11. Find the volume generated by rotating an ellipse of semi-axes a and b ($a > b$) about its major axis.

12. Set up the integrals that give (a) the area of a quadrant of the circle $x^2 + y^2 = a^2$, (b) the area of a quadrant of the ellipse $b^2x^2 + a^2y^2 = a^2b^2$. Show that the integral in (b) is b/a times the integral in (a) and deduce the area of the ellipse from the known area of the circle.

13. An ellipsoid is generated by rotating an ellipse about its major axis. The inside surface of the ellipsoid is silvered to produce a mirror. Show that a ray of light emanating from one focus will be reflected to the other focus. (Sound waves also follow such paths and this property of ellipsoids accounts for phenomena in certain "whispering galleries.")

14. Find the length of the chord perpendicular to the major axis of the ellipse $b^2x^2 + a^2y^2 = a^2b^2$ and passing through a focus. (This chord is called the "latus rectum" of the ellipse.)

15. Find the equation of an ellipse of eccentricity $\frac{2}{3}$ if the line $x = 9$ is one directrix and the corresponding focus is at $(4, 0)$.

16. Find the values of the constants A, B, and C if the ellipse $4x^2 + y^2 + Ax + By + C = 0$ is to be tangent to the x-axis at the origin and to pass through the point $(-1, 2)$.

17. Show that the line tangent to the ellipse $(x^2/a^2) + (y^2/b^2) = 1$ at the point $P_1(x_1, y_1)$ on it is

$$\frac{xx_1}{a^2} + \frac{yy_1}{b^2} = 1.$$

18. Graph the locus of $P(x, y)$ if $9x^2 + 16y^2 < 144$.

19. Graph the locus of $P(x, y)$ if

$$(x^2 + 4y)(2x - y - 3)(x^2 + y^2 - 25)(x^2 + 4y^2 - 4) = 0.$$

20. Graph the locus of $P(x, y)$ if $(x^2 + y^2 - 1)(9x^2 + 4y^2 - 36) < 0$.

11–8   The hyperbola.

DEFINITION. *A hyperbola is the locus of $P(x, y)$ if the difference of its distances from two fixed points is constant.*

Taking the fixed points at $F_1(-c, 0)$ and $F_2(c, 0)$ and the constant equal to $2a$ (see Fig. 11–42, p. 484), we have the condition

$$\sqrt{(x + c)^2 + y^2} - \sqrt{(x - c)^2 + y^2} = 2a$$

or

$$\sqrt{(x - c)^2 + y^2} - \sqrt{(x + c)^2 + y^2} = 2a.$$

The second equation is like the first, with $2a$ replaced by $-2a$. Hence we write the first one with $\pm 2a$, transpose one radical to the right side of the equation, square, and simplify. One radical still remains. We isolate it and square again. We then obtain the equation

$$\frac{x^2}{a^2} + \frac{y^2}{a^2 - c^2} = 1. \tag{1}$$

So far, this is just like the equation for an ellipse. But now $a^2 - c^2$ is negative, because the *difference* in two sides of the triangle F_1F_2P is less than the third side:

$$2a < 2c.$$

So in this case $c^2 - a^2$ is positive and has a real positive square root which we call b:

$$b = \sqrt{c^2 - a^2}, \tag{2a}$$

or

$$a^2 - c^2 = -b^2. \tag{2b}$$

The equation of the hyperbola now becomes

$$\boxed{\frac{x^2}{a^2} - \frac{y^2}{b^2} = 1,} \tag{3}$$

which is analogous to the equation of an ellipse; the only differences are the minus sign in the equation of the hyperbola, and the new relation among a, b, and c given by Eq. (2b). The hyperbola, like the ellipse, is symmetric with respect to both axes and the origin, but it has no real y-intercepts and in fact no portion of the curve lies between the lines $x = a$ and $x = -a$.

If we start with a point $P(x, y)$ whose coordinates satisfy Eq. (3), the distances $|PF_1|$ and $|PF_2|$ will be given by

$$|PF_1| = \sqrt{(x + c)^2 + y^2} = \left| a + \frac{c}{a} x \right|, \tag{4a}$$

$$|PF_2| = \sqrt{(x - c)^2 + y^2} = \left| a - \frac{c}{a} x \right|, \tag{4b}$$

as for the ellipse. But now c is greater than a, and P is either to the right of the line $x = a$, that is

$$x > a,$$

or else P is to the left of the line $x = -a$, and then

$$x < -a.$$

The absolute values in Eqs. (4) work out to be

$$
\left.
\begin{aligned}
|PF_1| &= a + \frac{c}{a}\,x \\
|PF_2| &= \frac{c}{a}\,x - a
\end{aligned}
\right\} \text{if } x > a
\qquad (5a)
$$

and

$$
\left.
\begin{aligned}
|PF_1| &= -\left(a + \frac{c}{a}\,x\right) \\
|PF_2| &= a - \frac{c}{a}\,x
\end{aligned}
\right\} \text{if } x < -a.
\qquad (5b)
$$

Thus, when P is to the right of the line $x = a$, the condition $|PF_1| - |PF_2| = 2a$ is satisfied, while if P is to the left of $x = -a$, the condition $|PF_2| - |PF_1| = 2a$ is fulfilled (Fig. 11–42). In either case, *any point P that satisfies the geometric conditions must satisfy the algebraic equation and, conversely, any point that satisfies the algebraic equation does also satisfy the geometric conditions.*

The left side of (3) can be factored and the equation written in the form

$$
\left(\frac{x}{a} - \frac{y}{b}\right)\left(\frac{x}{a} + \frac{y}{b}\right) = 1
$$

or

$$
\frac{x}{a} - \frac{y}{b} = \frac{ab}{bx + ay} .
\qquad (6a)
$$

Analysis of (3) shows that one branch of the curve lies in the first quadrant and has infinite extent. If the point P moves along this branch so that x and y both become infinite, then the right side of (6a) tends to zero; hence the left side must do likewise. That is

$$
\lim_{\substack{x \to \infty \\ y \to \infty}} \left(\frac{x}{a} - \frac{y}{b}\right) = 0,
\qquad (6b)
$$

which leads us to speculate that the straight line

Figure 11–42

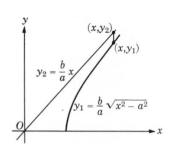

Figure 11–43

$$\frac{x}{a} - \frac{y}{b} = 0 \qquad (7\mathrm{a})$$

may be an asymptote of the curve. To see that this is definitely so, we investigate the vertical distance $(y_2 - y_1)$ between the curve and the line where we take

$$y_2 = \frac{b}{a} x$$

on the line, and

$$y_1 = \frac{b}{a} \sqrt{x^2 - a^2}$$

on the curve (Fig. 11–43). We then multiply both sides of Eq. (6b) by b, and see that

$$\lim_{x \to \infty} (y_2 - y_1) = 0.$$

Since this vertical distance tends to zero, certainly the perpendicular distance from the line to the curve also approaches zero, and the line in Eq. (7a) is an asymptote of the hyperbola.

By symmetry, the line

$$\frac{x}{a} + \frac{y}{b} = 0 \qquad (7\mathrm{b})$$

is also an asymptote of the hyperbola. Both asymptotes may be obtained by simply replacing the "one" on the right side of (3) by a zero and then factoring. In sketching a hyperbola (Fig. 11–42), it is convenient to mark off distances a to the right and to the left of the origin along the x-axis and distances b above and below the origin along the y-axis, and to construct a rectangle with sides passing through these points, parallel to the coordinate axes. The diagonals of this rectangle, extended, are then the asymptotes of the hyperbola. The semidiagonal

$$c = \sqrt{a^2 + b^2}$$

can also be used as the radius of a circle that will cut the x-axis in two points, $F_1(-c, 0)$ and $F_2(c, 0)$, which are the foci of the hyperbola.

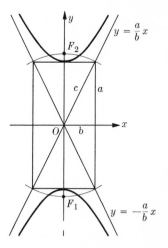

Fig. 11–44. Hyperbola
$(y^2/a^2) - (x^2/b^2) = 1.$

If we interchange x and y in Eq. (3), the new equation

$$\frac{y^2}{a^2} - \frac{x^2}{b^2} = 1 \qquad\qquad (8)$$

represents a hyperbola with foci on the y-axis. Its graph is shown in Fig. 11–44.

Center not at the origin. The *center* of a hyperbola is the point of intersection of its axes of symmetry. If the center is $C(h, k)$, we may introduce a translation to new coordinates

$$x' = x - h, \qquad y' = y - k \qquad\qquad (9)$$

with origin O' at the center. In terms of the new coordinates, the equation of the hyperbola is either

$$\frac{x'^2}{a^2} - \frac{y'^2}{b^2} = 1 \qquad\qquad (10a)$$

or

$$\frac{y'^2}{a^2} - \frac{x'^2}{b^2} = 1. \qquad\qquad (10b)$$

EXAMPLE 1. Analyze the equation $x^2 - 4y^2 + 2x + 8y - 7 = 0$.

Solution. We complete the squares in the x and y terms separately and reduce to standard form:

$$(x^2 + 2x) - 4(y^2 - 2y) = 7,$$
$$(x^2 + 2x + 1) - 4(y^2 - 2y + 1) = 7 + 1 - 4,$$
$$\frac{(x+1)^2}{4} - (y - 1)^2 = 1.$$

The translation of axes

$$x' = x + 1, \qquad y' = y - 1$$

reduces the equation to

$$\frac{x'^2}{4} - \frac{y'^2}{1} = 1,$$

which represents a hyperbola with center at $x' = 0$, $y' = 0$ or $x = -1, y = 1$, having

$$a^2 = 4, \qquad b^2 = 1, \qquad c^2 = a^2 + b^2 = 5$$

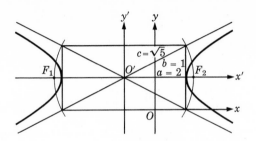

Figure 11-45

and asymptotes

$$\frac{x'}{2} - y' = 0, \qquad \frac{x'}{2} + y' = 0.$$

The foci have coordinates $(\pm\sqrt{5}, 0)$ relative to the new axes or, since

$$x = x' - 1, \qquad y = y' + 1,$$

the coordinates relative to the original axes are $(-1 \pm \sqrt{5}, 1)$. The curve is sketched in Fig. 11-45.

EXAMPLE 2. $\qquad x^2 - 4y^2 - 2x + 8y - 2 = 0.$

Proceeding as before, we obtain

$$(x - 1)^2 - 4(y - 1)^2 = 2 + 1 - 4 = -1.$$

The standard form requires a plus one on the right side of the equation, so we change signs and have

$$4(y - 1)^2 - (x - 1)^2 = 1.$$

Comparison with (10) indicates that we should write the first term of this equation as $(y - 1)^2$ divided by 0.25:

$$\frac{(y - 1)^2}{0.25} - \frac{(x - 1)^2}{1} = 1.$$

The translation $x' = x - 1$, $y' = y - 1$ replaces this by

$$\frac{y'^2}{0.25} - \frac{x'^2}{1} = 1,$$

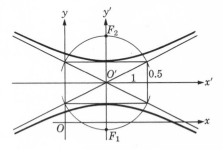

Figure 11-46

which represents a hyperbola with center at $x' = y' = 0$, or $x = y = 1$. The curve has intercepts at $(0, \pm0.5)$ on the y'-axis but does not cross the x'-axis.

Here (10b) applies, with

$$a^2 = 0.25, \qquad b^2 = 1, \qquad c^2 = a^2 + b^2 = 1.25.$$

The lines (Fig. 11–46)

$$\frac{y'}{0.5} - x' = 0, \qquad \frac{y'}{0.5} + x' = 0$$

are the asymptotes, while the foci are at $(0, \pm\sqrt{1.25})$ on the y'-axis.

It is worth noting that there is no restriction $a > b$ for the hyperbola as there is for the ellipse, and the direction in which the hyperbola opens is controlled by the *signs* rather than by the relative *sizes* of the coefficients of the quadratic terms.

In our further discussion of the hyperbola, we shall assume that it has been referred to axes through its center and that its equation has the form

$$\frac{x^2}{a^2} - \frac{y^2}{b^2} = 1. \tag{11}$$

Then

$$b = \sqrt{c^2 - a^2}$$

and

$$\boxed{c^2 = a^2 + b^2.} \tag{12}$$

As for the ellipse, we define the *eccentricity e* to be

$$\boxed{e = \frac{c}{a},}$$

and since $c \geq a$, the eccentricity of a hyperbola is never less than unity. The lines

$$x = \frac{a}{e}, \qquad x = -\frac{a}{e}$$

are the *directrices*.

We shall now verify that a point $P(x, y)$ whose coordinates satisfy Eq. (11) also has the property that

$$|PF_1| = e \cdot |PD_1| \tag{13a}$$

and

$$|PF_2| = e \cdot |PD_2|, \tag{13b}$$

where $F_1(-c, 0)$ and $F_2(c, 0)$ are the foci while $D_1(-a/e, y)$ and $D_2(a/e, y)$ are the points nearest P on the directrices.

We shall content ourselves with establishing the results (13a, b) for any point P on the right branch of the hyperbola; the method is the same

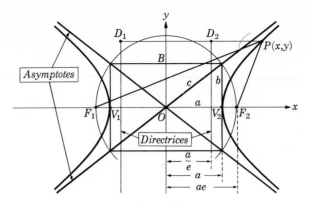

Figure 11–47

when P is on the left branch. Reference to Eqs. (5a) then shows that

$$|PF_1| = \frac{c}{a} x + a = e\left(x + \frac{a}{e}\right),$$
$$|PF_2| = \frac{c}{a} x - a = e\left(x - \frac{a}{e}\right),$$

(14a)

while we see from Fig. 11–47 that

$$|PD_1| = x + \frac{a}{e}, \qquad |PD_2| = x - \frac{a}{e}. \tag{14b}$$

These results combine to establish the "focus-and-directrix" properties of the hyperbola expressed in Eqs. (13a, b). Conversely, if Eqs. (14a) are satisfied, it is also true that

$$\boxed{|PF_1| - |PF_2| = 2a;}$$

that is, P satisfies the requirement that the difference of its distances from the two foci is constant.

It is possible to devise various schemes for sketching a hyperbola. In one method (see Fig. 11–48) we exploit the equation

$$|PF_1| = 2a + |PF_2|$$

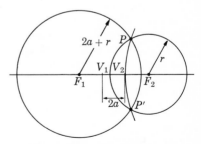

Figure 11–48

by constructing a circle of radius r with center at F_2 and another circle of radius $2a + r$ with center at F_1. The points P, P' where the two circles intersect are points on the hyperbola.

By varying r, as many points on the hyperbola as desired may be obtained. Interchanging the roles of the two foci F_1 and F_2 will give points on the other branch of the hyperbola.

PROBLEMS

1. Sketch each of the following hyperbolas:

(a) $\dfrac{x^2}{9} - \dfrac{y^2}{16} = 1,$ (b) $\dfrac{x^2}{16} - \dfrac{y^2}{9} = 1,$

(c) $\dfrac{y^2}{9} - \dfrac{x^2}{16} = 1,$ (d) $\dfrac{x^2}{9} - \dfrac{y^2}{16} = -1.$

In each of the following problems (2 through 8), find the center, vertices, foci, and asymptotes of the given hyperbola. Sketch the curve.

2. $9(x - 2)^2 - 4(y + 3)^2 = 36$ 3. $4(x - 2)^2 - 9(y + 3)^2 = 36$

4. $4(y + 3)^2 - 9(x - 2)^2 = 1$ 5. $5x^2 - 4y^2 + 20x + 8y = 4$

6. $4x^2 = y^2 - 4y + 8$ 7. $4y^2 = x^2 - 4x$

8. $4x^2 - 5y^2 - 16x + 10y + 31 = 0$

9. Show that the line tangent to the hyperbola $b^2x^2 - a^2y^2 = a^2b^2$ at a point $P(x_1, y_1)$ on it has an equation which may be written in the form $b^2xx_1 - a^2yy_1 = a^2b^2$.

10. Find the volume generated when the area bounded by the hyperbola $b^2x^2 - a^2y^2 = a^2b^2$ and the line $x = c$, through its focus $(c, 0)$, is rotated about the y-axis.

11. Show that the equation

$$\frac{x^2}{9 - C} + \frac{y^2}{5 - C} = 1$$

represents (a) an ellipse if C is any constant less than 5, (b) a hyperbola if C is any constant between 5 and 9, (c) no real locus if C is greater than 9. Show that each ellipse in (a) and each hyperbola in (b) has foci at the two points $(\pm 2, 0)$, independent of the value of C.

12. Find the equation of the hyperbola with foci at $(0, 0)$ and $(0, 4)$ if it is required to pass through the point $(12, 9)$.

13. One focus of a hyperbola is located at the point $(1, -3)$ and the corresponding directrix is the line $y = 2$. Find the equation of the hyperbola if its eccentricity is $\frac{3}{2}$.

14. Find out what you can about the DECCA system of air navigation. [See *Time*, Feb. 23, 1959, p. 87.]

11–9   **Second degree curves.** The circle, parabola, ellipse, and hyperbola are curves whose equations are all special cases of the following general equation of the second degree:

$$Ax^2 + Bxy + Cy^2 + Dx + Ey + F = 0. \tag{1}$$

For example, the circle

$$(x - h)^2 + (y - k)^2 = r^2$$

may be obtained from Eq. (1) by taking

$$A = C = 1, \quad B = 0, \quad D = -2h,$$
$$E = -2k, \quad F = h^2 + k^2 - r^2,$$

and the parabola

$$x^2 = 4py$$

is obtained by taking

$$A = 1, \quad E = -4p, \quad B = C = D = F = 0.$$

In fact, even the straight line is a special case of (1) with $A = B = C = 0$, but this reduces (1) to a *linear* equation instead of maintaining its status as a second degree equation. The terms Ax^2, Bxy, and Cy^2 are the second degree, or quadratic terms, and we shall presently investigate the nature of the curve represented by Eq. (1) when at least one of these quadratic terms is present.

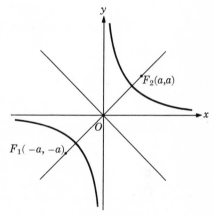

Figure 11–49

The so-called "cross-product" term, Bxy, has not appeared in the equations we found in Articles 11–5 to 11–8. This is a consequence of the way in which we chose coordinate axes, namely, such that at least one of them is parallel to an axis of symmetry of the curve in question. However, suppose we seek to find the equation of a hyperbola with foci at $F_1(-a, -a)$ and $F_2(a, a)$ for example, and with $||PF_1| - |PF_2|| = 2a$ (Fig. 11–49). Then

$$\sqrt{(x + a)^2 + (y + a)^2} - \sqrt{(x - a)^2 + (y - a)^2} = \pm 2a,$$

and when we transpose one radical, square, solve for the radical that still appears, and square again, this reduces to

$$2xy = a^2, \tag{2}$$

which is a special case of Eq. (1) in which the cross-product term is present. The asymptotes of the hyperbola in Eq. (2) are the x- and y-axes, and the transverse axis of the hyperbola (which is the axis of symmetry on which the foci lie) makes an angle of 45° with the coordinate axes. In fact, the cross-product term is present only in some similar circumstance, where the axes have been "tilted."

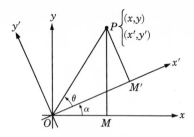

Figure 11-50

We shall now see how the equation of a curve is modified if it is referred to $x'y'$-axes by a rotation through an angle α in the counterclockwise direction. Referring to Fig. 11–50, we have

$$x = |OM| = |OP| \cos (\theta + \alpha),$$
$$y = |MP| = |OP| \sin (\theta + \alpha), \tag{3a}$$

while

$$x' = |OM'| = |OP| \cos \theta,$$
$$y' = |M'P| = |OP| \sin \theta. \tag{3b}$$

Using the relationships

$$\cos (\theta + \alpha) = \cos \theta \cos \alpha - \sin \theta \sin \alpha,$$
$$\sin (\theta + \alpha) = \sin \theta \cos \alpha + \cos \theta \sin \alpha,$$

in (3a) and taking account of (3b), we find

$$\boxed{\begin{aligned} x &= x' \cos \alpha - y' \sin \alpha, \\ y &= x' \sin \alpha + y' \cos \alpha, \end{aligned}} \tag{4}$$

which are known as the equations for *rotation of axes*.

To illustrate their application, suppose that we take $\alpha = 45°$ and find the equation of the hyperbola of (2) in terms of the new coordinates. Since $\cos 45° = \sin 45° = \sqrt{\frac{1}{2}}$, we substitute

$$x = \frac{x' - y'}{\sqrt{2}}, \qquad y = \frac{x' + y'}{\sqrt{2}}$$

into Eq. (2) and obtain

$$(x')^2 - (y')^2 = a^2,$$

which is like Eq. (3), Article 11–8, with $b = a$.

If we apply the general rotation of axes of equations (4) to the general quadratic equation (1), we obtain a new quadratic equation of the form

$$A'x'^2 + B'x'y' + C'y'^2 + D'x' + E'y' + F' = 0, \qquad (5)$$

with new coefficients related to the old as follows:

$$
\left.
\begin{aligned}
A' &= A\cos^2\alpha + B\cos\alpha\sin\alpha + C\sin^2\alpha, \\
B' &= B(\cos^2\alpha - \sin^2\alpha) + 2(C - A)\sin\alpha\cos\alpha, \\
C' &= A\sin^2\alpha - B\sin\alpha\cos\alpha + C\cos^2\alpha, \\
D' &= D\cos\alpha + E\sin\alpha, \\
E' &= -D\sin\alpha + E\cos\alpha, \\
F' &= F.
\end{aligned}
\right\}
\qquad (6)
$$

If we start with an equation in which the cross-product term is present, $B \neq 0$, we can always find an angle of rotation α such that the new cross-product term is eliminated. To find the angle α that does this, we simply put $B' = 0$ in (6_2) and solve for α. It is easier to do this if we note that

$$\cos^2\alpha - \sin^2\alpha = \cos 2\alpha,$$

$$2\sin\alpha\cos\alpha = \sin 2\alpha,$$

so that

$$B' = B\cos 2\alpha + (C - A)\sin 2\alpha.$$

Hence B' will vanish if we choose α so that

$$\boxed{\cot 2\alpha = \frac{A - C}{B}.}\qquad (7)$$

For example, the curve whose equation is

$$x^2 + xy + y^2 = 3$$

has $A = B = C = 1$. Choosing α according to Eq. (7),

$$\cot 2\alpha = 0, \qquad 2\alpha = 90°, \qquad \alpha = 45°,$$

and substituting

$$x = \frac{x' - y'}{\sqrt{2}}, \qquad y = \frac{x' + y'}{\sqrt{2}}$$

according to (4), we obtain

$$3(x')^2 + (y')^2 = 6.$$

This may be identified as an ellipse with its foci on the new y'-axis.

Since axes may be rotated to eliminate the cross-product term, there is no loss in generality in assuming that this has been done. Then the quadratic equation (5), with $B' = 0$, will look like Eq. (1), with $B = 0$:

$$Ax^2 + Cy^2 + Dx + Ey + F = 0. \tag{8}$$

Eq. (8) represents:

(a) A straight line if $A = C = 0$, and not both D and E vanish.
(b) A circle if $A = C \neq 0$. In special cases the locus may reduce to a single point, or no real locus.
(c) A parabola if (8) is quadratic in one variable, linear in the other.
(d) An ellipse if A and C are both positive or both negative. In special cases the locus may reduce to a single point, or no real locus.
(e) A hyperbola if A and C are of opposite signs, both different from zero. In special cases the locus may reduce to a pair of intersecting straight lines. (For example: $x^2 - y^2 = 0$.)

We have already seen how to reduce (8) to the standard form for the equation of a circle, parabola, ellipse, or hyperbola by completing the squares (as needed) and translating to new axes.

Summary. Any second degree equation in x and y represents a circle, parabola, ellipse, or hyperbola (except for certain special cases in which the locus may reduce to a point, a line, a pair of lines, or fail to exist, as noted above). Conversely, any of these curves has an equation of the second degree. To find the curve, given its equation, we

first, rotate axes (if necessary)
to eliminate the cross-product term,

and

second, translate axes (if desired) to reduce the
equation to a standard form which we recognize.

1. Show that the equation $x^4 + 6x^2y^2 + y^4 = 32$ becomes $x'^4 + y'^4 = 16$ under a 45° rotation of axes. Sketch the curve and the two sets of axes.

2. Use the definition of an ellipse to find the equation of an ellipse with foci at $F_1(-1, 0)$ and $F_2(0, \sqrt{3})$ if it passes through the point $(1, 0)$. Through

what angle α should the axes be rotated to eliminate the cross-product term from the equation found?

3. Show that the equation $x^2 + y^2 = r^2$ becomes $x'^2 + y'^2 = r^2$ for every choice of the angle α in the equations for rotation of axes.

4. Show that $A' + C' = A + C$ for every choice of the angle α in Eqs. (6).

5. Show that $B'^2 - 4A'C' = B^2 - 4AC$ for every choice of the angle α in Eqs. (6).

6. Show that a rotation of the axes through 45° will eliminate the cross-product term from Eq. (1) whenever $A = C$.

7. Find the equation of the curve $x^2 + 2xy + y^2 = 1$ after a rotation of axes which makes $A' = 0$ in Eq. (6).

By means of a rotation of axes, transform each of the following equations into an equation that has no cross-product term.

8. $3x^2 + 2xy + 3y^2 = 19$ 9. $x^2 - 3xy + y^2 = 5$

10. $3x^2 + 4\sqrt{3}xy - y^2 = 7$

11–10 Invariants and the discriminant. It is sometimes useful to apply directly to the equation

$$Ax^2 + Bxy + Cy^2 + Dx + Ey + F = 0 \tag{1}$$

a criterion that will tell whether the curve is a parabola, an ellipse, or a hyperbola, without first performing a rotation of axes to eliminate the cross-product term. Our discussion has shown that a rotation of axes through an angle α determined by

$$\boxed{\cot 2\alpha = \frac{A - C}{B}} \tag{2}$$

will transform the equation to the equivalent form

$$A'x'^2 + B'x'y' + C'y'^2 + D'x' + E'y' + F' = 0 \tag{3}$$

with new coefficients $A', \ldots, F'$ related to the old as in Eq. (6), Article 9–9, and with $B' = 0$ for the particular choice of α satisfying Eq. (2) above.

Now the nature of the curve whose equation is (3) with cross-product term removed is determined as follows:

(a) a *parabola* if A' or $C' = 0$, that is, if $A'C' = 0$,
(b) an *ellipse* if A' and C' have the same sign, that is, if $A'C' > 0$, and
(c) a *hyperbola* if A' and C' have opposite signs, that is, if $A'C' < 0$.

But it has been discovered and can easily be verified by use of Eq. (6), Article 11–9, that the coefficients A, B, C and A', B', C' satisfy the following condition:

$$B^2 - 4AC = B'^2 - 4A'C' \qquad (4)$$

for *any* rotation of axes. That is, the quantity $B^2 - 4AC$ is *invariant* under a rotation of axes. But when the particular rotation is performed that makes $B' = 0$, the right side of (4) becomes simply $-4A'C'$. The criteria above, expressed in terms of A' and C', can now be expressed in terms of the *discriminant:*

$$\text{discriminant} = B^2 - 4AC. \qquad (5)$$

Namely, the curve is

> (a) a *parabola* if $B^2 - 4AC = 0$,
> (b) an *ellipse* if $B^2 - 4AC < 0$,
> (c) a *hyperbola* if $B^2 - 4AC > 0$,

with the understanding that certain degenerate cases may arise.

Another invariant associated with Eqs. (1) and (3) is the sum of the coefficients of the squared terms. For it is evident from Eq. (6), Article 11–9, that

$$A' + C' = A\,(\cos^2\alpha + \sin^2\alpha) + C\,(\sin^2\alpha + \cos^2\alpha)$$

or

$$A' + C' = A + C, \qquad (6)$$

since

$$\sin^2\alpha + \cos^2\alpha = 1$$

for any angle α.

The two invariants (4) and (6) may be used as a check against numerical errors in performing a rotation of axes of a quadratic equation. They may also be used to find the new coefficients of the quadratic terms

$$A'x'^2 + B'x'y' + C'y'^2,$$

with

$$B' = 0,$$

as in the following example.

EXAMPLE. Determine the equation to which

$$x^2 + xy + y^2 = 1$$

reduces when the axes are rotated to eliminate the cross-product term.

Solution. From the original equation we find

$$B^2 - 4AC = -3, \qquad A + C = 2.$$

Then, taking $B' = 0$, we have from (4) and (6),

$$-4A'C' = -3, \qquad A' + C' = 2.$$

Substituting $C' = 2 - A'$ from the second of these into the first, we obtain the quadratic equation

$$4A'^2 - 8A' + 3 = 0,$$

which factors into

$$(2A' - 3)(2A' - 1) = 0$$

and gives

$$A' = \tfrac{3}{2} \quad \text{or} \quad A' = \tfrac{1}{2}.$$

The corresponding values of C' are

$$C' = \tfrac{1}{2} \quad \text{or} \quad C' = \tfrac{3}{2}.$$

The equation therefore is

$$\tfrac{3}{2}x'^2 + \tfrac{1}{2}y'^2 = 1$$

or

$$\tfrac{1}{2}x'^2 + \tfrac{3}{2}y'^2 = 1$$

in the new coordinates. Hence the curve is an ellipse.

It should be noted that when no first power terms are present in the original equation, they will also be absent in the new equation. This is due to the fact that a rotation of axes preserves the algebraic degree of each term of the equation; or we may refer to Eq. (6), Article 11–9, which shows that D' and E' are both zero if D and E vanish.

PROBLEMS

Use the discriminant and classify each of the following second degree equations as representing a circle, an ellipse, a parabola, or a hyperbola.

1. $x^2 + y^2 + xy + x - y = 3$ 2. $2x^2 - y^2 + 4xy - 2x + 3y = 6$
3. $x^2 + 4xy + 4y^2 - 3x = 6$ 4. $x^2 + y^2 + 3x - 2y = 10$
5. $xy + y^2 - 3x = 5$ 6. $3x^2 + 6xy + 3y^2 - 4x + 5y = 12$
7. $x^2 - y^2 = 1$ 8. $2x^2 + 3y^2 - 4x = 7$
9. $x^2 - 3xy + 3y^2 + 6y = 7$

10. When $B^2 - 4AC$ is negative, the equation $Ax^2 + Bxy + Cy^2 = 1$ represents an ellipse. If the semiaxes have lengths a and b, the area of the ellipse is πab. Show that the area of the ellipse given above is $2\pi/\sqrt{4AC - B^2}$.

11. Show, by reference to Eq. (6), Article 11–9, that $D'^2 + E'^2 = D^2 + E^2$ for every angle of rotation α.

12. If $C = -A$ in Eq. (1), show that there is a rotation of axes for which $A' = C' = 0$ in the resulting Eq. (3). Find the angle α that makes $A' = C' = 0$ in this case. [*Hint:* Since $A' + C' = 0$, one need only make the further requirement that $A' = 0$ in Eq. (3).]

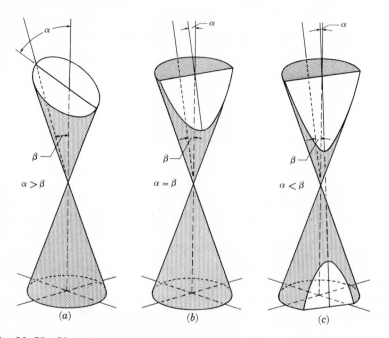

Fig. 11-51. **Plane intersecting cone in (a) ellipse, (b) parabola, (c) hyperbola.**

11–11   **Sections of a cone.** The circle, parabola, ellipse, and hyperbola are known as *conic* sections because each may be obtained by cutting a cone by a plane. If the cutting plane is perpendicular to the axis of the cone, the section is a circle.

More generally, suppose the cutting plane makes an angle α with the axis of the cone and let the generating angle of the cone be β. Then the section is:

(a) a circle if $\alpha = 90°$,   (b) an ellipse if $\beta < \alpha < 90°$,

(c) a parabola if $\alpha = \beta$,   (d) a hyperbola if $0 \leq \alpha < \beta$.

Figure 11–52

The connection between these curves as we have defined them and the sections from a cone is readily made by reference to Fig. 11–52. The figure is drawn to illustrate the case of an ellipse, but the argument holds for the other cases as well.

A sphere is inscribed tangent to the cone along a circle C, and tangent to the cutting plane at a point F. Point P is any point on the conic section, and we shall see that F is a focus and the line L in which the cutting plane and the plane of the circle C intersect is a directrix of the curve. To this end let Q be the point where the line through P parallel to the axis of the cone intersects the plane of C, let A be the point where the line joining P to the vertex of the cone touches C, and let $\overleftrightarrow{PD}$ be perpendicular to line L at D. Then $\overleftrightarrow{PA}$ and $\overleftrightarrow{PF}$ are two lines tangent to the same sphere from a common point P and hence have the same length;

$$|PA| = |PF|.$$

Also, from the right triangle PQA, we have

$$|PQ| = |PA| \cos \beta$$

and from the right triangle PQD, we find

$$|PQ| = |PD| \cos \alpha. \,|$$

Hence

$$|PA| \cos \beta = |PD| \cos \alpha$$

or

$$\frac{|PA|}{|PD|} = \frac{\cos \alpha}{\cos \beta}.$$

But since $|PA| = |PF|$, this means that

$$\frac{|PF|}{|PD|} = \frac{\cos \alpha}{\cos \beta}. \tag{1}$$

Since α and β are constant for a given cone and a given cutting plane, Eq. (1) has the form

$$|PF| = e \cdot |PD|.$$

This characterizes P as belonging to a parabola, an ellipse, or a hyperbola, with focus at F and directrix L, according as $e = 1$, $e < 1$, or $e > 1$ respectively, where

$$e = \frac{\cos \alpha}{\cos \beta}$$

is thus identified with the eccentricity.

PROBLEMS

1. Sketch a figure similar to Fig. 11–52 when the conic section is a parabola, and carry through the argument of Article 11–11 on the basis of such a figure.

2. Sketch a figure similar to Fig. 11–52 when the conic section is a hyperbola and carry through the argument of Article 11–11 on the basis of such a figure.

3. Which parts of the construction described in Article 11–11 become impossible when the conic section is a circle?

4. Let one directrix be the line $x = -p$ and take the corresponding focus at the origin. Using Eq. (15) of Article 11–7, derive the equation of the general conic section of eccentricity e. If e is neither 0 nor 1, show that the center of the conic section has coordinates

$$\left(\frac{pe^2}{1 - e^2}, \ 0\right).$$

11–12   Curve fitting using determinants. It is often of interest to see if a curve of given type can be made to pass through certain given points. When it can be done, we want to know the equation of the curve. Of course the given points do not uniquely determine the equation of the curve, since other curves of different types might also go through the same points. For example, a circle or a parabola might be made to go through three noncollinear points. But if it is to be a circle, that circle is unique.

Determinants may often be used to advantage in writing down an equation for a curve, as in the following examples.

EXAMPLE 1.

$$\begin{vmatrix} x & y & 1 \\ x_1 & y_1 & 1 \\ x_2 & y_2 & 1 \end{vmatrix} = 0$$

is the equation of a straight line through $P_1(x_1, y_1)$ and $P_2(x_2, y_2)$.

EXAMPLE 2.

$$\begin{vmatrix} x^2 + y^2 & x & y & 1 \\ x_1^2 + y_1^2 & x_1 & y_1 & 1 \\ x_2^2 + y_2^2 & x_2 & y_2 & 1 \\ x_3^2 + y_3^2 & x_3 & y_3 & 1 \end{vmatrix} = 0$$

is the equation of a circle through $P_1(x_1, y_1)$, $P_2(x_2, y_2)$, and $P_3(x_3, y_3)$, provided the cofactor

$$A_{11} = \begin{vmatrix} x_1 & y_1 & 1 \\ x_2 & y_2 & 1 \\ x_3 & y_3 & 1 \end{vmatrix}$$

is not zero. This is the same as requiring that the three points be noncollinear, from Example 1.

EXAMPLE 3.

$$\begin{vmatrix} y & x^2 & x & 1 \\ y_1 & x_1^2 & x_1 & 1 \\ y_2 & x_2^2 & x_2 & 1 \\ y_3 & x_3^2 & x_3 & 1 \end{vmatrix} = 0$$

is an equation of the form

$$Ay + Bx^2 + Cx + D = 0$$

and represents a parabola through $P_1(x_1, y_1)$, $P_2(x_2, y_2)$, and $P_3(x_3, y_3)$, provided $AB \neq 0$, where

$$A = \begin{vmatrix} x_1^2 & x_1 & 1 \\ x_2^2 & x_2 & 1 \\ x_3^2 & x_3 & 1 \end{vmatrix} = (x_1 - x_2)(x_1 - x_3)(x_2 - x_3)$$

and

$$B = - \begin{vmatrix} y_1 & x_1 & 1 \\ y_2 & x_2 & 1 \\ y_3 & x_3 & 1 \end{vmatrix} = \begin{vmatrix} x_1 & y_1 & 1 \\ x_2 & y_2 & 1 \\ x_3 & y_3 & 1 \end{vmatrix}.$$

The condition $A \neq 0$ is the same as x_1, x_2, x_3 all different; while $B \neq 0$ is the condition that P_1, P_2, P_3 be noncollinear.

EXAMPLE 4.

$$\begin{vmatrix} x^2 & xy & y^2 & x & y & 1 \\ x_1^2 & x_1 y_1 & y_1^2 & x_1 & y_1 & 1 \\ x_2^2 & x_2 y_2 & y_2^2 & x_2 & y_2 & 1 \\ x_3^2 & x_3 y_3 & y_3^2 & x_3 & y_3 & 1 \\ x_4^2 & x_4 y_4 & y_4^2 & x_4 & y_4 & 1 \\ x_5^2 & x_5 y_5 & y_5^2 & x_5 & y_5 & 1 \end{vmatrix} = 0$$

is the general equation of a conic section

$$Ax^2 + Bxy + Cy^2 + Dx + Ey + F = 0$$

through the five points $P_i(x_i, y_i); i = 1, 2, 3, 4, 5$.

PROBLEMS

1. Write a determinantal equation for a curve of the form

$$by = a_0x^n + a_1x^{n-1} + a_2x^{n-2} + \cdots + a_{n-1}x + a_n$$

through $n + 1$ points $P_i(x_i, y_i); i = 1, 2, \ldots, n + 1$. When the x_i's are all different, prove that there is such a curve with $b \neq 0$.

2. Find a parabola of the form

$$Ax + By^2 + Cy + D = 0$$

through the three points $P_1(-1, 0)$, $P_2(2, 1)$, $P_3(1, -1)$. Find the vertex and axis of the parabola, and sketch.

3. Find a conic of the form

$$Ax^2 + Bxy + Cy^2 = D$$

through the three points $P_1(3, 0)$, $P_2(1, 2)$, $P_3(-1, -1)$.

REVIEW QUESTIONS AND EXERCISES FOR CHAPTER 11

1. Discuss criteria for symmetry of a curve with respect to: (a) the x-axis, (b) the y-axis, (c) the origin, (d) the line $y = x$.

2. Define *asymptote*. How do you find vertical and horizontal asymptotes of a curve if its equation is given in the form $y = f(x)/g(x)$?

3. How do you find the extent of a curve (or, alternatively, strips of the plane from which the curve is excluded)?

4. Name the conic sections.

5. What kind of equation characterizes the conic sections?

6. If the equation of a conic section is given, and it contains no xy-term, how can you tell by inspection whether it is a parabola, circle, ellipse, or hyperbola? How can you tell what the curve is if there is an xy-term in the equation?

7. What are the equations of transformation of coordinates:

(a) for a translation of axes? (b) for a rotation of axes?

Illustrate with diagrams.

8. What two quantities that are associated with the equation of a conic section remain invariant under a rotation of axes?

9. Sketch a parabola and label its vertex, focus, axis, and directrix. What is the definition of a parabola? What is the equation of your parabola?

10. How can one find the equation of a line tangent to a given curve $y = f(x)$ at a given point (x_1, y_1) on the curve?

11. What is the normal to a curve at a given point $P_1(x_1, y_1)$?

12. Explain briefly Newton's method for approximating roots of equations. When can it be used?

13. Given two points $P_1(x_1, y_1)$ and $P_2(x_2, y_2)$, write the formula which can be used to find the distance d between them.

14. Sketch an ellipse and label its vertices, foci, axes, and directrices. What is the definition of an ellipse? What is the equation of your ellipse?

15. Sketch a hyperbola and label its vertices, foci, axes, asymptotes, and directrices. What is the definition of a hyperbola? What is the equation of your hyperbola?

16. A ripple tank is made by bending a strip of tin around the perimeter of an ellipse for the wall of the tank and soldering a flat bottom onto this. An inch or two of water is put in the tank and the experimenter pokes a finger into it, right at one focus of the ellipse. Ripples radiate outward through the water, reflect from the strip around the edge of the tank, and (in a short time) a drop of water spurts up at the second focus. Why?

MISCELLANEOUS PROBLEMS FOR CHAPTER 11

In Problems 1 through 9 determine the following properties of the curves whose equations are given: (A) symmetry, (B) extent, (C) intercepts, (D) asymptotes, (E) slope at intercepts. Use this information in sketching the curves.

1. (a) $y^2 = x(4 - x)$; (b) $y^2 = x(x - 4)$; (c) $y^2 = \dfrac{x}{4 - x}$

2. (a) $y = x + \dfrac{1}{x^2}$; (b) $y^2 = x + \dfrac{1}{x^2}$; (c) $y = x^2 + \dfrac{1}{x}$

3. (a) $y = x(x + 1)(x - 2)$; (b) $y^2 = x(x + 1)(x - 2)$

4. (a) $y = \dfrac{8}{4 + x^2}$; (b) $y = \dfrac{8}{4 - x^2}$; (c) $y = \dfrac{8x}{4 + x^2}$

5. (a) $xy = x^2 + 1$; (b) $y = \dfrac{x^2}{x - 1}$

6. (a) $y^2 = x^4 - x^2$; (b) $y^2 = \dfrac{x - 1}{x - 2}$

7. $x^2y - y = 4(x - 2)$

8. $y = \dfrac{x^2 + 1}{x^2 - 1}$

9. $x^2 + xy + y^2 = 3$

10. Let C be the curve in Problem 9. Let $P(x, y)$ be a point on C. Let $P'(kx, ky)$ be a point on the line $\overleftrightarrow{OP}$ from the origin to P. If k is held constant, what is the equation of the locus described by P' as P traces out the curve C?

11. Sketch the graph whose equation is $(y - x + 2)(2y + x - 4) = 0$.

12. A certain graph has an equation of the form

$$ay^2 + by = \frac{cx + d}{ex^2 + fx + g},$$

where a, b, c, d, e, f, and g are constants whose value in each case is either 0 or 1. From the following information about the graph, determine the constants and give a reason for your choice in each case:

Extent. The curve does not exist for $x < -1$. All values of y are permissible.

Symmetry. The curve is symmetric about the x-axis.

Intercepts. No y-intercept; x-intercept at $(-1, 0)$.

Asymptotes. Both axes; no others.

Sketch the graph.

13. Each of the following inequalities describes one or more regions of the xy-plane. Sketch first the locus obtained by replacing the inequality sign by an equal sign, then indicate the region that contains the points whose coordinates satisfy the given inequality.

(a) $x < 3$, (b) $x < y$, (c) $x^2 < y$, (d) $x^2 + y^2 > 4$, (e) $x^2 + xy + y^2 < 3$,
(f) $x^2 + xy + y^2 > 3$, (g) $y^2 < \dfrac{x}{4 - x}$.

14. Write an equation of the tangent, at $(2, 2)$, to the curve

$$x^2 - 2xy + y^2 + 2x + y - 6 = 0.$$

15. Sketch the curves $xy = 2$ and $x^2 - y^2 = 3$ in one diagram, and show that they intersect orthogonally.

16. Find equations of the lines that are tangent to the curve $y = x^3 - 6x + 2$ and are parallel to the line $y = 6x - 2$.

17. Prove that if a line is drawn tangent to the curve $y^2 = kx$ at a point $P(x, y)$ not at the origin, then the portion of the tangent that lies between the x-axis and P is bisected by the y-axis.

18. Through the point $P(x, y)$ on the curve $y^2 = kx$, lines are drawn parallel to the axes. The rectangular area bounded by these two lines and the axes is divided into two portions by the given curve. (a) If these two areas are rotated about the y-axis, show that they generate two solids whose volumes are in the ratio of four to one. (b) What is the ratio of the volumes of the solids generated when these areas are rotated about the x-axis?

19. Show that the curves $2x^2 + 3y^2 = a^2$ and $ky^2 = x^3$ are orthogonal for all values of the constants a and k ($a \neq 0, k \neq 0$). Sketch the four curves corresponding to $a = 2$, $a = 4$, $k = \frac{1}{2}$, $k = -2$ in one diagram.

20. Show, analytically, that an angle inscribed in a semicircle is a right angle.

21. Two points P, Q are called symmetric with respect to a circle if P and Q lie on the same ray through the center and if the product of their distances from the center is equal to the square of the radius. Given that Q describes the straight line $x + 2y - 5 = 0$, find the locus of the point P that is symmetric to Q with respect to the circle $x^2 + y^2 = 4$.

22. A point $P(x, y)$ moves so that the ratio of its distances from two fixed points is a constant k. Show that the locus is a circle if $k \neq 1$, and is a straight line if $k = 1$.

23. Show that the centers of all chords of the parabola $x^2 = 4py$ with slope m lie on a straight line and find its equation.

24. The line through the focus F and the point $P(x_1, y_1)$ on the parabola $y^2 = 4px$ intersects the parabola in a second point $Q(x_2, y_2)$. Find the coordinates of Q in terms of y_1 and p. If O is the vertex and $\overleftrightarrow{PO}$ cuts the directrix at R, prove that $\overleftrightarrow{QR}$ is parallel to the axis of the parabola.

25. Find the point (or points) on the curve $x^2 = y^3$ nearest the point $P(0, 4)$. Sketch the curve and the shortest line from P to the curve.

26. Prove that every line through the center of the circle $(x - h)^2 + (y - k)^2 = r^2$ is orthogonal to the circle.

27. Find all points on the curve $x^2 + 2xy + 3y^2 = 3$, where the tangent line is perpendicular to the line $x + y = 1$.

28. A line $\overleftrightarrow{PT}$ is drawn tangent to the curve $xy = x + y$ at the point $P(-2, \frac{2}{3})$. Find equations of two lines that are normal to the curve and perpendicular to $\overleftrightarrow{PT}$.

29. Sketch the loci described by each of the following equations:

(a) $(x + y)(x^2 + y^2 - 1) = 0$;   (b) $(x + y)(x^2 + y^2 - 1) = 1$.

[*Hint:* In part (b), consider intersections of the locus with the line $x + y = k$ for different values of the constant k.]

30. Find the center and radius of the circle through the two points $A(2, 0)$ and $B(6, 0)$ and tangent to the curve $y = x^2$.

31. Find the center of the circle that passes through the point $(0, 1)$ and is tangent to the curve $y = x^2$ at $(2, 4)$.

32. Let L_1, L_2, L_3 be three straight lines, no two of which are parallel. Let $L_i = a_i x + b_i y + c_i = 0$, $i = 1, 2, 3$, be the equation of the line L_i.

(a) Describe the locus whose equation is $L_1 L_2 + h L_2 L_3 + k L_1 L_3 = 0$, assuming h and k are constants.

(b) Use the method of part (a) and determine h and k so that the equation represents a circle through the points of intersection of the lines

$$x + y - 2 = 0, \qquad x - y + 2 = 0, \qquad y - 2x = 0.$$

(c) Find a parabola, axis vertical, through the points of intersection of the lines in (b).

33. A comet moves in a parabolic orbit with the sun at the focus. When the comet is 4×10^7 miles from the sun, the line from the sun to it makes an angle of $60°$ with the axis of the orbit (drawn in the direction in which the orbit opens). Find how near the comet comes to the sun.

34. Sketch in one diagram the curves $y^2 = 4x + 4$, $y^2 = 64 - 16x$, and find the angles at which they intersect.

35. Find an equation of the curve such that the distance from any point $P(x, y)$ on the curve to the line $x = 3$ is the same as its distance to the point $(4, 0)$. Sketch the curve.

36. Two radar stations lying along an east-west line are separated by 20 mi. Choose a coordinate system such that their positions are $(-10, 0)$ and $(10, 0)$. A low-flying plane traveling from west to east is known to have a speed of v_0 mi/sec. At $t = 0$ a signal is sent from the station at $(-10, 0)$, bounces off the plane, and is received at $(10, 0)$ $30/c$ sec later (c is the velocity of the signal). When $t = 10/v_0$, another signal is sent out from the station at $(-10, 0)$, reflects off the plane, and is once again received $30/c$ sec later by the other station. What is the position of the plane when it reflects the second signal, providing that one assumes $v_0 \ll c$ (that is, v_0 is much less than c)?

37. A line is drawn tangent to the parabola $y^2 = 4px$ at a point $P(x, y)$ on the curve. Let A be the point where this tangent line crosses the axis of the parabola, let F be the focus, and let $\overleftrightarrow{PD}$ be the line parallel to the axis of the parabola and intersecting the directrix at D. Prove that $AFPD$ is a rhombus.

38. Find the equation of the locus of a point $P(x, y)$ if the distance from P to the vertex is twice the distance from P to the focus of the parabola $x^2 = 8y$. Name the locus.

39. Prove that the tangent to a parabola at a point P cuts the axis of the parabola at a point whose distance from the vertex equals the distance from P to the tangent at the vertex.

40. Discuss the locus of the equation $x^4 - (y^2 - 9)^2 = 0$ and sketch its graph.

41. Show that the curve $C: x^4 - (y^2 - 9)^2 = 1$ approaches part of the curve $x^4 - (y^2 - 9)^2 = 0$ as the point $P(x, y)$ moves farther and farther away from the origin. Sketch. Do any points of C lie inside the circle $x^2 + y^2 = 9$? Give a reason for your answer.

42. The ellipse $(x^2/a^2) + (y^2/b^2) = 1$ divides the plane into two regions; one inside the ellipse, the other outside. Show that points in one of these regions have coordinates that satisfy the inequality $(x^2/a^2) + (y^2/b^2) < 1$, while in the other, $(x^2/a^2) + (y^2/b^2) > 1$. (Consider the effect of replacing x, y in the given equation by $x' = kx$, $y' = ky$, with $k < 1$ in one case and $k > 1$ in the other.)

43. Find an equation of an ellipse with foci at $(1, 0)$ and $(5, 0)$, and one vertex at the origin.

44. Let $F_1 = (3, 0)$, $F_2 = (0, 5)$, $P = (-1, 3)$. (a) Find the distances $|F_1P|$ and $|F_2P|$. (b) Does the origin O lie inside or outside the elllipse that has F_1 and F_2 as its foci and that passes through the point P? Why?

45. Find the greatest area of a rectangle inscribed in the ellipse $(x^2/a^2) + (y^2/b^2) = 1$, with sides parallel to the coordinate axes.

46. Show that the line $y = mx + c$ is tangent to the conic section $Ax^2 + y^2 = 1$ if and only if the constants A, m, and c satisfy the condition $A(c^2 - 1) = m^2$.

47. Starting from the general equation for the conic, find the equation of the conic with the following properties: (a) it is symmetric with respect to the origin, (b) it passes through the point $(1, 0)$, (c) the tangent to it at the point $(-2, 1)$ on it is the line $y = 1$.

48. Find an ellipse with one vertex at the point $(3, 1)$, the nearer focus at the point $(1, 1)$, and eccentricity $\frac{2}{3}$.

49. By a suitable rotation of axes, show that the equation $xy - x - y = 1$ represents a hyperbola. Sketch.

50. Find an equation of a hyperbola with eccentricity equal to $\sqrt{2}$ and with vertices at the points $(2, 0)$ and $(-2, 0)$.

51. Sketch the conic $\sqrt{2}y - 2xy = 3$. Locate its center and find its eccentricity.

52. If c is a fixed positive constant, then

$$\frac{x^2}{t^2} + \frac{y^2}{t^2 - c^2} = 1 \qquad (c^2 < t^2)$$

defines a family of ellipses, any member of which is characterized by a particular value of t. Show that every member of the family

$$\frac{x^2}{t^2} - \frac{y^2}{c^2 - t^2} = 1 \qquad (t^2 < c^2)$$

intersects any member of the first family at right angles.

53. Sketch the locus $|x| + |y| = 1$ and find the area it encloses.

54. Show that if the tangent to a curve at a point $P(x, y)$ passes through the origin, then $dy/dx = y/x$ at the point. Hence show that no tangent can be drawn from the origin to the hyperbola $x^2 - y^2 = 1$.

55. (a) Find the coordinates of the center and the foci, the lengths of the axes, and the eccentricity of the ellipse $x^2 + 4y^2 - 4x + 8y - 1 = 0$. (b) Do likewise with the hyperbola $3x^2 - y^2 + 12x - 3y = 0$, and in addition find equations of its asymptotes.

56. If the ends of a line segment of constant length move along perpendicular lines, show that a point P on the segment, at distances a and b from the ends, describes an ellipse.

57. Sketch the loci:

(a) $(9x^2 + 4y^2 - 36)(4x^2 + 9y^2 - 36) = 0$,

(b) $(9x^2 + 4y^2 - 36)(4x^2 + 9y^2 - 36) = 1$.

Is the curve in (b) bounded or does it extend to points arbitrarily far from the origin? Give a reason for your answer.

58. Let p, q be positive numbers such that $q < p$. If r is a third number, prove that the equation $[x^2/(p - r)] + [y^2/(q - r)] = 1$ represents (a) an ellipse if $r < q$, (b) a hyperbola if $q < r < p$, (c) nothing if $p < r$. Prove that all these ellipses and hyperbolas have the same foci, and find these foci.

59. Find the eccentricity of the hyperbola $xy = 1$.

60. On a level plane the sound of a rifle and that of the bullet striking the target are heard at the same instant. What is the locus of the hearer?

61. Show that any tangent to the hyperbola $xy = a^2$ determines with its asymptotes a triangle of area $2a^2$.

62. Given the hyperbola $9x^2 - 4y^2 - 18x - 16y + 29 = 0$. Find the coordinates of the center and foci, and the equations of the asymptotes. Sketch.

63. By an appropriate rotation, eliminate the xy-term from the equation,

$$7x^2 - 8xy + y^2 = 9.$$

64. Show that the tangent to the conic section

$$Ax^2 + Bxy + Cy^2 + Dx + Ey + F = 0$$

at a point (x_1, y_1) on it has an equation that may be written in the form

$$Axx_1 + B\left(\frac{x_1 y + xy_1}{2}\right) + Cyy_1$$

$$+ D\left(\frac{x + x_1}{2}\right) + E\left(\frac{y + y_1}{2}\right) + F = 0.$$

65. (a) Find the eccentricity and center of the conic

$$x^2 + 12y^2 - 6x - 48y + 9 = 0.$$

(b) Find the vertex of the conic

$$x^2 - 6x - 12y + 9 = 0.$$

(c) Sketch the conics in one diagram.

66. Find an equation of the circle passing through the three points common to the conics of Problem 65.

67. Two vertices A, B of a triangle are fixed and the vertex $C(x, y)$ moves in such a way that $\angle A = 2(\angle B)$. Find the locus of C.

68. Find the equation into which $x^{1/2} + y^{1/2} = a^{1/2}$ is transformed by a rotation of axes through 45°, and elimination of radicals.

69. Show that $dx^2 + dy^2$ is invariant under any rotation of axes about the origin.

70. Show that $x\, dy - y\, dx$ is invariant under any rotation of axes about the origin.

71. Graph the locus $x^{2n} + y^{2n} = a^{2n}$ for the following values of n: (a) 1, (b) 2, (c) 100. In each instance find where the curve cuts the line $y = x$.

Polar
Coordinates

12-1   The polar coordinate system. We know that a point can be located in a plane by giving its abscissa and ordinate relative to a given
coordinate system. Such x- and y-coordinates are called *Cartesian* coordinates, in honor of the French mathematician-philosopher René
Descartes* (1596–1650), who is credited with discovering this method
of fixing the position of a point in a plane.

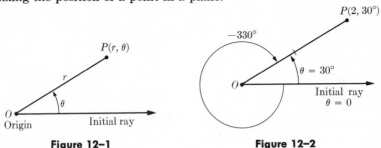

| Figure 12–1 | Figure 12–2 |

Another useful way to locate a point in a plane is by *polar coordinates*,
Fig. 12–1. First, we fix an *origin* O and an *initial ray* † from O. The point
P has polar coordinates r, θ, with

$$r = \text{directed distance from } O \text{ to } P, \qquad (1a)$$

and

$$\theta = \text{directed angle from initial ray to } OP. \qquad (1b)$$

As in trigonometry, the angle θ is *positive* when measured counterclockwise and negative when measured clockwise (Fig. 12–1). But the angle
associated with a given point is not unique (Fig. 12–2). For instance,
the point 2 units from the origin, along the ray $\theta = 30°$, has polar co-

---

* For an interesting biographical account together with an excerpt from
Descartes' own writings, see *World of Mathematics*, Vol. 1, pp. 235–253.
  † A *ray* is a half-line consisting of a vertex and points of a line on one side of
the vertex. For example, the origin and positive x-axis is a ray. The points
on the line $y = 2x + 3$ with $x \geq 1$ is another ray; its vertex is $(1, 5)$. We shall
denote the ray OP with initial point O by $\overrightarrow{OP}$.

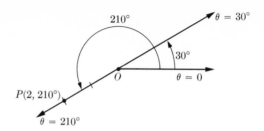

Figure 12–3

ordinates $r = 2$, $\theta = 30°$. It also has coordinates $r = 2$, $\theta = -330°$, or $r = 2$, $\theta = 390°$.

There are occasions when we wish to allow r to be negative. That's why we say "directed distance" in Eq. (1a). The ray $\theta = 30°$ and the ray $\theta = 210°$ together make up a complete line through O (Fig. 12–3). The point $P(2, 210°)$ 2 units from O on the ray $\theta = 210°$ has polar coordinates $r = 2$, $\theta = 210°$. It can be reached by a person standing at O and facing out along the initial ray, if he first turns $210°$ counterclockwise, and then goes forward 2 units. He would reach the same point by turning only $30°$ counterclockwise from the initial ray and then going *backward* 2 units. So we say that the point also has polar coordinates $r = -2$, $\theta = 30°$.

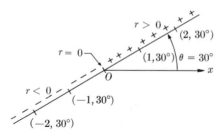

Figure 12–4

Whenever the angle between two rays is $180°$, the rays actually make a straight line. We then say that either ray is the negative of the other. Points on the ray $\theta = \alpha$ have polar coordinates (r, α) with $r \geq 0$. Points on the negative ray, $\theta = \alpha + 180°$, have coordinates (r, α) with $r \leq 0$. The origin is $r = 0$. (See Fig. 12–4 for the ray $\theta = 30°$ and its negative. Caution: the "negative" of the ray $\theta = 30°$ is the ray $\theta = 30° + 180° = 210°$ and *not* the ray $\theta = -30°$. "Negative" refers to the directed distance r.)

There is a great advantage in being able to use both polar and Cartesian coordinates. To do this, we use a common origin and take the ini-

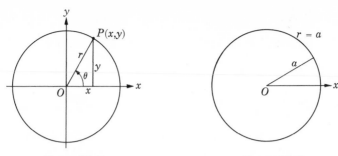

Figure 12-5   **Figure 12-6**

tial ray as the positive x-axis, the ray $\theta = 90°$ as the positive y-axis. The coordinates (Fig. 12-5) are then related by the equations

$$x = r \cos \theta, \qquad y = r \sin \theta. \tag{2}$$

These are the equations that define $\sin \theta$ and $\cos \theta$ when r is positive. They are also valid if r is negative, because $\cos (\theta + 180°) = -\cos \theta$, $\sin (\theta + 180°) = -\sin \theta$, so positive r's on the ray $\theta + 180°$ correspond to negative r's associated with the ray θ. When $r = 0$, then $x = y = 0$, and P is the origin.

If we impose the condition

$$r = a \qquad (a \text{ constant}), \tag{3}$$

then the locus of P is a circle with center O, radius a, and P describes the circle once as θ varies from 0 to 360° (Fig. 12-6). On the other hand, if we let r vary and hold θ fixed, say

$$\theta = 30°, \tag{4}$$

the locus of P is the straight line shown in Fig. 12-4.

We adopt the convention that r may be any real number, $-\infty < r < \infty$. Then $r = 0$ corresponds to $x = 0$, $y = 0$ in Eqs. (2), regardless of θ. That is,

$$r = 0, \qquad \theta \text{ any value} \tag{5}$$

is the origin. Positive values of r with θ fixed give points on the terminal side of the angle θ; *negative* values of r give points on the negative ray.

The same point may be represented in several different ways in polar coordinates. For example, the point $(2, 30°)$, or $(2, \pi/6)$, has the following representations: $(2, 30°)$, $(2, -330°)$, $(-2, 210°)$, $(-2, -150°)$.

These and all others are summarized in the two formulas

$$(2, 30° + n\,360°), \quad (-2, 210° + n\,360°) \qquad [n = 0, \pm 1, \pm 2, \ldots]$$

or, if we represent the angles in radians,

$$\left(2, \frac{\pi}{6} + 2n\pi\right), \quad \left(-2, \frac{7\pi}{6} + 2n\pi\right), \qquad [n = 0, \pm 1, \pm 2, \ldots].$$

The fact that the same point may be represented in several different ways in polar coordinates makes added care necessary in certain situations. For example, the point $(2a, \pi)$ is on the curve

$$r^2 = 4a^2 \cos \theta \tag{6}$$

even though its coordinates as given do not satisfy the equation, because the same point is represented by $(-2a, 0)$ and these coordinates do satisfy the equation. The same point $(2a, \pi)$ is on the curve

$$r = a(1 - \cos \theta), \tag{7}$$

and hence this point should be included among the points of intersection of the two curves represented by Eqs. (6) and (7). But if we solve the equations simultaneously by substituting $\cos \theta = r^2/4a^2$ from (6) into (7) and then solving the resulting quadratic equation

$$\left(\frac{r}{a}\right)^2 + 4\left(\frac{r}{a}\right) - 4 = 0$$

for

$$\frac{r}{a} = -2 \pm 2\sqrt{2}, \tag{8}$$

we do *not* obtain the point $(2a, \pi)$ as a point of intersection. The reason is simple enough; namely, the point is not on the curves "simultaneously" in the sense of being reached at the "same time," since it is reached in the one case when $\theta = 0$ and in the other case when $\theta = \pi$. It is as though two ships describe paths which intersect at a point, but the ships do not collide because they reach the point of intersection at different times! The curves represented by Eqs. (6) and (7) are shown in Fig. 12–9(c), and they are seen to intersect at the four points

$$(0, 0), \quad (2a, \pi), \quad (r_1, \theta_1), \quad (r_1, -\theta_1), \tag{9a}$$

where

$$r_1 = (-2 + 2\sqrt{2})a,$$
$$\cos \theta_1 = 1 - \frac{r_1}{a} = 3 - 2\sqrt{2}. \tag{9b}$$

Only the last two of these points are found from the simultaneous solution; the first two are disclosed only by the graphs of the curves.

PROBLEMS

1. Plot the following points, given in polar form, and find *all* polar coordinates of each point:

(a) $(3, \pi/4)$,   (b) $(-3, \pi/4)$,   (c) $(3, -\pi/4)$,   (d) $(-3, -\pi/4)$.

2. Graph the locus of points $P(r, \theta)$ whose polar coordinates satisfy the given equation, inequality, or inequalities:

(a) $r = 2$,   (b) $r < 2$,   (c) $r > 1$,   (d) $1 < r < 2$,
(e) $0° \le \theta \le 30°, r \ge 0$,   (f) $\theta = 120°, r \le -2$,
(g) $\theta = 60°, -1 \le r \le 3$,   (h) $\theta = 495°, r \ge -1$.

3. Find Cartesian coordinates of the points in Problem 1.
4. Graph the loci:

(a) $r \cos \theta = 2$,   (b) $r \sin \theta = -1$,
(c) $r \cos (\theta - 60°) = 3$, [*Hint:* rotate axes so that $\theta' = \theta - 60°$.]
(d) $r \sin (\theta + 45°) = 4$,   (e) $r \cos (30° - \theta) = 0$.

5. Show that $(2, \frac{3}{4}\pi)$ is on the curve $r = 2 \sin 2\theta$.
6. Show that $(\frac{1}{2}, \frac{3}{2}\pi)$ is on the curve $r = -\sin (\theta/3)$.
7. Show that the equations $r = \cos \theta + 1$, $r = \cos \theta - 1$, represent the same curve.

Find some intersections of the following pairs of curves (a = constant):

8. $r^2 = 2a^2 \sin 2\theta$, $r = a$ 9. $r = a \sin \theta$, $r = a \cos \theta$
10. $r = a(1 + \cos \theta)$, $r = a(1 - \sin \theta)$
11. $r = a(1 + \sin \theta)$, $r = 2a \cos \theta$ 12. $r = a \cos 2\theta$, $r = a(1 + \cos \theta)$

12–2   Graphs of polar equations.   The graph of an equation

$$F(r, \theta) = 0$$

consists of all those points whose coordinates (in some form) satisfy the equation. Frequently the equation gives r explicitly in terms of θ, as

$$r = f(\theta).$$

As many points as desired may then be obtained by substituting values of θ and calculating the corresponding values of r. In particular, it is desirable to plot the points where r is a maximum or a minimum and to find the values of θ when the curve passes through the origin, if that occurs.

Certain types of *symmetry* are readily detected. For example, the curve is:

(a) symmetric about the origin if the equation is unchanged when r is replaced by $-r$,

(b) symmetric about the x-axis if the equation is unchanged when θ is replaced by $-\theta$,

(c) symmetric about the y-axis if the equation is unchanged when θ is replaced by $\pi - \theta$.

These and certain other tests for symmetry are readily verified by considering the symmetrically located points in Fig. 12–7. [*Question:* What kind of symmetry occurs if the equation is unaltered when r and θ are replaced by $-r$ and $-\theta$ respectively?]

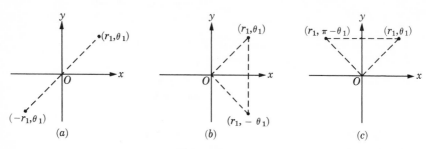

Figure 12–7

EXAMPLE 1. As an illustration of the method to be used, we shall discuss and sketch the curve

$$r = a(1 - \cos \theta),$$

where a is a positive constant.

Discussion. Since

$$\cos (-\theta) = \cos \theta,$$

the equation is unaltered when θ is replaced by $-\theta$; hence the curve is symmetric about the x-axis (Fig. 12–7b). Also, since

Figure 12–8

$$-1 \leq \cos \theta \leq 1,$$

the values of r vary between 0 and $2a$. The minimum value, $r = 0$, occurs at $\theta = 0$, and the maximum value, $r = 2a$, occurs at $\theta = \pi$. Moreover, as θ varies from 0 to π, $\cos \theta$ decreases from 1 to -1, hence $1 - \cos \theta$ increases from 0 to 2; that is, r increases from 0 to $2a$ as the radius vector $\overrightarrow{OP}$ swings from $\theta = 0$ to $\theta = \pi$. We mark the points from the following table:

θ:	0	60°	90°	120°	180°
r:	0	$a/2$	a	$3a/2$	$2a$

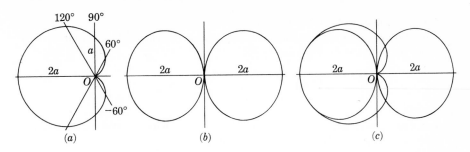

Figure 12-9

and sketch a smooth curve through them (Fig. 12–8) in such a way that r increases as θ increases, since

$$\frac{dr}{d\theta} = a \sin \theta$$

is positive for $0 < \theta < \pi$. Then we exploit the symmetry of the curve and reflect this portion across the x-axis. The result is the curve shown in Fig. 12–9(a), which is called a *cardioid* because of its heart-shaped appearance. Its behavior at the origin and the angles between its tangents and the coordinate axes at the other intercepts are more easily discussed at a later time. However, we may investigate the slope of the cardioid at the origin as follows. Let P be a point on the curve in the first quadrant, where P is destined to approach O along the curve.

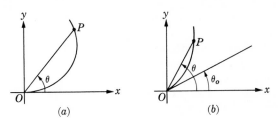

Figure 12-10

Then

$$\text{the slope of } \overleftrightarrow{OP} = \tan \theta$$

approaches

$$\text{the slope of the tangent at } O$$

as $P \to O$. But $P \to O$ as $\theta \to 0$, and hence

$$\lim_{\theta \to 0} (\text{slope of } \overleftrightarrow{OP}) = \lim_{\theta \to 0} \tan \theta = 0.$$

That is, the slope of the tangent to the curve at the origin is zero.

In fact, if any curve passes through the origin, say when $\theta = \theta_0$, then the discussion above would be modified only to the extent of saying that $P \to O$ along the curve as $\theta \to \theta_0$, and hence

$$\left(\frac{dy}{dx}\right)_{\theta=\theta_0} = \lim_{\theta \to \theta_0} (\tan \theta) = \tan \theta_0.$$

But $(dy/dx)_{\theta=\theta_0}$ is also the tangent of the angle between the x-axis and the curve at this point. Hence the line $\theta = \theta_0$ is tangent to the curve at the origin. In other words, whenever a curve passes through the origin for a value θ_0 of θ, it does so *tangent* to the line $\theta = \theta_0$. See Fig. 12–10(b).

EXAMPLE 2. $r^2 = 4a^2 \cos \theta$. This curve is symmetric about the origin. Two values,

$$r = \pm 2a\sqrt{\cos \theta},$$

correspond to each value of θ for which $\cos \theta > 0$, namely,

$$-\frac{\pi}{2} < \theta < \frac{\pi}{2}.$$

Furthermore, the curve is symmetric about the x-axis, since θ may be replaced by $-\theta$ without altering the value of $\cos \theta$. The curve passes through the origin at $\theta = \pi/2$ and is tangent to the y-axis at this point. Since $\cos \theta$ never exceeds unity, the maximum value of r is $2a$, which occurs at $\theta = 0$. As θ increases from 0 to $\pi/2$, $|r|$ decreases from $2a$ to 0. The curve is sketched in Fig. 12–9(b).

EXAMPLE 3. $r\theta = a$, where a is a positive constant. When $\theta = 0$ the equation becomes $0 = a$, which is not true. That is, there is no point on the curve for $\theta = 0$. However, suppose θ is a *small* positive angle. Then from $r = a/\theta$, we see that r is large and positive. Consider the situation in Fig.

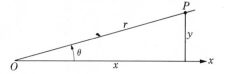

Figure 12–11

12–11. No matter how small the positive angle θ may be, if r is sufficiently large the point P may be far above the x-axis. In fact, we need to see what happens to

$$y = r \sin \theta = \frac{a}{\theta} \sin \theta$$

for small positive values of θ. We know, of course, that

$$\lim_{\theta \to 0} \frac{\sin \theta}{\theta} = 1,$$

hence

$$\lim_{\theta \to 0} y = \lim_{\theta \to 0} a \frac{\sin \theta}{\theta} = a.$$

This shows that the line $y = a$ is an asymptote of this curve. So we think of the

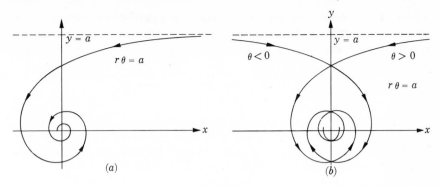

Figure 12–12

curve being traced by a point P that starts far out near the line $y = a$ for $\theta = 0+$ and moves in the direction indicated by the arrows in Fig. 12–12(a) as θ increases and r decreases. As the radius vector $\overrightarrow{OP}$ continues to rotate about the origin, it shrinks in length, and P describes a spiral which coils around the origin with r tending to zero as θ increases indefinitely.

When r and θ are replaced by $-r$ and $-\theta$ respectively, the equation is unaltered. Hence for every point (r_1, θ_1) on the curve in Fig. 12–12(a), there is a point $(-r_1, -\theta_1)$ symmetrically located with respect to the y-axis also on the curve $r\theta = a$. We therefore reflect the curve in Fig. 12–12(a) in the y-axis, obtaining another spiral which coils around the origin in the clockwise sense as θ approaches minus infinity. The complete curve is indicated in Fig. 12–12(b). It is called a *hyperbolic spiral*, the adjective "hyperbolic" being used because the equation $r\theta = a$ is analogous to the equation $xy = a$, which represents a hyperbola in Cartesian coordinates.

PROBLEMS

1. Find the polar form of the equation of the line $3x + 4y = 5$.

2. If the polar coordinates (r, θ) of a point P satisfy the equation $r = 2a \cos \theta$, what equation is satisfied by the Cartesian coordinates (x, y) of P?

Discuss and sketch each of the following curves:

3. $r = a(1 + \cos \theta)$ 4. $r = a(1 - \sin \theta)$

5. $r = a \sin 2\theta$ 6. $r^2 = 2a^2 \cos 2\theta$

7. $r = a(2 + \sin \theta)$ 8. $r = a(1 + 2 \sin \theta)$

9. $r = \theta$ 10. $r = a \sin \theta/2$

11. Find the points on the curve $r = a(1 + \cos \theta)$, where the tangent is (a) parallel to the x-axis, (b) parallel to the y-axis. [*Hint.* Express x and y in terms of θ. Then calculate dy/dx.]

12. Sketch the curves $r = a(1 + \cos \theta)$ and $r = 3a \cos \theta$ in one diagram and find the angle between their tangents at the point of intersection that lies in the first quadrant.

12–3   Polar equations of the conic sections and other curves.   The relationships given in Article 12–1 between Cartesian and polar coordinates enable us to change any Cartesian equation into a polar equation for the same curve.

For example, the circle

$$x^2 + y^2 - 2ax = 0, \tag{1}$$

with center at $(a, 0)$ and radius a, becomes

$$(r \cos \theta)^2 + (r \sin \theta)^2 - 2a(r \cos \theta) = 0,$$

which reduces to

$$r(r - 2a \cos \theta) = 0.$$

The locus obtained by putting the first factor equal to zero, $r = 0$, is just one point, the origin. The other factor vanishes when

$$r = 2a \cos \theta. \tag{2}$$

This includes the origin among its points and hence represents the entire locus given by Eq. (1).

The example illustrates one method of finding the polar equation for a curve, namely by transforming its Cartesian equation into polar form. An alternative method is to derive the polar equation directly from some geometric property. For example, take the circle in Fig. 12–13(b) and let $P(r, \theta)$ be a representative point on the circle. Then angle OPA is a right angle (why?) and from the right triangle OPA, we read

$$\frac{r}{2a} = \cos \theta \qquad \text{or} \qquad r = 2a \cos \theta,$$

which is the same equation obtained above.

(a)   (b)

Figure 12–13

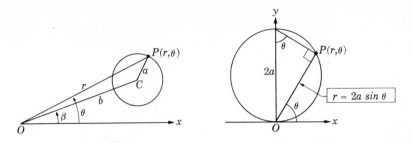

Figure 12–14   **Figure 12–15**

We shall apply this second method to obtain equations of various curves in the following examples.

EXAMPLE 1. Find the polar equation of the circle of radius a with center at (b, β).

Solution. We let $P\ (r, \theta)$ be a representative point on the circle and apply the law of cosines to the triangle OCP (Fig. 12–14) to obtain

$$a^2 = b^2 + r^2 - 2br \cos (\theta - \beta). \tag{3}$$

If the circle passes through the origin, then $b = a$ and the equation takes the simpler form

$$r[r - 2a \cos (\theta - \beta)] = 0$$

or

$$r = 2a \cos (\theta - \beta). \tag{4}$$

In particular, if $\beta = 0$, Eq. (4) reduces to the result we have obtained before, while if $\beta = 90°$, so that the center of the circle lies on the y-axis, Eq. (4) reduces to

$$r = 2a \sin \theta. \tag{5}$$

EXAMPLE 2. The normal from the origin to the line L intersects L at the point $N(p, \beta)$. Find the polar equation of L.

Solution. We let $P(r, \theta)$ be a representative point on the line L in Fig. 12–16 and from the right triangle ONP read the result

$$r \cos (\theta - \beta) = p. \tag{6}$$

This equation is simply a more general form of the equation

$$r \cos \theta = p, \tag{7}$$

which is the polar form of the line

$$x = p.$$

Figure 12–16

Figure 12–17

In fact, if we perform a rotation of axes as in Fig. 12–17, the new polar coordinates (r', θ') are related to the old polar coordinates as follows:

$$r' = r, \qquad \theta' = \theta - \beta. \tag{8}$$

If we apply this rotation to Eq. (6), we get

$$r' \cos \theta' = p.$$

But

$$r' \cos \theta' = x',$$

so the equation is the same as

$$x' = p,$$

which represents a straight line p units from and parallel to the y'-axis.

EXAMPLE 3. Find the polar locus of P if the product of its distances to the two points $F_1(a, \pi)$ and $F_2(a, 0)$ is a constant, say b^2.

Figure 12–18

Solution. We let $P(r, \theta)$ be a representative point on the locus and determine the equation satisfied by the coordinates r and θ in order to fulfill the requirement

$$d_1 d_2 = b^2, \tag{9}$$

where $d_1 = |PF_1|$ and $d_2 = |PF_2|$ (Fig. 12–18). We apply the law of cosines twice: once to the triangle OPF_2,

$$d_2^2 = r^2 + a^2 - 2ar \cos \theta,$$

and again to the triangle OPF_1,

$$d_1^2 = r^2 + a^2 - 2ar \cos (\pi - \theta).$$

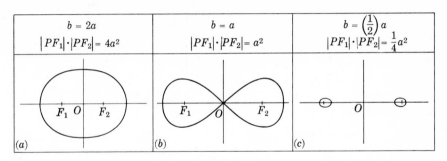

Figure 12–19

But

$$\cos(\pi - \theta) = -\cos\theta,$$

so that

$$d_1^2 = r^2 + a^2 + 2ar\cos\theta.$$

Hence

$$d_1^2 d_2^2 = (r^2 + a^2)^2 - (2ar\cos\theta)^2$$

or

$$b^4 = a^4 + r^4 + 2a^2r^2(1 - 2\cos^2\theta).$$

The trigonometric identity $\cos 2\theta = 2\cos^2\theta - 1$ enables us to put our equation in the form

$$b^4 = a^4 + r^4 - 2a^2r^2\cos 2\theta. \tag{10}$$

One special case allows the locus to pass through the origin, namely, if $b = a$. Then the equation simplifies still further to the form

$$r^2 = 2a^2\cos 2\theta. \tag{11}$$

The graphs of the curves represented by (10) for different values of the ratio b/a are shown in Fig. 12–19(a)–(c). The curves in both (a) and (b) are called lemniscates, and the curve in (c) consists of two separate closed portions known as "ovals of Cassini."

EXAMPLE 4. Find the polar equation of the conic section of eccentricity e if the focus is at the origin and the associated directrix is the line $x = -k$.

Solution. We adopt the notation of Fig. 12–20 and use the focus-and-directrix property

$$|PF| = e \cdot |PD|, \tag{12}$$

which allows us to handle the parabola, ellipse, and hyperbola all at the same time.

By taking the origin at the focus F, we have

$$|PF| = r,$$

while

$$|PD| = |AB|$$

and

$$|AB| = |AF| + |FB| = k + r \cos \theta.$$

Then Eq. (12) is the same as

$$r = e(k + r \cos \theta).$$

If we solve this equation for r, we get

$$r = \frac{ke}{1 - e \cos \theta}. \qquad (13)$$

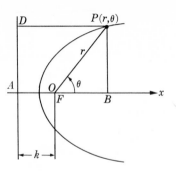

Figure 12-20

Typical special cases of (13) are obtained by taking

$$e = 1, \qquad r = \frac{k}{1 - \cos \theta} = \frac{k}{2} \csc^2 \frac{\theta}{2}, \qquad (14a)$$

which represents a *parabola;*

$$e = \tfrac{1}{2}, \qquad r = \frac{k}{2 - \cos \theta}, \qquad (14b)$$

which represents an *ellipse;*

$$e = 2, \qquad r = \frac{2k}{1 - 2 \cos \theta}, \qquad (14c)$$

which represents a *hyperbola.*

It is worth noting that the denominator in Eq. (14b) for the ellipse can never vanish, so that r remains finite for all values of θ. But r becomes infinite as θ approaches 0 in (14a) and as θ approaches $\pi/3$ in (14c).

By replacing the constant ke in Eq. (13) by its equivalent value

$$ke = a(1 - e^2)$$

when $e < 1$, we may let $e \to 0$ and get

$$r = a$$

in the limit. That is, the circle of radius a and center at O is a limiting case of the curves represented by Eq. (13).

PROBLEMS

1. A line segment of length $2a$ slides with its ends on the x- and y-axes. Find the polar equation of the locus described by the point $P(r, \theta)$ in which the perpendicular from the origin intersects the moving line. Sketch the curve.

2. $\overline{OA}$ is a diameter of a circle of radius a, $\overleftrightarrow{AC}$ is tangent to the circle, and $\overrightarrow{OC}$ intersects the circle at B. On $\overleftrightarrow{OC}$ the point $P(r, \theta)$ is found such that $|OP| = |BC|$. With O as origin, $\overrightarrow{OA}$ as x-axis, and angle AOP as θ, find the polar equation

of the locus of P and sketch the curve. Show that the line $x = 2a$ is an asymptote. The curve is called a "cissoid," meaning "ivy-like."

In Problems 3–7 determine the polar equation and sketch the given curve.

3. $x^2 + y^2 - 2ay = 0$
4. $(x^2 + y^2)^2 + 2ax(x^2 + y^2) - a^2y^2 = 0$
5. $x \cos \alpha + y \sin \alpha = p$ (α, p constants)
6. $y^2 = 4ax + 4a^2$ 7. $(x^2 + y^2)^2 = x^2 - y^2$

In Problems 8–13 determine the Cartesian equation and sketch the given curve.

8. $r = 4 \cos \theta$ 9. $r = 6 \sin \theta$
10. $r = \sin 2\theta$ 11. $r^2 = 2a^2 \cos 2\theta$
12. $r = 8/(1 - 2 \cos \theta)$ 13. $r = a(1 + \sin \theta)$

14. Sketch the following loci:

(a) $r = 2 \cos (\theta + 45°)$,   (b) $r = 4 \csc (\theta - 30°)$,
(c) $r = 5 \sec (60° - \theta)$,   (d) $r = 3 \sin (\theta + 30°)$,
(e) $r = a + a \cos (\theta - 30°)$,   (f) $0 \le r \le 2 - 2 \cos \theta$.

15. (a) How can the angle β and the distance p [see Fig. 12–16 and Eq. (6)] be determined from the Cartesian equation $ax + by = c$ for a straight line? (b) Specifically, find p, β, and the polar equation for the straight line $\sqrt{3}x + y = 6$.

16. The focus of a parabola is at the origin and its directrix is the line $4 = r \cos (\theta + \pi/3)$. Find the polar equation of the parabola.

17. One focus of a hyperbola of eccentricity $\frac{5}{4}$ is at the origin and the corresponding directrix is the line $r \cos \theta = 9$. Find the polar coordinates of the second focus. Also determine the polar equation of the hyperbola and sketch.

18. From the origin a line is drawn perpendicular to a tangent of the circle $r = 2a \cos \theta$. Find the locus of the point of intersection and sketch the curve.

19. Find the maximum and minimum values of r that satisfy Eq. (10), first in terms of a and b, and then specifically for the cases $b = 2a$, $b = a$, and $b = a/2$.

20. Determine the slopes of the lines that are tangent to the lemniscate $r^2 = 2a^2 \cos 2\theta$ at the origin.

21. Equation (14b), $r = k/(2 - \cos \theta)$, represents an ellipse with one focus at the origin. Sketch the curve and its directrices for the case $k = 2$ and locate the center of the ellipse.

22. In the case $e > 1$, Eq. (13) represents a hyperbola. From the polar form of the equation, determine the slopes of the asymptotes of the hyperbola of eccentricity e.

23. Show, by reference to a figure, that the distance from the line

$$r \cos (\theta - \beta) = p$$

to the point $P_1(r_1, \theta_1)$ is $|r_1 \cos (\theta_1 - \beta) - p|$.

12–4   The angle ψ between the radius vector and the tangent line.   In Cartesian coordinates, when we want to discuss the direction of a curve at a point, we use the angle ϕ from the positive x-axis to the tangent line. In polar coordinates, it is more convenient to make use of the angle ψ (psi) from the *radius vector* to the tangent line. Then the relationship

$$\phi = \theta + \psi, \tag{1}$$

which can be read from Fig. 12–21, makes it a simple matter to find ϕ if that angle is desired instead of ψ.

Suppose the equation of the curve is given in the form $r = f(\theta)$, where $f(\theta)$ is a differentiable function of θ. Then from

$$x = r \cos \theta, \qquad y = r \sin \theta, \tag{2}$$

we see that x and y are differentiable functions of θ with

$$\frac{dx}{d\theta} = -r \sin \theta + \cos \theta \, \frac{dr}{d\theta},$$

$$\frac{dy}{d\theta} = r \cos \theta + \sin \theta \, \frac{dr}{d\theta}. \tag{3}$$

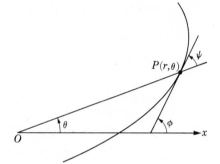

Figure 12–21

Since $\psi = \phi - \theta$ from (1),

$$\tan \psi = \tan (\phi - \theta) = \frac{\tan \phi - \tan \theta}{1 + \tan \phi \tan \theta},$$

while

$$\tan \phi = \frac{dy/d\theta}{dx/d\theta}, \qquad \tan \theta = \frac{y}{x}.$$

Hence

$$\tan \psi = \frac{\dfrac{dy/d\theta}{dx/d\theta} - \dfrac{y}{x}}{1 + \dfrac{y}{x}\dfrac{dy/d\theta}{dx/d\theta}} = \frac{x \dfrac{dy}{d\theta} - y \dfrac{dx}{d\theta}}{x \dfrac{dx}{d\theta} + y \dfrac{dy}{d\theta}}. \tag{4}$$

The numerator in the last expression in Eq. (4) is found by substitution from Eqs. (2) and (3) to be

$$x \frac{dy}{d\theta} - y \frac{dx}{d\theta} = r^2.$$

Similarly, the denominator is

$$x \frac{dx}{d\theta} + y \frac{dy}{d\theta} = r \frac{dr}{d\theta}.$$

When we substitute these into Eq. (4), we obtain the very simple final result

$$\tan \psi = \frac{r}{dr/d\theta} \cdot \tag{5}$$

This formula for $\tan \psi$ is much simpler than the formula

$$\tan \phi = \frac{r \cos \theta + (\sin \theta)\, dr/d\theta}{-r \sin \theta + (\cos \theta)\, dr/d\theta}, \tag{6}$$

that one obtains by calculating

$$\frac{dy}{dx} = \frac{dy/d\theta}{dx/d\theta}$$

from (3). This is why it is usually preferable to work with the angle ψ rather than with ϕ in the case of polar coordinates.

One may also obtain a simple expression for the differential element of arc length ds by squaring and adding the differentials

$$dx = -r \sin \theta\, d\theta + \cos \theta\, dr,$$

$$dy = r \cos \theta\, d\theta + \sin \theta\, dr.$$

We find that

$$ds^2 = dx^2 + dy^2 = r^2\, d\theta^2 + dr^2.$$

This result and the result for $\tan \psi$ are both easily remembered in the form

$$
\begin{aligned}
(1) \quad &\tan \psi = \frac{r\, d\theta}{dr}, \\
(2) \quad &ds^2 = r^2\, d\theta^2 + dr^2
\end{aligned}
\tag{7}
$$

Fig. 12–22. Arc length.

if we refer to the "differential triangle" shown in Fig. 12–22. We simply treat dr and $r\, d\theta$ as the two legs and ds as the hypotenuse of an ordinary right triangle with the angle ψ opposite the side $r\, d\theta$. If we realize that certain terms of higher order are being neglected, we may think of dr as the component of displacement along the radius vector and $r\, d\theta$ as the component at right angles to this produced by the displacement ds along the curve. The relationships (7) may be read at once from this triangle. We should realize, of course, that the *proof* of these equations did not depend upon any such "differential triangle" and that the latter represents only a mnemonic device.

To find the angle ψ, we use (7_1); and to find the length of a polar curve, we find ds from (7_2) and integrate between appropriate limits as illustrated in the following examples.

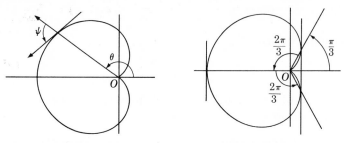

Figure 12–23   Figure 12–24

EXAMPLE 1. Find the angle ψ for the cardioid (Fig. 12–23)

$$r = a(1 - \cos \theta). \tag{8a}$$

Solution. From the equation of the curve, we get

$$dr = a \sin \theta \, d\theta, \tag{8b}$$

so that

$$\tan \psi = \frac{r \, d\theta}{dr} = \frac{a(1 - \cos \theta) \, d\theta}{a \sin \theta \, d\theta} = \tan \frac{\theta}{2}.$$

As θ varies from 0 to 2π, the angle ψ varies from 0 to π according to the equation $\psi = \theta/2$. Thus at the y-intercepts the tangent line makes an angle of 45° with the vertical, at the origin the curve is tangent to the x-axis, and at $(2a, \pi)$ the tangent line makes an angle of 90° with the negative x-axis.

Suppose we ask for the points on the cardioid where the tangent line is vertical. Denoting the inclination angle of the tangent line by ϕ and recalling that

$$\phi = \psi + \theta$$

and

$$\psi = \tfrac{1}{2}\theta,$$

we get

$$\phi = \tfrac{3}{2}\theta.$$

Since the tangent is vertical when

$$\phi = \frac{\pi}{2} + n\pi,$$

the values of θ satisfy

$$\theta = \frac{2}{3}\phi = \frac{\pi}{3} + \frac{2}{3}n\pi.$$

Taking $n = 0, -1, 1, -2, 2, \ldots$, we obtain

$$\theta = \frac{\pi}{3}, \frac{-\pi}{3}, \pi, -\pi, \frac{5}{3}\pi, \ldots$$

These lead to three distinct points, namely,

$$\left(\frac{a}{2}, \pm\frac{\pi}{3}\right) \quad \text{and} \quad (2a, \pi),$$

whose radius vectors are evenly spaced 120° apart. (See Fig. 12–24.)

EXAMPLE 2. Find the length of the cardioid $r = a(1 - \cos\theta)$.

Solution. Substituting dr and r from (8b, a) into (7_2), we have

$$ds^2 = a^2\,d\theta^2\,[\sin^2\theta + (1 - \cos\theta)^2]$$
$$= 2a^2\,d\theta^2(1 - \cos\theta)$$

and

$$ds = a\sqrt{2}\,\sqrt{1 - \cos\theta}\,d\theta.$$

In order to integrate the expression on the right, we recall the trigonometric identity

$$1 - \cos\theta = 2\sin^2\frac{\theta}{2}$$

and have

$$ds = 2a\left|\sin\frac{\theta}{2}\right|d\theta.$$

Since $\sin\theta/2$ is not negative when θ varies from 0 to 2π, we obtain

$$s = \int_0^{2\pi} 2a\sin\frac{\theta}{2}\,d\theta$$

$$= -4a\cos\frac{\theta}{2}\Big]_0^{2\pi} = 8a.$$

We observe in passing that in letting θ range from 0 to 2π, we start at the cusp at the origin, go once around the smooth portion of the cardioid and return to the cusp. In doing this we do not pass *across* the cusp (Fig. 12–23). If, on the other hand, we take the cardioid $r = a(1 + \cos\theta)$, the appropriate procedure for avoiding the cusp (Fig. 12–25) is to let θ increase from $-\pi$ to π, or we may use the symmetry of the curve and calculate half of the total length by letting θ vary from 0 to π.

Figure 12–25   Figure 12–26

EXAMPLE 3. The lemniscate

$$r^2 = 2a^2 \cos 2\theta$$

is revolved about the y-axis. Find the area of the surface generated.

Solution. An element of arc length ds (Fig. 12–26) generates a portion of surface area

$$dS = 2\pi x \, ds,$$

where

$$x = r \cos \theta, \qquad ds = \sqrt{dr^2 + r^2 \, d\theta^2}.$$

That is,

$$dS = 2\pi r \cos \theta \sqrt{dr^2 + r^2 \, d\theta^2} = 2\pi \cos \theta \sqrt{r^2 \, dr^2 + r^4 \, d\theta^2}.$$

From the equation of the curve, we get

$$r \, dr = -2a^2 \sin 2\theta \, d\theta.$$

Then

$$(r^2 \, dr^2 + r^4 \, d\theta^2) = (2a^2 \, d\theta)^2 (\sin^2 2\theta + \cos^2 2\theta)$$

and

$$dS = 4\pi a^2 \cos \theta \, d\theta.$$

The total surface area is generated by the loop of the lemniscate to the right of the y-axis between $\theta = -\pi/4$ and $\theta = +\pi/4$, so that

$$S = \int_{-\pi/4}^{\pi/4} 4\pi a^2 \cos \theta \, d\theta = 4\pi a^2 \sqrt{2}.$$

PROBLEMS

1. For the hyperbolic spiral $r\theta = a$ show that $\psi = 135°$ when $\theta = 1$ radian, and that $\psi \to 90°$ as the spiral winds around the origin. Sketch the curve and indicate ψ for $\theta = 1$ radian.

2. Show, by reference to a figure, that the angle β between the tangents to two curves at a point of intersection may be found from the formula

$$\tan \beta = \frac{\tan \psi_2 - \tan \psi_1}{1 + \tan \psi_2 \tan \psi_1}.$$

When will the two curves intersect orthogonally?

3. Find a point of intersection of the parabolas

$$r = \frac{1}{1 - \cos \theta} \quad \text{and} \quad r = \frac{3}{1 + \cos \theta}$$

and find the angle between the tangents to these curves at this point.

4. Find points on the cardioid $r = a(1 + \cos \theta)$ where the tangent line is horizontal.

5. Find the length of the cardioid $r = a(1 + \cos \theta)$. [*Hint:* $\int \sqrt{1 + \cos \theta}\, d\theta = \int \sqrt{2}\, |\cos \theta/2|\, d\theta$.]

6. A thin, uniform wire is bent into the shape of the cardioid $r = a(1 + \cos \theta)$. Find its center of gravity $(\bar{x}, \bar{y})$. [*Hint:* $\int \cos \theta \cos \theta/2\, d\theta$ can be evaluated by substituting $\cos \theta = 1 - 2 \sin^2 \theta/2$ and then letting $u = \sin \theta/2$.]

7. The lemniscate $r^2 = 2a^2 \cos 2\theta$ is rotated about the x-axis. Find the area of the surface generated.

8. Find the length of the curve $r = a \sin^2 \theta/2$ from $\theta = 0$ to $\theta = \pi$. Sketch the curve.

9. Find the length of the parabolic spiral $r = a\theta^2$ between $\theta = 0$ and $\theta = \pi$. Sketch the curve.

10. Find the length of the curve $r = a \sin^3 \theta/3$ between $\theta = 0$ and $\theta = \pi$. Sketch the curve.

11. Find the surface area generated by rotating the curve $r = 2a \cos \theta$ about the line $\theta = \pi/2$. Sketch.

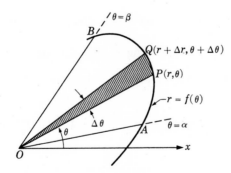

Figure 12–27

12–5   Plane areas in polar coordinates. The area AOB in Fig. 12–27 is bounded by the rays $\theta = \alpha$, $\theta = \beta$, and the curve $r = f(\theta)$. We imagine the angle AOB as being divided into n parts

$$\Delta \theta = \frac{\beta - \alpha}{n},$$

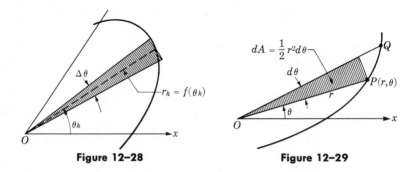

Figure 12–28   **Figure 12–29**

and we approximate the area in a typical sector POQ by the area of a *circular* sector of radius r and central angle $\Delta\theta$, that is,

$$\text{area of } POQ \approx \tfrac{1}{2}r^2\,\Delta\theta,$$

and hence the entire area AOB is approximately

$$\sum_{\theta=\alpha}^{\beta} \tfrac{1}{2}r^2\,\Delta\theta.$$

In fact, if the function $r = f(\theta)$ which represents the polar curve is a continuous function of θ for $\alpha \le \theta \le \beta$, then there is a θ_k between θ and $\theta + \Delta\theta$ such that the circular sector of radius

$$r_k = f(\theta_k)$$

and central angle $\Delta\theta$ gives the *exact* area of POQ (Fig. 12–28). Then the entire area is given exactly by

$$A = \sum \tfrac{1}{2}r_k^2\,\Delta\theta = \sum \tfrac{1}{2}[f(\theta_k)]^2\,\Delta\theta.$$

If we let $\Delta\theta \to 0$, we may apply the Fundamental Theorem of the integral calculus and obtain

$$A = \lim_{\Delta\theta\to 0} \sum \tfrac{1}{2}[f(\theta_k)]^2\,\Delta\theta = \tfrac{1}{2}\int_\alpha^\beta [f(\theta)]^2\,d\theta,$$

or

$$A = \int_\alpha^\beta \tfrac{1}{2}r^2\,d\theta. \tag{1}$$

This result may also be remembered as the integral of the differential element of area (Fig. 12–29):

$$dA = \tfrac{1}{2}r^2\,d\theta,$$

taken between the appropriate limits on θ.

EXAMPLE. Find the area that is inside the circle $r = a$ and outside the cardioid $r = a(1 - \cos \theta)$. (See Fig. 12–30.)

Solution. We take a representative element of area

$$dA = dA_1 - dA_2,$$

where

$$dA_1 = \tfrac{1}{2}r_1^2 \, d\theta, \qquad dA_2 = \tfrac{1}{2}r_2^2 \, d\theta$$

with

$$r_1 = a, \qquad r_2 = a(1 - \cos \theta).$$

Such elements of area belong to the region inside the circle and outside the cardioid provided θ lies between

$$-\frac{\pi}{2} \quad \text{and} \quad +\frac{\pi}{2},$$

where the curves intersect. Hence

$$A = \int_{-\pi/2}^{\pi/2} \tfrac{1}{2}(r_1^2 - r_2^2) \, d\theta$$

$$= \int_{-\pi/2}^{\pi/2} \frac{a^2}{2} (2 \cos \theta - \cos^2 \theta) \, d\theta$$

$$= a^2 \int_{-\pi/2}^{\pi/2} \cos \theta \, d\theta - \frac{a^2}{2} \int_{-\pi/2}^{\pi/2} \frac{1 + \cos 2\theta}{2} \, d\theta$$

$$= a^2 \left(2 - \frac{\pi}{4}\right).$$

Figure 12–30

As a check against gross errors, we observe that this is roughly 80% of the area of a semicircle of radius a and this seems reasonable when we look at the area in Fig. 12–30.

PROBLEMS

[*Note:* The trigonometric identities

$$\sin^2 \theta = \tfrac{1}{2}(1 - \cos 2\theta), \qquad \cos^2 \theta = \tfrac{1}{2}(1 + \cos 2\theta)$$

should be used to evaluate $\int \sin^2 \theta \, d\theta$ and $\int \cos^2 \theta \, d\theta$ in certain of the problems that follow.]

1. Find the total area inside the cardioid $r = a(1 + \cos \theta)$.
2. Find the total area inside the circle $r = 2a \sin \theta$.
3. Find the total area inside the lemniscate $r^2 = 2a^2 \cos 2\theta$.
4. Find that portion of the area inside the lemniscate $r^2 = 2a^2 \cos 2\theta$ that is not included in the circle $r = a$. Sketch.

5. Find the area inside the curve $r = a(2 + \cos \theta)$.

6. Find the area common to the circles $r = 2a \cos \theta$ and $r = 2a \sin \theta$. Sketch.

7. Find the area inside the circle $r = 3a \cos \theta$ and outside the cardioid $r = a(1 + \cos \theta)$.

REVIEW QUESTIONS AND EXERCISES FOR CHAPTER 12

1. Make a diagram to show the standard relations between Cartesian coordinates (x, y) and polar coordinates (r, θ). Express each set of coordinates in terms of the other kind.

2. If a point has polar coordinates (r_1, θ_1), what other polar coordinates represent the same point?

3. What is the expression for area between curves in polar coordinates?

4. What is the expression for length of arc of a curve in polar coordinates? For area of a surface of revolution?

5. What are some criteria for symmetry of a curve if its polar coordinates satisfy the equation $r = f(\theta)$? Illustrate your discussion with specific examples.

6. An artificial satellite is in an orbit that passes over the North and South Poles of the earth. When it is over the North Pole it is at the highest point of its orbit, 1000 miles above the earth's surface. Above the South Pole it is at the lowest point of its orbit, 300 miles above the earth's surface. (a) Assuming that the orbit (with reference to the earth) is an ellipse with one focus at the center of the earth, find its eccentricity. (Take the diameter of the earth to be 8000 miles.) (b) Using the north-south axis of the earth as polar axis, and the center of the earth as origin, find a polar equation of the orbit.

Discuss and sketch each of the curves in Problems 1–13 (where a is a positive constant).

1. $r = a\theta$

2. $r = a(1 + \cos 2\theta)$

3. (a) $r = a \sec \theta$;   (b) $r = a \csc \theta$;   (c) $r = a \sec \theta + a \csc \theta$

4. $r = a \sin\left(\theta + \dfrac{\pi}{3}\right)$

5. $r^2 + 2r (\cos \theta + \sin \theta) = 7$

6. $r = a \cos \theta - a \sin \theta$

7. $r \cos \dfrac{\theta}{2} = a$

8. $r^2 = a^2 \sin \theta$

9. $r^2 = 2a^2 \sin 2\theta$

10. $r = a(1 - 2 \sin 3\theta)$

11. (a) $r = \cos 2\theta$
    (b) $r^2 = \cos 2\theta$

12. (a) $r = 1 + \cos \theta$

    (b) $r = \dfrac{1}{1 + \cos \theta}$

13. (a) $r = \dfrac{2}{1 - \cos \theta}$

    (b) $r = \dfrac{2}{1 + \sin \theta}$

14. Sketch and discuss the graph whose equation in polar coordinates is

$$r = 1 - \tan^2\theta.$$

Show that it has no vertical asymptotes.

Sketch each of the pairs of curves in Problems 15–20, and find all points of intersection and the angle between their tangents at each point of intersection.

15. $r = a$, $r = 2a \sin \theta$

16. $r = a$, $r = a(1 - \sin \theta)$

17. $r = a \sec \theta$, $r = 2a \sin \theta$

18. $r = a \cos \theta$,

19. $r = a(1 + \cos 2\theta)$,

      $r = a(1 + \cos \theta)$

      $r = a \cos 2\theta$

20. $r^2 = 4 \cos 2\theta$, $r^2 = \sec 2\theta$

21. Find the equation, in polar coordinates, of a parabola whose focus is at $r = 0$ and whose vertex is at $r = 1$, $\theta = 0$.

22. Find the polar equation of the straight line with intercepts a and b on the lines $\theta = 0$, $\theta = \pi/2$.

23. Find the equation of a circle with center on the line $\theta = \pi$, of radius a, and passing through the origin.

24. Find the polar equation of a parabola with focus at the origin and vertex at $(a, \pi/4)$.

25. Find the polar equation of an ellipse with one focus at the origin, the other at $(2, 0)$, and a vertex at $(4, 0)$.

26. Find the polar equation of a hyperbola with one focus at the origin, center at $(2, \pi/2)$, and vertex at $(1, \pi/2)$.

27. Three loran stations are located (in polar coordinates) at $(a, 0)$, $(0, 0)$, and $(a, \pi/4)$. Radio signals are sent out from the three stations simultaneously.

A plane receiving the signals notes that the signals from the second and third stations arrive $a/2v$ sec later than that from the first. If v is the velocity of a radio signal, what is the location of the plane in polar coordinates?

28. Show that the parabolas $r = a/(1 + \cos\theta)$, $r = b/(1 - \cos\theta)$ are orthogonal at each point of intersection ($ab \neq 0$).

29. Find the angle between the line $\theta = \pi/2$ and the cardioid $r = a(1 - \cos\theta)$ at their intersection.

30. Find the angle between the line $r = 3\sec\theta$ and the curve $r = 4(1 + \cos\theta)$ at one of their intersections.

31. Find the slope of the tangent line to the curve $r = a\tan(\theta/2)$ at $\theta = \pi/2$.

32. Check that the two curves $r = 1/(1 - \cos\theta)$ and $r = 3/(1 + \cos\theta)$ intersect at the point $(2, \pi/3)$. Find the angle between the tangents to these curves at this point.

33. The equation $r^2 = 2\csc 2\theta$ represents a curve in polar coordinates. (a) Sketch the curve. (b) Find the equation of the curve in rectangular coordinates. (c) Find the angle at which the curve intersects the line $\theta = \pi/4$.

34. A given curve cuts all rays $\theta =$ constant at the constant angle α. (a) Show that the area bounded by the curve and two rays $\theta = \theta_1$, $\theta = \theta_2$, is proportional to $r_2^2 - r_1^2$, where (r_1, θ_1) and (r_2, θ_2) are polar coordinates of the ends of the arc of the curve between these rays. Find the factor of proportionality. (b) Show that the length of the arc of the curve in part (a) is proportional to $r_2 - r_1$ and find the proportionality constant.

35. The cardioid $r = a(1 - \cos\theta)$ is rotated about the initial line. (a) Find the area of the surface generated. [*Hint:* You may use the fact that $\sin\theta = 2\sin(\theta/2)\cos(\theta/2)$, and $1 - \cos\theta = 2\sin^2(\theta/2)$ to evaluate your integral.] (b) Set up the definite integral (or integrals) that would be used to find the centroid of the area in part (a). (c) Find the centroid of the area in part (a).

36. Let P be a point on the hyperbola $r^2\sin 2\theta = 2a^2$. Show that the triangle formed by $\overleftrightarrow{OP}$, the tangent at P, and the initial line is isosceles.

37. Verify that the formula for finding the length of a curve in polar form gives the correct result for the circumference of the circles (a) $r = a$, (b) $r = a\cos\theta$, (c) $r = a\sin\theta$.

38. If $r = a\cos^3(\theta/3)$, show that $ds = a\cos^2(\theta/3)\,d\theta$ and determine the perimeter of the curve.

39. Find the area that lies inside the curve $r = 2a\cos 2\theta$ and outside the curve $r = a\sqrt{2}$.

40. Sketch the curves $r = 2a\cos^2(\theta/2)$ and $r = 2a\sin^2(\theta/2)$, and find the area they have in common.

Find the total area enclosed by each of the curves in Problems 41–47.

41. $r^2 = a^2\cos 2\theta$ 　　　　　　　　　　42. $r = a(2 - \cos\theta)$

43. $r = a(1 + \cos 2\theta)$ 　　　　　　　　44. $r = 2a\cos\theta$

45. $r = 2a\sin 3\theta$ 　　　　　　　　　　46. $r^2 = 2a^2\sin 3\theta$

47. $r^2 = 2a^2\cos^2(\theta/2)$

48. Find the area that is inside the cardioid $r = a(1 + \sin\theta)$ and outside the circle $r = a\sin\theta$.

49. Find the area that is inside the circle $r = 4 \cos \theta$ and outside $r = 2$.

50. Find the area that is inside $r^2 = 2a^2 \cos 2\theta$ and outside the circle $r = a$.

51. Find the area that is inside the circle $r = 5 \cos \theta$ and outside the curve $r = 2 + \cos \theta$.

52. Find the area of the region between the two loops of the limaçon $r = 2 + 4 \cos \theta$.

Hyperbolic Functions

13–1   Introduction. In this chapter we shall consider certain combinations of the exponentials e^x and e^{-x} which are called "hyperbolic functions." There are two reasons why we study these functions. One reason is that they are used in solving certain engineering problems. For example, the tension at any point in a cable suspended by its ends and hanging under its own weight, such as an electric transmission line, may be computed in terms of hyperbolic functions. We shall investigate the hanging cable in some detail in Article 13–6. A second reason for studying the hyperbolic functions is that they are useful in connection with differential equations.

13–2   Definitions and identities. The combinations $\frac{1}{2}(e^u + e^{-u})$ and $\frac{1}{2}(e^u - e^{-u})$ occur with sufficient frequency that it has been found convenient to give special names to them. It may not be clear at this particular time why the names about to be introduced are especially appropriate. But it will become more apparent as we proceed that these functions have many properties analogous, respectively, to $\cos u$ and $\sin u$. And just as $\cos u$ and $\sin u$ are easily identified with the point (x, y) on the unit circle $x^2 + y^2 = 1$, where by properly defining u we may take $x = \cos u$ and $y = \sin u$, so it is also possible to identify

$$
\begin{aligned}
\cosh u &= \tfrac{1}{2}(e^u + e^{-u}), \\
\sinh u &= \tfrac{1}{2}(e^u - e^{-u}),
\end{aligned}
\tag{1}
$$

with the coordinates of the point (x, y) on the "unit hyperbola" $x^2 - y^2 = 1$.

Equations (1) are the *definitions* of the *hyperbolic cosine* of u ($\cosh u$, which is often pronounced to rhyme with "gosh you") and of the *hyperbolic sine* of u ($\sinh u$, which is pronounced as though it were spelled "cinch u").

Suppose we check the statement that the point (x, y) with $x = \cosh u$ and $y = \sinh u$ lies on the unit hyperbola. We simply substitute the defining relations (1) into the equation of the hyperbola, and see whether or not these coordinates do satisfy the equation:

$$x^2 - y^2 = 1,$$

$$\cosh^2 u - \sinh^2 u \overset{?}{=} 1,$$

$$\tfrac{1}{4}(e^{2u} + 2 + e^{-2u}) - \tfrac{1}{4}(e^{2u} - 2 + e^{-2u}) \overset{?}{=} 1,$$

$$\tfrac{1}{4}(e^{2u} + 2 + e^{-2u} - e^{2u} + 2 - e^{-2u}) \overset{?}{=} 1,$$

$$\tfrac{1}{4}(4) \overset{?}{=} 1. \quad \text{(Yes!)}$$

Actually, if we let

$$x = \cosh u = \tfrac{1}{2}(e^u + e^{-u}),$$

$$y = \sinh u = \tfrac{1}{2}(e^u - e^{-u}),$$

(2)

then when u varies from $-\infty$ to $+\infty$, the point $P(x, y)$ describes the right-hand branch of the hyperbola $x^2 - y^2 = 1$. The sense in which the curve is described is indicated by the arrows in Fig. 13–1. Since e^u is always positive and $e^{-u} = 1/e^u$ is also positive, it follows that $x = \cosh u = \tfrac{1}{2}(e^u + e^{-u})$ is positive for all real values of u, $-\infty < u < +\infty$. Hence the point (x, y) remains always to the right of the y-axis.

The first bit of hyperbolic trigonometry that we have just established is the basic identity

$$\boxed{\cosh^2 u - \sinh^2 u = 1.}$$

(3)

This is analogous to, but not the same as, the ordinary trigonometric identity, $\cos^2 u + \sin^2 u = 1$. We shall now investigate additional points of analogy between these two types of functions.

The remaining hyperbolic functions are *defined* in terms of $\sinh u$ and $\cosh u$ as follows:

$$\tanh u = \frac{\sinh u}{\cosh u} = \frac{e^u - e^{-u}}{e^u + e^{-u}},$$

$$\coth u = \frac{\cosh u}{\sinh u} = \frac{e^u + e^{-u}}{e^u - e^{-u}},$$

(4)

$$\operatorname{sech} u = \frac{1}{\cosh u} = \frac{2}{e^u + e^{-u}},$$

$$\operatorname{csch} u = \frac{1}{\sinh u} = \frac{2}{e^u - e^{-u}}.$$

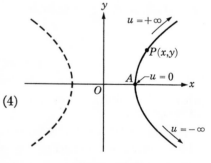

Figure 13–1

If we divide the identity (3) by $\cosh^2 u$, we get

$$1 - \tanh^2 u = \operatorname{sech}^2 u,$$

(5a)

and if we divide it by $\sinh^2 u$, we get

$$\coth^2 u - 1 = \operatorname{csch}^2 u.$$

(5b)

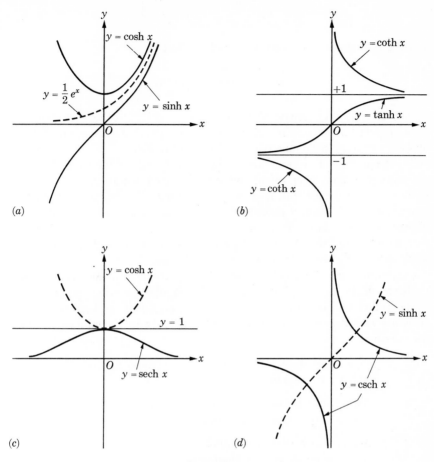

Figure 13-2

Since from (1) we find

$$\cosh u + \sinh u = e^u, \tag{6a}$$

$$\cosh u - \sinh u = e^{-u}, \tag{6b}$$

it is apparent that *any* combination of the exponentials e^u and e^{-u} can be replaced by a combination of $\sinh u$ and $\cosh u$, and conversely. Also, since e^{-u} is positive, (6b) shows that $\cosh u$ is always greater than $\sinh u$. But for large values of u, e^{-u} is small, and $\cosh u \approx \sinh u$.

The graphs of the hyperbolic functions are shown in Fig. 13-2(a—d).

At $x = 0$, $\cosh x = 1$ and $\sinh x = 0$, so the hyperbolic functions all have the same values at 0 that the corresponding trigonometric functions have. The hyperbolic cosine is an *even function*, that is,

$$\boxed{\cosh\,(-x) = \cosh x,}\tag{7}$$

and the hyperbolic sine is an *odd function*, that is,

$$\boxed{\sinh\,(-x) = -\sinh x;}\tag{8}$$

so one curve is symmetric about the y-axis and the other is symmetric with respect to the origin. Here again the hyperbolic functions behave like the ordinary trigonometric (or circular) functions.

The hyperbolic functions are so important and useful that their numerical values have been calculated and tabulated just as have the circular functions, at least for $\sinh x$, $\cosh x$, and $\tanh x$. The values of the other functions can be readily expressed in terms of these, and hence it is unnecessary to tabulate them also. Some slide rules also have $\sinh x$ and $\cosh x$ scales, and the values of these functions may be read directly in the same way that e^x may be read from the LL-scales.

Certain major differences between the hyperbolic and the circular functions should be noted. For example, the circular functions are periodic: $\sin\,(x + 2\pi) = \sin x$, $\tan\,(x + \pi) = \tan x$, etc. But *the hyperbolic functions are not periodic*. Again, they differ greatly in the range of values they assume:

$\sin x$ varies between -1 and $+1$, oscillates;
$\sinh x$ varies from $-\infty$ to $+\infty$, steadily increases;

$\cos x$ varies between -1 and $+1$, oscillates;
$\cosh x$ varies from $+\infty$ to $+1$ to $+\infty$;

$|\sec x|$ is never less than unity;
$\operatorname{sech} x$ is never greater than unity, is always positive;

$\tan x$ varies from $-\infty$ to $+\infty$;
$\tanh x$ varies from -1 to $+1$.

Another difference is exhibited in the behavior of the functions as $x \to \pm\infty$. In the case of the circular functions, $\sin x$, $\cos x$, $\tan x$, etc., we can say nothing very specific about their behavior for large values of x. On the other hand, the hyperbolic functions behave very much like $e^x/2$, $e^{-x}/2$, unity, or zero as follows:

For x large and positive:

$\cosh x \approx \sinh x \approx \frac{1}{2}e^x$

$\tanh x \approx \coth x \approx 1$

$\operatorname{sech} x \approx \operatorname{csch} x \approx 2e^{-x} \approx 0$

For x negative, $|x|$ large:

$\cosh x \approx -\sinh x \approx \frac{1}{2}e^{-x}$

$\tanh x \approx \coth x \approx -1$ $\qquad(9)$

$\operatorname{sech} x \approx -\operatorname{csch} x \approx 2e^x \approx 0$

Additional analogies will be apparent when we study the calculus of hyperbolic functions in the next article. We conclude this article with certain formulas which the reader may readily verify. The following identities require only some algebraic calculations combined with the definitions (1), namely,

$$\sinh (x + y) = \sinh x \cosh y + \cosh x \sinh y,$$
$$\cosh (x + y) = \cosh x \cosh y + \sinh x \sinh y.$$

(10)

These in turn give

$$\sinh 2x = 2 \sinh x \cosh x, \tag{11a}$$

$$\cosh 2x = \cosh^2 x + \sinh^2 x, \tag{11b}$$

when we take $y = x$. The second of these leads to certain useful "half-angle" formulas when we combine it with the basic identity

$$1 = \cosh^2 x - \sinh^2 x. \tag{3}$$

For if we add (11b) and (3), we have

$$\cosh 2x + 1 = 2 \cosh^2 x, \tag{12a}$$

while if we subtract (3) from (11b), we get

$$\cosh 2x - 1 = 2 \sinh^2 x. \tag{12b}$$

Thus practically all the circular trigonometric identities have hyperbolic analogies. The formulas (3) and (10) are easily verified in terms of the definitions (1). The others follow from these by straightforward algebraic manipulations.

PROBLEMS

1. Show that $x = -\cosh u$, $y = \sinh u$ represents a point on the left branch of the hyperbola $x^2 - y^2 = 1$.

2. Using the definitions of $\cosh u$ and $\sinh u$ given by Eq. (1), show that $\cosh (-u) = \cosh u$ and $\sinh (-u) = -\sinh u$.

3. Verify Eqs. (10) for $\sinh (x + y)$ and $\cosh (x + y)$.

4. Show that $(\cosh x + \sinh x)^n = \cosh nx + \sinh nx$.

5. Let L be the line tangent to the hyperbola $x^2 - y^2 = 1$ at the point $P_1(x_1, y_1)$, where $x_1 = \cosh u$, $y_1 = \sinh u$. Show that L cuts the x-axis at the point (sech u, 0) and the y-axis at (0, $-$csch u).

6. In each of the following problems, one of the six hyperbolic functions of u is given; determine the remaining five.

(a) $\sinh u = -\frac{3}{4}$,   (b) $\cosh u = \frac{17}{15}$,   (c) $\tanh u = -\frac{7}{25}$,

(d) $\coth u = \frac{13}{12}$,   (e) $\operatorname{sech} u = \frac{3}{5}$,   (f) $\operatorname{csch} u = \frac{5}{12}$.

7. Show that the distance r from the origin O to the point $P(\cosh u, \sinh u)$ on the hyperbola $x^2 - y^2 = 1$ is $r = \sqrt{\cosh 2u}$.

8. Show that the line tangent to the hyperbola at its vertex A in Fig. 13–1 intersects the line $\overrightarrow{OP}$ in the point $(1, \tanh u)$. This gives a geometric representation of $\tanh u$.

9. If θ lies in the interval $-\pi/2 < \theta < \pi/2$ and $\sinh x = \tan \theta$, show that $\cosh x = \sec \theta$, $\tanh x = \sin \theta$, $\coth x = \csc \theta$, $\operatorname{csch} x = \cot \theta$, and $\operatorname{sech} x = \cos \theta$.

13–3   **Derivatives and integrals.** Let u be a differentiable function of x and differentiate

$$\sinh u = \tfrac{1}{2}(e^u - e^{-u}), \qquad \cosh u = \tfrac{1}{2}(e^u + e^{-u}), \qquad (1)$$

with respect to x. Applying the formulas

$$\frac{de^u}{dx} = e^u \frac{du}{dx}, \qquad \frac{de^{-u}}{dx} = e^{-u} \frac{d(-u)}{dx} = -e^{-u} \frac{du}{dx},$$

we get

$$\frac{d(\sinh u)}{dx} = \cosh u \frac{du}{dx}, \qquad\qquad \text{XXI}$$

$$\frac{d(\cosh u)}{dx} = \sinh u \frac{du}{dx}. \qquad\qquad \text{XXII}$$

Then, if we let

$$y = \tanh u = \frac{\sinh u}{\cosh u}$$

and differentiate as a fraction, we get

$$\frac{d(\tanh u)}{dx} = \frac{\cosh u \dfrac{d(\sinh u)}{dx} - \sinh u \dfrac{d(\cosh u)}{dx}}{\cosh^2 u}$$

$$= \frac{\cosh^2 u \dfrac{du}{dx} - \sinh^2 u \dfrac{du}{dx}}{\cosh^2 u}$$

$$= \frac{(\cosh^2 u - \sinh^2 u) \dfrac{du}{dx}}{\cosh^2 u} = \frac{1}{\cosh^2 u} \frac{du}{dx}$$

$$= \operatorname{sech}^2 u \frac{du}{dx}.$$

In a similar manner, we may establish the rest of the formulas in the following list:

$$\frac{d(\tanh u)}{dx} = \operatorname{sech}^2 u \frac{du}{dx}, \qquad\qquad \text{XXIII}$$

$$\frac{d(\coth u)}{dx} = -\operatorname{csch}^2 u \frac{du}{dx}, \qquad\qquad \text{XXIV}$$

$$\frac{d(\operatorname{sech} u)}{dx} = -\operatorname{sech} u \tanh u \frac{du}{dx}, \qquad\qquad \text{XXV}$$

$$\frac{d(\operatorname{csch} u)}{dx} = -\operatorname{csch} u \coth u \frac{du}{dx}. \qquad\qquad \text{XXVI}$$

Note that aside from the pattern of algebraic signs, these formulas are the exact analogs of the formulas for the corresponding circular functions. Again, exactly half of them have minus signs, but we no longer attach the minus signs to the derivatives of the cofunctions, but rather notice that the first three, sinh u, cosh u, tanh u, have positive derivatives and the last three have negative derivatives.

Each of these derivative formulas has a matching differential formula. These in turn may be integrated at once to produce the following integration formulas:

$$\text{(1)} \quad \int \sinh u \, du = \cosh u + C.$$

$$\text{(2)} \quad \int \cosh u \, du = \sinh u + C.$$

$$\text{(3)} \quad \int \operatorname{sech}^2 u \, du = \tanh u + C.$$

$$\text{(4)} \quad \int \operatorname{csch}^2 u \, du = -\coth u + C. \qquad\qquad (2)$$

$$\text{(5)} \quad \int \operatorname{sech} u \tanh u \, du = -\operatorname{sech} u + C.$$

$$\text{(6)} \quad \int \operatorname{csch} u \coth u \, du = -\operatorname{csch} u + C.$$

EXAMPLE 1. Show that $y = a \cosh (x/a)$ satisfies the differential equation

$$\frac{d^2 y}{dx^2} = \frac{w}{H} \sqrt{1 + \left(\frac{dy}{dx}\right)^2}, \qquad\qquad (3)$$

provided $a = H/w$, where H and w are constants.

Solution. By differentiating $y = a \cosh (x/a)$, we find

$$\frac{dy}{dx} = a \sinh \frac{x}{a} \cdot \frac{1}{a} = \sinh \frac{x}{a}, \qquad \frac{d^2y}{dx^2} = \cosh \frac{x}{a} \cdot \frac{1}{a}.$$

We substitute these into (3) and obtain

$$\frac{1}{a} \cosh \frac{x}{a} \overset{?}{=} \frac{w}{H} \sqrt{1 + \sinh^2 \frac{x}{a}} \qquad \text{(a)}$$

$$= \frac{w}{H} \sqrt{\cosh^2 \frac{x}{a}} \qquad \text{(b)}$$

$$= \frac{w}{H} \cosh \frac{x}{a}, \qquad \text{(c)}$$

which is a true equation provided $a = H/w$.

Remark 1. In going from (a) to (b) above, we used the fundamental identity

$$\cosh^2 u - \sinh^2 u = 1$$

in the form

$$1 + \sinh^2 u = \cosh^2 u.$$

In going from (b) to (c), we used the fact that $\cosh u$ is always positive, and hence

$$\sqrt{\cosh^2 u} = |\cosh u| = \cosh u.$$

Remark 2. The differential equation (3) expresses the condition for equilibrium of forces acting on a section AP of a hanging cable (Fig. 13–3). We imagine the rest of the cable as having been removed and the section AP from the lowest point A to the representative point $P(x, y)$ as being in equilibrium under the forces

(1) H = horizontal tension pulling on the cable at A,

(2) T = tangential tension pulling on the cable at P,

(3) $W = ws$ = weight of s feet of the cable at w pounds per foot of length from A to P.

Then equilibrium of the cable requires that the horizontal and vertical components of T balance H and W respectively:

$$T \cos \phi = H, \qquad T \sin \phi = W = ws.$$

$$\text{(4)}$$

By division, we get

$$\frac{T \sin \phi}{T \cos \phi} = \tan \phi = \frac{W}{H}$$

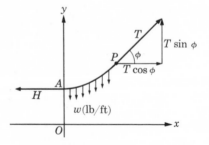

Figure 13–3

or

$$\frac{dy}{dx} = \frac{ws}{H}, \tag{5}$$

since $\tan \phi = dy/dx$. The arc length s in Eq. (5) would be found by integrating

$$ds = \sqrt{1 + \left(\frac{dy}{dx}\right)^2}\, dx$$

from A to P. But instead of doing so, we may differentiate Eq. (5) with respect to x:

$$\frac{d^2y}{dx^2} = \frac{w}{H}\frac{ds}{dx},$$

and then substitute $\sqrt{1 + (dy/dx)^2}$ in place of ds/dx to obtain Eq. (3) above.

Remark 3. In Example 1, above, we pulled the equation $y = a \cosh(x/a)$ out of the hat, so to speak, and showed by substitution that it satisfies the differential equation (3). In Article 13–6, we shall adopt the more straightforward approach of simply solving Eq. (3) subject to the initial conditions

$$\frac{dy}{dx} = 0 \quad\text{and}\quad y = y_0 \quad\text{when}\quad x = 0.$$

By choosing the origin so that $y_0 = a = H/w$, we shall find that the solution is indeed the one given above, namely,

$$y = a \cosh\frac{x}{a} \quad\text{with}\quad a = \frac{H}{w}. \tag{6}$$

EXAMPLE 2. Show that the tension in the cable at $P(x, y)$ in Fig. 13–3 is

$$T = wy.$$

Solution. We make use of the fact that

$$\frac{dy}{dx} = \tan \phi,$$

since T acts along the tangent, and

$$T = \frac{H}{\cos \phi} = H \sec \phi,$$

by Eq. (4a). Then, differentiating (6), we have

$$\tan \phi = \frac{dy}{dx} = \sinh\frac{x}{a}$$

and

$$\sec \phi = \sqrt{\sec^2 \phi} = \sqrt{1 + \tan^2 \phi} = \sqrt{1 + \left(\frac{dy}{dx}\right)^2}$$

$$= \sqrt{1 + \sinh^2\frac{x}{a}} = \sqrt{\cosh^2\frac{x}{a}} = \cosh\frac{x}{a}.$$

Therefore

$$T = H \sec \phi = H \cosh \frac{x}{a}, \quad (7a)$$

where

$$a = \frac{H}{w} \quad \text{or} \quad H = wa. \quad (7b)$$

Combining (7a) and (7b), we have

$$T = wa \cosh \frac{x}{a}$$

or, when we take account of Eq. (6),

$$T = wy.$$

Figure 13–4

This means that the tension at P is equal to the weight of y feet of the cable. Thus if the end of the cable to the right of P is allowed to hang down over a smooth peg while the cable is held at P so that it does not slip, and if the cable is then cut off at the point Q where it crosses the x-axis (Fig. 13–4), it may then be released at P and the weight wy of the section of cable PQ will be just sufficient to prevent the cable from slipping. If this is carried out at two different points P and P', the cable may be draped over two smooth pegs without slipping, provided the free ends reach just to the x-axis. The curve, $y = a \cosh (x/a)$, is called a *catenary* from the Latin word *catena*, meaning chain. The x-axis is called the directrix of the catenary.

PROBLEMS

1. Establish the validity of the formulas **XXIV–XXVI**.

Find dy/dx in each of the following:

2. $y = \sinh 3x$

3. $y = \cosh^2 5x$

4. $y = \cosh^2 5x - \sinh^2 5x$

5. $y = \tanh 2x$

6. $y = \coth (\tan x)$

7. $y = \operatorname{sech}^3 x$

8. $y = 4 \operatorname{csch} (x/4)$

9. $\sinh y = \tan x$

Integrate each of the following:

10. $\displaystyle\int \cosh (2x + 1)\, dx$

11. $\displaystyle\int \tanh x\, dx$

12. $\displaystyle\int \frac{\sinh x}{\cosh^4 x}\, dx$

13. $\displaystyle\int \frac{4\, dx}{(e^x + e^{-x})^2}$

14. $\displaystyle\int \frac{e^x - e^{-x}}{e^x + e^{-x}}\, dx$

15. $\displaystyle\int \tanh^2 x\, dx$

16. $\displaystyle\int \frac{\sinh \sqrt{x}}{\sqrt{x}}\, dx$

17. $\displaystyle\int \cosh^2 3x\, dx$

18. $\displaystyle\int \sqrt{\cosh x - 1}\, dx$

19. Find the area of the hyperbolic sector AOP bounded by the arc AP and the lines $\overleftrightarrow{OA}$, $\overleftrightarrow{OP}$ through the origin, in Fig. 13–1.

20. Show that the straight line $y = x/2 + 1$ and the catenary $y = \cosh x$ intersect at the two points $(0, 1)$ and $(0.930, 1.465)$. (Consult tables for $\cosh x$.)

21. Two successive poles supporting an electric power line are 100 feet apart, the supporting members being at the same level. If the wire dips 25 feet at the center, (a) find the length of the wire between supports, and (b) find the tension in the wire at its lowest point if its weight is $w = 0.3$ lb/ft. [*Hint:* First find a from the equation $25/a + 1 = \cosh 50/a$, which can be related to Problem 20 with $x = 50/a$.]

22. The equation $\sinh x = \tan \theta$, $-\pi/2 < \theta < \pi/2$, defines θ as a function of x:

$$\theta = \tan^{-1} (\sinh x),$$

to which the name "gudermannian of x" has been attached, written

$$\theta = \text{gd } x.$$

Show that

$$\frac{d\theta}{dx} = \frac{1}{\cosh x} = \frac{1}{\sec \theta},$$

so that $\sec \theta \, d\theta = dx$ and

$$\int \sec \theta \, d\theta = \text{gd}^{-1} \theta + C = \sinh^{-1} (\tan \theta) + C.$$

23. Sketch the curve $\theta = \text{gd } x$ (see Problem 22) by the following procedure. First sketch the curves $y = \sinh x$ and $y = \tan \theta$ $(-\pi/2 < \theta < \pi/2)$ on separate xy- and θy-planes. Starting in the xy-plane with any value of x, $-\infty < x < +\infty$, determine the corresponding value of y from the curve $y = \sinh x$. Transfer this y reading to the y-axis in the θy-plane and determine the corresponding value of θ from the curve $y = \tan \theta$. Use this value of θ as ordinate and the original value of x as abscissa to plot a point on the curve $\theta = \text{gd } x$.

24. Show that the curve $\theta = \text{gd } x$ (see Problems 22 and 23) has the lines $\theta = \pm\pi/2$ as horizontal asymptotes, is always rising (from left to right), has a point of inflection at the origin, and is symmetric with respect to the origin.

13–4 Geometric significance of the hyperbolic radian.

We are now in a position to illustrate the meaning of the variable u in the equations

$$x = \cosh u, \qquad y = \sinh u \tag{1}$$

as they relate to the point $P(x, y)$ on the unit hyperbola

$$x^2 - y^2 = 1. \tag{2}$$

Before we do so, however, we shall find the analogous meaning of the variable θ in the equations

$$x = \cos \theta, \qquad y = \sin \theta \tag{3}$$

as they relate to the point $P(x, y)$ on the
unit circle

$$x^2 + y^2 = 1. \qquad (4)$$

The most familiar interpretation of θ is, of
course, that it is the radian measure of the
angle AOP in Fig. 13–5, that is

$$\theta = \frac{\text{arc } AP}{\text{radius } OA}.$$

Figure 13–5

But we also recall that the area of a circular sector of radius r and central
angle θ (radians) is given by $(\frac{1}{2})r^2\theta$. Since we are here dealing with a unit
circle, this says that

$$\text{area of sector } AOP = \tfrac{1}{2}\theta$$

or, if we solve this for θ,

$$\boxed{\theta = \text{twice the area of the sector } AOP.} \qquad (5)$$

Of course we must realize that θ is a pure (dimensionless) number and
Eq. (5) really says that the value of θ which Eqs. (3) associate with the
point $P(x, y)$ on the unit circle is twice the *number* of square units of area
that the radius vector $\overrightarrow{OP}$ sweeps out as P moves along the circle from A
to its final position P. Thus when the area of the sector AOP is one-half
the area of a square having $\overline{OA}$ as a side, then $\theta = 1$ and the coordinates
of P represent cos 1 and sin 1. Negative values of θ would be interpreted
as corresponding to areas swept over
in a clockwise rotation of $\overline{OA}$.

Now for the unit hyperbola,

$$x^2 - y^2 = 1,$$

we shall find an analogous interpretation for the variable u in the equations

$$x = \cosh u, \qquad y = \sinh u.$$

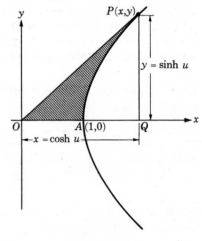

To see that this is indeed the case,
we shall calculate the area of the
sector AOP in Fig. 13–6. This area
is clearly equal to the area of the
triangle OQP minus the area AQP
bounded above by the curve, below

Figure 13–6

by the x-axis, and on the right by the vertical line $\overleftrightarrow{QP}$. But this area is simply

$$\text{area } AQP = \int_A^P y \, dx = \int_A^P \sinh u \, d(\cosh u)$$

$$= \int_A^P \sinh^2 u \, du = \tfrac{1}{2} \int_A^P (\cosh 2u - 1) \, du \quad [\text{Eq. (12b)},$$
$$\text{Article 13–2}]$$

$$= \tfrac{1}{2} \Big[\tfrac{1}{2} \sinh 2u - u \Big]_{A\,(u=0)}^{P\,(u=u)}$$

$$= \tfrac{1}{4} \sinh 2u - \tfrac{1}{2}u = \tfrac{1}{2} \sinh u \cosh u - \tfrac{1}{2}u.$$

Hence,

$$\text{area of sector } AOP = \text{area of } OQP - \text{area of } AQP$$
$$= \tfrac{1}{2} \sinh u \cosh u - (\tfrac{1}{2} \sinh u \cosh u - \tfrac{1}{2}u)$$
$$= \tfrac{1}{2}u,$$

or solving for u,

$$u = \text{twice the area of the sector } AOP. \qquad (6)$$

As for the circle, a positive value of u is associated with an area above the x-axis and a negative value with an area below the x-axis, and areas are to be measured in terms of the unit square having $\overline{OA}$ as side. The term *hyperbolic radian* is sometimes used in connection with the variable u in Eq. (6), but here again, u is just a dimensionless real number. For example, $\cosh 2$ and $\sinh 2$ may be interpreted as the coordinates of P when the area of the sector AOP is just equal to the area of a square having $\overline{OA}$ as side.

13–5   The inverse hyperbolic functions. If we start with

$$x = \sinh y, \qquad (1)$$

then as y varies continuously from $-\infty$ to $+\infty$, x does likewise. Graphically, this means that we may start with any real value on the y-axis in Fig. 13–7 and draw a horizontal line to the curve. Then a vertical line to the x-axis locates exactly one value of x such that the point (x, y) is on the curve. On the other hand, we could equally well reverse these steps and start with any real value x on the x-axis, go along a vertical line to the curve, then on a horizontal line to the y-axis. This latter procedure gives us y as a function of x, and the notation we use is

$$y = \sinh^{-1} x. \qquad (2)$$

Figure 13–7

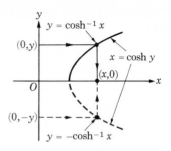

Figure 13–8

Here we have no problem about principal values, as we did in the case of the inverses of the circular functions, since the correspondence between the real numbers x and the real numbers y in Eq. (1) is one-to-one. Equation (1) says exactly the same thing as Eq. (2).

$$y = \sinh^{-1} x \qquad \text{means} \qquad x = \sinh y.$$

The inverse hyperbolic cosine, however, is double-valued and it is desirable to prescribe a principal branch. For if we start with the equation

$$x = \cosh y, \tag{3}$$

then y and $-y$ both give the same value of x; that is, the correspondence between y-values and x-values is two-to-one, so that if x is considered the independent variable, there are *two* corresponding values of y. This is analogous to the situation surrounding the equation $x = y^2$, which defines x as a single-valued function of y; but when x is given and we ask for y, the result is $y = \pm\sqrt{x}$. In the case of the inverse hyperbolic cosine, we take the positive values of y as the principal branch:

$$\boxed{y = \cosh^{-1} x \qquad \text{means} \qquad x = \cosh y, \quad y \geq 0, \quad x \geq 1.} \tag{4}$$

Thus in Fig. 13–8 the equation $x = \cosh y$ represents the entire curve, but $y = \cosh^{-1} x$ represents only that portion above the x-axis, while the portion below the x-axis is given by $y = -\cosh^{-1} x$.

Reference to Fig. 13–2 shows that the only other double-valued inverse is the inverse hyperbolic secant, and again we select the positive branch. That is,

$$y = \operatorname{sech}^{-1} x, \qquad y > 0, \qquad 0 < x \leq 1 \tag{5}$$

defines the principal branch and the numbers x and y satisfy

$$x = \operatorname{sech} y. \tag{6}$$

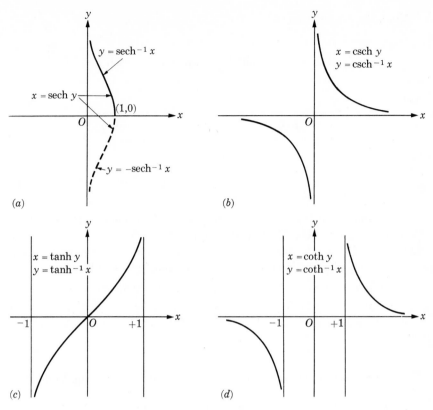

Figure 13–9

Since

$$\text{sech } y = \frac{1}{\cosh y},$$

Eq. (6) is equivalent to

$$\cosh y = \frac{1}{x}$$

and the restriction $y > 0$ defines the same branch as in (5), so that

$$y = \cosh^{-1} \frac{1}{x}.$$

That is,

$$\text{sech}^{-1} x = \cosh^{-1} \frac{1}{x}.$$

Similarly, we see that

$$y = \operatorname{csch}^{-1} x = \sinh^{-1} \frac{1}{x} \qquad \text{means} \qquad \operatorname{csch} y = x. \tag{7}$$

Also,

$$y = \tanh^{-1} x \qquad \text{means} \qquad x = \tanh y, \tag{8a}$$

and

$$y = \coth^{-1} x \qquad \text{means} \qquad x = \coth y. \tag{8b}$$

The graphs of the various inverse hyperbolic functions are given in Figs. 13–7, 13–8, 13–9. Numerical values of $\sinh^{-1} x$, $\cosh^{-1} x$, and $\tanh^{-1} x$ may be read from the tables of $\sinh x$, $\cosh x$, and $\tanh x$ respectively in the same way that antilogarithms are read from tables of logarithms.

For example, suppose it is required to find $\tanh^{-1} 0.25$. If we let

$$x = \tanh^{-1} 0.25,$$

then

$$\tanh x = 0.25.$$

We consult a table of hyperbolic tangents and we find the following entries:

x	$\tanh x$	$\tanh x$ (rounded off)
0.25	0.24492	0.24
0.26	0.25430	0.25

Since we want the entry which corresponds to $\tanh x = 0.25$, we may simply round off the tabular entries to two significant figures and read $x = 0.26$. Or else we may take $\tanh x = 0.25000$ and interpolate between the readings listed above. Using ordinary proportional parts, we have

$$x_1 = 0.25, \qquad \tanh x_1 = 0.24492,$$

$$x = (?), \qquad \tanh x = 0.25000,$$

$$x_2 = 0.26, \qquad \tanh x_2 = 0.25430,$$

$$\frac{x - x_1}{x_2 - x_1} = \frac{\tanh x - \tanh x_1}{\tanh x_2 - \tanh x_1},$$

$$\frac{x - x_1}{0.01} = \frac{508}{938} = 0.54,$$

$$x = 0.2554 = \tanh^{-1} 0.25000.$$

An alternative method for evaluating the inverse hyperbolic functions is to express each of them in terms of logarithms, as illustrated below for $\tanh^{-1} x$. Let $y = \tanh^{-1} x$, then $\tanh y = x$ or

$$x = \frac{\sinh y}{\cosh y} = \frac{\frac{1}{2}(e^y - e^{-y})}{\frac{1}{2}(e^y + e^{-y})} = \frac{e^y - \dfrac{1}{e^y}}{e^y + \dfrac{1}{e^y}} = \frac{e^{2y} - 1}{e^{2y} + 1}.$$

We now solve this equation for e^{2y}:

$$x e^{2y} + x = e^{2y} - 1$$

or

$$1 + x = e^{2y}(1 - x),$$

and

$$e^{2y} = \frac{1 + x}{1 - x}.$$

Hence

$$y = \tanh^{-1} x = \frac{1}{2} \ln \frac{1 + x}{1 - x}, \qquad |x| < 1. \tag{9}$$

The variable x in Eq. (9) is restricted to the domain $|x| < 1$, since $x = \tanh y$ lies in this interval for all real values of y, $-\infty < y < +\infty$.

For example,

$$\tanh^{-1} 0.25 = \frac{1}{2} \ln \frac{1.25}{0.75} = \frac{1}{2} \ln \frac{5}{3}$$

$$= \tfrac{1}{2}(\ln 5 - \ln 3) = 0.25542.$$

The expressions for the other inverse hyperbolic functions in terms of logarithms are found in a similar manner. They are:

$$
\begin{aligned}
\sinh^{-1} x &= \ln\left(x + \sqrt{x^2 + 1}\right), \qquad -\infty < x < \infty, \\
\cosh^{-1} x &= \ln\left(x + \sqrt{x^2 - 1}\right), \qquad x \geq 1, \\
\operatorname{sech}^{-1} x &= \ln\left(\frac{1 + \sqrt{1 - x^2}}{x}\right) = \cosh^{-1}\left(\frac{1}{x}\right), \qquad 0 < x \leq 1, \\
\operatorname{csch}^{-1} x &= \ln\left(\frac{1}{x} + \frac{\sqrt{1 + x^2}}{|x|}\right) = \sinh^{-1}\left(\frac{1}{x}\right), \qquad x \neq 0, \\
\coth^{-1} x &= \frac{1}{2} \ln \frac{x + 1}{x - 1} = \tanh^{-1}\left(\frac{1}{x}\right), \qquad |x| > 1.
\end{aligned}
\tag{10}
$$

It should be evident that the logarithmic expressions are, on the whole, rather cumbersome, and that the inverse hyperbolic functions do provide a useful shorthand wherever these expressions arise.

The chief merit of the inverse hyperbolic functions lies in their usefulness in integration. This will easily be understood after we have derived the following formulas for their derivatives:

$$\frac{d(\sinh^{-1} u)}{dx} = \frac{1}{\sqrt{1 + u^2}} \frac{du}{dx}, \qquad\qquad \text{XXVII}$$

$$\frac{d(\cosh^{-1} u)}{dx} = \frac{1}{\sqrt{u^2 - 1}} \frac{du}{dx}, \qquad\qquad \text{XXVIII}$$

$$\frac{d(\tanh^{-1} u)}{dx} = \frac{1}{1 - u^2} \frac{du}{dx}, \quad |u| < 1, \qquad \text{XXIX}$$

$$\frac{d(\coth^{-1} u)}{dx} = \frac{1}{1 - u^2} \frac{du}{dx}, \quad |u| > 1, \qquad \text{XXX}$$

$$\frac{d(\text{sech}^{-1} u)}{dx} = \frac{-du/dx}{u\sqrt{1 - u^2}}, \qquad\qquad \text{XXXI}$$

$$\frac{d(\text{csch}^{-1} u)}{dx} = \frac{-du/dx}{|u|\sqrt{1 + u^2}}. \qquad\qquad \text{XXXII}$$

The proofs of these all follow the same method. We illustrate for the case of $\cosh^{-1} u$. To this end, let

$$y = \cosh^{-1} u;$$

then

$$\cosh y = u,$$

$$\sinh y \frac{dy}{dx} = \frac{du}{dx},$$

and

$$\frac{dy}{dx} = \frac{1}{\sinh y} \frac{dy}{dx}.$$

But

$$\cosh^2 y - \sinh^2 y = 1,$$

$$\cosh y = u,$$

so that

$$\sinh y = \pm\sqrt{\cosh^2 y - 1}$$

$$= \pm\sqrt{u^2 - 1}$$

and
$$\frac{dy}{dx} = \frac{1}{\pm\sqrt{u^2 - 1}} \frac{du}{dx}.$$

The ambiguous sign will be $+$ if we restrict attention to the principal value, $y = \cosh^{-1} u$, $y \geq 0$, for then $\sinh v \geq 0$ and the ambiguous sign is the same as the sign of $\sinh y$. Thus XXVIII is established. The identities (5a) and (5b) of Article 13–2, with y in place of u, will be found to be useful in proving formulas XXIX to XXXII. The reader should have no difficulty in deriving these results.

The restrictions $|u| < 1$ and $|u| > 1$ in XXIX and XXX respectively are due to the fact that if
$$y = \tanh^{-1} u,$$

then
$$u = \tanh y,$$

and since
$$-1 < \tanh y < 1,$$

this means $|u| < 1$. Similarly,
$$y = \coth^{-1} u, \qquad u = \coth y$$

requires $|u| > 1$. The distinction becomes important when we invert the formulas to get integration formulas, since otherwise we would be unable to tell whether we should write $\tanh^{-1} u$ or $\coth^{-1} u$ for
$$\int \frac{du}{1 - u^2}.$$

The following integration formulas follow at once from the differential formulas XXVII′ to XXXII′, that are obtained by multiplying both sides of XXVII to XXXII by dx:

(1) $\displaystyle\int \frac{du}{\sqrt{1 + u^2}} = \sinh^{-1} u + C,$

(2) $\displaystyle\int \frac{du}{\sqrt{u^2 - 1}} = \cosh^{-1} u + C,$

(3) $\displaystyle\int \frac{du}{1 - u^2} = \begin{cases} \tanh^{-1} u + C & \text{if } |u| < 1 \\ \coth^{-1} u + C & \text{if } |u| > 1 \end{cases} = \frac{1}{2} \ln \left|\frac{1 + u}{1 - u}\right| + C,$ (11)

(4) $\displaystyle\int \frac{du}{u\sqrt{1 - u^2}} = -\operatorname{sech}^{-1} |u| + C = -\cosh^{-1}\left(\frac{1}{|u|}\right) + C,$

(5) $\displaystyle\int \frac{du}{u\sqrt{1 + u^2}} = -\operatorname{csch}^{-1} |u| + C = -\sinh^{-1}\left(\frac{1}{|u|}\right) + C.$

PROBLEMS

1. Solve the equation $x = \sinh y = \frac{1}{2}(e^y - e^{-y})$ for e^y in terms of x, and thus show that $y = \ln(x + \sqrt{1 + x^2})$. (This equation expresses $\sinh^{-1} x$ as a logarithm.)

2. Express $\cosh^{-1} x$ in terms of logarithms by using the method of Problem 1.

3. Establish formula XXVII.

4. Establish formula XXIX.

5. Establish formula XXXI.

Find dy/dx in each of the following:

6. $y = \sinh^{-1}(2x)$ 7. $y = \tanh^{-1}(\cos x)$

8. $y = \cosh^{-1}(\sec x)$ 9. $y = \coth^{-1}(\sec x)$

10. $y = \operatorname{sech}^{-1}(\sin 2x)$

Evaluate each of the following integrals:

11. $\displaystyle\int \frac{dx}{\sqrt{1 + 4x^2}}$ 12. $\displaystyle\int \frac{dx}{\sqrt{4 + x^2}}$ 13. $\displaystyle\int_0^{0.5} \frac{dx}{1 - x^2}$

14. $\displaystyle\int_{5/4}^{2} \frac{dx}{1 - x^2}$ 15. $\displaystyle\int \frac{dx}{x\sqrt{4 + x^2}}$

16. If a body of mass m falling from rest under the action of gravity encounters an air resistance proportional to the square of the velocity, then the velocity v at time t satisfies the differential equation $m(dv/dt) = mg - kv^2$, where k is a constant of proportionality and $v = 0$ when $t = 0$. Show that $v = \sqrt{mg/k} \tanh (\sqrt{gk/m}\, t)$, and hence deduce that the body approaches a "limiting velocity" $= \sqrt{mg/k}$ as $t \to \infty$.

13–6   The hanging cable.

We conclude this chapter by deriving the solution of the differential equation

$$\frac{d^2 y}{dx^2} = \frac{w}{H} \sqrt{1 + \left(\frac{dy}{dx}\right)^2}, \tag{1}$$

which is the equation of equilibrium of forces on a hanging cable discussed in Article 13–3, Example 1. Since Eq. (1) involves the second derivative, we shall require two conditions to determine the constants of integration. By choosing the y-axis to be the vertical line through the lowest point of the cable, one condition becomes

$$\frac{dy}{dx} = 0 \quad \text{when} \quad x = 0. \tag{2a}$$

Then we may still move the x-axis up or down to suit our convenience. That is, we let

$$y = y_0 \quad \text{when} \quad x = 0, \tag{2b}$$

and we may choose y_0 so as to give us the simplest form in our final answer.

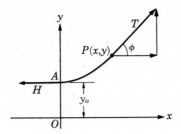

Figure 13–10

It is customary, when solving an equation such as (1), to introduce a single letter to represent dy/dx. The letter p is most often used. Thus we let

$$\frac{dy}{dx} = p, \tag{3a}$$

and then we may write

$$\frac{d^2y}{dx^2} = \frac{dp}{dx}, \tag{3b}$$

so that Eq. (1) takes the form

$$\frac{dp}{dx} = \frac{w}{H}\sqrt{1 + p^2}.$$

We may now separate the variables to get

$$\frac{dp}{\sqrt{1 + p^2}} = \frac{w}{H}\,dx$$

or

$$\int \frac{dp}{\sqrt{1 + p^2}} = \frac{w}{H}x + C_1. \tag{4a}$$

The integral on the left is of the same form, with p in place of u, as (11_1), Article 13–5. Hence (4a) becomes

$$\sinh^{-1} p = \frac{w}{H}x + C_1. \tag{4b}$$

Since $p = dy/dx = 0$ when $x = 0$, we determine the constant of integration

$$\sinh^{-1} 0 = C_1,$$

from which (see Fig. 13–7)

$$C_1 = 0.$$

Hence

$$\sinh^{-1} p = \frac{w}{H}x$$

or

$$p = \sinh\left(\frac{w}{H}x\right). \qquad (5a)$$

We substitute $p = dy/dx$, multiply by dx, and have

$$dy = \sinh\left(\frac{w}{H}x\right)dx$$

or

$$y = \int \sinh\left(\frac{w}{H}x\right)dx$$

$$= \frac{H}{w}\int \sinh\left(\frac{w}{H}x\right)d\left(\frac{w}{H}x\right)$$

$$= \frac{H}{w}\cosh\left(\frac{w}{H}x\right) + C_2. \qquad (5b)$$

The condition $y = y_0$ when $x = 0$ determines C_2:

$$y_0 = \frac{H}{w}\cosh 0 + C_2,$$

$$C_2 = y_0 - \frac{H}{w}, \qquad (5c)$$

and hence

$$y = \frac{H}{w}\cosh\left(\frac{w}{H}x\right) + y_0 - \frac{H}{w}. \qquad (5d)$$

Clearly, this equation will have a simpler form if we choose y_0 so that

$$y_0 = \frac{H}{w}.$$

We do so. The answer then takes the form

$$y = \frac{H}{w}\cosh\left(\frac{w}{H}x\right)$$

or

$$y = a\cosh\frac{x}{a} \quad\text{with}\quad a = \frac{H}{w}. \qquad (6)$$

PROBLEMS

1. Find the length of arc of the catenary $y = a\cosh x/a$ from $A(0, a)$ to $P_1(x_1, y_1)$, $x_1 > 0$.

2. Show that the area bounded by the x-axis, the catenary $y = a\cosh x/a$, the y-axis, and the vertical line through $P_1(x_1, y_1)$, $x_1 > 0$, is the same as the

area of a rectangle of altitude a and base s, where s is the length of the arc from $A(0, a)$ to P_1. (See Problem 1.)

3. The catenary $y = a \cosh x/a$ is revolved about the x-axis. Find the surface area generated by the portion of the curve between the points $A(0, a)$ and $P_1(x_1, y_1)$, $x_1 > 0$.

4. Find the center of gravity of the arc of the catenary $y = a \cosh x/a$ between two symmetrically located points $P_0(-x_1, y_1)$ and $P_1(x_1, y_1)$.

5. Find the volume generated when the area of Problem 2 is revolved about the x-axis.

6. (a) The length of the arc AP (Fig. 13–10) is $s = a \sinh x/a$. (See Problem 1.) Show that the coordinates of $P(x, y)$ may be expressed as functions of the arc length s as follows:

$$x = a \sinh^{-1} \frac{s}{a}, \qquad y = \sqrt{s^2 + a^2}.$$

(b) Calculate dx/ds and dy/ds from part (a) above and verify that $(dx/ds)^2 + (dy/ds)^2 = 1$.

7. A cable 32 feet long and weighing 2 pounds per foot has its ends fastened at the same level to two posts 30 feet apart.

(a) Show that the constant a in Eq. (6) must satisfy the equation

$$\sinh u = \frac{16}{15} u, \qquad u = \frac{15}{a}. \qquad \text{(See Problem 6a.)}$$

(b) Sketch graphs of the curves $y_1 = \sinh u$, $y_2 = \frac{16}{15} u$ and show (by consulting tables) that they intersect at $u = 0$ and $u = \pm 0.6$ (approximately).

(c) Using the results of part (b), find the dip in the cable at its center.

(d) Using the results of part (b), find the tension in the cable at its lowest point.

REVIEW QUESTIONS AND EXERCISES FOR CHAPTER 13

1. Define each of the hyperbolic functions.

2. State three trigonometric identities [such as formulas for $\sin (A + B)$, $\cos (A - B)$, $\cos^2 A + \sin^2 A = 1$, etc.]. What are the corresponding hyperbolic identities? Verify them.

3. Develop formulas for derivatives of the six hyperbolic functions.

4. What is the domain of the hyperbolic sine? What is its range?

5. What are the domain and range of the hyperbolic cosine? Of the hyperbolic tangent?

6. State some differences between the graphs of the trigonometric functions and their hyperbolic counterparts (for example, sine and sinh, cosine and cosh, tangent and tanh).

7. If $y = A \sin (at) + B \cos (at)$, then $y'' = -a^2 y$. What is the corresponding differential equation satisfied by $y = A \sinh (at) + B \cosh (at)$?

8. Define $\sinh^{-1}$ and $\cosh^{-1}$ functions. What are their domains? What are their ranges? What are their derivatives?

1. Prove the hyperbolic identity $\cosh 2x = \cosh^2 x + \sinh^2 x$.

2. Verify that $\tanh x = \sinh 2x/(1 + \cosh 2x)$.

3. Sketch the curves $y = \cosh x$ and $y = \sinh x$ in one diagram. To each positive value of x corresponds a point P on $y = \sinh x$ and a point Q on $y = \cosh x$. Calculate the limit of the distance $|PQ|$ as x becomes infinitely large.

4. If $\cosh x = \frac{5}{4}$, find $\sinh x$ and $\tanh x$.

5. If $\operatorname{csch} x = -\frac{9}{40}$, find $\cosh x$ and $\tanh x$.

6. If $\tanh x > \frac{5}{13}$, show that $\sinh x > 0.4$ and $\operatorname{sech} x < 0.95$.

7. Let $P(x, y)$ be a point on the curve $y = \tanh x$ (Fig. 13-2b). Let $\overline{AB}$ be the vertical line segment through P with A and B on the asymptotes of the curve. Let C be a semicircle with $\overline{AB}$ as diameter. Let L be a line through P perpendicular to $\overline{AB}$ and cutting C in a point Q. Show that $|PQ| = \operatorname{sech} x$.

8. Prove that $\sinh 3u = 3 \sinh u + 4 \sinh^3 u$.

9. Find equations of the asymptotes of the hyperbola represented by the equation $y = \tanh (\frac{1}{2} \ln x)$.

10. A particle moves along the x-axis according to one of the following laws: (a) $x = a \cos kt + b \sin kt$, (b) $x = a \cosh kt + b \sinh kt$. In both cases, show that the acceleration is proportional to x, but that in the first case it is always directed toward the origin while in the second case it is directed away from the origin.

11. Show that $y = \cosh x$, $\sinh x$, $\cos x$, and $\sin x$ all satisfy the relationship $d^4y/dx^4 = y$.

Find dy/dx in each of Problems 12–21.

12. $y = \sinh^2 3x$

13. $\tan x = \tanh^2 y$

14. $\sin^{-1} x = \operatorname{sech} y$

15. $\sinh y = \sec x$

16. $\tan^{-1} y = \tanh^{-1} x$

17. $y = \tanh (\ln x)$

18. $x = \cosh (\ln y)$

19. $y = \sinh (\tan^{-1} e^{3x})$

20. $y = \sinh^{-1} (\tan x)$

21. $y^2 + x \cosh y + \sinh^2 x = 50$

Evaluate each of the following integrals, Problems 22–31:

22. $\displaystyle\int \frac{d\theta}{\sinh \theta + \cosh \theta}$

23. $\displaystyle\int \frac{\cosh \theta \, d\theta}{\sinh \theta + \cosh \theta}$

24. $\displaystyle\int \sinh^3 x \, dx$

25. $\displaystyle\int e^x \sinh 2x \, dx$

26. $\displaystyle\int \frac{e^{2x} - 1}{e^{2x} + 1} \, dx$

27. $\displaystyle\int_0^1 \frac{dx}{4 - x^2}$

28. $\displaystyle\int_3^5 \frac{dx}{4 - x^2}$

29. $\displaystyle\int \frac{e^t \, dt}{\sqrt{1 + e^{2t}}}$

30. $\displaystyle\int \frac{\sin x \, dx}{1 - \cos^2 x}$

31. $\displaystyle\int \frac{\sec^2 \theta \, d\theta}{\sqrt{\tan^2 \theta - 1}}$

Sketch the following loci, Problems 32–34:

32. $y = \dfrac{1}{2} \ln \dfrac{1 + \tanh x}{1 - \tanh x}$

33. $y = \tan\left(\dfrac{\pi}{2} \tanh x\right)$

34. $\cosh y = 1 + \dfrac{x^2}{2}$

35. If the arc s of the catenary $y = \cosh(x/a)$ is measured from the lowest point, show that $dy/dx = s/a$.

36. A body starting from rest falls under the attraction of gravity but encounters resistance proportional to the square of its velocity. Show that if the body could continue to fall indefinitely under these same conditions, its velocity would approach a limiting value and find the distance it would fall in time t.

37. Evaluate the limit, as $x \to \infty$, of $\cosh^{-1} x - \ln x$.

38. Evaluate $\lim\limits_{x \to \infty} \displaystyle\int_1^x \left(\dfrac{1}{\sqrt{1 + t^2}} - \dfrac{1}{t}\right) dt$.

Vectors and Parametric Equations

14–1 Parametric equations in kinematics. In Newtonian mechanics, the motion of a particle in a plane is usually described by means of a pair of differential equations expressing Newton's second law of motion*

$$\mathbf{F} = \frac{d(m\mathbf{v})}{dt}. \tag{1}$$

Here $\mathbf{F}$ is the vector force acting on the particle of mass m at time t and $\mathbf{v}$ is its vector velocity at time t. When the x- and y-components of Eq. (1) are separated, the equivalent equations are

$$F_x = \frac{d(mv_x)}{dt}, \qquad F_y = \frac{d(mv_y)}{dt}. \tag{2}$$

In addition to these laws of motion, we require a knowledge of the position and velocity of the particle at some given instant. Then the position of the particle at all later instants is determined by the prescribed forces. The result of integrating the second-order differential equations (2) subject to the given initial conditions usually yields equations that determine the x- and y-coordinates of the particle as functions of t:

$$x = f(t), \qquad y = g(t). \tag{3}$$

These equations are called *parametric equations* of the path of the particle and t is called the *parameter*. Equations (3) contain more information about the motion of the particle than does the *Cartesian equation*

$$y = F(x), \tag{4}$$

that one obtains from (3) by eliminating t. The parametric equations tell *where* the particle goes and *when* it gets to any given place, whereas the Cartesian equation tells only the curve along which the particle travels.

We shall illustrate these ideas by determining the path of a projectile. Suppose the projectile is fired with an initial velocity v_0 at an angle of elevation α. Assuming that gravity is the only force acting on the projectile, we shall find its motion.

---

* Vectors are indicated by bold-faced Roman letters. In handwritten work, it is customary to indicate them by a small arrow over each letter which represents a vector, for instance $\overrightarrow{OA}$.

We introduce coordinate axes with origin at the point where the projectile begins its motion, as in Fig. 14–1. The initial conditions may then be taken to be

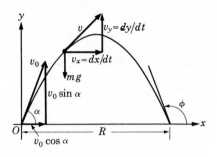

Figure 14–1

$$t = 0: \quad v_x \left(= \frac{dx}{dt} \right) = v_0 \cos \alpha, \qquad (5)$$

$$v_y \left(= \frac{dy}{dt} \right) = v_0 \sin \alpha,$$

$$x = 0, \qquad y = 0.$$

The force components at time t, with appropriate sign, are

$$F_x = 0, \qquad F_y = -mg,$$

so that the differential equations (2) become

$$0 = m \frac{d^2 x}{dt^2}, \qquad -mg = m \frac{d^2 y}{dt^2}. \qquad (6)$$

Each of Eqs. (6) requires two integrations. This introduces a total of four constants of integration. These may be evaluated by using the initial conditions (5). Thus by integration one obtains from (6_1):

$$\frac{d^2 x}{dt^2} = 0, \qquad \frac{dx}{dt} = c_1, \qquad x = c_1 t + c_2, \qquad (7\text{a})$$

and from (6_2):

$$\frac{d^2 y}{dt^2} = -g, \qquad \frac{dy}{dt} = -gt + c_3, \qquad y = -\tfrac{1}{2}gt^2 + c_3 t + c_4. \qquad (7\text{b})$$

From the initial conditions, we find

$$c_1 = v_0 \cos \alpha, \qquad c_2 = 0, \qquad c_3 = v_0 \sin \alpha, \qquad c_4 = 0. \qquad (7\text{c})$$

The position of the projectile at time t (seconds, say, after firing) is given by

$$x = (v_0 \cos \alpha) t, \qquad y = -\tfrac{1}{2}gt^2 + (v_0 \sin \alpha) t. \qquad (8)$$

For a given angle of elevation α and a given muzzle velocity v_0, the position of the projectile at any time may be determined from the parametric equations, (8). The equations may be used to answer such questions as the following:

1. How high does the projectile rise vertically?
2. How far does the projectile travel horizontally?

3. What is the range of the projectile (horizontally) in terms of the angle of elevation? What angle produces the maximum range?

The projectile will attain maximum height when its y velocity component is zero, that is, when

$$\frac{dy}{dt} = -gt + v_0 \sin \alpha = 0$$

or when

$$t = t_m = \frac{v_0 \sin \alpha}{g} .$$

Then

$$y_{\max} = -\tfrac{1}{2}g(t_m)^2 + (v_0 \sin \alpha)t_m = \frac{(v_0 \sin \alpha)^2}{2g} .$$

To find the horizontal range of the projectile, we find the time when it strikes the ground, that is, when $y = 0$. From (8_2), we have

$$y = t(-\tfrac{1}{2}gt + v_0 \sin \alpha) = 0$$

when

$$t = 0 \quad \text{or} \quad t = \frac{2v_0 \sin \alpha}{g} = 2t_m.$$

Clearly, $t = 0$ corresponds to the instant when the projectile is fired, so that $t = 2t_m$ gives the range $x = R$:

$$R = v_0 \cos \alpha \, \frac{2v_0 \sin \alpha}{g} = \frac{v_0^2}{g} \sin 2\alpha.$$

For a given muzzle velocity, this shows that the maximum range is obtained when $\sin 2\alpha = 1$, that is, when $\alpha = 45°$.

The slope of the path of the projectile at any point may also be found directly from (8), namely,

$$\frac{dy}{dx} = \frac{dy/dt}{dx/dt} = \frac{-gt + v_0 \sin \alpha}{v_0 \cos \alpha} .$$

At $y = 0$, $x = R$, we found

$$t = \frac{2v_0 \sin \alpha}{g} ,$$

and hence

$$\frac{dy}{dx} = \frac{-2v_0 \sin \alpha + v_0 \sin \alpha}{v_0 \cos \alpha} = -\tan \alpha.$$

This shows that the angle ϕ (Fig. 14–1) is $\pi - \alpha$, so that the projectile returns to the earth at the same angle as that at which it was fired.

Finally, the Cartesian equation of the path is readily obtained from (8); for we need only substitute

$$t = \frac{x}{v_0 \cos \alpha}$$

from (8_1) into (8_2) to eliminate t and obtain

$$y = -\left(\frac{g}{2v_0^2 \cos^2 \alpha}\right) x^2 + (\tan \alpha)x. \tag{9}$$

Since this equation is linear in y and quadratic in x, it represents a *parabola*. Thus the path of a projectile (in vacuo, that is, neglecting air resistance) is a parabola.

When air resistance is taken into account, the differential equations obtained are too complicated for straightforward integration. The M.I.T. differential analyzers were used to solve such problems during World War II in order to build up "range tables." Against a moving target, in particular, the *time* is also of great importance, so that equations or tables which give x and y in terms of t are preferred over the Cartesian form.

PROBLEMS

In Problems 1–4, the projectile is assumed to obey the laws of motion discussed above, in which air resistance is neglected.

1. Find two values of the angle of elevation that will enable a projectile to reach a target on the same level as the gun and 25,000 feet distant from it if the initial velocity is 1000 ft/sec. Determine the times of flight corresponding to these two angles.

2. Show that doubling of the initial velocity of a projectile multiplies both the maximum height and the range by a factor of four.

3. Show that a projectile attains three-quarters of its maximum height in one-half the time required to reach that maximum.

4. Suppose a target moving at the constant rate of a ft/sec is level with and b ft away from a gun at the instant the gun is fired. If the target moves in a horizontal line directly away from the gun, show that the muzzle velocity v_0 and angle of elevation α must satisfy the equation.

$$v_0^2 \sin 2\alpha - 2a\, v_0 \sin \alpha - bg = 0$$

if the projectile is to strike the target.

In Problems 5–7, find parametric equations and sketch the curve described by the point $P(x, y)$ for $t \geq 0$ if its coordinates satisfy the given differential equations and initial conditions.

5. $\dfrac{dx}{dt} = x, \quad \dfrac{dy}{dt} = -x^2; \quad t = 0, \quad x = 1, \quad y = -4.$

6. $\dfrac{dx}{dt} = y$, $\dfrac{dy}{dt} = y^2$; $t = 0$, $x = 0$, $y = 1$.

7. $\dfrac{dx}{dt} = \sqrt{1 - x^2}$, $\dfrac{dy}{dt} = x^2$; $t = 0$, $x = 0$, $y = 1$.

14–2 Parametric equations in analytic geometry. The solutions of differential equations of motion are not the only ways in which parametric equations arise. For example, we have frequently had occasion to use equations such as

$$x = a \cos \theta, \qquad y = a \sin \theta \qquad (1)$$

to represent a circle. Here θ is the parameter and Eqs. (1) are parametric equations of the circle (Fig. 14–2). Similarly,

$$x = a \cos \phi, \qquad y = b \sin \phi \qquad (2)$$

are parametric equations of an ellipse whose Cartesian equation is

$$\frac{x^2}{a^2} + \frac{y^2}{b^2} = 1.$$

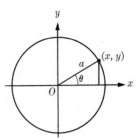

The parabola

$$y^2 = 4px \qquad (3)$$

Figure 14–2

can be parametrized in several ways. One method is to use as parameter the slope

$$t = \frac{dy}{dx}$$

of the tangent to the curve at (x, y) (Fig. 14–3a). Since

$$2y \frac{dy}{dx} = 4p \qquad \text{or} \qquad \frac{dy}{dx} = \frac{2p}{y},$$

the parametric equations in this case are

$$y = \frac{2p}{t}, \qquad x = \frac{p}{t^2}. \qquad (4)$$

If we use the parameter defined (Fig. 14–3b) by

$$m = \frac{y}{x},$$

Figure 14-3

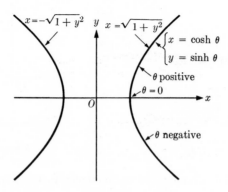

Figure 14-4

we have

$$y^2 = m^2 x^2 \quad \text{and} \quad y^2 = 4px,$$

which lead to

$$x = \frac{4p}{m^2}, \qquad y = \frac{4p}{m} \tag{5}$$

as the parametric equations.

Sometimes the parametric equations of a locus and the Cartesian equation are not coextensive.

For example, suppose the parametric equations of a curve are

$$x = \cosh \theta, \qquad y = \sinh \theta. \tag{6}$$

Then the hyperbolic identity

$$\cosh^2 \theta - \sinh^2 \theta = 1$$

enables us to eliminate θ and write

$$x^2 - y^2 = 1 \qquad (7)$$

as the Cartesian equation of the curve. Closer scrutiny, however, shows that Eq. (7) *includes too much.* For $x = \cosh \theta$ is never less than unity, so the parametric equations represent a curve lying wholly to the right of the y-axis, whereas the Cartesian equation (7) represents both the right- and left-hand branches of the hyperbola (Fig. 14–4). The left-hand branch could be excluded by taking only positive values of x. That is,

$$x = \sqrt{1 + y^2} \qquad (8)$$

does represent the same curve as (6).

As a second example, consider the curve whose parametric equations are

$$x = \cos 2\theta, \qquad y = \cos \theta. \qquad (9)$$

It is certainly restricted to lie within the square $-1 \le x \le 1, -1 \le y \le 1$. But we eliminate θ as follows:

$$x = \cos 2\theta = 2 \cos^2 \theta - 1 = 2y^2 - 1.$$

Thus every point on the locus of (9) also lies on the curve

$$x = 2y^2 - 1 \qquad (10)$$

and, in addition, is restricted by

$$|x| \le 1, \qquad |y| \le 1.$$

If we omit these restrictions, Eq. (10) represents the complete parabola

$$y^2 = \tfrac{1}{2}(x + 1)$$

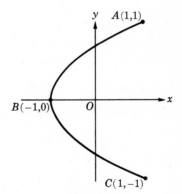

Figure 14–5

with vertex at $(-1, 0)$ and opening to the right, as shown in Fig. 14–5. The parametric equations, on the other hand, represent only the arc ABC. Referring to Eqs. (9), we readily see that the point starts at $A(1, 1)$ when $\theta = 0$, moves along AB to $B(-1, 0)$ as θ varies from 0 to $\pi/2$, and continues to $C(1, -1)$ as θ increases to π. As θ varies from π to 2π, the point traverses the arc CBA back to A. Since both x and y are periodic functions of θ of period 2π, further variations in θ result in retracing the same portion of the parabola.

The following example illustrates further how parametric equations may be derived from geometric properties of a curve. A wheel of radius

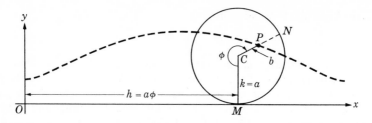

Figure 14-6

a rolls along a horizontal straight line without slipping. Find the locus described by a point on a spoke of the wheel at distance b from its center. Such a curve is called a *trochoid*. When $b = a$ the tracing point is on the circumference of the wheel and the trochoid in this case is called a *cycloid*.

In Fig. 14–6, we take the x-axis as the line the wheel rolls along, with the y-axis through a low point of the trochoid. Point P describes the curve in question. It is customary to use the angle ϕ through which $\overline{CP}$ has rotated as the parameter. We introduce $x'y'$-axes parallel to the xy-axes but having their origin at the center of the circle C (Fig. 14–7). If (h, k) are the coordinates of C relative to the xy-axes, then the xy-coordinates of P are related to its $x'y'$-coordinates as follows:

$$x = h + x', \qquad y = k + y'. \tag{11}$$

From the fact that the circle rolls along the x-axis without slipping, we see that the distance $|OM|$ that the wheel has moved horizontally is just equal to the arc $MN = a\phi$. (Roll the wheel back; then N will fall at the origin O.) The xy-coordinates of C are therefore

$$h = a\phi, \qquad k = a. \tag{12}$$

From Fig. 14–7 we may immediately read

$$x' = b \cos \theta, \qquad y' = b \sin \theta,$$

or, since

$$\theta = \frac{3\pi}{2} - \phi,$$

$$x' = -b \sin \phi, \qquad y' = -b \cos \phi. \tag{13}$$

We substitute these results and Eqs. (12) into (11) and obtain

$$x = a\phi - b \sin \phi,$$
$$\tag{14}$$
$$y = a - b \cos \phi$$

Figure 14-7

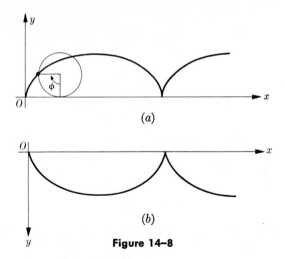

(a)

(b)

Figure 14-8

as parametric equations of the trochoid. The cycloid (Fig. 14–8a),

$$x = a(\phi - \sin \phi), \qquad y = a(1 - \cos \phi), \qquad (15)$$

obtained from (14) by taking $b = a$, is the most important special case of a trochoid.

If we reflect both the cycloid and the y-axis across the x-axis, Eqs. (15) still apply and the resulting curve (Fig. 14–8b) has several interesting properties, one of which we shall now discuss without proof. The proofs belong to a branch of mathematics known as the calculus of variations. Much of the fundamental theory of this subject is attributable to the Bernoulli brothers, John and James, who were friendly rivals and stimulated each other with mathematical problems in the form of challenges. One of these, the brachistochrone problem, was: Among all smooth curves joining two given points, to find that one along which a bead might slide, subject only to the force of gravity, *in the shortest time.*

The two points, labeled P_0 and P_1 in Fig. 14–9, may be taken to lie at the origin and at (x_1, y_1) respectively in a vertical plane. We can formulate the problem in mathematical terms as follows. The kinetic energy of the bead at the start is zero, since its velocity is zero. The work done by gravity in moving the particle from $(0, 0)$ to any point (x, y) is mgy and this must be equal to the change in kinetic energy; that is,

$$mgy = \tfrac{1}{2}mv^2 - \tfrac{1}{2}m(0)^2.$$

Thus the velocity

$$v = ds/dt$$

that the particle has when it reaches $P(x,y)$ is

$$v = \sqrt{2gy}.$$

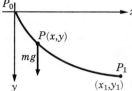

Figure 14-9

That is,

$$\frac{ds}{dt} = \sqrt{2gy}$$

or

$$dt = \frac{ds}{\sqrt{2gy}} = \frac{\sqrt{1 + \left(\frac{dy}{dx}\right)^2}\, dx}{\sqrt{2gy}}.$$

The time t_1 required for the bead to slide from P_0 to P_1 depends upon the particular curve $y = f(x)$ along which it moves and is given by

$$t_1 = \int_0^{x_1} \sqrt{\frac{1 + (f'(x))^2}{2gf(x)}}\, dx. \tag{16}$$

The problem is *to find the curve* $y = f(x)$ that passes through the points $P_0(0, 0)$ and $P_1(x_1, y_1)$ and minimizes the value of the integral in Eq. (16). (*Brachistochrone* is derived from two Greek words that together mean "shortest time.")

At first sight, one might guess that the straight line joining P_0 and P_1 would also yield the shortest time, but a moment's reflection will cast some doubt on this conjecture. For there may be some gain in time by having the particle start to fall vertically at first, thereby building up its velocity more quickly than if it were to slide along an inclined path. With this increased velocity, one may be able to afford to travel over a longer path and still reach P_1 in a shorter time. The solution of the problem is beyond the present book, but the brachistochrone curve is actually an arc of a cycloid through P_0 and P_1, having a cusp at the origin. [The interested reader is referred to the book *Calculus of Variations* by G. A. Bliss, The Mathematical Association of America (1925), for a discussion of this problem and others belonging to this branch of mathematics.]

If we write Eq. (16) in the equivalent form

$$t_1 = \int \sqrt{\frac{dx^2 + dy^2}{2gy}}$$

and then substitute Eqs. (15) into this, we obtain

$$t_1 = \int_{\phi=0}^{\phi_1} \sqrt{\frac{a^2(2 - 2\cos\phi)}{2ga(1 - \cos\phi)}}\, d\phi = \phi_1 \sqrt{\frac{a}{g}}$$

as the time required for the particle to slide from P_0 to P_1. The time required to reach the bottom of the arc is obtained by taking $\phi_1 = \pi$. Now it is a remarkable fact, which we shall soon demonstrate, that the time required to slide along the cycloid from $(0, 0)$ to the lowest point $(a\pi, 2a)$ is the same as the time required for the particle, starting from rest, to slide from *any intermediate point* of the arc, say (x_0, y_0), to $(a\pi, 2a)$. For the latter case, one has

$$v = \sqrt{2g(y - y_0)}$$

as the velocity at $P(x, y)$, and the time required is

$$T = \int_{\phi_0}^{\pi} \sqrt{\frac{a^2(2 - 2\cos\phi)}{2ag(\cos\phi_0 - \cos\phi)}} \, d\phi = \sqrt{\frac{a}{g}} \int_{\phi_0}^{\pi} \sqrt{\frac{1 - \cos\phi}{\cos\phi_0 - \cos\phi}} \, d\phi$$

$$= \sqrt{\frac{a}{g}} \int_{\phi_0}^{\pi} \sqrt{\frac{2\sin^2\frac{\phi}{2}}{\left(2\cos^2\frac{\phi_0}{2} - 1\right) - \left(2\cos^2\frac{\phi}{2} - 1\right)}} \, d\phi$$

$$= 2\sqrt{\frac{a}{g}} \left[-\sin^{-1}\frac{\cos\frac{\phi}{2}}{\cos\frac{\phi_0}{2}} \right]_{\phi_0}^{\pi} = 2\sqrt{\frac{a}{g}} (-\sin^{-1}0 + \sin^{-1}1) = \pi\sqrt{\frac{a}{g}}.$$

Since this answer is independent of the value of ϕ_0, it follows that the same length of time is required to reach the lowest point on the cycloid no matter where on the arc the particle is released from rest. Thus, in Fig. 14–10, three particles which start at the same time from O, A, and B will reach C simultaneously. In this sense, the cycloid is also a tautochrone (meaning "the same time") as well as being a brachistochrone.

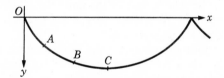

Figure 14–10

PROBLEMS

In each of Problems 1–10, sketch the graph of the curve described by the point $P(x, y)$ as the parameter t varies over the domain given. Also determine the Cartesian equation of the curve in each case.

1. $x = \cos t, \quad y = \sin t, \quad 0 \le t \le 2\pi$
2. $x = \cos 2t, \quad y = \sin t, \quad 0 \le t \le 2\pi$
3. $x = \sec t, \quad y = \tan t, \quad -\pi/2 < t < \pi/2$
4. $x = 2 + 4\sin t, \quad y = 3 - 2\cos t, \quad 0 \le t \le 2\pi$
5. $x = 2t + 3, \quad y = 4t^2 - 9, \quad -\infty < t < \infty$
6. $x = \cosh t, \quad y = 2\sinh t, \quad 0 \le t < \infty$
7. $x = 2 + 1/t, \quad y = 2 - t, \quad 0 < t < \infty$
8. $x = t + 1, \quad y = t^2 + 4, \quad 0 \le t < \infty$
9. $x = t^2 + t, \quad y = t^2 - t, \quad -\infty < t < \infty$

10. $x = 3 + 2 \operatorname{sech} t$, $\quad y = 4 - 3 \tanh t$, $\quad -\infty < t < \infty$

11. Find parametric equations of the semicircle

$$x^2 + y^2 = a^2, \qquad y > 0,$$

using as parameter the slope $t = dy/dx$ of the tangent to the curve at (x, y).

12. Find parametric equations of the semicircle

$$x^2 + y^2 = a^2, \qquad y > 0,$$

using as parameter the variable θ defined by the equation $x = a \tanh \theta$.

13. Find parametric equations of the circle

$$x^2 + y^2 = a^2,$$

using as parameter the arc length s measured counterclockwise from the point $(a, 0)$ to the point (x, y).

14. Find parametric equations of the catenary $y = a \cosh x/a$, using as parameter the length of arc s from the point $(0, a)$ to the point (x, y), with the sign of s taken to be the same as the sign of x.

15. If a string wound around a fixed circle is unwound while held taut in the plane of the circle, its end traces an *involute* of the circle. Let the fixed circle be located with its center at the origin O and have radius a. Let the initial position of the tracing point P be $A(a, 0)$ and let the unwound portion of the string $\overline{PT}$ be tangent to the circle at T. Derive parametric equations of the involute, using the angle AOT as the parameter ϕ.

16. When a circle rolls externally on the circumference of a second, fixed circle, any point P on the circumference of the rolling circle describes an *epicycloid*. Let the fixed circle have its center at the origin O and have radius a. Let the radius of the rolling circle be b and let the initial position of the tracing point P be $A(a, 0)$. Determine parametric equations of the epicycloid, using as parameter the angle θ from the positive x-axis to the line of centers.

17. When a circle rolls on the inside of a fixed circle any point P on the circumference of the rolling circle describes a *hypocycloid*. Let the fixed circle be $x^2 + y^2 = a^2$, let the radius of the rolling circle be b, and let the initial position of the tracing point P be $A(a, 0)$. Use the angle θ from the positive x-axis to the line of centers as parameter and determine parametric equations of the hypocycloid. In particular, if $b = a/4$, show that

$$x = a \cos^3 \theta, \qquad y = a \sin^3 \theta.$$

18. Find the length of one arch of the cycloid

$$x = a(\phi - \sin \phi), \qquad y = a(1 - \cos \phi).$$

19. Show that the slope of the cycloid

$$x = a(\phi - \sin \phi), \qquad y = a(1 - \cos \phi)$$

is $dy/dx = \cot \phi/2$. In particular, the tangent to the cycloid is vertical when ϕ is 0 or 2π.

20. Show that the slope of the trochoid

$$x = a\phi - b \sin \phi, \quad y = a - b \cos \phi$$

is always finite if $b < a$.

21. The *witch* is a bell-shaped curve that may be constructed as follows: Let C be a circle of radius a having its center at $(0, a)$ on the y-axis. The variable line $\overleftrightarrow{OA}$ through the origin O intersects the line $y = 2a$ in the point A and intersects the circle in the point B. A point P on the witch is now located by taking the intersection of lines through A and B parallel to the y- and x-axes respectively. Find parametric equations of the witch, using as parameter the angle θ from the x-axis to the line $\overleftrightarrow{OA}$. Also find the Cartesian equation.

14-3   Vector components and the unit vectors i and j. Some physical quantities are completely determined when their magnitudes, in terms of specific units, are given. Such quantities are called *scalars* and are exemplified by mass and length. Other quantities, like forces and velocities, in which the direction as well as the magnitude is important, are called *vectors*. It is customary to represent a vector by a directed line segment whose direction represents the direction of the vector and whose length (in terms of some chosen unit of length) represents the magnitude.

The most satisfactory algebra of vectors is based on a representation of each vector in terms of its components parallel to the axes of a Cartesian coordinate system. This is accomplished by using the same unit of length on both the x- and y-axes with unit vectors along these axes used as basic components in terms of which every vector in the plane may be expressed. Thus, in Fig. 14–11, the vector from $(0, 0)$ to $(1, 0)$ is the unit vector **i**, while **j** is the unit vector from $(0, 0)$ to $(0, 1)$. Then $a\mathbf{i}$, a being a scalar, represents a vector parallel to the x-axis, having magnitude $|a|$ and pointing to the right if a is positive, to the left if a is negative. Similarly, $b\mathbf{j}$ is a vector parallel to the y-axis and having the same sense as **j** or the opposite sense, according as b is positive or negative.

We shall ordinarily deal with "free vectors," meaning that a vector is free to move about under parallel displacements. We say that two vectors are *equal* provided they have the same direction and the same magnitude. The same condition may be expressed algebraically by saying that

$$a\mathbf{i} + b\mathbf{j} = a'\mathbf{i} + b'\mathbf{j} \quad \text{if and only if} \quad a = a' \quad \text{and} \quad b = b'.$$

That is, two vectors are equal if and only if their corresponding components are equal. Thus, in Fig. 14–11, the vector $\overrightarrow{AB} = a\mathbf{i}$ and the vector $\overrightarrow{OP}$ from $(0, 0)$ to the point $(a, 0)$ on the x-axis is also equal to $a\mathbf{i}$.

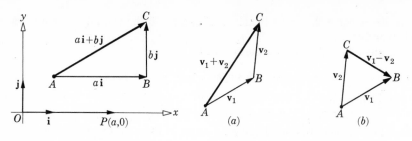

Figure 14–11   **Figure 14–12**

Addition. Two vectors, $\mathbf{v}_1$ and $\mathbf{v}_2$ are *added* by drawing a vector $\mathbf{v}_1$, say from A to B in Fig. 14–12(a), and then a vector equal to $\mathbf{v}_2$ starting from the terminal point of $\mathbf{v}_1$; thus $\mathbf{v}_2 = \overrightarrow{BC}$ in Fig. 14–12(a). The sum $\mathbf{v}_1 + \mathbf{v}_2$ is then the vector from the starting point A of $\mathbf{v}_1$ to the terminal point C of $\mathbf{v}_2$:

$$\mathbf{v}_1 = \overrightarrow{AB}, \qquad \mathbf{v}_2 = \overrightarrow{BC},$$

$$\mathbf{v}_1 + \mathbf{v}_2 = \overrightarrow{AB} + \overrightarrow{BC} = \overrightarrow{AC}.$$

If we apply this principle to the vectors $a\mathbf{i}$ and $b\mathbf{j}$ in Fig. 14–11, we see that $a\mathbf{i} + b\mathbf{j}$ is the vector hypotenuse of a right triangle whose vector sides are $a\mathbf{i}$ and $b\mathbf{j}$ respectively. If the vectors $\mathbf{v}_1$ and $\mathbf{v}_2$ are given in terms of components

$$\mathbf{v}_1 = a_1\mathbf{i} + b_1\mathbf{j},$$

$$\mathbf{v}_2 = a_2\mathbf{i} + b_2\mathbf{j},$$

then

$$\boxed{\mathbf{v}_1 + \mathbf{v}_2 = (a_1 + a_2)\mathbf{i} + (b_1 + b_2)\mathbf{j}} \qquad (1)$$

has x- and y-components obtained by adding the x- and y-components of $\mathbf{v}_1$ and $\mathbf{v}_2$.

Subtraction. To *subtract* one vector $\mathbf{v}_2$ from another vector $\mathbf{v}_1$ geometrically, we draw them both from a common initial point and then draw the vector from the tip of $\mathbf{v}_2$ to the tip of $\mathbf{v}_1$. Thus in Fig. 14–12(b), we have

$$\mathbf{v}_1 = \overrightarrow{AB}, \qquad \mathbf{v}_2 = \overrightarrow{AC},$$

and

$$\mathbf{v}_1 - \mathbf{v}_2 = -\mathbf{v}_2 + \mathbf{v}_1 = \overrightarrow{CA} + \overrightarrow{AB} = \overrightarrow{CB}.$$

In terms of components, vector subtraction follows the simple algebraic law

$$\mathbf{v}_1 - \mathbf{v}_2 = (a_1 - a_2)\mathbf{i} + (b_1 - b_2)\mathbf{j},$$

which says that corresponding components are subtracted.

Multiplication by scalars. The algebraic operation of multiplying a vector $\mathbf{v} = a\mathbf{i} + b\mathbf{j}$ by a scalar c is also simple, namely,

$$c(a\mathbf{i} + b\mathbf{j}) = (ca)\mathbf{i} + (cb)\mathbf{j}.$$

Geometrically, $c\mathbf{v}$ is a vector whose length is $|c|$ times the length of $\mathbf{v}$ and whose direction is the same as, or opposite to, that of $\mathbf{v}$ respectively according as c is positive or negative. Thus $3\mathbf{v}$ has the same sense as $\mathbf{v}$ and is three times as long; while $-2\mathbf{v}$ is twice as long as $\mathbf{v}$ but is directed in the opposite sense (Fig. 14–13).

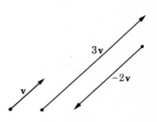

Figure 14–13

The unit vectors $\mathbf{i}$ and $\mathbf{j}$ serve the useful purpose of allowing us to keep the components separated from one another when we operate on the vectors algebraically.

The length of the vector $\mathbf{v}$ is usually denoted by $|\mathbf{v}|$, which is read "magnitude of v." Reference to Fig. 14–11 shows that $\mathbf{v} = a\mathbf{i} + b\mathbf{j}$ is the hypotenuse of a right triangle whose legs have lengths $|a|$ and $|b|$ respectively. Hence we may apply the theorem of Pythagoras to obtain

$$|a\mathbf{i} + b\mathbf{j}| = \sqrt{a^2 + b^2}. \tag{2}$$

Zero vector. Any vector whose length is zero is called the *zero vector*, **0**. The vector

$$a\mathbf{i} + b\mathbf{j} = \mathbf{0}, \qquad \text{if and only if} \qquad a = b = 0.$$

Unit vector. Any vector $\mathbf{u}$ whose length is equal to the unit of length used along the coordinate axes is called a *unit vector*. If $\mathbf{u}$ is a unit vector obtained by rotating the unit vector $\mathbf{i}$ through an angle θ in the positive direction, then (see Fig. 14–14) $\mathbf{u}$ has a horizontal component

$$u_x = \cos\theta$$

and a vertical component

$$u_y = \sin\theta,$$

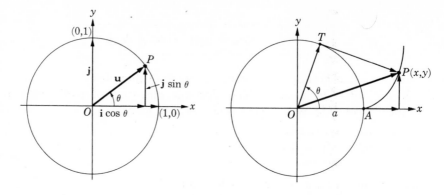

Figure 14–14   **Figure 14–15**

so that

$$\boxed{\mathbf{u} = \mathbf{i} \cos \theta + \mathbf{j} \sin \theta.} \tag{3}$$

If we allow the angle θ in Eq. (3) to vary from 0 to 2π, say, then the point P traces out the unit circle $x^2 + y^2 = 1$ precisely once in the counterclockwise direction.

As an illustration of how vector methods may be applied to problems in geometry, we shall derive parametric equations of the involute of a circle. This is the locus described by the end point P of a string that is held taut as it is unwound from the circle. In Fig. 14–15, the origin is taken at the center of the circle whose radius is a. The x-axis passes through the point A where P started when the string was all wound onto the circle. The figure illustrates the position of P after a length of string

$$|TP| = \text{arc } AT = a\theta$$

has been unwound. The line $\overleftrightarrow{TP}$ is drawn tangent to the circle, since the string is held taut as it is unwound. Now the vector from the origin O to the point P is simply

$$\overrightarrow{OP} = \mathbf{i}x + \mathbf{j}y. \tag{4}$$

On the other hand, the same vector is also given by

$$\overrightarrow{OP} = \overrightarrow{OT} + \overrightarrow{TP}, \tag{5}$$

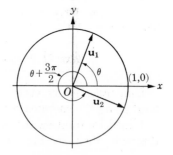

Figure 14–16

and if we express the right side in terms of the parameter θ, we may equate the two right sides of (4) and (5) and separate the components to obtain x and y

in terms of θ. Now

$$\overrightarrow{OT} = a\mathbf{u}_1$$

and

$$\overrightarrow{TP} = (a\theta)\mathbf{u}_2,$$

where $\mathbf{u}_1$ and $\mathbf{u}_2$ are unit vectors making angles θ and $\theta + 3\pi/2$ respectively with the x-axis. (See Fig. 14–16.) Then, applying (3), we have

$$\mathbf{u}_1 = \mathbf{i} \cos \theta + \mathbf{j} \sin \theta$$

and

$$\mathbf{u}_2 = \mathbf{i} \cos \left(\theta + \frac{3\pi}{2}\right) + \mathbf{j} \sin \left(\theta + \frac{3\pi}{2}\right)$$

$$= \mathbf{i} \sin \theta - \mathbf{j} \cos \theta.$$

Therefore

$$\overrightarrow{OP} = a\mathbf{u}_1 + (a\theta)\,\mathbf{u}_2$$

$$= a\,(\mathbf{i} \cos \theta + \mathbf{j} \sin \theta) + a\theta(\mathbf{i} \sin \theta - \mathbf{j} \cos \theta)$$

$$= a\,(\cos \theta + \theta \sin \theta)\,\mathbf{i} + a\,(\sin \theta - \theta \cos \theta)\,\mathbf{j}.$$

We equate this to $x\mathbf{i} + y\mathbf{j}$ and, since corresponding components must be equal, we obtain the parametric equations

$$x = a\,(\cos \theta + \theta \sin \theta), \qquad y = a\,(\sin \theta - \theta \cos \theta). \qquad (6)$$

PROBLEMS

In Problems 1–10 express each of the vectors in the form $a\mathbf{i} + b\mathbf{j}$. Indicate all quantities graphically.

1. $\overrightarrow{P_1P_2}$ if P_1 is the point $(1, 3)$ and P_2 is the point $(2, -1)$.

2. $\overrightarrow{OP_3}$ if O is the origin and P_3 is the mid-point of the vector $\overrightarrow{P_1P_2}$ joining $P_1(2, -1)$ and $P_2(-4, 3)$.

3. The vector from the point $A(2, 3)$ to the origin.

4. The sum of the vectors $\overrightarrow{AB}$ and $\overrightarrow{CD}$, given the four points $A(1, -1)$, $B(2, 0)$, $C(-1, 3)$, and $D(-2, 2)$.

5. A unit vector making an angle of $30°$ with the positive x-axis.

6. The unit vector obtained by rotating $\mathbf{j}$ through $120°$ in the clockwise direction.

7. A unit vector having the same direction as the vector $3\mathbf{i} - 4\mathbf{j}$.

8. A unit vector tangent to the curve $y = x^2$ at the point $(2, 4)$.

9. A unit vector normal to the curve $y = x^2$ at the point $P(2, 4)$ and pointing from P toward the concave side of the curve (that is, an "inner" normal).

10. A unit vector tangent to the involute of a circle whose parametric equations are given in Eq. (6).

Find the lengths of each of the following vectors and the angle that each makes with the positive x-axis.

11. $\mathbf{i} + \mathbf{j}$ 12. $2\mathbf{i} - 3\mathbf{j}$ 13. $\sqrt{3}\,\mathbf{i} + \mathbf{j}$

14. $-2\mathbf{i} + 3\mathbf{j}$ 15. $5\mathbf{i} + 12\mathbf{j}$ 16. $-5\mathbf{i} - 12\mathbf{j}$

17. Use vector methods and determine parametric equations for the trochoid of Fig. 14–6, by taking
$$\mathbf{R} = \overrightarrow{OP} = \overrightarrow{OM} + \overrightarrow{MC} + \overrightarrow{CP}.$$

18. Let A, B, C, D be the vertices, in order, of a quadrilateral. Let A', B', C', D' be the mid-points of the sides $\overline{AB}$, $\overline{BC}$, $\overline{CD}$, and $\overline{DA}$, in order. Prove that $A'B'C'D'$ is a parallelogram. [*Hint:* First show that $\overrightarrow{A'B'} = \overrightarrow{D'C'} = \frac{1}{2}\overrightarrow{AC}$.]

19. Using vectors, show that the diagonals of a parallelogram bisect each other. [*Method:* Let A be one vertex and let M and N be the mid-points of the diagonals. Then show that $\overrightarrow{AM} = \overrightarrow{AN}$.]

14–4   Differentiation of vectors. We shall be interested in applications of vectors to problems in physics. For applications to *statics*, we need only a knowledge of the *algebra* of vectors. But for applications to *dynamics*, we also require a knowledge of the *calculus* of vectors.

Position vector. Suppose the point P moves along a curve in the xy-plane and suppose we know its position at any time t. This means that the motion of P is described by a pair of functions f and g:
$$x = f(t), \qquad y = g(t). \tag{1}$$

The vector from the origin to P is customarily called the *position vector* of P, although it might be appropriate to call it the "radar" vector. This vector is a function of t given by

$$\boxed{\mathbf{R} = \mathbf{i}x + \mathbf{j}y} \tag{2a}$$

or

$$\mathbf{R} = \mathbf{i}f(t) + \mathbf{j}g(t). \tag{2b}$$

Velocity vector. We now raise the question as to what we might mean by the *derivative* of $\mathbf{R}$ with respect to t, both mathematically and physically. Mathematically, we would simply *define* the derivative as

$$\frac{d\mathbf{R}}{dt} = \lim_{\Delta t \to 0} \frac{\Delta \mathbf{R}}{\Delta t}, \tag{3}$$

where $\mathbf{R}$ is given by (2a) and

$$\mathbf{R} + \Delta\mathbf{R} = \mathbf{i}(x + \Delta x) + \mathbf{j}(y + \Delta y). \tag{4}$$

Here, $P(x, y)$ represents the position of the particle at time t, while $Q(x + \Delta x, y + \Delta y)$ gives its position at time $t + \Delta t$. By subtracting (2a) from (4), we obtain

$$\Delta \mathbf{R} = \mathbf{i}\,\Delta x + \mathbf{j}\,\Delta y, \qquad (5)$$

which is the vector $\overrightarrow{PQ}$ in Fig. 14–17. The remaining calculations needed to give $d\mathbf{R}/dt$ proceed as follows:

$$\frac{\Delta \mathbf{R}}{\Delta t} = \mathbf{i}\,\frac{\Delta x}{\Delta t} + \mathbf{j}\,\frac{\Delta y}{\Delta t},$$

$$\lim_{\Delta t \to 0} \frac{\Delta \mathbf{R}}{\Delta t} = \lim_{\Delta t \to 0}\left(\mathbf{i}\,\frac{\Delta x}{\Delta t} + \mathbf{j}\,\frac{\Delta y}{\Delta t}\right)$$

$$= \mathbf{i}\lim_{\Delta t \to 0}\frac{\Delta x}{\Delta t} + \mathbf{j}\lim_{\Delta t \to 0}\frac{\Delta y}{\Delta t},$$

$$\boxed{\frac{d\mathbf{R}}{dt} = \mathbf{i}\,\frac{dx}{dt} + \mathbf{j}\,\frac{dy}{dt}.} \qquad (6)$$

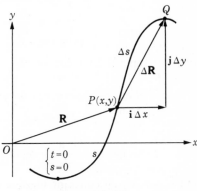

Figure 14–17

The result (6) is equivalent to what would be obtained by differentiating both sides of (2a) with respect to t, holding $\mathbf{i}$ and $\mathbf{j}$ constant. The geometric significance of (6) may be learned by calculating the direction and the magnitude as follows:

$$\text{slope of } \frac{d\mathbf{R}}{dt} = \frac{\text{rise}}{\text{run}} = \frac{dy/dt}{dx/dt} = \frac{dy}{dx},$$

$$\text{magnitude} = \left|\frac{d\mathbf{R}}{dt}\right| = \left|\mathbf{i}\,\frac{dx}{dt} + \mathbf{j}\,\frac{dy}{dt}\right| = \sqrt{\left(\frac{dx}{dt}\right)^2 + \left(\frac{dy}{dt}\right)^2} = \left|\frac{ds}{dt}\right|. \qquad (7)$$

Here s represents arc length along the curve measured from some starting point (x_0, y_0).

If we draw a vector equal to $d\mathbf{R}/dt$, placing its initial point at P, the resulting vector will

(a) be tangent to the curve at P, since its slope equals dy/dx, which is the same as the slope of the curve at P, and

(b) have magnitude $= |ds/dt|$, which gives the instantaneous speed of the particle at P.

Thus, physically, the vector $d\mathbf{R}/dt$, when drawn from P, is a suitable representation of the *velocity vector* which has the same two properties (a) and (b).

We may now summarize by saying that if we differentiate the position vector

$$\boxed{\mathbf{R} = \mathbf{i}x + \mathbf{j}y}$$

with respect to time, the result gives the *velocity vector*

$$\boxed{\mathbf{v} = \frac{d\mathbf{R}}{dt} = \mathbf{i}\frac{dx}{dt} + \mathbf{j}\frac{dy}{dt}.}$$

It is customary to think of the velocity vector as being drawn at the point P.

Acceleration. The acceleration vector $\mathbf{a}$ is obtained from $\mathbf{v}$ by a further differentiation:

$$\boxed{\mathbf{a} = \frac{d\mathbf{v}}{dt} = \mathbf{i}\frac{d^2x}{dt^2} + \mathbf{j}\frac{d^2y}{dt^2}.} \tag{8}$$

For a particle of constant mass m moving under the action of an applied force $\mathbf{F}$, Newton's second law of motion states that

$$\mathbf{F} = m\mathbf{a}. \tag{9}$$

Since one ordinarily visualizes the force vector as being *applied at P*, it is customary to adopt the same viewpoint about the acceleration vector $\mathbf{a}$.

EXAMPLE 1. A particle $P(x, y)$ moves on the hyperbola

$$x = r \cosh \omega t, \quad y = r \sinh \omega t, \tag{10}$$

where r and ω are positive constants. Then

$$\mathbf{R} = \mathbf{i}(r \cosh \omega t) + \mathbf{j}(r \sinh \omega t),$$

$$\mathbf{v} = \frac{d\mathbf{R}}{dt} = \mathbf{i}(\omega r \sinh \omega t) + \mathbf{j}(\omega r \cosh \omega t)$$

and

$$\mathbf{a} = \mathbf{i}(\omega^2 r \cosh \omega t) + \mathbf{j}(\omega^2 r \sinh \omega t)$$

$$= \omega^2 \mathbf{R}.$$

This means that the force $\mathbf{F} = m\mathbf{a} = m\omega^2\mathbf{R}$ has a magnitude $m\omega^2|\mathbf{R}| = m\omega^2|\overrightarrow{OP}|$ which is directly proportional to the distance OP, and that its direction is the same as the direction of $\mathbf{R}$. Thus the force is directed away from O (Fig. 14–18).

The next example illustrates how we obtain the path of motion by integrating Eq. (9) when the force $\mathbf{F}$ is a given function of time and the

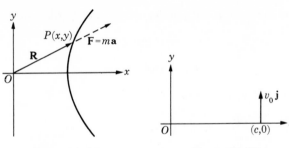

Figure 14-18   Figure 14-19

initial position and initial velocity of the particle are given. In general, the force **F** may depend upon the position of P as well as upon the time and the problem of integrating the differential equations so obtained is usually discussed in textbooks on that subject. [For example, see Martin and Reissner, *Elementary Differential Equations*, Addison-Wesley Publishing Company (1956).]

EXAMPLE 2. (Fig. 14-19.) The force acting on a particle P of mass m is given as a function of t by

$$\mathbf{F} = \mathbf{i} \cos t + \mathbf{j} \sin t.$$

If the particle starts at the point $(c, 0)$ with initial velocity $v_0\mathbf{j}$ perpendicular to the x-axis, find the curve it describes.

Solution. If we denote the position vector by

$$\mathbf{R} = \mathbf{i}x + \mathbf{j}y,$$

we may restate the problem as follows. Find **R** if

$$\mathbf{F} = m \frac{d^2\mathbf{R}}{dt^2} = \mathbf{i} \cos t + \mathbf{j} \sin t \tag{11}$$

and

$$\text{at } t = 0: \quad \mathbf{R} = \mathbf{i}c, \quad \frac{d\mathbf{R}}{dt} = \mathbf{j}v_0. \tag{12}$$

In (11) we let $\mathbf{v} = d\mathbf{R}/dt$, and separate the variables to obtain

$$m d\mathbf{v} = (\mathbf{i} \cos t + \mathbf{j} \sin t) \, dt.$$

Integrating this, we have

$$m\mathbf{v} = m \frac{d\mathbf{R}}{dt} = \mathbf{i} \sin t - \mathbf{j} \cos t + \mathbf{C}_1, \tag{13}$$

where the constant of integration is a *vector* denoted by $\mathbf{C}_1$. The value of $\mathbf{C}_1$

may be found by using the initial velocity, (12_2), in (13) with $t = 0$:

$$m\mathbf{j}v_0 = -\mathbf{j} + \mathbf{C}_1,$$

$$\mathbf{C}_1 = (mv_0 + 1)\mathbf{j}.$$

Substituting this into (13), we have

$$m\frac{d\mathbf{R}}{dt} = \mathbf{i}\sin t + (mv_0 + 1 - \cos t)\mathbf{j}.$$

Another integration gives

$$m\mathbf{R} = -\mathbf{i}\cos t + \mathbf{j}(mv_0 t + t - \sin t) + \mathbf{C}_2.$$

The initial condition (12_1) enables us to evaluate $\mathbf{C}_2$:

$$m c\mathbf{i} = -\mathbf{i} + \mathbf{C}_2, \qquad \mathbf{C}_2 = \mathbf{i}(mc + 1),$$

so that the position vector $\mathbf{R}$ is given by

$$\mathbf{R} = \frac{1}{m}[\mathbf{i}(mc + 1 - \cos t) + \mathbf{j}(mv_0 t + t - \sin t)].$$

The parametric equations of the curve are found by equating components of the above equation and

$$\mathbf{R} = \mathbf{i}x + \mathbf{j}y,$$

which gives

$$x = c + \frac{1 - \cos t}{m}, \qquad y = v_0 t + \frac{t - \sin t}{m}.$$

PROBLEMS

In Problems 1–8, $\mathbf{R} = \mathbf{i}x + \mathbf{j}y$ is the vector from the origin to the moving point $P(x, y)$ at time t. Find the velocity and acceleration vectors for any t. Also find these vectors and the speed at the particular instant given.

1. $\mathbf{R} = (a\cos \omega t)\mathbf{i} + (a\sin \omega t)\mathbf{j}$, a and ω being positive constants; $t = \pi/(3\omega)$.
2. $\mathbf{R} = (2\cos t)\mathbf{i} + (3\sin t)\mathbf{j}$, $t = \pi/4$
3. $\mathbf{R} = (t + 1)\mathbf{i} + (t^2 - 1)\mathbf{j}$, $t = 2$
4. $\mathbf{R} = (\cos 2t)\mathbf{i} + (2\sin t)\mathbf{j}$, $t = 0$
5. $\mathbf{R} = e^t\mathbf{i} + e^{-2t}\mathbf{j}$, $t = \ln 3$
6. $\mathbf{R} = (\sec t)\mathbf{i} + (\tan t)\mathbf{j}$, $t = \pi/6$
7. $\mathbf{R} = (\cosh 3t)\mathbf{i} + (2\sinh t)\mathbf{j}$, $t = 0$
8. $\mathbf{R} = [\ln (t + 1)]\mathbf{i} + t^2\mathbf{j}$, $t = 1$

9. If the force that acts on a particle P of mass m is

$$\mathbf{F} = -mg\mathbf{j},$$

where m and g are constants, and the particle starts from the origin with velocity

$$\mathbf{v}_0 = (v_0 \cos \alpha)\mathbf{i} + (v_0 \sin \alpha)\mathbf{j}$$

at time $t = 0$, find the vector $\mathbf{R} = i x + j y$ from the origin to P at time t.

10. Problem 9 describes the motion of a projectile in vacuo. If the projectile encounters a resistance proportional to the velocity, the force is

$$\mathbf{F} = -mg\mathbf{j} - k\,\frac{d\mathbf{R}}{dt}.$$

Show that one integration of $\mathbf{F} = md^2\mathbf{R}/dt^2$ leads to the differential equation

$$\frac{d\mathbf{R}}{dt} + \frac{k}{m}\,\mathbf{R} = \mathbf{v}_0 - gt\mathbf{j}.$$

(This differential equation can in turn be integrated by means of the following device: multiply both sides of the equation by $e^{(k/m)t}$. Then the left side is the derivative of the product $\mathbf{R}e^{(k/m)t}$ and both sides can be integrated.)

14–5   Tangential vectors.

As the point P moves along a given curve in the xy-plane, we may imagine its position as being specified by the length of arc s from some arbitrarily chosen reference point P_0 on the curve. The vector

$$\mathbf{R} = i x + j y$$

from O to $P(x, y)$ is therefore a function of s and we shall now investigate the properties of $d\mathbf{R}/ds$. To this end, let P have coordinates (x, y) corresponding to the value s, while $Q(x + \Delta x, y + \Delta y)$ corresponds to $s + \Delta s$. Then

$$\frac{\Delta \mathbf{R}}{\Delta s} = i\,\frac{\Delta x}{\Delta s} + j\,\frac{\Delta y}{\Delta s} = \frac{\overrightarrow{PQ}}{\Delta s} \tag{1}$$

is a *vector* whose magnitude is chord $|PQ|$ divided by the length of the arc PQ, and this approaches unity as $\Delta s \to 0$. Hence

$$\frac{d\mathbf{R}}{ds} = \lim_{\Delta s \to 0} \frac{\Delta \mathbf{R}}{\Delta s} \tag{2}$$

is a *unit* vector. The *direction* of this unit vector is the limiting direction approached by the direction of $\Delta \mathbf{R}/\Delta s$ as $\Delta s \to 0$. Now

$$\frac{\Delta \mathbf{R}}{\Delta s} = \frac{\overrightarrow{PQ}}{\Delta s}$$

has the same direction as $\overrightarrow{PQ}$ in case (a) when Δs is positive, or else it has the same direction as $\overrightarrow{QP}$ in case (b) when Δs is negative. Figures 14–20(a) and (b) illustrate these two cases and show that in *either* case,

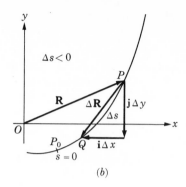

(a)   (b)

Figure 14–20

$\Delta R/\Delta s$ is directed along the chord through P and Q and points in the direction of increasing s (that is, upward to the right in both figures). As $\Delta s \to 0$ and $Q \to P$, the direction of the chord through P and Q approaches the direction of the *tangent* to the curve at P. Thus the limiting direction of $\Delta R/\Delta s$, in other words the *direction of dR/ds*, is along the *tangent to the curve at P* and its sense is that which points in the direction of increasing arc length s (that is, away from P_0 when s is positive, or toward P_0 when s is negative).

That is,

$$\frac{dR}{ds} = T \tag{3}$$

is a *unit vector, tangent to the curve at P* (Fig. 14–21).

If we let $\Delta s \to 0$ in Eq. (1), we find that

$$\frac{dR}{ds} = i\,\frac{dx}{ds} + j\,\frac{dy}{ds} \tag{4}$$

and this may be used to find T at any point of a curve whose equation is given.

EXAMPLE. (Fig. 14–22.) Find the unit vector T tangent to the circle

$$x = a\,\cos\,\theta,$$

$$y = a\,\sin\,\theta,$$

at any point $P(x, y)$.

Solution. From the equations of the curve,

$$dx = -a\,\sin\,\theta\,d\theta, \qquad dy = a\,\cos\,\theta\,d\theta,$$

Figure 14–21

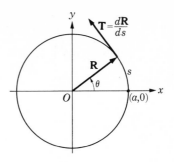

Figure 14–22

and

$$ds^2 = dx^2 + dy^2 = a^2 (\sin^2 \theta + \cos^2 \theta) \, d\theta^2 = a^2 \, d\theta^2,$$

so that

$$ds = \pm a \, d\theta.$$

If we measure arc length in the counterclockwise direction, with $s = 0$ at $(a, 0)$, s will be an increasing function of θ, so that the $+$ sign should be taken:

$$ds = a \, d\theta.$$

Then

$$\mathbf{T} = \frac{d\mathbf{R}}{ds} = \mathbf{i}\frac{dx}{ds} + \mathbf{j}\frac{dy}{ds} = \mathbf{i}\left(\frac{-a\sin\theta\,d\theta}{a\,d\theta}\right) + \mathbf{j}\left(\frac{a\cos\theta\,d\theta}{a\,d\theta}\right)$$

$$= -\mathbf{i}\sin\theta + \mathbf{j}\cos\theta.$$

PROBLEMS

In each of the following problems (1 through 5), $\mathbf{R} = \mathbf{i}x + \mathbf{j}y$ is the vector from the origin O to $P(x, y)$. For each of these motions, find the unit tangent vector $\mathbf{T} = d\mathbf{R}/ds$.

1. $\mathbf{R} = 2\mathbf{i}\cos t + 2\mathbf{j}\sin t$ 2. $\mathbf{R} = e^t\mathbf{i} + t^2\mathbf{j}$

3. $\mathbf{R} = (\cos^3 t)\mathbf{i} + (\sin^3 t)\mathbf{j}$ 4. $\mathbf{R} = \mathbf{i}x + \mathbf{j}x^2$

5. $\mathbf{R} = (\cos 2t)\mathbf{i} + (2 \cos t)\mathbf{j}$

14-6   Curvature and normal vectors.   Our next step is to consider the rate of change of the unit tangent vector $\mathbf{T}$ as P moves along the curve. Of course the length of $\mathbf{T}$ is constant, always being equal to unity. But the direction of $\mathbf{T}$ changes, since it is tangent to the curve and this tangent changes direction from point to point unless the curve is a straight line.

We may specify the direction of $\mathbf{T}$ by means of the angle ϕ from the x-axis to $\mathbf{T}$ (Fig. 14–23). The instantaneous rate of change of this slope

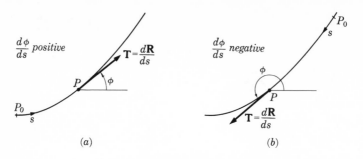

Figure 14–23

angle ϕ with respect to arc length s (measured in radians per unit of length) is taken as the mathematical *definition of the curvature* of the curve at P. The Greek letter κ (kappa) is used to denote curvature, and its definition is given by the equation

$$\kappa = \frac{d\phi}{ds},$$
(1)

where

$$\tan \phi = \frac{dy}{dx}$$

and

$$ds = \pm\sqrt{dx^2 + dy^2}.$$

One may derive a formula for κ from the equations above in a straightforward manner. Namely,

$$\phi = \tan^{-1} \frac{dy}{dx},$$

$$\frac{d\phi}{dx} = \frac{\dfrac{d^2y}{dx^2}}{1 + \left(\dfrac{dy}{dx}\right)^2},$$

and

$$\frac{ds}{dx} = \pm\sqrt{1 + \left(\frac{dy}{dx}\right)^2},$$

so that

$$\kappa = \frac{d\phi}{ds} = \frac{d\phi/dx}{ds/dx} = \frac{\pm\dfrac{d^2y}{dx^2}}{\left[1 + \left(\dfrac{dy}{dx}\right)^2\right]^{3/2}}.$$
(2a)

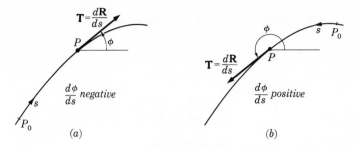

Figure 14–24

The ambiguous sign in (2a) is plus if ds/dx is positive, that is, if s increases as we move along the curve from left to right (as on the lower half of the circle in Fig. 14–22). But the ambiguous sign is minus if ds/dx is negative (as on the upper half of the circle in Fig. 14–22).

It is desirable for our purposes to have κ carry the same sign as $d\phi/ds$; hence we shall need to keep the ambiguous sign in Eq. (2a), subject to the discussion above. The sign of $d\phi/ds$ depends, of course, upon whether ϕ increases or decreases as s increases. Geometric considerations (Figs. 14–23 and 14–24) show that

> κ is positive if the concave side of the curve lies on our left and
>
> κ is negative if the concave side of the curve lies on our right,

as we "walk" along the curve in the direction of increasing s.

In Fig. 14–23(a), we indicate that s increases as we go from left to right along the curve. If we go from P to a nearby point P' to the right of P (corresponding to a positive Δs), we see that the tangent at P' is steeper than at P; hence $\Delta\phi$ is also positive, so that

$$d\phi/ds = \lim_{\Delta s \to 0} (\Delta\phi/\Delta s)$$

is positive at P. We also see that the concave side of the curve is on our left as we travel along the curve in the direction indicated.

A similar analysis of the situation illustrated by Fig. 14–23(b) leads to the conclusion that $d\phi/ds$ is negative at P, since a small increase in s causes a decrease in ϕ. In this case, κ is negative and the concave side of the curve is on our right as we go along the curve in the direction of increasing s.

Finally, the two cases illustrated in Fig. 14–24(a) and (b) show that the geometric interpretation of the sign of κ which was given above holds valid in every case. It should be pointed out that some writers take the sign of κ to be the same as the sign of d^2y/dx^2, which corresponds to assuming that ds/dx is positive.

We may arrive at a formula for κ in terms of dx/dy and d^2x/dy^2 if we use

$$\phi = \cot^{-1} \frac{dx}{dy}$$

and

$$\kappa = \frac{d\phi}{ds} = \frac{d\phi/dy}{ds/dy}.$$

The result, which corresponds to (2a), is

$$\kappa = \frac{\pm \dfrac{d^2x}{dy^2}}{\left[1 + \left(\dfrac{dx}{dy}\right)^2\right]^{3/2}}. \tag{2b}$$

If the equation of the curve is given in parametric form,

$$x = f(t), \qquad y = g(t),$$

then

$$\phi = \tan^{-1}\left(\frac{dy/dt}{dx/dt}\right),$$

and if we use

$$\kappa = \frac{d\phi/dt}{ds/dt},$$

the calculations are as follows:

$$\frac{d\phi}{dt} = \frac{1}{1 + \left(\dfrac{dy/dt}{dx/dt}\right)^2} \frac{\dfrac{dx}{dt}\dfrac{d^2y}{dt^2} - \dfrac{dy}{dt}\dfrac{d^2x}{dt^2}}{\left(\dfrac{dx}{dt}\right)^2} = \frac{\dot{x}\ddot{y} - \dot{y}\ddot{x}}{\dot{x}^2 + \dot{y}^2} \left[\dot{x} = \frac{dx}{dt}, \quad \ddot{x} = \frac{d^2x}{dt^2}\right]$$

and

$$\frac{ds}{dt} = \pm\sqrt{\dot{x}^2 + \dot{y}^2},$$

so that

$$\kappa = \pm \frac{\dot{x}\ddot{y} - \dot{y}\ddot{x}}{[\dot{x}^2 + \dot{y}^2]^{3/2}}. \tag{2c}$$

On a straight line, ϕ is constant, so $d\phi/ds$ is zero and Eq. (2a) says that *the curvature of a straight line is zero.*

If we apply (2), or (1), to a circle of radius a, we find that the curvature

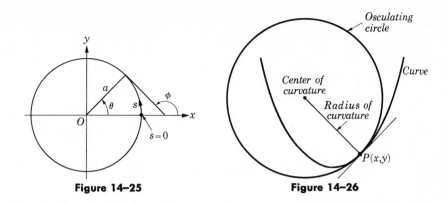

Figure 14–25   **Figure 14–26**

of a circle is constant in magnitude. In fact, we see from Fig. 14–25 that both s and ϕ may be expressed in terms of the angle θ as follows:

$$s = a\theta, \qquad \phi = \theta + \frac{\pi}{2}, \tag{3}$$

so that

$$\kappa = \frac{d\phi}{ds} = \frac{d\theta}{a\,d\theta} = \frac{1}{a}.$$

That is, the curvature of a circle traversed in the positive direction is equal to the reciprocal of its radius. The smaller the circle, the greater its curvature. "Turning around on a dime" indicates a more rapid change of direction per unit of arc length than does turning around on a silver dollar!

Circle and radius of curvature. The circle that is tangent to a given curve at P, whose center lies on the concave side of the curve and that has the same curvature as the curve has at P, is called the *circle of curvature*. Its radius is $1/|\kappa|$. We define the *radius of curvature* at P to be $|\rho|$, where

$$\rho = \frac{1}{\kappa} = \frac{\left[1 + \left(\dfrac{dy}{dx}\right)^2\right]^{3/2}}{\pm\,\dfrac{d^2y}{dx^2}}. \tag{4}$$

As we have defined it, ρ has the same sign as κ. The center of the circle of curvature is called the center of curvature. The circle of curvature has its first and second derivatives equal respectively to the first and second derivatives of the curve itself at this point. For this reason it has a higher degree of contact with the curve at P than has any other circle, so it is also called the *osculating* circle! (See Fig. 14–26.) Since velocity

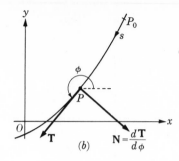

Figure 14–27

and acceleration involve only the first and second time derivatives of the coordinates of P, it is natural to anticipate that the instantaneous velocity and acceleration of a particle moving on any curve may be expressed in terms of instantaneous velocity and acceleration of an associated particle moving on the osculating circle. This will be investigated in the next article.

Unit normal vector. We return once more to the question of the rate of change of the unit vector $\mathbf{T}$ as P moves along the curve. In terms of the slope angle ϕ (Fig. 14–27), we may write

$$\mathbf{T} = \mathbf{i} \cos \phi + \mathbf{j} \sin \phi, \tag{5}$$

and then the derivative

$$\frac{d\mathbf{T}}{d\phi} = -\mathbf{i} \sin \phi + \mathbf{j} \cos \phi \tag{6}$$

has magnitude

$$\left| \frac{d\mathbf{T}}{d\phi} \right| = \sqrt{\sin^2 \phi + \cos^2 \phi} = 1.$$

Its slope is

$$\frac{\cos \phi}{-\sin \phi} = \frac{-1}{\tan \phi},$$

which is the negative reciprocal of the slope of $\mathbf{T}$. Therefore $d\mathbf{T}/d\phi$ is perpendicular to $\mathbf{T}$. In fact, we see from Eq. (6) that

$$\boxed{\frac{d\mathbf{T}}{d\phi} = \mathbf{N},} \tag{7}$$

where $\mathbf{N}$ is the *unit normal* vector obtained by rotating the unit tangent vector $\mathbf{T}$ through 90° in the counterclockwise direction, since

$$\mathbf{N} = \mathbf{i} \cos (\phi + 90°) + \mathbf{j} \sin (\phi + 90°) = -\mathbf{i} \sin \phi + \mathbf{j} \cos \phi.$$

If we combine Eqs. (7) and (1), we have

$$\frac{d\mathbf{T}}{ds} = \frac{d\mathbf{T}}{d\phi}\frac{d\phi}{ds} = \mathbf{N}\kappa. \qquad (8)$$

We observe in passing that whether κ is positive or negative, $\mathbf{N}\kappa$ is always directed toward the concave side of the curve. (See Figs. 14–23, 14–24, 14–27.)

PROBLEMS

Find the curvature of each of the curves in the following problems (1 through 9).

1. $y = a\cosh(x/a)$ 2. $y = \ln(\cos x)$

3. $y = e^{2x}$ 4. $x = a\cos^3 t,\quad y = a\sin^3 t$

5. $x = a(\cos\theta + \theta\sin\theta),$ 6. $x = a(\theta - \sin\theta),$

   $y = a(\sin\theta - \theta\cos\theta)$ $y = a(1 - \cos\theta)$

7. $x = \ln\sec y$ 8. $x = \frac{1}{3}(y^2 + 2)^{3/2}$

9. $x = \dfrac{y^4}{4} + \dfrac{1}{8y^2}$

10. Find the equation of the osculating circle associated with the curve $y = e^x$ at the point $(0, 1)$. By calculating dy/dx and d^2y/dx^2 at the point $(0, 1)$ from the equation of this circle, verify that these derivatives have the same values there as do the corresponding derivatives for the curve $y = e^x$. Sketch the curve and the osculating circle.

11. Show that when x and y are considered as functions of arc length s, the unit vectors $\mathbf{T}$ and $\mathbf{N}$ may be expressed as follows:

$$\mathbf{T} = \mathbf{i}\frac{dx}{ds} + \mathbf{j}\frac{dy}{ds}, \qquad \mathbf{N} = -\mathbf{i}\frac{dy}{ds} + \mathbf{j}\frac{dx}{ds},$$

where $dx/ds = \cos\phi$, $dy/ds = \sin\phi$, and ϕ is the angle from the positive x-axis to the tangent line.

14–7   Tangential and normal components of the velocity and acceleration vectors. In mechanics it is useful to be able to discuss the motion of a particle P in terms of its instantaneous speed ds/dt, acceleration along its path d^2s/dt^2, and the curvature of the path. This is easy if we refer the velocity and acceleration vectors to the unit vectors $\mathbf{T}$ and $\mathbf{N}$, rather than using horizontal and vertical components.

In Article 14–4 we found the velocity vector to be given by

$$\mathbf{v} = \frac{d\mathbf{R}}{dt}, \qquad (1)$$

where $\mathbf{R} = \mathbf{i}x + \mathbf{j}y$ is the position vector $\overrightarrow{OP}$. We may also write this in the form

$$\mathbf{v} = \frac{d\mathbf{R}}{dt} = \frac{d\mathbf{R}}{ds}\frac{ds}{dt}$$

or

$$\boxed{\mathbf{v} = \mathbf{T}\frac{ds}{dt}} \qquad (2)$$

if we use the result of Eq. (3), Article 14–5. This is in keeping with our earlier remark that the velocity vector is tangent to the curve and has magnitude $|ds/dt|$. (See Fig. 14–28.)

To obtain the acceleration vector, we differentiate Eq. (2) with respect to t:

$$\mathbf{a} = \frac{d\mathbf{v}}{dt} = \mathbf{T}\frac{d^2s}{dt^2} + \frac{ds}{dt}\frac{d\mathbf{T}}{dt}.$$

By Eq. (8), Article 14–6,

$$\frac{d\mathbf{T}}{dt} = \frac{d\mathbf{T}}{ds}\frac{ds}{dt} = \mathbf{N}\kappa\frac{ds}{dt},$$

so that

$$\boxed{\mathbf{a} = \mathbf{T}\frac{d^2s}{dt^2} + \mathbf{N}\kappa\left(\frac{ds}{dt}\right)^2.} \qquad (3)$$

Equation (3) expresses the acceleration vector in terms of its tangential and normal components. The *tangential component*, d^2s/dt^2, is simply the derivative of the speed ds/dt of the particle in its path. The *normal component* is directed toward the concave side of the curve and has magnitude

$$|\kappa|\left(\frac{ds}{dt}\right)^2 = \frac{(ds/dt)^2}{|\rho|} = \frac{v^2}{|\rho|},$$

where v is the instantaneous speed of the particle and $|\rho|$ is the radius of curvature of the path at the point in question. This explains why a large normal force, which must be supplied by friction between the tires and the roadway, is required to hold an automobile on a level road if it makes a sharp turn (small $|\rho|$) or a moderate turn at high speed (large v^2). (See Sears: *Mechanics*, p. 187, for a discussion of the banking of curves.)

If the particle is moving in a circle with *constant* speed $v = ds/dt$, then d^2s/dt^2 is zero, and the only acceleration is the normal acceleration v^2/ρ toward the center of the circle. If the speed is not constant, the acceleration vector $\mathbf{a}$ is the resultant of the tangential and normal components, as in Fig. 14–29.

Figure 14–28

Figure 14–29

The following example illustrates how the tangential and normal components of velocity and acceleration may be computed when the equations of motion are known. In particular, it should be noted that the equation

$$|\mathbf{a}|^2 = a_x^2 + a_y^2 = a_T^2 + a_N^2 \qquad (4)$$

is used to determine the normal component of acceleration

$$a_N = \sqrt{|\mathbf{a}|^2 - a_T^2}. \qquad (5)$$

EXAMPLE. The coordinates of a moving particle at time t are given by

$$x = \cos t + t \sin t, \qquad y = \sin t - t \cos t.$$

Then

$$\mathbf{v} = \mathbf{i}\frac{dx}{dt} + \mathbf{j}\frac{dy}{dt} = \mathbf{i}[-\sin t + t \cos t + \sin t] + \mathbf{j}[\cos t + t \sin t - \cos t]$$

$$= \mathbf{i}t \cos t + \mathbf{j}t \sin t$$

and

$$\mathbf{a} = \frac{d\mathbf{v}}{dt} = \mathbf{i}[-t \sin t + \cos t] + \mathbf{j}[t \cos t + \sin t].$$

Now the tangential component of velocity is

$$\frac{ds}{dt} = |\mathbf{v}| = \sqrt{(t \cos t)^2 + (t \sin t)^2} = t$$

and the tangential component of acceleration is

$$a_T = \frac{d^2s}{dt^2} = \frac{d}{dt}\left(\frac{ds}{dt}\right) = \frac{d}{dt}(t) = 1.$$

We use Eq. (5) to determine the normal component of acceleration:

$$a_N = \sqrt{|\mathbf{a}|^2 - a_T^2} = \sqrt{(-t \sin t + \cos t)^2 + (t \cos t + \sin t)^2 - 1} = t.$$

Here the tangential acceleration has constant magnitude and the normal acceleration starts with zero magnitude at $t = 0$ and increases with time. The equations of motion are the same as the parametric equations for the involute of a circle of unit radius with $\theta = t$.
(See Figs. 14–15, 14–30.) We could also readily find the radius of curvature without any complicated calculations from the equation

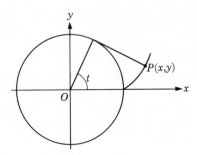

$$a_N = \frac{v^2}{\rho},$$

since $v^2 = |\mathbf{v}|^2 = t^2$ and $a_N = t$, hence

$$\rho = \frac{v^2}{a_N} = \frac{t^2}{t} = t.$$

Figure 14–30

PROBLEMS

1. With the book closed, derive vector expressions for the velocity and acceleration in terms of tangential and normal components. Check your derivations with those given in the text.

In each of the following problems (2 through 6), find the velocity and acceleration vectors, then find the speed ds/dt and the tangential and normal components of acceleration.

2. $\mathbf{R} = \mathbf{i} \cosh 2t + \mathbf{j} \sinh 2t$ 3. $\mathbf{R} = (2t + 3)\mathbf{i} + (t^2 - 1)\mathbf{j}$

4. $\mathbf{R} = a \cos \omega t\, \mathbf{i} + a \sin \omega t\, \mathbf{j}$,   5. $\mathbf{R} = \mathbf{i} \ln (t^2 + 1) + \mathbf{j}(t - 2 \tan^{-1} t)$
   a and ω positive constants   6. $\mathbf{R} = \mathbf{i} e^t \cos t + \mathbf{j} e^t \sin t$

7. Deduce from Eq. (3) that a particle will move in a straight line if the normal component of acceleration is zero.

8. Show that the radius of curvature is given by the formula

$$\rho = \frac{\pm(\dot{x}^2 + \dot{y}^2)}{\sqrt{\ddot{x}^2 + \ddot{y}^2 - \ddot{s}^2}},$$

where

$$\dot{x} = \frac{dx}{dt}, \quad \ddot{x} = \frac{d^2x}{dt^2}, \text{ etc.,} \quad \text{and} \quad \ddot{s} = \frac{d}{dt}\left(\sqrt{\dot{x}^2 + \dot{y}^2}\right).$$

9. If a particle moves in a curve with constant speed, show that the force is always directed along the normal.

10. If the force acting on a particle is at all times perpendicular to the direction of motion, show that the speed remains constant.

14–8 Polar coordinates. If the particle P moves on a curve whose equation is given in polar coordinates, it is convenient to express the velocity and acceleration vectors in terms of still a third set of unit vectors. We introduce **unit vectors**

$$\mathbf{u}_r = \mathbf{i} \cos \theta + \mathbf{j} \sin \theta, \qquad \mathbf{u}_\theta = -\mathbf{i} \sin \theta + \mathbf{j} \cos \theta, \qquad (1)$$

that point respectively along the radius vector $\overrightarrow{OP}$ and at right angles to $\overrightarrow{OP}$ and in the direction of increasing θ, as shown in Fig. 14–31. Then, from (1), we find

$$\frac{d\mathbf{u}_r}{d\theta} = -\mathbf{i} \sin \theta + \mathbf{j} \cos \theta = \mathbf{u}_\theta,$$

$$\frac{d\mathbf{u}_\theta}{d\theta} = -\mathbf{i} \cos \theta - \mathbf{j} \sin \theta = -\mathbf{u}_r. \qquad (2)$$

This says that the result of differentiating either one of the unit vectors $\mathbf{u}_r$ or $\mathbf{u}_\theta$ with respect to θ is equivalent to rotating that vector through 90° in the positive (counterclockwise) direction.

Since the vectors $\mathbf{R} = \overrightarrow{OP}$ and $r\mathbf{u}_r$ have the same direction, and the length of $\mathbf{R}$ is the absolute value of the polar coordinate r of $P(r, \theta)$, we have

$$\mathbf{R} = r\mathbf{u}_r. \qquad (3)$$

Figure 14–31

To obtain the velocity, we must differentiate this with respect to t, remembering that both r and $\mathbf{u}_r$ may be variables. From (2) it is clear that

$$\frac{d\mathbf{u}_r}{dt} = \frac{d\mathbf{u}_r}{d\theta} \frac{d\theta}{dt} = \mathbf{u}_\theta \frac{d\theta}{dt}, \qquad \frac{d\mathbf{u}_\theta}{dt} = \frac{d\mathbf{u}_\theta}{d\theta} \frac{d\theta}{dt} = -\mathbf{u}_r \frac{d\theta}{dt}. \qquad (4)$$

Hence,

$$\mathbf{v} = \frac{d\mathbf{R}}{dt} = \mathbf{u}_r \frac{dr}{dt} + r \frac{d\mathbf{u}_r}{dt}$$

becomes

$$\mathbf{v} = \mathbf{u}_r \frac{dr}{dt} + \mathbf{u}_\theta r \frac{d\theta}{dt}. \qquad (5)$$

Figure 14–32   Figure 14–33

Of course this velocity vector is tangent to the curve at P and has magnitude

$$|\mathbf{v}| = \sqrt{(dr/dt)^2 + r^2(d\theta/dt)^2} = |ds/dt| \, .$$

In fact, if the three sides of the "differential triangle" of sides dr, $rd\theta$, and ds are all divided by dt (Fig. 14–32), the result will be a similar triangle having sides dr/dt, $r\, d\theta/dt$, and ds/dt, which illustrates the vector equation

$$\mathbf{v} = \mathbf{T}\, \frac{ds}{dt} = \mathbf{u}_r\, \frac{dr}{dt} + \mathbf{u}_\theta r\, \frac{d\theta}{dt} \, .$$

The acceleration vector is found by differentiating the velocity vector in (5) as follows:

$$\mathbf{a} = \frac{d\mathbf{v}}{dt} = \left(\mathbf{u}_r\, \frac{d^2r}{dt^2} + \frac{dr}{dt}\, \frac{d\mathbf{u}_r}{dt} \right) + \left(\mathbf{u}_\theta r\, \frac{d^2\theta}{dt^2} + \mathbf{u}_\theta\, \frac{dr}{dt}\, \frac{d\theta}{dt} + \frac{d\mathbf{u}_\theta}{dt}\, r\, \frac{d\theta}{dt} \right).$$

When Eqs. (4) are used to evaluate the derivatives of $\mathbf{u}_r$ and $\mathbf{u}_\theta$ and the components are separated, the result becomes

$$\mathbf{a} = \mathbf{u}_r \left[\frac{d^2r}{dt^2} - r\left(\frac{d\theta}{dt} \right)^2 \right] + \mathbf{u}_\theta \left[r\, \frac{d^2\theta}{dt^2} + 2\, \frac{dr}{dt}\, \frac{d\theta}{dt} \right]. \qquad (6)$$

The polar form is particularly convenient in discussing the motion of a particle in what is called a "central force field." By this we mean that the force acting on the particle is always directed toward a single point, the center of force, which we choose as origin (Fig. 14–33). Then from $\mathbf{F} = m\mathbf{a}$, we see that the $\mathbf{u}_\theta$ component of acceleration must vanish. That is, in any central force field

$$r\, \frac{d^2\theta}{dt^2} + 2\, \frac{dr}{dt}\, \frac{d\theta}{dt} = 0 \qquad (7)$$

where the origin is at the center of force. (For instance, the sun would be chosen as the origin in discussing the gravitational attraction between the sun and a planet.) To integrate the differential equation (7), let

$$u = \frac{d\theta}{dt};$$

then

$$r \frac{du}{dt} + 2u \frac{dr}{dt} = 0$$

or

$$r\, du = -2u\, dr, \qquad \frac{du}{u} = -2 \frac{dr}{r},$$

$$\ln |u| = -2 \ln |r| + c_1,$$

$$\ln |ur^2| = c_1, \qquad |ur^2| = e^{c_1} = C,$$

or

$$r^2 \frac{d\theta}{dt} = \pm C. \tag{8}$$

We recognize the left side of this equation as $2\, dA/dt$, where $dA = \frac{1}{2}r^2\, d\theta$ is the area swept over as the radius vector $\overrightarrow{OP}$ rotates through a small angle $d\theta$. Hence, Eq. (8) says that the radius vector *sweeps over area at a constant rate* in a central force field. This is Kepler's second law of planetary motion, and it is thus seen to be a consequence of the fact that the field of gravitational attraction of the sun for the planets is a central force field.

PROBLEMS

1. With the book closed, derive vector expressions for the velocity and acceleration in terms of components along and at right angles to the radius vector. Check your derivations with those given in the text.

In Problems 2–6, find the velocity and acceleration vectors in terms of the unit vectors $\mathbf{u}_r$ and $\mathbf{u}_\theta$ if:

2. $r = a(1 - \cos \theta)$ and $\dfrac{d\theta}{dt} = 3$ \qquad 3. $r = a \sin 2\theta$ and $\dfrac{d\theta}{dt} = 2t$

4. $r = e^{a\theta}$ and $\dfrac{d\theta}{dt} = 2$ \qquad\qquad 5. $r = a(1 + \sin t)$ and $\theta = 1 - e^{-t}$

6. $r = 2 \cos 4t$ and $\theta = 2t$

7. If a particle moves in an ellipse whose polar equation is $r = c/(1 - e \cos \theta)$ and the force is directed toward the origin, show that the magnitude of the force is proportional to $1/r^2$.

REVIEW QUESTIONS AND EXERCISES FOR CHAPTER 14

1. When are two vectors equal?

2. How are two vectors added? Subtracted?

3. If a vector is multiplied by a scalar, how is the result related to the original vector? In your discussion include all possible values of the scalar: positive, negative, and zero.

4. Define the derivative of a vector function.

5. Develop formulas for the derivatives, with respect to θ, of the unit vectors $\mathbf{u}_r$ and $\mathbf{u}_\theta$.

6. Develop vector formulas for velocity and acceleration of a particle moving in a plane curve:

   (a) in terms of Cartesian coordinates,

   (b) in terms of polar coordinates,

   (c) in terms of distance traveled along the curve and unit vectors tangent and normal to the curve.

7. (a) Define *curvature* of a plane curve. (b) Define radius of curvature. (c) Define center of curvature. (d) Define osculating circle.

8. Develop a formula for the curvature of a curve whose parametric equations are $x = f(t)$, $y = g(t)$.

9. In what way does the curvature of a curve affect the acceleration of a particle moving along the curve? In particular, discuss the case of constant-speed motion along a curve.

10. State and derive Kepler's second law concerning motion in a central force field.

11. Give examples of two ways in which parametric equations of a curve may arise.

12. What is the relation between a locus represented by parametric equations and the locus represented by the Cartesian equations that we may get when we eliminate the parameter? Illustrate with an example.

MISCELLANEOUS PROBLEMS FOR CHAPTER 14

In each of Problems 1–10, find parametric equations of the locus of $P(x, y)$ for the data given.

1. $\dfrac{dx}{dt} = x^2$, $\dfrac{dy}{dt} = x$; $t = 0$, $x = 1$, $y = 1$

2. $\dfrac{dx}{dt} = \cos^2 x$; $\dfrac{dy}{dt} = x$; $t = 0$, $x = \dfrac{\pi}{4}$, $y = 0$

3. $\dfrac{dx}{dt} = e^t$, $\dfrac{dy}{dt} = xe^x$; $t = 0$, $x = 1$, $y = 0$

4. $\dfrac{dx}{dt} = 6 \sin 2t$, $\dfrac{dy}{dt} = 4 \cos 2t$; $t = 0$, $x = 0$, $y = 4$

5. $\dfrac{dx}{dt} = 1 - \cos t$, $\dfrac{dy}{dt} = \sin t$; $t = 0$, $x = 0$, $y = 0$

6. $\dfrac{dx}{dt} = \sqrt{1 + y}$, $\dfrac{dy}{dt} = y$; $t = 0$, $x = 0$, $y = 1$

7. $\dfrac{dx}{dt} = \text{sech } x$, $\dfrac{dy}{dt} = x$; $t = 0$, $x = 0$, $y = 0$

8. $\dfrac{dx}{dt} = \cosh \dfrac{t}{2}$, $\dfrac{dy}{dt} = x$; $t = 0$, $x = 2$, $y = 0$

9. $\dfrac{dx}{dt} = y$, $\dfrac{dy}{dt} = -x$; $t = 0$, $x = 0$, $y = 4$

10. $\dfrac{d^2x}{dt^2} = -\dfrac{dx}{dt}$, $\dfrac{dy}{dt} = x$; $t = 0$, $x = 1$, $\dfrac{dx}{dt} = 1$, $y = 1$

11. A particle is projected with velocity v at an angle α to the horizontal from a point that is at the foot of a hill inclined at an angle ϕ to the horizontal $[0 < \phi < \alpha < (\pi/2)]$. Show that it reaches the ground at a distance $[(2v^2 \cos \alpha)/(g \cos^2 \phi)] \sin (\alpha - \phi)$ measured up the face of the hill. Hence show that the greatest range achieved for a given v is when $\alpha = (\phi/2) + (\pi/4)$.

12. A wheel of radius 4 in. rolls along the x-axis with angular velocity 2 rad/sec. Find the locus described by a point on a spoke and 2 in. from the center of the wheel if it starts from the point $(0, 2)$ at time $t = 0$.

13. $\overline{OA}$ is the diameter of a circle of radius a. $\overrightarrow{AN}$ is tangent to the circle at A. A line through O making angle θ with diameter $\overline{OA}$ intersects the circle at M and tangent line at N. On $\overrightarrow{ON}$ a point P is located so that $|OP| = |MN|$. Taking O as origin, $\overline{OA}$ along the y-axis, and angle θ as parameter, find parametric equations of the locus described by P.

14. Let a line $\overleftrightarrow{AB}$ be the x-axis of a system of rectangular coordinates. Let the point C be the point $(0, 1)$. Let the line $\overleftrightarrow{DE}$ through C intersect $\overleftrightarrow{AB}$ at F. Let P and P' be the points on $\overleftrightarrow{DE}$ such that $|PF| = |P'F| = a$. Find parametric equations of the loci of P and P' in terms of the angle $\theta = \angle CFB$.

15. For the curve $x = a(t - \sin t)$, $y = a(1 - \cos t)$, find the following quantities: (a) The area bounded by the x-axis and one loop of the curve. (b) The length of one loop. (c) The radius of curvature. (d) The area of the surface of revolution obtained by rotating one loop about the x-axis. (e) The coordinates of the center of gravity of the area in part (a).

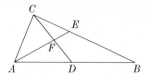

16. In the accompanying figure, D is the mid-point of side $\overline{AB}$ and E is one-third of the way between C and B. *Using vectors*, prove that F is the mid-point of $\overline{CD}$.

17. The vectors $2\mathbf{i} + 3\mathbf{j}$, $4\mathbf{i} + \mathbf{j}$, and $5\mathbf{i} + y\mathbf{j}$ have their initial points at the origin. Find the value of y so that the vectors terminate on one straight line.

18. **A** and **B** are vectors from the origin to the two points A and B. The point P is determined by the vector $\overrightarrow{OP} = x\mathbf{A} + y\mathbf{B}$ where x and y are positive quantities, neither of which is zero, and whose sum is equal to one. Prove that P lies on the line segment $\overline{AB}$.

19. Using vector methods, prove that the line joining the mid-points of two sides of a triangle is parallel to, and half the length of, the third side.

20. Let ABC be a triangle and let M be the mid-point of $\overline{AB}$. Let P be the point on $\overline{CM}$ that is two-thirds of the way from C to M. Let O be any point in space. (a) Show that

$$\overrightarrow{OP} = \left(\frac{\overrightarrow{OA} + \overrightarrow{OB} + \overrightarrow{OC}}{3} \right).$$

(b) Show how the result in part (a) leads to the conclusion that the medians of a triangle meet in a point.

21. A, B, C are the vertices of a triangle and a, b, c are the mid-points of the opposite sides. Show that $\overrightarrow{Aa} + \overrightarrow{Bb} + \overrightarrow{Cc} = 0$. Interpret the result geometrically.

22. Vectors are drawn from the center of a regular polygon to its vertices. Show that their sum is zero.

23. Let **A**, **B**, **C** be vectors from a common point O to points A, B, C. (a) If A, B, C are collinear, show that three constants x, y, z (not all zero) exist such that $x + y + z = 0$ and $x\mathbf{A} + y\mathbf{B} + z\mathbf{C} = 0$. (b) Conversely, if three constants x, y, z (not all zero) exist such that $x + y + z = 0$ and $x\mathbf{A} + y\mathbf{B} + z\mathbf{C} = 0$, show that A, B, C are collinear.

24. A particle moves in the xy-plane, according to the time law: $x = 1/\sqrt{1 + t^2}$, $y = t/\sqrt{1 + t^2}$. (a) Compute the velocity vector and acceleration vector, when $t = 1$. (b) At what time is the speed of the particle a maximum?

25. A circular wheel with unit radius rolls along the x-axis uniformly, rotating one half turn per second. The position of a point P on the circumference is given by the formula $\overrightarrow{OP} = \mathbf{R} = \mathbf{i}(\pi t - \sin \pi t) + \mathbf{j}(1 - \cos \pi t)$. (a) Determine the velocity (*vector*) **v** and the acceleration (*vector*) **a** at time t. (b) Determine the slopes (as functions of t) of the two straight lines $\overleftrightarrow{PC}$ and $\overrightarrow{PQ}$ joining P to

the center C of the wheel and to the point Q that is topmost at the instant. (c) Show that the directions of the vectors $\mathbf{v}$ and $\mathbf{a}$ can be expressed in terms of the straight lines described in (b).

26. The motion of a particle in the xy-plane is given by

$$\mathbf{R} = \mathbf{i}at\cos t + \mathbf{j}at\sin t.$$

Find the speed, and the tangential and normal components of the acceleration.

27. A particle moves in such a manner that the derivative of the position vector is always perpendicular to the position vector. Show that the particle moves on a circle with center at the origin.

28. The position of a point at time t is given by the formulas $x = e^t\cos t$, $y = e^t\sin t$. (a) Show that $\mathbf{a} = 2\mathbf{v} - 2\mathbf{r}$. (b) Show that the angle between the radius vector $\mathbf{r}$ and the acceleration vector $\mathbf{a}$ is constant, and find this angle.

29. Given the instantaneous velocity $\mathbf{v} = a\mathbf{i} + b\mathbf{j}$ and acceleration $\mathbf{a} = c\mathbf{i} + d\mathbf{j}$ of a particle at a point P on its path of motion, determine the curvature of the path at P.

30. Find the parametric equations, in terms of the parameter θ, of the locus of the center of curvature of the cycloid $x = a(\theta - \sin\theta)$, $y = a(1 - \cos\theta)$.

31. Find the point on the curve $y = e^x$ for which the radius of curvature is a minimum.

32. (a) Given a closed curve having the property that every line parallel to the x-axis or the y-axis has at most two points in common with the curve. Let

$$x = x(t), \qquad y = y(t), \qquad \alpha \le t \le \beta$$

be equations of the curve. Prove that if dx/dt and dy/dt are continuous, then the area bounded by the curve is

$$\frac{1}{2}\left|\int_\alpha^\beta \left\{x(t)\frac{dy}{dt} - y(t)\frac{dx}{dt}\right\}dt\right|.$$

(b) Use the result of part (a) to find the area inside the ellipse $x = a\cos\phi$, $y = b\sin\phi$, $0 \le \phi \le 2\pi$. What does the answer become when $a = b$?

33. For the curve defined by the equations

$$x = \int_0^\theta \cos\left(\tfrac{1}{2}\pi t^2\right)dt, \qquad y = \int_0^\theta \sin\left(\tfrac{1}{2}\pi t^2\right)dt,$$

calculate the curvature κ as a function of the length of arc s, where s is measured from $(0, 0)$.

34. The curve for which the length of the tangent intercepted between the point of contact and the y-axis is always equal to 1 is called the *tractrix*. Find its equation. Show that the radius of curvature at each point of the curve is inversely proportional to the length of the normal intercepted between the point on the curve and the y-axis. Calculate the length of arc of the tractrix, and find the parametric equations in terms of the length of arc.

35. Let $x = x(t)$, $y = y(t)$ be a closed curve. A constant length p is measured

off along the normal to the curve. The extremity of this segment describes a curve which is called a *parallel curve* to the original curve. Find the area, the length of arc, and the radius of curvature of the parallel curve.

36. Given the curve represented by the parametric equations $x = 32t$, $y = 16t^2 - 4$. (a) Calculate the radius of curvature of the curve at the point where $t = 3$. (b) Find the length of the curve between the points where $t = 0$ and $t = 1$.

37. Find the velocity, acceleration, and speed of a particle whose position at time t is $x = 3 \sin t$, $y = 2 \cos t$. Also find the tangential and normal components of the acceleration.

38. The position of a particle at time t is given by the equations $x = 1 + \cos 2t$, $y = \sin 2t$. Find (a) the normal and tangential components of acceleration at time t; (b) the radius of curvature of the path; (c) the equation of the path in polar coordinates, using the x-axis as the line $\theta = 0$ and the y-axis as the line $\theta = \pi/2$.

39. A particle moves so that its position at time t has the polar coordinates $r = t$, $\theta = t$. Find the velocity $\mathbf{v}$, the acceleration $\mathbf{a}$, and the curvature κ at any time t.

40. Find an expression for the curvature of the curve whose equation in polar coordinates is $r = f(\theta)$.

41. (a) Find the equation in *polar coordinates* of the curve $x = e^{2t} \cos t$, $y = e^{2t} \sin t$. (b) Find the length of this curve from $t = 0$ to $t = 2\pi$.

42. Express the velocity vector in terms of $\mathbf{u}_r$ and $\mathbf{u}_\theta$ for a point moving in the xy-plane according to the law $\mathbf{r} = (t + 1)\mathbf{i} + (t - 1)\mathbf{j}$.

43. The polar coordinates of a particle at time t are $r = e^{\omega t} + e^{-\omega t}$, $\theta = t$, where ω is a constant. Find the acceleration vector when $t = 0$.

44. A slender rod, passing through the fixed point O, is rotating about O in a plane at the constant rate of 3 rad/min. An insect is crawling along the rod toward O at the constant rate of 1 in/min. Use polar coordinates in the plane, with point O as the origin, and assume that the insect starts at the point $r = 2$, $\theta = 0$. (a) Find, in polar form, the vector velocity and vector acceleration of the insect when it is halfway to the origin. (b) What will be the length of the path, in the plane, that the insect has traveled when it reaches the origin?

45. A smooth ball rolls inside a long hollow tube while the tube rotates with constant angular velocity ω about an axis perpendicular to the axis of the tube. Assuming no friction between the ball and the sides of the tube, show that the distance r from the axis of rotation to the ball satisfies the differential equation $d^2r/dt^2 - \omega^2 r = 0$. If at time $t = 0$ the ball is at rest (relative to the tube) at $r = a > 0$, find r as a function of t.

46. Find the orbit of a planet relative to the sun, assuming the sun to be fixed at the origin and the force acting on the planet to be directed toward the sun with magnitude $\gamma mM/r^2$ where γ is the universal gravitational constant, M is the mass of the sun, m is the mass of the planet, and r is its distance from the sun. Choose the initial line to pass through the perihelion point of the orbit, and assume the velocity at perihelion is v_0. Show that the path is a circle, ellipse, parabola, or hyperbola according as $v_0^2 r_0/\gamma M$ equals one, lies between one and two, equals two, or is greater than two.

CHAPTER 1

Article 1–2

1–15. If P is the point (x, y), the other points are $Q(x, -y)$, $R(-x, y)$, $S(-x, -y)$, $T(y, x)$.

17. 2   19. -1

Article 1–3

1. $(3, 1)$;   2; 3; $\sqrt{13}$ 3. $(2, 2)$;   3; -3; $3\sqrt{2}$

5. $(1, -1)$;   2; 3; $\sqrt{13}$ 7. $(-1, 2)$; 2; -4; $2\sqrt{5}$

9. $(-1, -2)$; 2; 1; $\sqrt{5}$

11. (a) $x^2 + y^2 = 25$ (b) $x^2 + y^2 - 10x = 0$

   (c) $x^2 + y^2 - 6x - 8y = 0$ (d) $(x - h)^2 + (y - k)^2 = 25$

Article 1–4

1. $-3; \frac{1}{3}$ 3. $-\frac{1}{3}; 3$ 5. $-1; 1$ 7. $0; \infty$

9. $-1; 1$ 11. $\frac{2}{3}; -\frac{3}{2}$ 13. $0; \infty$ 15. $-b/a; a/b$

17. Parallelogram   19. Parallelogram   21. $(1, 2)$

27. Yes   29. Center $(\frac{3}{2}, \frac{3}{2})$; radius $= \dfrac{\sqrt{34}}{2}$

Article 1–5

1. $3x - 2y = 0$ 3. $x = 1$ 5. $x = -2$

7. $y = 0$ 9. $x + y = 1$ 11. 3

13. -1 15. $\frac{1}{2}$ 17. $\frac{4}{3}$

19. $-b/a$ 21. $x + 2y = 5$ 23. $y - 4 = \sqrt{3}(x - 1)$

Article 1–6

1. $-1 < 0$ 3. $2 < 3$ 5. $-3 < -2$ 7. $\sqrt{2} < 2$ 9. $\frac{1}{3} < \frac{1}{2}$

Article 1–7

1. $\{x \mid -4 < x < 4\}$ 3. $\{x \mid -3 \leq x \leq 7\}$

5. $\{x \mid x \leq -\frac{1}{2} \text{ or } x > \frac{9}{2}\}$ 7. $\{x \mid x < -1 \text{ or } x > 5\}$

9. $\{x \mid -\frac{7}{2} \leq x \leq \frac{1}{2}\}$ 11. $\{x \mid 0 \leq x \leq 3\}$

13. $\{(x, y) \mid -1 < x < 1\}$ 15. $\{(x, y) \mid x = y \text{ or } x = -y\}$

17. $\{(x, y) \mid y > x, y > -x, y < x, y < -x\}$

19. $\{(x, y) \mid -2 < x + y < 2\}$

21. $\{(x, y) \mid y = 1 - x \text{ or } x - 1 \text{ for } 0 \leq x \leq 1 \text{ and } y = x + 1 \text{ or } -x - 1$ for $-1 \leq x \leq 0\}$

23. $\{(x, y) \mid 2 < x < 4 \text{ and } -3 < y < 7\}$

Article 1–8

3. True   5. False, e.g., if $|a| = 1$ and $|b| = 0.5$

7. False, e.g., $|a| = 1$ and $|b| = \frac{1}{2}$

Article 1–9

1. $\{t \mid -3 < t < 7, t \neq 2\}$; this deleted neighborhood is 10 units in length.
3. $t + 2; 4$ 5. $-1/tx, -1/x^2$

CHAPTER 1: MISCELLANEOUS

1. (b) $-\frac{3}{2}, \frac{2}{3}, -\frac{3}{2}, \frac{2}{3}, 0, \infty$

   (c) Yes, $ABCD$ (d) Yes, AEB (e) Yes, C and D

   (f) $2y + 3x = 26; 2y + 3x = 0; 3y - 2x + 13 = 0; y = 6; x = 2$

(g)

L	$\overleftrightarrow{AB}$	$\overleftrightarrow{CD}$	$\overleftrightarrow{AD}$	$\overleftrightarrow{CE}$	$\overleftrightarrow{BD}$
y-intercept	13	0	$-\frac{13}{3}$	6	none
x-intercept	$\frac{26}{3}$	0	$\frac{13}{2}$	none	2

3. (a) No   (b) No   (c) Outside   (d) $(-2, -\frac{9}{7})$
5. $[(x_1 + x_2)/2, (y_1 + y_2)/2]$
7. (a) $-a/b$ (b) $-c/b$ (c) $-c/a$ (d) $ay - bx = 0$
9. Four; centers: $(0, \sqrt{5} - 2), (0, -\sqrt{5} - 2), (-\sqrt{5} - 1, 1), (\sqrt{5} - 1, 1)$
   Radii (in same order): $(3\sqrt{2} - \sqrt{10})/2, (3\sqrt{2} + \sqrt{10})/2,$
   $$(\sqrt{10} + \sqrt{2})/2, (\sqrt{10} - \sqrt{2})/2$$
13. $x + 5y = \pm 5\sqrt{2}$
17. $|t + 3| < |t - b|$ 19. $|t - 2| > |t - b|$
21. $x \geq 1, x \leq -1$ 23. $-4 \leq x \leq -3$

CHAPTER 2

Article 2–1

1. (a) Increasing   (b) Bounded below by -1, above by 9.
3. (c) None   (d) $(0, 1)$
5. (a) Neither increasing or decreasing in $[-\pi, \pi]$.
   (c) One at $x = 0$ (d) $[-1, 1]$

Article 2–2

1. Range: $\{f(x) \mid f(x) = 2 \text{ or } 0 \leq f(x) \leq 1\}$
   Two, one, many
   $\{f(x) = 2 \text{ for } -3 \leq x < 0\}$
3. $f(x) = -2x, -3 \leq x \leq 0$ 5. $f(x) = -\sin x, -\pi \leq x < 0$
   $\quad\quad = 2x, 0 \leq x \leq 3$ $\quad\quad = \sin x, 0 \leq x \leq \pi$
7. $f(x) = x - 2, 2 \leq x \leq 5$ 9. $f(x) = x - 1, 1 \leq x \leq 3$
   $\quad\quad = -x + 2, 0 \leq x < 2$ $\quad\quad = -x + 1, -1 \leq x < 1$

11. $\{x \mid x > 1\}$

13. $\{x \mid x \le 1, x \ne 0\}$

15. $\{x \mid -1 \le x \le 3\}$

17. $\{x \mid -1 \le x \le 0, x \ge 1\}$

19. $\{x \mid -\infty < x < \infty\}$

21. $\{x \mid x \ne 0\}$

23. $|1 - x| = 1 - x$ if $x \le 1; |1 - x| = x - 1$ if $x \ge 1$

Article 2–3

3. $r(x) = s(x) = v(x)$

5. $f(x) = x^2 + 1/x; f(2) = 4\frac{1}{2}; f(-1) = 0$

   $f(1/x) = 1/x^2 + x; f(x + \Delta x) = (x + \Delta x)^2 + 1/(x + \Delta x)$

11. $h = \dfrac{V}{lw}$

13. (a) If $h = 0$, then $\Delta f(x, h) = 0$.

   (b) $\Delta f(0, 0) = 0$

   $\Delta f(-2, 4) = 0$

   $\Delta f(0.0001, -0.0001) = -10^{-8}$

   (c) $-5 \le \Delta f < 7$

Article 2–4

1. $D_f = \{x \mid -\infty < x < \infty\}$

   $D_g = \{x \mid x \ge 1\}$

   $D_{f+g} = D_{f \cdot g} = D_{g/f} = \{x \mid x \ge 1\}$

   $D_{f/g} = \{x \mid x > 1\}$

3. $D_f = \{x \mid x \ge 0\}$

   $D_g = \{x \mid x \ge -1\}$

   $D_{f+g} = D_{f \cdot g} = D_{f/g} = \{x \mid x \ge 0\}$

   $D_{g/f} = \{x \mid x > 0\}$

7. (a) $D_g = (-8, 8)$ (b) $D_h = (-4/3, 4/3)$ (c) $D_k = (-1, 1)$

   $\quad\quad R_g = [0, 6)$ $R_h = [0, 6)$ $R_k = [0, 6)$

9. $R_f = \{0, \frac{1}{3}, \frac{2}{3}\}$

Article 2–5

1. (a) $m(h) = 2; m(4) = 2$

   (c) $m(h) = \dfrac{-1}{x_1(x_1 + h)}; m\left(\dfrac{1}{4}\right) = -\dfrac{4}{5}$

   (e) $m(h) = \dfrac{|x_1 + h| - |x_1|}{h}; m\left(\dfrac{1}{2}\right) = -1$

3. True   5. False   7. True

9. $L = 4, \epsilon = 0.6$ 11. $L = 6, \epsilon \ge \frac{3}{4}$

Article 2–6

1. 0   3. 0   5. -8 7. 0   9. $3 - 8a$

m	horizontal tangent
11. $2x - 2$	$x = 1$
13. $-2x$	$x = 0$
15. $2x + 3$	$x = -3/2$
17. $6x^2 + 6x - 12$	$x = -2, x = 1$
19. $3x^2 - 2$	$x = 2, x = -2$
21. $3x^2 - 6x$	$x = 0, x = 2$
23. $\dfrac{2x\lvert x^2 - 4\rvert}{x^2 - 4}$	$x = 0$
25. $\dfrac{-2(x + 2)}{(x^2 + 4x)^2}$	$x = -2$

Article 2–7

1. 2 3. $3x^2$ 5. $-\dfrac{1}{x^2}$ 7. $\dfrac{-2}{(2x + 1)^2}$ 9. $4x - 1$

11. $4x^3$ 13. $\dfrac{x^2 + 1}{x^2}$ 15. $(2x)^{-1/2}$ 17. $(2x + 3)^{-1/2}$

19. $-(2x + 3)^{-3/2}$ 21. $R_{f^1} = \{-1, 1\}; f'(x) = \dfrac{\lvert x\rvert}{x}, x \neq 0$

Article 2–8

3. $gt + v_0$ 5. $2t - 3$ 7. $8t + 12$ 9. $-4t$

11. (a) 32 ft/sec   (b) -16 ft/sec   (c) 0 ft/sec

13. (a) $2\pi r + \pi \, \Delta r$ (b) $2\pi r$ 15. πh^2

CHAPTER 2: MISCELLANEOUS

1. $x = \sqrt{(y + 2)/(y - 1)}; y \leq -2, y > 1$

3. (a) $D = \{x \mid x \neq -1; R = \{y \mid y \neq 0\}$

   (c) $D = \{x \mid x \geq 0\}; R = \{y \mid 0 < y \leq 1\}$

5. For $y \leq 4, x = y - 2$; for $y > 4, x = (y + 2)/3$

7. $x = \dfrac{y + \sqrt{y^2 - 4}}{2}$ or $x = \dfrac{y - \sqrt{y^2 - 4}}{2}, \lvert y\rvert \geq 2$

9. (a) $f(-2) = -3$

   $f(x_1 + \Delta x) = x_1^2 + 2x_1 \, \Delta x + (\Delta x)^2 + 2x_1 + 2 \, \Delta x - 3$

11. $R = \{y \mid -2 \leq y \leq 6\}$ 19. $2/(x + 1)^2$

21. $\frac{1}{3}x^{-2/3}$ 23. $-1/3x^2 + 2$ 25. (a) 6 (b) $P(0, 2)$

27. $m = 180 - 32x_1$; horizontal tangent at $(5\frac{5}{8}, 506\frac{1}{4})$

29. (a) $-1/V^2$ (b) $-\frac{1}{4}$

31. (a) Weakly increasing and weakly decreasing

   (c) Weakly increasing   (e) Increasing

   (g) Not monotone; strongly monotone, if domain is divided into the parts
   $x < 0$ and $x > 0$.

CHAPTER 3

Article 3–1

1. $L = -1, N = \left\{ x \mid 0 < |x - 2| < \frac{\epsilon}{3} \right\}$

3. $L = 2, N = \left\{ x \mid 0 < |x - 2| < \frac{2\epsilon}{2 + \epsilon} \right\}$

5. $L = 6, N = \{ x \mid 0 < |x - 5| < \epsilon \}$

7. $L = -\frac{1}{9} ; N = \left\{ x \mid 0 < |x - 3| < N \quad \text{where} \right.$

$$N = \min \left\{ \left| \frac{-27\epsilon}{1 + 9\epsilon} \right|, \ \left| \frac{27\epsilon}{1 - 9\epsilon} \right| \right\} \right\}$$

Article 3–2

1. 4   3. 4   5. 2   7. 5   9. 4   11. 1   13. 25

15. 1   17. 1   19. $f(x) = \dfrac{x^2 + x - 1}{x} ; \ g(x) = \dfrac{x + 1}{x}$

Article 3–3

1. (a) -10 (b) -20 3. 18   5. 36   7. 2   9. 4   11. -1

13. (a) $\frac{2}{5}$ (b) $\frac{2}{15}$ 15. 10   17. $\frac{1}{10}$ 19. 0   21. $f(x) = 1/x; \ g(x) = x^2$

Article 3–4

1. $\frac{2}{5}$ 3. ∞ 5. 0   7. ∞ 9. $\frac{1}{2}$

11. ∞ 17. (a) Yes   (b) Yes   (c) No   19. 2

CHAPTER 3: MISCELLANEOUS

1. $\frac{1}{2}$ 3. $\frac{3}{7}$ 5. Does not exist   7. 0   9. $\sqrt{x}/2x$ 11. ∞

13. $-\frac{1}{10}$ 21. 0   25. -1 27. 0   29. Does not exist   31. 4

CHAPTER 4

Article 4–1

1. $v = 2t - 4, a = 2$ 3. $v = gt + v_\circ, a = g$ 5. $v = 8t + 12, a = 8$

7. $y' = 15(x^2 - x^4)$ 9. $y' = x^3 - x^2 + x - 1$
$\ \ \ y'' = 30(x - 2x^3)$ $y'' = 3x^2 - 2x + 1$

11. $y' = 2x^3 - 3x - 1$ 13. $y' = 5x^4 - 2x$
$\ \ \ \ y'' = 6x^2 - 3$ $\ \ \ y'' = 20x^3 - 2$

15. $y' = 12x + 13$ 17. $y = 8x - 5$
$\ \ \ \ y'' = 12$

19. $(-1, 27), (2, 0)$ 21. $a = -3, b = 2, c = 1$

Article 4–2

1. $x^2 - x + 1$ 3. $10x(x^2 + 1)^4$

5. $-2(2x^2 + 3x - 1)(x + 1)(x^2 + 1)^{-4}$ 7. $-19/(3x - 2)^2$

9. $(1 - t^2)/(t^2 + 1)^2$ 11. $-2(2t - 1)(t^2 - t)^{-3}$

13. $(2 - 6t^2)/(3t^2 + 1)^2$ 15. $3(2t + 3)(t^2 + 3t)^2$

Article 4–3

1. $-x/y$

3. $-(2x+y)/x$

5. $\dfrac{3x^2}{2y}$

7. $-(y/x)^{1/2}$

9. $\dfrac{y}{x} - (x+y)^2$

11. $(2x^2+1)(x^2+1)^{-1/2}$

13. $\dfrac{1-2y}{2x+2y-1}$

15. $\dfrac{2x}{y(x^2+1)^2}$

17. $5(3x+7)^4/(2y^2)$

19. $-y^2/x^2$

21. $(2x-1)/(2y)$

23. $-\dfrac{x^2+9}{3x^2(x^2+3)^{2/3}}$

25. $dy/dx = -x/y;\ d^2y/dx^2 = -1/y^3$

27. $dy/dx = -x^{-1/3}y^{1/3};\ d^2y/dx^2 = \frac{1}{3}x^{-4/3}y^{-1/3}$

31. $3x - 4y = 25;\ 4x + 3y = 0$ 33. $x - 3y = 0;\ 3x + y = 10$

Article 4–4

1. (a) $(2x+2)\,\Delta x + (\Delta x)^2$ (b) $(2x+2)\,\Delta x$ (c) $(\Delta x)^2$

3. (a) $(3x^2-1)\,\Delta x + 3x\,(\Delta x)^2 + (\Delta x)^3$ (c) $3x\,(\Delta x)^2 + (\Delta x)^3$

5. (a) $-\dfrac{\Delta x}{x(x+\Delta x)}$ (b) $-\Delta x/x^2$ (c) $\dfrac{(\Delta x)^2}{x^2(x+\Delta x)}$

7. 1.96   9. 5.16

Article 4–5

1. $9y = (x-1)^2$ 3. $y = \left(\dfrac{x}{1+x}\right)^2$ 5. -3

7. $\dfrac{1}{2(x+1)^2}$ 9. $18x + \dfrac{1}{3x^2}$

Article 4–7

1. $(3x^2-6x+5)\,dx$ 3. $-\dfrac{2xy+y^2}{2xy+x^2}\,dx$ 5. $\dfrac{1-2x^2}{\sqrt{1-x^2}}\,dx$

7. $3(1-x)^2(2x-1)(2-3x)^{-2}\,dx$

9. 12.04   11. 2.03   13. 79.69

15. (c) $15x - y = 20$ 17. (c) $9x + y = 6$ 19. $-4t^3(t^2-1)^{-3}$

Article 4–8

3. Continuous   5. Max $= 1$, min $= 0$

7. Take $a = 0, b = 1$, and $N = 0$ in Theorem 3, part (ii).

CHAPTER 4: MISCELLANEOUS

1. $-4(x^2-4)^{-3/2}$ 3. $-y/(x+2y)$ 5. $-\dfrac{y^2+2xy}{x^2+2xy}$

7. $(1-x^2)^{-3/2}$ 9. $(x+1)^{-2}$

11. $(3x^3 - 2a^2x)/\sqrt{x^2-a^2}$ 13. $2x(1-x^2)^{-2}$

15. $-\dfrac{2x+1}{2}\,(x^2+x-1)^{-3/2}$ 17. $\dfrac{4x+5}{2}\,\sqrt{2x^2+5x}$

19. $-\dfrac{y}{x}\left(\dfrac{2y\sqrt{xy}+1}{4y\sqrt{xy}+1}\right)$ 21. $-(y/x)^{1/3}$ 23. $-y/x$

25. $-\dfrac{1}{2}\left(\dfrac{x+2y+y^2}{x+2y+xy}\right)$ 27. $\dfrac{1}{2y(x+1)^2}$ 29. $-\dfrac{y+2}{x+3}$

31. $\dfrac{4x+8}{\sqrt{4x^2+16x+15}}$ 33. $2x\left[1+\dfrac{(1-x^2)}{(1+x^2)^3}\right]$

35. $y+2x=6$ 37. $m=2,\,y-2x=-5$

39. (a) $10(x^2+2x)^4(x+1)$ (b) $(3t^2-2t)^{-1/2}$

   (c) $r[(r^2+5)^{-1/2}+(r^2-5)^{-1/2}]$ (d) $\dfrac{4x}{(x^2+1)^2}$

41. $y+x=3$ 43. $-6(2-3x),\,f(x)=(2-3x)^2$

45. $6\pi(\Delta r)^2$; a shell around the can with thickness Δr.

47. $x_1=40$, fare $=20\not{c}$ 49. $(x-1)(2x-1)$ 51. 56 ft/sec

53. (a) $h+2k=5$ (b) $h=-4,\,k=\frac{9}{2},\,r=5\sqrt{5}/2$

55. $\dfrac{2}{3(2y+1)(2x+1)\sqrt{x^2+x}}$ 57. $\dfrac{3}{(x+1)^2}\sin\left[\left(\dfrac{2x-1}{x+1}\right)^2\right]$

59. $a=-32$ 61. $-\frac{3}{32}$

67. $\sqrt{26}\approx5.1$ $\sqrt[3]{26}\approx2.963,\,y=x^{1/3}$. $x=27,\,\Delta x=-1$

69. $14\pm.046$ ft   75. $m=\frac{1}{2},\,C=\sqrt{2}$

CHAPTER 5

Article 5–1

1. Falling $x<\frac{1}{2}$, rising $x>\frac{1}{2}$. Low point at $(\frac{1}{2},\frac{3}{4})$.

3. Rising $x<0$, falling $0<x<1$, rising $x>1$.   High at $(0,3)$, low at $(1,2)$.

5. Falling $x<-2$, rising $-2<x<0$, falling $0<x<2$, rising $x>2$. Low points $(\pm2,0)$, high $(0,16)$.

Article 5–2

1. $\dfrac{dA}{dt}=2\pi r\dfrac{dr}{dt}$ 3. $\dfrac{8}{5\pi}$ ft/min   5. $\dfrac{ax+by}{\sqrt{x^2+y^2}}$ ft/sec

7. $\dfrac{10\sqrt{21}}{21}=2.2$ ft/sec   9. $\dfrac{125}{144\pi}$ ft/min

11. 8 ft/sec toward the lamppost.   13. 1500 ft/sec
   Decreasing 3 ft/sec.

15. Thickness decreasing at the rate of $\dfrac{5}{72\pi}$ in/min.   Area decreasing at the rate of $\frac{10}{3}$ in^2/min.

Article 5–4

1. (a) $x>2$ (b) $x<2$ (c) Always   (d) Never; $m(2,-1)$

3. (a) $-1<x<1$ (b) $x<-1,\,x>1$ (c) $x<0$
   (d) $x>0$; $M(1,6)$; $m(-1,2)$; $I(0,4)$

5. (a) $x<-2,\,x>2$ (b) $-2<x<2,\,x\ne0$ (c) $x>0$
   (d) $x<0$; $M(-2,-4)$; $m(2,4)$

In Problems 9 and 11: M = high turning point, m = low turning point.

9. $m(1, 1)$ 11. $m(2, 0)$ 13. $(1, -1)$ 15. $(2, 0), (1, \pm 1)$

19. Concave downward because $f''(x) = -\dfrac{1}{x^2}$ is negative.

21. (a) 3 times; on $(-\frac{5}{3}, -\frac{4}{3}), (-\frac{2}{3}, -\frac{1}{3}), (\frac{2}{3}, 1)$
    (b) Once; on $(-1.7, -1.6)$ (c) Once; on $(1.2, 1.3)$

Article 5–6

3. 32   5. Use one half of the fence parallel to the river.

7. $4'' \times 4'' \times 2''$ 9. 9 inches wide and 18 inches high

11. $(100 + c)/2$ 13. (a) 16   (b) -54 (c) -1
                                           (d) $f'(x) = 0$ when $2x^3 = a$ and then $f''(x) =$
                                               $+6$ or $+2$ according as $a \neq 0$ or $a = 0$

15. (a) $\dfrac{4L}{4 + 3\sqrt{3}}$ for the square, $\dfrac{3\sqrt{3}\,L}{4 + 3\sqrt{3}}$ for the triangle
    (b) Use it all for the square.

17. (a) $(c - \frac{1}{2}, \sqrt{c - \frac{1}{2}})$ (b) $(0, 0)$ 19. $\frac{4}{9}\pi r^3 \sqrt{3}$

21. Width $= \dfrac{2\sqrt{3}}{3}\, r$, depth $= \dfrac{2\sqrt{6}}{3}\, r$

23. $x = \dfrac{c\sqrt[3]{a}}{\sqrt[3]{a} + \sqrt[3]{b}}$ where x is the distance from the source of strength a.

25. $4/\pi$ 27. (a) 1   (b) 0

31. Before tax: production $= 7,500$; price $= \$1.25$, profit $= \$5,425$.
    After tax: production $= 7,000$; price $= \$1.30$; profit $= \$4,700$.
    To maximize his profit he should absorb 5¢ of the tax and add 5¢ to
    the price.

Article 5–8

1. $\frac{1}{2}$ 3. $\frac{8}{27}$ 5. $\frac{3}{2}$ 7. (a) $3\frac{1}{6}$ (b) 4.012   (c) 0.0101

CHAPTER 5: MISCELLANEOUS

1. (a) $x < \frac{9}{2}$ 3. (a) $x < 3$ 5. (a) $x > \sqrt[3]{2}$
   (b) $x > \frac{9}{2}$ (b) $x > 3$ (b) $x < \sqrt[3]{2}, x \neq 0$
   (c) No values   (c) $0 < x < 2$ (c) $x > 0, x < -\sqrt[3]{4}$
   (d) All values   (d) $x < 0, x > 2$ (d) $-\sqrt[3]{4} < x < 0$

7. (a) $x < 0$ 9. (a) $x \neq 0$ 11. (a) $x < -2b/a, x > 0$
   (b) $x > 0$ (b) Never   (b) $-2b/a < x < 0, x \neq -b/a$
   (c) $x \neq 0$ (c) $x < 0$ (c) $x > -b/a$
   (d) Never   (d) $x > 0$ (d) $x < -b/a$

13. (a) $x < -1, x > \frac{1}{3}$ (b) $-1 < x < \frac{1}{3}$
    (c) $x > -\frac{1}{3}$ (d) $x < -\frac{1}{3}$

15. (a) At $x = 1$; because y' goes from $+$ to $-$
    (b) At $x = 3$; because y' goes from $-$ to $+$

17. If $v = k/\sqrt{s}$, then $dv/dt = -k^2/2s^2$ 19. $\frac{1}{4}$ in/min

21. (a) Approx. 606 mph   (b) Approx. 0.83 mi

23. $-480\sqrt{2}/7$ 25. $a = -gR^2/s^2$

27. $(8/9\pi)$ ft/min   29. 10

31. $a = 1; b = -3; c = -9; d = 5$ 33. $r = 25$ ft

35. $r = 4, h = 4$ 37. $4\sqrt{3}$

39. (a) $(2, \pm\sqrt{3})$, (b) and (c) $(1, 0)$

41. Each $= S - b/2$ 53. 6 ft $\times$ 18 ft

55. $v = \sqrt[n]{\dfrac{a}{(n-1)b}}$ 57. Approx. 1.94 gal

59. (a) True;   (b) Not necessarily true; $f(x) = g(x) = 5 + x + x^3$ for $|x| \le 1, a = 0$.

61. Doesn't apply; derivative doesn't exist at $x = 0$.

63. $c = \pm \left(\dfrac{a^{2/3} + a^{1/3}b^{1/3} + b^{2/3}}{3} \right)^{3/2}$

CHAPTER 6

Article 6–2

1. $y = \dfrac{x^3}{3} + x + C$ 3. $y^2 = x^2 + C$

5. $y^{2/3} = x^{2/3} + C$ 7. $y = x^3 - x^2 + 5x + C$

9. $r = (2z + 1)^4/8 + C$ 11. $x^{1/2} = 4t + C$

13. $y = z^3/3 - z^{-1} + C$ 15. $\dfrac{x^3}{3} - \dfrac{2x^{3/2}}{3} + C$

17. $\dfrac{-3(2 - 7t)^{5/3}}{35} + C$ 19. $\dfrac{-1}{9x + 6} + C$

21. $\dfrac{(2x^2 + 1)^{3/2}}{6} + C$ 23. $\frac{1}{2}\sqrt{2y^2 + 1} + C$

25. $\frac{3}{4}(z^2 + 2z + 2)^{2/3} + C$

Article 6–3

1. $s = t^3 + s_0$ 3. $s = \frac{1}{3}(t + 1)^3 + s_0 - \frac{1}{3}$

5. $s = -(t + 1)^{-1} + s_0 + 1$ 7. $v = gt + v_0$
    $s = \frac{1}{2}gt^2 + v_0 t + s_0$

9. $v = \frac{3}{8}(2t + 1)^{4/3} + v_0 - \frac{3}{8}$
   $s = \frac{9}{112}(2t + 1)^{7/3} + (v_0 - \frac{3}{8})t + s_0 - \frac{9}{112}$

11. $v = \frac{1}{5}t^5 + \frac{2}{3}t^3 + t + v_0$
    $s = \frac{1}{30}t^6 + \frac{1}{6}t^4 + \frac{1}{2}t^2 + v_0 t + s_0$

13. $4\sqrt{y} = x^2 + 4$ 15. $y = \frac{1}{3}(1 + x^2)^{3/2} - \frac{10}{3}$

Article 6–4

9. $\cos^2 A + \sin^2 A = \cos 0 = 1$

11. $\tan (A - B) = \dfrac{\tan A - \tan B}{1 + \tan A \tan B}$

15. $\cos 2A = \cos^2 A - \sin^2 A$, $\sin 2A = 2 \sin A \cos A$

Article 6–5

1. 1 3. 2 5. $\frac{5}{3}$ 7. 0 9. $\frac{1}{2}$ 11. $\frac{3}{5}$

13. 2π 15. $\frac{1}{2}$ 17. 2 19. $-\sin a$

21. $3 \cos (3x + 4)$ 23. $(x \cos x - \sin x)/x^2$

25. $3x^2 \cos 3x + 2x \sin 3x$ 27. 0

29. $6 \cos 2x + 8 \sin 2x$ 31. $2(\cos^2 x - \sin^2 x)$ or $2 \cos 2x$

33. $-6 \cos 3x \sin 3x$ or $-3 \sin 6x$ 35. $\dfrac{\sin 2y + 2y \sin 2x}{\cos 2x - 2x \cos 2y}$

41. $\frac{1}{2} \sin (2x + 4) + C$ 43. $2 \sin \sqrt{x} + C$

45. $\frac{1}{3} \sin (3\theta - 1) + C$ 47. $\sin^2 z + C$

49. $-\frac{1}{6} \cos^3 2y + C$ 51. $1/\cos x + C$

53. $\frac{2}{9}(2 + \sin 3t)^{3/2} + C$ 55. $\dfrac{1}{2} \sin^4 \dfrac{y}{2} + C$

57. $-\dfrac{1}{2} \cos^3 \dfrac{2x}{3} + C$ 59. $-\frac{3}{2} \cos 2x + \frac{4}{3} \sin 3x + C$

Article 6–6

1. 1.75, 2.25 3. $\pi/(2\sqrt{2}) \approx 1.12$, $(\pi/2)(1 + \sqrt{2}/2) \approx 2.68$

5. 4.146, 6.146

Article 6–8

1. 12 3. $8\frac{2}{3}$ 5. $\frac{1}{15}$ 7. 10 9. 1

11. $\frac{1}{2}$ 13. 2 15. $\frac{4}{3}$ 17. $\pi/6$

Article 6–9

1. (a) $c_k = \frac{1}{2}(x_k + x_{k-1})$

(b) $c_k = \pm \sqrt{\dfrac{x_{k-1}^2 + x_{k-1}x_k + x_k^2}{3}}$,

the sign being determined by the interval x_{k-1}, x_k.

(c) $c_k = \sqrt[3]{\dfrac{x_{k-1}^3 + x_{k-1}^2 x_k + x_{k-1}x_k^2 + x_k^3}{4}}$

(d) $c_k = \left(\dfrac{\sqrt{x_{k-1}} + \sqrt{x_k}}{2}\right)^2$

5. $S_n = 2(\sqrt{b} - 1)$ 7. $\frac{7}{3}$ 9. $\frac{13}{3}$

11. 0 13. $\frac{1}{2}$ 15. π/ω

17. (a) $A = \lim\limits_{n \to \infty} \sum\limits_{k=1}^{n} (18 - 2x_k^2) \Delta x_k$, $(x_1 = -3, x_{n+1} = 3)$

(b) $A = \int_{-3}^{3} (18 - 2x^2)\, dx = 72$

19. $\sqrt{1 + x^2}$ 21. $\sqrt{1 - x^2}$

23. $2 \cos (4x^2)$ 25. $(-\cos x)/(2 + \sin x)$

Article 6–10   (I $=$ integral, A $=$ approximation)

3. I $= 4$, A $= 4.25$ 5. I $= \frac{1}{2}$, A ≈ 0.53

Article 6–12

1. $\int_{a}^{b} f(t)\, dt = -\int_{b}^{a} f(t)\, dt$

$\int_{a}^{c} f(t)\, dt = \int_{a}^{b} f(t)\, dt + \int_{b}^{c} f(t)\, dt$

$\dfrac{d}{dx} \int_{a}^{x} f(t)\, dt = f(x)$

$\int_{a}^{b} f(t)\, dt = f(c) \cdot (b - a)$

$\int_{a}^{b} f(t)\, dt = F(b) - F(a)$

3. (a) $F'(\frac{1}{2}) = \frac{1}{2}$, $F'(\frac{3}{2}) = -1$

(b) $F'(\frac{1}{2}) = \sqrt{2}/2$, $F'(\frac{3}{2}) = (\frac{9}{2})^{-1/3}$

(c) $F'(\frac{1}{2}) = \frac{2}{3}$, $F'(\frac{3}{2}) = -\frac{2}{5}$

CHAPTER 6: MISCELLANEOUS

1. $x^2 y + 2 = cy$

3. $y^3 + 3y = x^3 - 3x + c$

5. $(y - 3)^{-1} = (x + 2)^{-1} + c$

7. Yes; $y = x$ is such a curve.

9. $(2\sqrt{2}/3)b^{3/4}$

11. $v = t^2 + 3t + 4$, $\Delta s = 61\frac{1}{3}$

13. $h(10) = h(0) = 5$

15. (a) $k = 38.72$ ft/sec^2 (b) 25 ft

17. $h = 96t - 16t^2$; 144 ft

19. (a) ≈ 1.75 (b) ≈ 1.72

21. $(x^2/2) - x^{-1} + c$

23. $-\frac{1}{8}(1 + t^{4/3})^{-6} + c$

25. $-\frac{3}{5}(7 - 5r)^{1/3} + c$

27. $\frac{1}{9} \sin^3 3x + c$

29. $\frac{1}{2} \sin (2x - 1) + c$

31. $-\sqrt{2/t} + c$

33. $\frac{1}{3}(2 - 3x)^{-1} + c$

35. $-\csc^2 x$

37. $20 \sin^3 5x \cos 5x$

39. 0

45. Yes; no; applies to identities, but not to equations.

47. $|3a\omega \sin \theta \cos \theta|$

49. (a) $\frac{10}{3}$ (b) $\frac{5}{3}$ (c) $\frac{1}{2}$

51. $\int_{0}^{1} f(x)\, dx$

53. $d^2y/dx^2 = 4y$

CHAPTER 7

Article 7–2

1. (a) $\lim\limits_{\Delta y \to 0} \sum\limits_{a}^{b} (f(y) - g(y)) \Delta y$ (b) $\int_{a}^{b} (f(y) - g(y))\, dy$

3. $\frac{1}{12}$ 5. $\frac{32}{3}$ 7. $\frac{4}{3}$ 9. $\sqrt{2} - 1$ 11. $\frac{1}{6}$

Article 7–3

1. 6 ft
3. $3\frac{2}{3}$ ft
5. 6 ft
7. $2\sqrt{2}$ ft
9. $6 - \sin 2 \approx 5.09$ ft
11. $2g$
13. $3\frac{1}{6}$ ft
15. 6.45 ft; 3.22 ft/sec

Article 7–4

1. $\dfrac{8\pi}{3}$
3. $\dfrac{\pi}{30}$
5. $\dfrac{8\pi}{3}$
7. $\dfrac{256\pi}{5}$
9. (a) $\dfrac{\pi r^2 h}{3}$
(b) $\frac{2}{3}\pi h^2 r$

11. (a) 8π
(b) $\dfrac{512\pi}{15}$
(c) $\dfrac{256\pi}{5}$
(d) $\dfrac{1088\pi}{15}$
(e) $\dfrac{128\pi}{3}$

13. $\frac{4}{3}\pi ab^2$
15. $\dfrac{16a^3}{3}$
17. $\dfrac{8a^3}{3}$
19. 15,990 ft^3

Article 7–6

1. 12
3. $\frac{14}{3}$
5. $\frac{123}{32}$
7. $\dfrac{a\pi^2}{8}$
9. $\frac{21}{2}$

Article 7–7

1. $\dfrac{12\pi a^2}{5}$
3. $\dfrac{\pi}{27}(10\sqrt{10} - 1)$
5. $\dfrac{1823\pi}{18}$
7. $\dfrac{2\pi}{3}(26\sqrt{26} - 2\sqrt{2})$

Article 7–8

1. (a) $2/\pi$ (b) 0
3. $\frac{49}{12}$
5. $\dfrac{a+b}{2}\alpha + \beta$
7. $4a/\pi$
9. $2a^2$

Article 7–9

1. $\left(\dfrac{4a}{3\pi}, \dfrac{4a}{3\pi}\right)$
3. $\left(\dfrac{2a}{12 - 3\pi}, \dfrac{2a}{12 - 3\pi}\right)$

5. $(\frac{2}{5}, 1)$
7. $\frac{3}{5}h$

9. On the axis, $\frac{3}{5}h$ from vertex
11. $\left(0, \dfrac{\pi}{4}r\right)$

Article 7–10

1. $(0, \frac{2}{5}c^2)$
3. $(0, \frac{12}{5})$
5. $(\frac{3}{5}, 1)$
7. $(0, \frac{8}{3}, 0)$

9. On the axis, $\frac{2}{3}h$ from the vertex
11. $\dfrac{17\sqrt{17} - 1}{12}$

Article 7–11

1. $c = 5$ lb/in; 80 in-lb
3. $\frac{1}{2}k$, where k is the proportionality factor.

5. $\frac{1}{2}mgR$
9. $\dfrac{200\pi}{3}$ ft-tons

CHAPTER 7: MISCELLANEOUS

1. $\frac{9}{2}$
3. 1
5. $\frac{9}{2}$
7. 18
9. $a^2/6$
11. 8
13. $\frac{13}{3}$
15. $\frac{64}{3}$
17. (a) $\frac{3}{7}$ (b) $\frac{3}{8}$ (c) $y = 3/2(1 + 3x)^{-1/2}$ (d) $\frac{3}{7}$
19. (a) $3^5\pi/5$ (b) $189\pi/2$ (c) $81\pi/2$ (d) $2^9\pi/15$ (e) $2^7\pi/3$

21. $32\pi/3$ 23. $V = 2\pi \int_0^2 x^2/\sqrt{x^3 + 8}\, dx = (8\pi/3)(2 - \sqrt{2})$

25. $112\pi a^3/15$ 27. $\pi^2/4$ 29. $2\sqrt{3}a^3$ 31. $153\pi/40$

33. $\dfrac{a}{3}(3\sqrt{3} - 1)$ 35. (a) $f(x) = a \pm x\sqrt{A^2 - 1},\, |A| \geq 1$ (b) No

37. Vol. $= 401\pi$ cu units; Av. area $= 40.1\pi$ sq units   39. $(\frac{3}{2}, \frac{12}{5})$

41. $(\frac{3}{4}, \frac{3}{10})$ 43. (a) $(5a/7, 0)$ (b) $(2a/3, 0)$

45. $wr[1 - r/2R]$ ft-lb, $R =$ radius of earth in feet

CHAPTER 8

Article 8-1

13. $6x \sec^2 (3x^2)$

15. $-3 \csc^2 (3x + 5)$

17. 0

19. $3(1 + \sec^2 3x)$

21. $-\tan^2 x$

23. $-2 \csc x (\csc x + \cot x)^2$

25. $\frac{1}{2}(1 - \cos 2x)$, or $\sin^2 x$

27. $-\cos^3 (x/3)$

29. $\dfrac{x}{2} \sin \dfrac{x}{2}$

31. $3(\sin^2 x \cos x - \cos 3x)$

33. $-\dfrac{\cos^2 (xy) + y}{x}$

35. max $y = 3/2$ when $x = \pi/6$,
    min $y = 1$ when $x = 0$ or $\pi/2$

39. $120°$

41. $\frac{1}{2} \tan 2\theta + C$

43. $\frac{1}{3} \sec^3 x + C$

45. $\frac{1}{2}y + \frac{1}{4} \sin 2y + C$

47. $-3 \cot (\theta/3) + C$

49. $\pi \left(1 - \dfrac{\pi}{4}\right)$

Article 8-2

1. $\dfrac{\sqrt{3}}{2}, \dfrac{\sqrt{3}}{3}, \dfrac{2\sqrt{3}}{3}, 2$ 3. π

5. $-\pi/3$

Article 8-3

5. $\dfrac{1}{\sqrt{4 - x^2}}$

7. $\dfrac{1}{|x|\sqrt{25x^2 - 1}}$

9. $\dfrac{4}{4 + x^2}$

11. $\dfrac{1}{x^2 + 1}$

13. $(\sin^{-1} x)^2$

15. $\sqrt{b(a + b)}$ ft

17. $\pi/2$

19. $-\pi/12$

21. $\pi/6$

Article 8-4

1. 0.1826 3. 0.6938 5. (a) Circumscribed   (b) Inscribed

7. $\ln 2 \approx \frac{2}{3}$ 9. (d) $n \geq 4$

Article 8-5

1. $\dfrac{2x + 2}{x^2 + 2x}$

3. $-\tan x$

5. $\dfrac{2x^2 + 1}{x^3 + x}$

7. $\ln x$

9. $\dfrac{1}{1 - x^2}$

11. $\dfrac{2}{x(2 + 3x)}$

13. $\dfrac{\tan^{-1} x}{x^2}$

15. $2 \cos (\ln x)$

17. $\ln (a^2 + x^2)$

19. $\frac{1}{2} \ln |2x + 3| + C$ 21. $\frac{1}{8} \ln (4x^2 + 1) + C$ 23. $\ln |\sin x| + C$

25. $x - \ln |x + 1| + C$ 27. $-\frac{1}{2} \ln |1 - x^2| + C$ 29. $\frac{1}{3} (\ln x)^3 + C$

Article 8–6

1. $4a$ 3. $3a/2$ 5. $2a - 2b$ 7. $2b - 3a$ 9. $2b - a$

Article 8–7

3. Slope at $(x, y) = y$. Concave up, because $y'' = y' = y$ is positive.

7. $\log_{10} N = \dfrac{\ln N}{\ln 10}$

Article 8–8

1. (a) x (b) x (c) x^{-2} (d) $-x^2$

   (e) $1/x$ (f) $-x$ (g) $1/x$ (h) x

   (i) $2x$ (j) x^2 (k) $x - x^2$ (l) $-2x + 2 \ln x$

   (m) xe^x (n) x/y^2

3. $13e^{2x} \cos 3x$ 5. $\frac{1}{2}(e^x + e^{-x})$ 7. $\dfrac{4}{(e^x + e^{-x})^2}$

9. $-4xe^{-2x}$ 11. xe^{ax} 13. $2e^{-x^2}(x - x^3)$

15. $\dfrac{e^x}{1 + e^{2x}}$ 17. $\frac{2}{3}e^{2x} \sec (x + 3y) - \frac{1}{3}$

19. $(\cos^2 y)\left(e^x + \dfrac{1}{x}\right)$ 23. $\frac{1}{2}e^{x^2} + C$

25. $3e^{x/3} + C$ 27. $\frac{1}{2} \ln |1 + 2e^x| + C$ 29. $\ln |e^x + e^{-x}| + C$

Article 8–9

1. $\dfrac{y(2x + 1)}{2x(x + 1)}$ 3. $\dfrac{y(4x^3 + 6x^2 + x + 3)}{3x(x + 1)(x^2 + 1)}$

5. $y\left[\dfrac{\sin x}{x} + \cos x \cdot \ln x\right]$ 7. $y(\sec x \tan x) \ln 2$

11. $\frac{3}{8}$ 13. $(4 \ln 4)^{-1} \approx 0.180$ 15. $(2 \ln 4)^{-1} \approx 0.360$

Article 8–10

1. (a) 2 (b) $\frac{5}{3}$ (c) -2 (d) -2

3. $\log_{1.5} 2 = \dfrac{\ln 2}{\ln 1.5}$ 7. (a) 1.46 (b) 0.68 (c) 2.48

9. (a) $3^{\tan x} \sec^2 x \ln 3$ (b) $y\left[\dfrac{1}{x} \ln (x^2 + 1) + \dfrac{2x}{x^2 + 1} \ln x\right]$

   (c) $-2t (\ln 2)2^{-t^2}$ (d) $e^{-2\theta}(1 - 2\theta)$

Article 8–11

1. $\dfrac{mv_0}{k} [e^{kt/m} - 1]$ where $k < 0$ is a constant of proportionality.

3. $N_0 e^{kt}$ 5. $-1, 2$ 7. $\pm 3, \pm 2$

CHAPTER 8: MISCELLANEOUS

1. $2 \cos 2x$ 3. $2 \cos x + 2 \cos 2x$ 5. $-\csc y$ or $\dfrac{-1}{\sqrt{1 - x^2}}$

7. $-2 \cos (x/2)$ 9. $1 - \cos x$

11. $\dfrac{x \cos x - 2 \sin x}{x^3}$ $\begin{cases} y \to \infty \text{ as } x \to 0 \\ y \to 0 \text{ as } x \to \infty \end{cases}$

13. $2x \sin \dfrac{1}{x} - \cos \dfrac{1}{x}$ $\begin{cases} y \to 0 \text{ as } x \to 0 \\ y \to \infty \text{ as } x \to \infty \end{cases}$

15. (a) $\frac{1}{2}(e^x - e^{-x})$ (b) $\frac{1}{2}(e^x + e^{-x})$ (c) $4(e^x + e^{-x})^{-2}$

17. (a) $1 + \ln x$ (b) $2x^{-1/2} \ln x + x^{-1/2}$

19. $e^{-x}(2 \cos 2x - \sin 2x)$

21. (a) $1 - e^x$ (b) $(1 - e^x)e^{(x - e^x)}$

23. $(1 - x^2)^{-1}$ 25. $\tan^{-1}(x/2) + 2x/(x^2 + 4)$

27. $2 \sec x$ 29. $2x(1 - x^4)^{-1/2} - (2x^2 + 1)e^{x^2}$

31. $2x(2 - x)(x^2 + 2)^{1-x} - (x^2 + 2)^{2-x} \ln (x^2 + 2)$

33. $1/x(x^2 + 1)$ 35. $(6x + 4)/(3x^2 + 4x)$

37. $3(1 + \ln x)$ 39. 1 41. e^x

43. (a) $(1 - x^2)/(1 + x^2)^2$
    (b) $\frac{2}{3}(x^2 + x - 1)x^{-2/3}(x - 2)^{-2/3}(x^2 + 1)^{-4/3}$

45. (a) $a^{x^2-x}(2x - 1) \ln a$ (b) $(1 + e^x)^{-1}$
    (c) $x^x(1 + \ln x)$ (d) $x^{(1-2x)/x}(1 - \ln x)$

49. $\dfrac{d^2y}{dx^2} = 4(e^x + e^{-x})^{-2}$ 53. $E = E_0 e^{-t/40}$
    $y = \ln (e^x + e^{-x}) + c$ $t = 92.1$ sec

55. $\pi^2/2$ 57. $y = 1 - \frac{1}{2}(e^x + e^{-x})$

59. $1 + 4 \ln \frac{3}{2}$ 61. $y = 2e^x/(2 - e^x)$

65. $3\pi/8$ 67. (a) $\sec x$ (b) $\ln (1 + \sqrt{2})$

69. $\pi(e^4 - 1)/2$ 71. $y^2 = 4x$

73. (a) $y' = \ln x$ (b) 1.33 75. (a) $\frac{1}{6}$ (b) $x + \ln |x| + c$
                                                          (c) $\frac{1}{2}x - \frac{1}{4} \ln |2x + 1| + c$

77. $\pi \ln 4$ 79. (a) $\frac{1}{3} \ln 2$ 81. 585 lb
                              (b) $\frac{1}{2}(e^8 - e^{-1})$
                              (c) $\ln 3$

91. $\frac{1}{3}$ 93. $\frac{1}{7}$ 95. ∞ 97. 0 99. $\frac{1}{6}$

CHAPTER 9

Article 9–1

1. $\frac{1}{3}(2x + 3)^{3/2} + C$ 3. $\dfrac{-1}{2(2x - 7)} + C$

5. $-\ln |2 + \cos x| + C$ 7. $-\frac{1}{4}\sqrt{1 - 4x^2} + C$

9. $\dfrac{-1}{12(3x^2+4)^2}+C$

11. $\frac{2}{3}(x^3+5)^{1/2}+C$

13. $\frac{1}{2}e^{2x}+C$

15. $-\frac{1}{3}e^{-3x}+C$

17. $-\frac{1}{3}\cos^3 x+C$

19. $-\frac{1}{4}\cot^4 x+C$

21. $\frac{1}{2}\ln\left|e^{2x}-e^{-2x}\right|+C$

23. $-\frac{1}{4}(1+\cos\theta)^4+C$

25. $\ln|\sin x|+C$

27. $\frac{1}{3}\sec^3 x+C$

29. $\frac{1}{3}e^{\tan 3x}+C$

31. $-\frac{1}{2}(\csc 2x+\cot 2x)+C$

33. $-\sqrt{1+\cot 2t}+C$

35. $\frac{1}{2}e^{\tan^{-1}2t}+C$

37. $\dfrac{3^x}{\ln 3}+C$

39. (a) $-1;\ \frac{1}{2}(\ln x)^2+C$ (b) $2;\ \frac{1}{3}e^{x^3}+C$ (c) $-\frac{1}{2};\ -2\cos\sqrt{x}+C$

Article 9–2

1. $-\frac{2}{3}(1+\cos t)^{3/2}+C$

3. $\frac{1}{2}\ln|1+\tan 2x|+C$

5. $\sin x-\frac{1}{3}\sin^3 x+C$

7. (a) $\frac{1}{5}\cos^5 x-\frac{1}{3}\cos^3 x+C$
   (b) $\cos x+\sec x+C$

9. $\dfrac{\tan^{n+1}x}{n+1}+C$ if $n\neq-1$

   $\ln|\tan x|+C$ if $n=-1$

11. $\dfrac{-\cos^{n+1}x}{n+1}+C$ if $n\neq-1$

   $-\ln|\cos x|+C$ if $n=-1$

13. $-\frac{1}{8}\cos^4 2x+C$

15. $\frac{1}{9}\tan^3 3x+\frac{1}{3}\tan 3x+C$

17. $\frac{1}{4}\tan^2 2x+\frac{1}{2}\ln|\cos 2x|+C$

19. $\frac{1}{3}\cos^3 x-\cos x+C$

21. $\ln|2+\tan x|+C$

23. $\ln|1+e^x|+C$

25. $\ln|\ln 3x|+C$

27. $-\frac{1}{6}\csc^3 2t+C$

29. $-\dfrac{\cot^{n-1}ax}{(n-1)a}-\displaystyle\int\cot^{n-2}ax\,dx,$ $-\dfrac{\cot^3 3x}{9}+\dfrac{\cot 3x}{3}+x+C$

Article 9–3

1. $\frac{1}{3}\sin^3 x-\frac{1}{5}\sin^5 x+C$

3. $\frac{1}{2}t-\frac{1}{8}\sin 4t+C$

5. $\dfrac{3}{8}x-\dfrac{1}{4a}\sin 2ax+\dfrac{1}{32a}\sin 4ax+C$

7. $\tan x+C$

9. $-\frac{1}{6}\csc^3 2t+C$

Article 9–4

1. $0.2\,|a|$

3. $\dfrac{\pi a^2}{4}$

5. $\frac{1}{2}\ln|\sec 2t+\tan 2t|+C$

7. $\pi/6$

9. $\frac{1}{2}\ln 2$

11. $\frac{1}{4}\ln 3$

13. $\dfrac{1}{a}\ln\left|\dfrac{x}{a+\sqrt{a^2+x^2}}\right|+C$

15. $\dfrac{\sqrt{5}}{5}\sin^{-1}(x\sqrt{5/2})+C$

17. $\dfrac{1}{|a|}\sec^{-1}\left|\dfrac{x}{a}\right|+C$

19. $\dfrac{1}{a^2}\left(\dfrac{x}{\sqrt{a^2-x^2}}\right)+C$

Article 9–5

1. $\pi/8$

3. $-2\sin^{-1}(1-x)-\sqrt{2x-x^2}+C$

5. $2 \sin^{-1} \dfrac{x-2}{3} - \sqrt{5 + 4x - x^2} + C$ 7. $\sqrt{8 + 2x - x^2} + C$

9. $\frac{1}{2} \ln (x^2 + 4x + 5) - 2 \tan^{-1} (x + 2) + C$

Article 9–6

1. $\frac{1}{6} \ln |(x + 5)^5 (x - 1)| + C$ 3. $\frac{2}{3} \ln |x + 5| + \frac{1}{3} \ln |x - 1| + C$

5. $\ln \left| \dfrac{x}{x + 1} \right| + \dfrac{1}{x + 1} + C$ 7. $\dfrac{1}{2} \ln \dfrac{x^2}{x^2 + x + 1} - \dfrac{1}{\sqrt{3}} \tan^{-1} \dfrac{2x + 1}{\sqrt{3}} + C$

9. $\ln \left| \dfrac{1 + e^t}{2 + e^t} \right| + C$ 11. $x - \dfrac{3}{2} \tan^{-1} x + \dfrac{1}{2} \dfrac{x}{1 + x^2} + C$

Article 9–7

1. $\dfrac{x^2}{2} \ln x - \dfrac{x^2}{4} + C$ 3. $\dfrac{x^2 + 1}{2} \tan^{-1} x - \dfrac{1}{2} x + C$

5. $\dfrac{1}{a^2} \sin ax - \dfrac{1}{a} x \cos ax + C$ 7. $\dfrac{x}{a} \tan ax + \dfrac{1}{a^2} \ln |\cos ax| + C$

9. $\dfrac{x}{2} [\sin (\ln x) - \cos (\ln x)] + C$

11. $x \ln (a^2 + x^2) - 2x + 2a \tan^{-1} \dfrac{x}{a} + C$

13. $\left(\dfrac{x^2}{2} - \dfrac{1}{4} \right) \sin^{-1} x + \dfrac{x}{4} \sqrt{1 - x^2} + C$

15. $\dfrac{4\pi - 3\sqrt{3}}{3}$ 17. (b) $\dfrac{x^4}{32} [8 (\ln x)^2 - 4 \ln x + 1] + C$

19. (b) $(x^3 - 3x^2 + 6x - 6)e^x + C$ 21. $P(x) = 1 - 3x^2$

Article 9–8

1. 2   3. $\tan x + \sec x + C$

5. $\dfrac{4}{\sqrt{3}} \tan^{-1} \left(\sqrt{3} \tan \dfrac{x}{2} \right) - x + C$ 7. 0

Article 9–9

1. $-x + 4\sqrt{x} - 4 \ln |1 + \sqrt{x}| + C$

3. $\dfrac{2(x + a)^{3/2}}{105} (15x^2 - 12ax + 8a^2) + C$

5. $\dfrac{b - a}{2} \left(\ln \left| \dfrac{u - 1}{u + 1} \right| - \dfrac{2u}{u^2 - 1} \right) + C$, where $u = \sqrt{\dfrac{a + x}{b + x}}$

7. $(3\sqrt{2} - 4)/2$ 9. $2 + 2 \ln (\frac{3}{2})$ 11. $-1 + 4 \ln (\frac{3}{2})$

13. $\frac{3}{2} y^{2/3} + \ln |1 + y^{1/3}| - \frac{1}{2} \ln |y^{2/3} - y^{1/3} + 1| - \sqrt{3} \tan^{-1} \dfrac{2y^{1/3} - 1}{\sqrt{3}} + C$

15. $\frac{2}{3}(\sqrt{t^3 - 1} - \tan^{-1} \sqrt{t^3 - 1}) + C$ 17. $2 + 4 \ln (\frac{2}{3})$

19. $\frac{1}{3} \ln |x + 1| - \frac{1}{6} \ln |x^2 - x + 1| + \dfrac{1}{\sqrt{3}} \tan^{-1} \dfrac{2x - 1}{\sqrt{3}} + C$

Article 9–10

1. $\pi/2$ 3. 6   5. 4
7. $\frac{1}{2}$ 9. Diverges   11. Converges
13. Converges   15. Diverges   17. Converges
19. Converges

Article 9–11

1. $\frac{8}{3}, \frac{8}{3}, \frac{8}{3}$ 3. $2\pi/3$, 2.28   5. 1.86, 1.85

CHAPTER 9: MISCELLANEOUS

1. $2\sqrt{1 + \sin x} + C$ 3. $(\tan^2 x)/2 + C$

5. $(2x^{3/2})/3 + C$ 7. $\ln |x + 1 + \sqrt{x^2 + 2x + 2}| + C$

9. $(x^2 - 2x + 2)e^x + C$ 11. $\tan^{-1}(e^t) + C$

13. $2\sqrt{x} - 2\ln(1 + \sqrt{x}) + C$ 15. $\frac{9}{25}(t^{5/3} + 1)^{5/3} + C$

17. $\ln \dfrac{\sqrt{1 + e^t} - 1}{\sqrt{1 + e^t} + 1} + C$ 19. $e^{\sec x} + C$

21. $\sin^{-1}(x - 1) + C$ 23. $\frac{1}{2}\ln |1 + \sin 2t| + C$

25. $(-2\cos x)/\sqrt{1 + \sin x} + C$ 27. $x/(a^2\sqrt{a^2 - x^2}) + C$

29. $\dfrac{1}{3}\ln \dfrac{1 - \cos x}{4 - \cos x} + C$ 31. $\displaystyle\sum_{k=0}^{m} \dfrac{(-1)^k}{k!(m-k)!}\ln |x + k| + C$

33. $\frac{1}{3}[(2y^3 + 1)^{-1} + \ln |y^3/(2y^3 + 1)|] + C$

35. $\ln |x/\sqrt{x^2 + 1}| + 1/2(x^2 + 1) + C$

37. $\ln |e^x - 1| - x + C$ 39. $x^{-1} + 2\ln |1 - x^{-1}| + C$

41. $-\dfrac{1}{4}\dfrac{e^u + e^{-u}}{e^u - e^{-u}} + C$ 43. $\frac{1}{3}\tan^{-1}[(5x + 4)/3] + C$

45. $e^x(\cos 2x + 2\sin 2x)/5 + C$ 47. $\ln |x| - 3\ln |1 + \sqrt[3]{x}| + C$

49. $\frac{1}{15}(8 - 4z^2 + 3z^4)(1 + z^2)^{1/2} + C$

51. $\frac{5}{2}(1 + x^{4/5})^{1/2} + C$

53. $\frac{1}{4}[(2x^2 - 1)\sin^{-1}x + x\sqrt{1 - x^2}] + C$

55. $x + \ln |(x - 1)/x| + C$

57. $\dfrac{2}{3}(3e^{2x} - 6e^x - 1)^{1/2} + \dfrac{1}{\sqrt{3}}\ln |e^x - 1 + \sqrt{e^{2x} - 2e^x - \frac{1}{3}}| + C$

59. $\tan^{-1}(2\sqrt{y^2 + y}) + C$

61. $\frac{3}{8}\sin^{-1}x + \frac{1}{8}(5x - 2x^3)\sqrt{1 - x^2} + C$

63. $x\tan x - (x^2/2) + \ln |\cos x| + C$

65. $\dfrac{x^2}{4} + \dfrac{x\sin 2x}{4} + \dfrac{\cos 2x}{8} + C$ 67. $\dfrac{x^2}{4} - \dfrac{x\sin 2x}{4} - \dfrac{\cos 2x}{8} + C$

69. $\frac{1}{12}[4u - 3\ln(1 + e^{2u}) + \ln(3 + e^{2u})] + C$

71. $(x^2 + 1)e^x + C$ 73. $-2x^{-2} + 2x^{-1} + \ln|x/(x+2)| + C$

75. $2 - \sqrt{2}\ln(1 + \sqrt{2})$ 77. $\dfrac{1}{4}\dfrac{e^u - e^{-u}}{e^u + e^{-u}} + C$

79. $\ln|\tan t - 2| - \ln|\tan t - 1| + C$

81. $\dfrac{1}{\sqrt{2}}\tan^{-1}\left(\dfrac{\tan x}{\sqrt{2}}\right) + C$ 83. $x\ln\sqrt{x^2 + 1} - x + \tan^{-1}x + C$

85. $\frac{1}{2}(x^2 - 1)e^{x^2} + C$ 87. $\sin^{-1}(3^{-1/2}\tan x) + C$

89. $\tan x - \sec x + C$

91. $-\dfrac{1}{2}\cot x \csc x + \dfrac{1}{4}\ln\dfrac{1 - \cos x}{1 + \cos x} + C$

93. $x(\sin^{-1}x)^2 - 2x + 2\sqrt{1 - x^2}\sin^{-1}x + C$

95. $\frac{1}{2}\ln(x^2 + 1) + \frac{1}{2}(x^2 + 1)^{-1} + C$

97. $\frac{1}{15}(3x - 1)(2x + 1)^{3/2} + C$

99. $x\ln(x - \sqrt{x^2 - 1}) + \sqrt{x^2 - 1} + C$

101. $x - e^{-x}\tan^{-1}(e^x) - \frac{1}{2}\ln(1 + e^{2x}) + C$

103. $x\ln(x + \sqrt{x}) - x + \sqrt{x} - \ln(1 + \sqrt{x}) + C$

105. $x\ln x + (x + 1)\ln(x + 1) - 2x + C$

107. $2\sqrt{x}\sin\sqrt{x} + 2\cos\sqrt{x} + C$

109. $(x + 2)\tan^{-1}\sqrt{x + 1} - \sqrt{x + 1} + C$

111. $\frac{1}{4}x^2 - \frac{1}{8}x\sin 4x - \frac{1}{32}\cos 4x + C$ 113. $\ln(\sqrt{e^{2t} + 1} - 1) - t + C$

115. $\dfrac{1}{ac}\ln\left|\dfrac{e^{ct}}{a + be^{ct}}\right| + C$ 117. $\dfrac{1}{\sqrt{2}}\ln\left|\csc\left(x - \dfrac{\pi}{4}\right) - \cot\left(x - \dfrac{\pi}{4}\right)\right| + C$

119. $x\ln(2x^2 + 4) + 2\sqrt{2}\tan^{-1}(x/\sqrt{2}) - 2x + C$

121. $\ln|2 + \ln x| + C$

123. $\dfrac{1}{3}\ln|x + 1| - \dfrac{1}{6}\ln(x^2 - x + 1) + \dfrac{1}{\sqrt{3}}\tan^{-1}\dfrac{2x - 1}{\sqrt{3}} + C$

125. $\tan^{-1}(e^x) + C$

127. $-2\sqrt{x + 1}\cos\sqrt{x + 1} + 2\sin\sqrt{x + 1} + C$

129. $\ln 2$ 131. $2/\pi$ 133. $\pi/4$

135. $\pi/2$ 137. -1 139. e^{-4}

141. Area $(\pi - 2)r^2/4$; centroid $2r\sqrt{2}/(3\pi - 6)$ from center.

143. $2\pi^2 kr^2$ 145. Only V is finite; integrals for A and for S diverge.

147. $(0.58, 0.93)$ 149. Approx. 2   151. Approx. 6.8

153. $2\pi[\sqrt{2} + \ln(1 + \sqrt{2})] \approx 14.4$

155. $(0, 0.6)$ for arch $|x| \le \pi/2$ 157. $6a$ 159. $12\pi a^2/5$

161. Converges, compare with $\displaystyle\int_1^\infty x^{-3/2}\,dx$.   165. $x = a\cos kt$

CHAPTER 10

Article 10–1

  1. 7   3. -32 5. $x = 1, y = 1$

Article 10–2

  1. 4   3. -9 5. -4 7. 6

Article 10–3

  1. Index of 4 3 2 1 is $3 + 2 + 1 = 6$

    Sign of $a_{14} \, a_{23} \, a_{32} \, a_{41}$ is $+$

Article 10–4

  1. $q = 4, r = 3, s = 0$ 5. 0

    $q' = 4, r' = 4, s' = 0$

Article 10–5

  1. Differentiate the elements of any one row of the determinant and leave the remaining unaltered. The sum of the n determinants which can be obtained in this manner is the derivative of the original nth order determinant.

Article 10–6

  1. $x = \frac{6}{7}, y = \frac{10}{7}, z = -\frac{2}{7}$

  3. Multiply the equations respectively by $-14, -7, +9$ and -3 and add to obtain $-50z = -50$.

Article 10–7

  1. 16.5

  5. $r = 0, A = -B; r = 3, A = 2B$

  7. $r = 0, A = -B; r = 2, A = B$

  9. $r = 1, A = B; r = -3, A = -B$

  11. $r = 2, A = 0, B$ arbitrary; $r = -2, A = -B$

CHAPTER 10: MISCELLANEOUS

  1. $x = y = 1$ 3. $\frac{14}{33}, -\frac{2}{33}, \frac{25}{33}$ 5. $x = y = z = 0$ 7. $1, -1, 0$

  9. No solution   17. $x = a, y = b, z = c$ 21. The converse is false.

CHAPTER 11

Article 11–1

  1. (a) About the x-axis

     (b) No curve for $0 < x < 2$

     (c) $(0, 0), (2, 0)$

     (e) ∞

  3. (a) About both axes, the origin and the line $y = x$

     (b) Curve is inside the square $|x| \leq 1, |y| \leq 1$

     (c) $(0, \pm 1), (\pm 1, 0)$

     (e) Slope is 0 at $(0, \pm 1)$, ∞ at $(\pm 1, 0)$

5. (a) About both axes and the
   origin
   (b) No curve for $|y| \leq 1$;
   no curve for $|x| \leq 1$
   (c) No intercepts
   (d) $x = \pm 1$; $y = \pm 1$

7. (a) About the y-axis
   (b) Curve is confined to $y \geq 1$
   (c) $(0, 1)$
   (e) 0

9. (a) About the y-axis   (b) $y \geq -1$
   (c) $(0, -1)$; $(\pm 1, 0)$ (e) 0; ± 2

Article 11–2

1. $x + y + 1 = 0$

3. $6x - y = 14$; $y - 6x = 18$

7. Yes; $(-2, -8)$

9. $2x + 3y = \pm 12$

11. $\left(-\frac{13}{4}, \frac{17}{16}\right)$

15. ± 16

17. $A = \tan^{-1} \frac{5}{3}$, $B = \tan^{-1} 5$, $C = \tan^{-1} \frac{10}{11}$

21. (a) $45°$ (b) $\tan^{-1} 3$ (c) $\tan^{-1} (5/\sqrt{3})$ (d) $\tan^{-1} \left(\frac{14}{3}\right)$

Article 11–3

1. 0.618

3. 1.165

5. -1.189

7. $x_1 = x_2 = x_3$, etc.

9. $m_1 = (q - 1)/q$, $m_2 = 1/q$

Article 11–4

1. $x - y = 1$

3. $(x^2 + y^2)^2 + 8(y^2 - x^2) = 0$

5. $3x^2 + 4y^2 - 20x + 12 = 0$

7. $x^2 = 10 - 2y + 6|y - 1|$

9. $(2, 2)$; $\sqrt{5}$

or $\begin{cases} x^2 = 4y + 4 & \text{when } y \geq 1 \\ x^2 = 16 - 8y & \text{when } y < 1 \end{cases}$

Article 11–5

1. $x^2 + y^2 - 4y = 0$

3. $x^2 + y^2 - 6x + 8y = 0$

5. $x^2 + y^2 + 4x + 2y = 1$

7. $(0, 1)$; 2

9. $(-1, 0)$; $2/\sqrt{3}$

11. $(-1, 2)$; 0

13. $x^2 + y^2 - 4x - 4y = 5$

15. $(x - 0.7)^2 + (y - 1.3)^2 = 12.58$

17. $x^2 + y^2 + 2x + 2y - 23 = 0$

19. Center of circle is $(1, 2)$; radius $\sqrt{2}$. Distance of $(0.1, 3.1)$ from center is $\sqrt{2.02}$. Point is outside the circle.

21. Center $(-1, 1)$, radius 5

Article 11–6

1. $x^2 = 8y$; $y = -2$

3. $(x + 2)^2 = 4(y - 3)$; $y = 2$

5. $(y - 1)^2 = 12(x + 3)$; $x = -6$

7. $y^2 = 8(x - 2)$; $F(4, 0)$

9. $(y - 1)^2 = -16(x + 3)$; $F(-7, 1)$

11. $(y - 1)^2 = 4x$; $F(1, 1)$ 13. $V(1, 1)$; $x = 1$; $F(1, -1)$; $y = 3$

15. $V(2, 0)$; $y = 0$; $F(1, 0)$; $x = 3$

17. $V(-1, -1)$; $x = -1$; $F(-1, 0)$; $y = -2$

19. $V(2, 1)$; $y = 1$; $F(\frac{29}{16}, 1)$; $x = \frac{35}{16}$

21. $V(2, -2)$; $x = 2$; $F(2, -\frac{4}{3})$; $y = -\frac{8}{3}$

23. Points above parabola $x^2 = 8y$ 27. $b^2 y = 4hx(b - x)$

Article 11–7

1. $x^2/12 + y^2/16 = 1$; $e = \frac{1}{2}$ 3. $9x^2 + 5(y - 2)^2 = 45$; $e = \frac{2}{3}$

5. $(x - 2)^2 + 10(y - 2)^2 = 10$; $e = 3/\sqrt{10}$

7. $(2, -3)$; $(2, 2)$, $(2, -8)$; $(2, 1)$, $(2, -7)$

9. $x^2 + 2y^2 - 4y = 0$ 11. $\frac{4}{3}\pi ab^2$ 15. $5x^2 + 9y^2 = 180$

19. Graph consists of parabola $x^2 + 4y = 0$, straight line $2x - y - 3 = 0$, circle $x^2 + y^2 - 25 = 0$, ellipse $x^2 + 4y^2 - 4 = 0$.

Article 11–8

3. $C(2, -3)$; $V(2 \pm 3, -3)$; $F(2 \pm \sqrt{13}, -3)$
   $A: 2(x - 2) = \pm 3(y + 3)$

5. $C(-2, 1)$; $V(-2 \pm 2, 1)$; $F(-2 \pm 3, 1)$
   $A: \sqrt{5}(x + 2) = \pm 2(y - 1)$

7. $C(2, 0)$; $V(2 \pm 2, 0)$, $F(2 \pm \sqrt{5}, 0)$
   $A: x - 2 = \pm 2y$

13. $4x^2 - 5y^2 - 8x + 60y + 4 = 0$

Article 11–9

7. $2(y')^2 = 1$ 9. $5(y')^2 - (x')^2 = 10$

Article 11–10

1. Ellipse   3. Parabola   5. Hyperbola   7. Hyperbola   9. Ellipse

Article 11–11

3. Line L and the point D do not exist.

4. $(1 - e^2)x^2 + y^2 - 2pe^2 x - p^2 e^2 = 0$

Article 11–12

1.
$$\begin{vmatrix} y & x^n & x^{n-1} & \cdots & x & 1 \\ y_1 & x_1^n & x_1^{n-1} & \cdots & x_1 & 1 \\ y_2 & x_2^n & x_2^{n-1} & \cdots & x_2 & 1 \\ \vdots & \vdots & \vdots & & \vdots & \vdots \\ y_{n+1} & x_{n+1}^n & x_{n+1}^{n-1} & \cdots & x_{n+1} & 1 \end{vmatrix} = 0$$

3.
$$\begin{vmatrix} x^2 & xy & y^2 & 1 \\ 9 & 0 & 0 & 1 \\ 1 & 2 & 4 & 1 \\ 1 & 1 & 1 & 1 \end{vmatrix} = 0, \quad \text{or} \quad x^2 + 12xy - 4y^2 = 9$$

CHAPTER 11: MISCELLANEOUS

1. (a) A. Symmetric about the x-axis
   B. $0 \le x \le 4, -2 \le y \le 2$
   C. $(0, 0), (4, 0)$
   D. None
   E. ∞ at both intercepts
   (b) A. Symmetric about the x-axis
   B. $x \le 0, x \ge 4$, all y
   C. $(0, 0), (4, 0)$
   D. Asymptotic to $y = \pm(x - 2)$
   E. ∞ at both intercepts
   (c) A. Symmetric, about the x-axis
   B. $0 \le x < 4$, all y
   C. $(0, 0)$
   D. Asymptotic to $x = 4$
   E. ∞ at $(0, 0)$

3. (a) A. None
   B. All y, all x
   C. $(0, 0), (-1, 0), (2, 0)$
   D. None
   E. -2 at $(0, 0)$
   3 at $(-1, 0)$
   6 at $(2, 0)$
   (b) A. Symmetric about the x-axis
   B. All y, $-1 \le x \le 0$, $x \ge 2$
   C. $(0, 0), (-1, 0), (2, 0)$
   D. None
   E. ∞ at all intercepts

5. (a) A. Symmetric about the origin
   B. $|y| \ge 2, |x| > 0$
   C. None
   D. $y = x, x = 0$
   (b) A. About $(1, 2)$
   B. $y \le 0, y \ge 4; x \ne 1$
   C. $(0, 0)$
   D. $x = 1, y = x + 1$
   E. 0
   Remark: Translate axes to new origin at $(1, 2)$; becomes same as 5(a).

7. A. None
   B. $y \le 4 - 2\sqrt{3}, y \ge 4 + 2\sqrt{3}$;
   $x^2 \ne 1$
   C. $(0, 8), (2, 0)$
   D. $x = \pm 1, y = 0$
   E. -4 at $(0, 8)$
   $\frac{4}{3}$ at $(2, 0)$

9. A. Symmetric about the origin
   B. $|x| \le 2, |y| \le 2$
   C. $(0, \pm\sqrt{3}), (\pm\sqrt{3}, 0)$
   D. None
   E. $-\frac{1}{2}$ at $(0, \pm\sqrt{3})$
   -2 at $(\pm\sqrt{3}, 0)$

21. $5x^2 + 5y^2 = 4x + 8y$

23. $x = 2pm$

25. $(\pm\frac{8}{9}\sqrt{3}, \frac{4}{3})$

27. $(-2, 1), (2, -1)$

31. $(-\frac{16}{5}, \frac{53}{10})$

33. 10^7 mi

35. $y^2 = 2x - 7$

41. No

43. $5x^2 + 9y^2 - 30x = 0$

45. $2ab$

47. $x^2 + 4xy + 5y^2 = 1$

51. Center at $(\frac{1}{2}\sqrt{2}, 0)$, $e = \sqrt{2}$

53. Square, area $= 2$

55. (a) Center $(2, -1)$, foci $\left(\dfrac{4 \pm 3\sqrt{3}}{2}, -1\right)$, major axis 6, minor axis 3,
   $e = \sqrt{3}/2$

   (b) Center $(-2, -\frac{3}{2})$, foci $(-2 \pm \sqrt{13}, -\frac{3}{2})$, major axis $= \sqrt{13}$, conjugate axis $= \sqrt{39}$, $e = 2$, asymptotes: $2y \pm 2\sqrt{3}x + (3 \pm 4\sqrt{3}) = 0$

57. (b) Bounded; both $9x^2 + 4y^2 - 36$ and $4x^2 + 9y^2 - 36$ exceed one when $4(x^2 + y^2) > 37$

59. $\sqrt{2}$

63. $9x^2 - y^2 = 9$ or $9y^2 - x^2 = 9$

65. (a) Center $(3, 2)$; $e = \sqrt{\frac{11}{12}}$ (b) $(3, 0)$

67. With $A(0, 0)$ and $B(c, 0)$, locus is the left branch of the hyperbola $3x^2 - y^2 - 4cx + c^2 = 0$.

CHAPTER 12

Article 12–1

1. (a) $\left(3, \frac{\pi}{4} + 2n\pi\right)$, $\left(-3, -\frac{3\pi}{4} + 2n\pi\right)$,

(b) $\left(-3, \frac{\pi}{4} + 2n\pi\right)$, $\left(3, -\frac{3\pi}{4} + 2n\pi\right)$,

where $n = 0, \pm 1, \pm 2, \ldots$

(c) $\left(3, -\frac{\pi}{4} + 2n\pi\right)$, $\left(-3, \frac{3\pi}{4} + 2n\pi\right)$,

(d) $\left(-3, -\frac{\pi}{4} + 2n\pi\right)$, $\left(3, \frac{3\pi}{4} + 2n\pi\right)$,

3. (a) $(3/\sqrt{2}, 3/\sqrt{2})$ (b) $(-3/\sqrt{2}, -3/\sqrt{2})$
   (c) $(3/\sqrt{2}, -3/\sqrt{2})$ (d) $(-3/\sqrt{2}, 3/\sqrt{2})$

5. $(2, \frac{3}{4}\pi)$ is the same as $\left(-2, -\frac{\pi}{4}\right)$ and $2 \sin\left(-\frac{\pi}{2}\right) = -2$.

7. If (r_1, θ_1) satisfies $r_1 = \cos\theta_1 + 1$, then the same point has coordinates $(-r_1, \theta_1 + \pi)$ which satisfy the second equation. Also, if (r_2, θ_2) satisfies the second equation, the coordinates $(-r_2, \theta_2 + \pi)$ of the same point satisfy the first equation.

9. The origin and $\left(\frac{a}{\sqrt{2}}, 45°\right)$ 11. The origin and $(\frac{8}{5}a, \sin^{-1}\frac{3}{5})$

Article 12–2

1. $r[3 \cos\theta + 4 \sin\theta] = 5$ 11. (a) $(\frac{3}{2}a, \pm 60°)$, $(0, 180°)$
    (b) $(2a, 0°)$, $(\frac{1}{2}a, \pm 120°)$

Article 12–3

1. $r = a \sin 2\theta$; rose of 4 leaves   3. $r = 2a \sin\theta$

5. $r \cos(\theta - \alpha) = p$ 7. $r^2 = \cos 2\theta$ 9. $x^2 + y^2 = 6y$

11. $(x^2 + y^2)^2 = 2a^2(x^2 - y^2)$ 13. $x^2 + y^2 - ay = a\sqrt{x^2 + y^2}$

15. (a) $p = \dfrac{|c|}{\sqrt{a^2 + b^2}}$, $\cos\beta = \dfrac{a}{\sqrt{a^2 + b^2}}$, $\sin\beta = \dfrac{b}{\sqrt{a^2 + b^2}}$

(b) $p = 3, \beta = 30°$

17. $(50, 0°)$, $r = \dfrac{45}{4 + 5 \cos\theta}$

19. (a) max $= \sqrt{a^2 + b^2}$
 min $= \sqrt{|a^2 - b^2|}$

(b) max $= a\sqrt{5}$, min $= a\sqrt{3}$
 max $= a\sqrt{2}$, min $= 0$
 max $= a\sqrt{5}/2$, min $= a\sqrt{3}/2$

21. $(\frac{2}{3}, 0°)$

Article 12–4

3. $(2, \pm 60°); 90°$ 5. $8a$ 7. $4\pi a^2 (2 - \sqrt{2})$

9. $\frac{a}{3}[(4 + \pi^2)^{3/2} - 8]$ 11. $4\pi^2 a^2$

Article 12–5

1. $\frac{3}{2}\pi a^2$ 3. $2a^2$ 5. $\frac{9}{2}\pi a^2$ 7. πa^2

CHAPTER 12: MISCELLANEOUS

15. $\pi/3$ at $(a, \pi/6)$ and $(a, 5\pi/6)$ 17. 0 at $(a\sqrt{2}, \pi/4)$

19. $\pi/4$ at $r = 0$; $2 \tan^{-1}(\sqrt{3}/6)$ at $(a/2, \theta_i)$ where $\theta_i = \pm\pi/3, \pm 2\pi/3$

21. $r = 2/(1 + \cos\theta)$ 23. $r = -2a\cos\theta$

25. $r = 8/(3 - \cos\theta)$ 27. $(0.75a, -3.44°)$, approx.

29. $\pi/4$ 31. -1

33. (b) $xy = 1$ (c) $\pi/2$

35. (a) $32\pi a^2/5$

(b) $\bar{y} = 0; \bar{x} = 5a \int_0^\pi \sin^6\frac{\theta}{2}\cos\frac{\theta}{2}\cos\theta\, d\theta$

(c) $\bar{x} = -50a/63$

39. $2a^2$ 41. a^2 43. $3\pi a^2/2$ 45. πa^2

47. $a^2(\pi + 2)$ 49. $2(2\pi + 3\sqrt{3})/3$ 51. $8\pi/3 + \sqrt{3}$

CHAPTER 13

Article 13–2

6. Values of $\sinh u$, $\cosh u$, $\tanh u$, $\coth u$, $\operatorname{sech} u$, $\operatorname{csch} u$ are listed in the order given:

(a) $-\frac{3}{4}, \frac{5}{4}, -\frac{3}{5}, -\frac{5}{3}, \frac{4}{5}, -\frac{4}{3}$

(b) $\pm\frac{8}{15}, \frac{17}{15}, \pm\frac{8}{17}, \pm\frac{17}{8}, \frac{15}{17}, \pm\frac{15}{8}$

(c) $-\frac{7}{24}, \frac{25}{24}, -\frac{7}{25}, -\frac{25}{7}, \frac{24}{25}, -\frac{24}{7}$

(d) $\frac{12}{5}, \frac{13}{5}, \frac{12}{13}, \frac{13}{12}, \frac{5}{13}, \frac{5}{12}$

(e) $\pm\frac{4}{3}, \frac{5}{3}, \pm\frac{4}{5}, \pm\frac{5}{4}, \frac{3}{5}, \pm\frac{3}{4}$

(f) Same as (d)

Article 13–3

3. $10\cosh 5x \sinh 5x = 5\sinh 10x$ 5. $2\operatorname{sech}^2 2x$

7. $-3\operatorname{sech}^3 x \tanh x$ 9. $\sec^2 x \operatorname{sech} y$

11. $\ln (\cosh x) + C$

13. $\tanh x + C$

15. $x - \tanh x + C$

17. $\frac{1}{2}x + \frac{1}{12} \sinh 6x + C$

19. $u/2$

21. (a) 115 ft   (b) 16 lb

Article 13–5

7. $-\csc x$

9. $-\csc x$

11. $\frac{1}{2} \sinh^{-1} 2x + C$

13. 0.5493

15. $-\frac{1}{2} \operatorname{csch}^{-1} \dfrac{|x|}{2} + C = -\frac{1}{2} \sinh^{-1} \dfrac{2}{|x|} + C$

Article 13–6

1. $a \sinh (x_1/a)$

3. $\dfrac{\pi a}{2} \left(2x_1 + a \sinh \dfrac{2x_1}{a} \right)$

5. $\dfrac{\pi a^2}{4} \left(2x_1 + a \sinh \dfrac{2x_1}{a} \right)$

7. (c) $a = 25$ ft, dip ≈ 4.6 ft
   (d) $H = 50$ lb

CHAPTER 13: MISCELLANEOUS

3. $\lim PQ = 0$

5. $\cosh x = \frac{41}{9}$, $\tanh x = -\frac{40}{41}$

9. $y = 1$

13. $\sec^2 x/(2 \tanh y \operatorname{sech}^2 y)$

15. $\tanh y \tan x$

17. $x^{-1} \operatorname{sech}^2 (\ln x) = 4x(x^2 + 1)^{-2}$

19. $3e^{3x} \cosh (\tan^{-1} e^{3x})/(1 + e^{6x})$

21. $-(\cosh y + \sinh 2x)/(2y + x \sinh y)$

23. $(2\theta - e^{-2\theta})/4 + C$

25. $(e^{3x} + 3e^{-x})/6 + C$

27. $\frac{1}{2} \tanh^{-1} (\frac{1}{2})$

29. $\sinh^{-1} (e^t) + C$

31. $\cosh^{-1} (\tan \theta) + C$

37. $\ln 2$

CHAPTER 14

Article 14–1

1. $\alpha_1 = \frac{1}{2} \sin^{-1} 0.8 = 26°34'$
   $\alpha_2 = 90° - \alpha_1 = 63°26'$

5. $x = e^t, y = -(7 + e^{2t})/2$

7. $x = \sin t, y = 1 + (t - \sin t \cos t)/2$, for $0 \le t \le \pi/2$;
   $x = 1, y = t + 1 - \pi/4$, for $t > \pi/2$

Article 14–2

1. $x^2 + y^2 = 1$

3. $x^2 - y^2 = 1; x > 0$

5. $y = x^2 - 6x$

7. $(x - 2)(y - 2) + 1 = 0; x > 2, y < 2$

9. $2(x + y) = (x - y)^2$

11. $x = \dfrac{-at}{\sqrt{t^2 + 1}}, \ y = \dfrac{a}{\sqrt{t^2 + 1}}$

13. $x = a \cos \dfrac{s}{a}, \ y = a \sin \dfrac{s}{a}$

15. $x = a \cos \phi + a\phi \sin \phi$
    $y = a \sin \phi - a\phi \cos \phi$

17. $x = (a - b) \cos \theta + b \cos \left(\dfrac{a - b}{b} \theta \right)$

    $y = (a - b) \sin \theta - b \sin \left(\dfrac{a - b}{b} \theta \right)$

21. (a) $x = 2a \cot \theta$, $y = 2a \sin^2 \theta$

(b) $y = \dfrac{8a^3}{x^2 + 4a^2}$

Article 14-3

1. $\mathbf{i} - 4\mathbf{j}$

3. $-2\mathbf{i} - 3\mathbf{j}$

5. $\frac{1}{2}\sqrt{3}\mathbf{i} + \frac{1}{2}\mathbf{j}$

7. $\frac{3}{5}\mathbf{i} - \frac{4}{5}\mathbf{j}$

9. $\dfrac{-4\mathbf{i} + \mathbf{j}}{\sqrt{17}}$

11. $\sqrt{2}$, $45°$

13. 2, $30°$

15. 13, $\tan^{-1} \frac{12}{5}$

Article 14-4

1. $\mathbf{v} = -a\omega \sin \omega t\mathbf{i} + a\omega \cos \omega t\mathbf{j}$, $\mathbf{a} = -a\omega^2 \cos \omega t\mathbf{i} - a\omega^2 \sin \omega t\mathbf{j} = -\omega^2 \mathbf{R}$;

when $\omega t = \dfrac{\pi}{3}$: $\mathbf{v} = a\omega \left(-\dfrac{\sqrt{3}}{2}\mathbf{i} + \dfrac{1}{2}\mathbf{j} \right)$, speed $= a\omega$,

$\mathbf{a} = -a\omega^2 \left(\dfrac{1}{2}\mathbf{i} + \dfrac{\sqrt{3}}{2}\mathbf{j} \right)$

3. $\mathbf{v} = \mathbf{i} + 2t\mathbf{j}$
$\mathbf{a} = 2\mathbf{j}$
$t = 2$: $\mathbf{v} = \mathbf{i} + 4\mathbf{j}$, $\mathbf{a} = 2\mathbf{j}$
speed $= \sqrt{17}$

5. $\mathbf{v} = e^t\mathbf{i} - 2e^{-2t}\mathbf{j}$
$\mathbf{a} = e^t\mathbf{i} + 4e^{-2t}\mathbf{j}$
$t = \ln 3$: $\mathbf{v} = 3\mathbf{i} - \frac{2}{9}\mathbf{j}$,
$\mathbf{a} = 3\mathbf{i} + \frac{4}{9}\mathbf{j}$,
speed $= \frac{1}{9}\sqrt{733}$

7. $\mathbf{v} = 3 \sinh 3t\mathbf{i} + 2 \cosh t\mathbf{j}$
$\mathbf{a} = 9 \cosh 3t\mathbf{i} + 2 \sinh t\mathbf{j}$
$t = 0$: $\mathbf{v} = 2\mathbf{j}$, $\mathbf{a} = 9\mathbf{i}$, speed $= 2$

9. $\mathbf{R} = -\frac{1}{2}gt^2\mathbf{j} + \mathbf{v}_0 t = tv_0 \cos \alpha\mathbf{i} + (tv_0 \sin \alpha - \frac{1}{2}gt^2)\mathbf{j}$

Article 14-5

1. $-\sin t\mathbf{i} + \cos t\mathbf{j}$

3. $-\cos t\mathbf{i} + \sin t\mathbf{j}$

5. $-\dfrac{2 \cos t\mathbf{i} + \mathbf{j}}{\sqrt{1 + 4 \cos^2 t}}$

Article 14-6

1. $\dfrac{1}{a} \text{sech}^2 \dfrac{x}{a}$

3. $\dfrac{4e^{2x}}{(1 + 4e^{4x})^{3/2}}$

5. $\dfrac{1}{a\theta}$

7. $-\cos y$

9. $\dfrac{48y^5}{(4y^6 + 1)^2}$

Article 14-7

3. $\mathbf{v} = 2\mathbf{i} + 2t\mathbf{j}$
$\mathbf{a} = 2\mathbf{j}$

5. $a_T = 0$, $a_N = \dfrac{2}{t^2 + 1}$

$\dfrac{ds}{dt} = |\mathbf{v}| = \sqrt{4 + 4t^2} = 2\sqrt{1 + t^2}$

$a_T = \dfrac{2t}{\sqrt{1 + t^2}}$, $a_N = \dfrac{2}{\sqrt{1 + t^2}}$

Article 14–8

3. $\mathbf{v} = 4at\cos 2\theta\mathbf{u}_r + 2at\sin 2\theta\mathbf{u}_\theta$
   $\mathbf{a} = (4a\cos 2\theta - 20at^2\sin 2\theta)\mathbf{u}_r + (2a\sin 2\theta + 16at^2\cos 2\theta)\mathbf{u}_\theta$

5. $\mathbf{v} = a\cos t\mathbf{u}_r + ae^{-t}(1 + \sin t)\mathbf{u}_\theta$
   $\mathbf{a} = -a[\sin t + e^{-2t}(1 + \sin t)]\mathbf{u}_r + ae^{-t}[2\cos t - 1 - \sin t]\mathbf{u}_\theta$

CHAPTER 14: MISCELLANEOUS

1. $x = (1 - t)^{-1},\ y = 1 - \ln(1 - t),\ t < 1$

3. $x = e^t,\ y = e^{e^t} - e$

5. $x = t - \sin t,\ y = 1 - \cos t$

7. $x = \sinh^{-1} t,\ y = t\sinh^{-1} t - \sqrt{1 + t^2} + 1$

9. $x = 4\sin t,\ y = 4\cos t$

13. $x = 2a\sin^2\theta\tan\theta,\ y = 2a\sin^2\theta$

15. (a) $3\pi a^2$ (b) $8a$ (c) $-4a\sin(t/2)$ (d) $64\pi a^2/3$
    (e) $(\pi a, 5a/6)$

17. 0

25. (a) $\mathbf{v} = \pi[(1 - \cos\pi t)\mathbf{i} + \sin\pi t\mathbf{j}],\ \mathbf{a} = \pi^2(\sin\pi t\mathbf{i} + \cos\pi t\mathbf{j})$
    (b) Slope of $PC = \cot\pi t$, slope of $PQ = \csc\pi t + \cot\pi t$
    (c) Slope of $\mathbf{v} = $ slope of PQ, slope of $\mathbf{a} = $ slope of PC

29. $|ad - bc|\,(a^2 + b^2)^{-3/2}$, provided $a^2 + b^2 \neq 0$

31. $(-\tfrac{1}{2}\ln 2,\ 1/\sqrt{2})$ 33. $\kappa = \pi s$

35. $s = s_0 + 2\pi p$, $A = A_0 + s_0 p + \pi p^2$, $R = R_0 + p$, where s_0, A_0, R_0 are the length of arc, area, and radius of curvature of the original curve.

37. $\mathbf{v} = 3\cos t\mathbf{i} - 2\sin t\mathbf{j}$
    $\mathbf{a} = -3\sin t\mathbf{i} - 2\cos t\mathbf{j}$
    Speed $= (4 + 5\cos^2 t)^{1/2}$
    $a_t = -5\sin t\cos t\,(4 + 5\cos^2 t)^{-1/2}$
    $a_n = 6(4 + 5\cos^2 t)^{-1/2}$

39. $\mathbf{v} = (\cos t - t\sin t)\mathbf{i} + (\sin t + t\cos t)\mathbf{j}$
    $\mathbf{a} = -(t\cos t + 2\sin t)\mathbf{i} - (t\sin t - 2\cos t)\mathbf{j}$
    $\kappa = (t^2 + 2)/(t^2 + 1)^{3/2}$

41. (a) $r = e^2$ (b) $\tfrac{1}{2}\sqrt{5}(e^{4\pi} - 1)$

43. $2(\omega^2 - 1)\mathbf{i}$ 45. $r = a\cosh\omega t$

TABLE 1

NATURAL TRIGONOMETRIC FUNCTIONS

Angle					Angle				
De-gree	Ra-dian	Sine	Co-sine	Tan-gent	De-gree	Ra-dian	Sine	Co-sine	Tan-gent
0°	0.000	0.000	1.000	0.000					
1°	0.017	0.017	1.000	0.017	46°	0.803	0.719	0.695	1.036
2°	0.035	0.035	0.999	0.035	47°	0.820	0.731	0.682	1.072
3°	0.052	0.052	0.999	0.052	48°	0.838	0.743	0.669	1.111
4°	0.070	0.070	0.998	0.070	49°	0.855	0.755	0.656	1.150
5°	0.087	0.087	0.996	0.087	50°	0.873	0.766	0.643	1.192
6°	0.105	0.105	0.995	0.105	51°	0.890	0.777	0.629	1.235
7°	0.122	0.122	0.993	0.123	52°	0.908	0.788	0.616	1.280
8°	0.140	0.139	0.990	0.141	53°	0.925	0.799	0.602	1.327
9°	0.157	0.156	0.988	0.158	54°	0.942	0.809	0.588	1.376
10°	0.175	0.174	0.985	0.176	55°	0.960	0.819	0.574	1.428
11°	0.192	0.191	0.982	0.194	56°	0.977	0.829	0.559	1.483
12°	0.209	0.208	0.978	0.213	57°	0.995	0.839	0.545	1.540
13°	0.227	0.225	0.974	0.231	58°	1.012	0.848	0.530	1.600
14°	0.244	0.242	0.970	0.249	59°	1.030	0.857	0.515	1.664
15°	0.262	0.259	0.966	0.268	60°	1.047	0.866	0.500	1.732
16°	0.279	0.276	0.961	0.287	61°	1.065	0.875	0.485	1.804
17°	0.297	0.292	0.956	0.306	62°	1.082	0.883	0.469	1.881
18°	0.314	0.309	0.951	0.325	63°	1.100	0.891	0.454	1.963
19°	0.332	0.326	0.946	0.344	64°	1.117	0.899	0.438	2.050
20°	0.349	0.342	0.940	0.364	65°	1.134	0.906	0.423	2.145
21°	0.367	0.358	0.934	0.384	66°	1.152	0.914	0.407	2.246
22°	0.384	0.375	0.927	0.404	67°	1.169	0.921	0.391	2.356
23°	0.401	0.391	0.921	0.424	68°	1.187	0.927	0.375	2.475
24°	0.419	0.407	0.914	0.445	69°	1.204	0.934	0.358	2.605
25°	0.436	0.423	0.906	0.466	70°	1.222	0.940	0.342	2.748
26°	0.454	0.438	0.899	0.488	71°	1.239	0.946	0.326	2.904
27°	0.471	0.454	0.891	0.510	72°	1.257	0.951	0.309	3.078
28°	0.489	0.469	0.883	0.532	73°	1.274	0.956	0.292	3.271
29°	0.506	0.485	0.875	0.554	74°	1.292	0.961	0.276	3.487
30°	0.524	0.500	0.866	0.577	75°	1.309	0.966	0.259	3.732
31°	0.541	0.515	0.857	0.601	76°	1.326	0.970	0.242	4.011
32°	0.559	0.530	0.848	0.625	77°	1.344	0.974	0.225	4.332
33°	0.576	0.545	0.839	0.649	78°	1.361	0.978	0.208	4.705
34°	0.593	0.559	0.829	0.675	79°	1.379	0.982	0.191	5.145
35°	0.611	0.574	0.819	0.700	80°	1.396	0.985	0.174	5.671
36°	0.628	0.588	0.809	0.727	81°	1.414	0.988	0.156	6.314
37°	0.646	0.602	0.799	0.754	82°	1.431	0.990	0.139	7.115
38°	0.663	0.616	0.788	0.781	83°	1.449	0.993	0.122	8.144
39°	0.681	0.629	0.777	0.810	84°	1.466	0.995	0.105	9.514
40°	0.698	0.643	0.766	0.839	85°	1.484	0.996	0.087	11.43
41°	0.716	0.656	0.755	0.869	86°	1.501	0.998	0.070	14.30
42°	0.733	0.669	0.743	0.900	87°	1.518	0.999	0.052	19.08
43°	0.750	0.682	0.731	0.933	88°	1.536	0.999	0.035	28.64
44°	0.768	0.695	0.719	0.966	89°	1.553	1.000	0.017	57.29
45°	0.785	0.707	0.707	1.000	90°	1.571	1.000	0.000	

TABLE 2

EXPONENTIAL FUNCTIONS

x	e^x	e^{-x}	x	e^x	e^{-x}
0.00	1.0000	1.0000	2.5	12.182	0.0821
0.05	1.0513	0.9512	2.6	13.464	0.0743
0.10	1.1052	0.9048	2.7	14.880	0.0672
0.15	1.1618	0.8607	2.8	16.445	0.0608
0.20	1.2214	0.8187	2.9	18.174	0.0550
0.25	1.2840	0.7788	3.0	20.086	0.0498
0.30	1.3499	0.7408	3.1	22.198	0.0450
0.35	1.4191	0.7047	3.2	24.533	0.0408
0.40	1.4918	0.6703	3.3	27.113	0.0369
0.45	1.5683	0.6376	3.4	29.964	0.0334
0.50	1.6487	0.6065	3.5	33.115	0.0302
0.55	1.7333	0.5769	3.6	36.598	0.0273
0.60	1.8221	0.5488	3.7	40.447	0.0247
0.65	1.9155	0.5220	3.8	44.701	0.0224
0.70	2.0138	0.4966	3.9	49.402	0.0202
0.75	2.1170	0.4724	4.0	54.598	0.0183
0.80	2.2255	0.4493	4.1	60.340	0.0166
0.85	2.3396	0.4274	4.2	66.686	0.0150
0.90	2.4596	0.4066	4.3	73.700	0.0136
0.95	2.5857	0.3867	4.4	81.451	0.0123
1.0	2.7183	0.3679	4.5	90.017	0.0111
1.1	3.0042	0.3329	4.6	99.484	0.0101
1.2	3.3201	0.3012	4.7	109.95	0.0091
1.3	3.6693	0.2725	4.8	121.51	0.0082
1.4	4.0552	0.2466	4.9	134.29	0.0074
1.5	4.4817	0.2231	5	148.41	0.0067
1.6	4.9530	0.2019	6	403.43	0.0025
1.7	5.4739	0.1827	7	1096.6	0.0009
1.8	6.0496	0.1653	8	2981.0	0.0003
1.9	6.6859	0.1496	9	8103.1	0.0001
2.0	7.3891	0.1353	10	22026	0.00005
2.1	8.1662	0.1225			
2.2	9.0250	0.1108			
2.3	9.9742	0.1003			
2.4	11.023	0.0907			

TABLE 3

NATURAL LOGARITHMS OF NUMBERS

n	$\log_e n$	n	$\log_e n$	n	$\log_e n$
0.0	*	4.5	1.5041	9.0	2.1972
0.1	7.6974	4.6	1.5261	9.1	2.2083
0.2	8.3906	4.7	1.5476	9.2	2.2192
0.3	8.7960	4.8	1.5686	9.3	2.2300
0.4	9.0837	4.9	1.5892	9.4	2.2407
0.5	9.3069	5.0	1.6094	9.5	2.2513
0.6	9.4892	5.1	1.6292	9.6	2.2618
0.7	9.6433	5.2	1.6487	9.7	2.2721
0.8	9.7769	5.3	1.6677	9.8	2.2824
0.9	9.8946	5.4	1.6864	9.9	2.2925
1.0	0.0000	5.5	1.7047	10	2.3026
1.1	0.0953	5.6	1.7228	11	2.3979
1.2	0.1823	5.7	1.7405	12	2.4849
1.3	0.2624	5.8	1.7579	13	2.5649
1.4	0.3365	5.9	1.7750	14	2.6391
1.5	0.4055	6.0	1.7918	15	2.7081
1.6	0.4700	6.1	1.8083	16	2.7726
1.7	0.5306	6.2	1.8245	17	2.8332
1.8	0.5878	6.3	1.8405	18	2.8904
1.9	0.6419	6.4	1.8563	19	2.9444
2.0	0.6931	6.5	1.8718	20	2.9957
2.1	0.7419	6.6	1.8871	25	3.2189
2.2	0.7885	6.7	1.9021	30	3.4012
2.3	0.8329	6.8	1.9169	35	3.5553
2.4	0.8755	6.9	1.9315	40	3.6889
2.5	0.9163	7.0	1.9459	45	3.8067
2.6	0.9555	7.1	1.9601	50	3.9120
2.7	0.9933	7.2	1.9741	55	4.0073
2.8	1.0296	7.3	1.9879	60	4.0943
2.9	1.0647	7.4	2.0015	65	4.1744
3.0	1.0986	7.5	2.0149	70	4.2485
3.1	1.1314	7.6	2.0281	75	4.3175
3.2	1.1632	7.7	2.0412	80	4.3820
3.3	1.1939	7.8	2.0541	85	4.4427
3.4	1.2238	7.9	2.0669	90	4.4998
3.5	1.2528	8.0	2.0794	95	4.5539
3.6	1.2809	8.1	2.0919	100	4.6052
3.7	1.3083	8.2	2.1041		
3.8	1.3350	8.3	2.1163		
3.9	1.3610	8.4	2.1282		
4.0	1.3863	8.5	2.1401		
4.1	1.4110	8.6	2.1518		
4.2	1.4351	8.7	2.1633		
4.3	1.4586	8.8	2.1748		
4.4	1.4816	8.9	2.1861		

Index